MAP OF THE WORLD

Each pattern shows the dominant age of sediments present; age and types of igneous rock not differentiated. Divisions correspond with those used in the text.

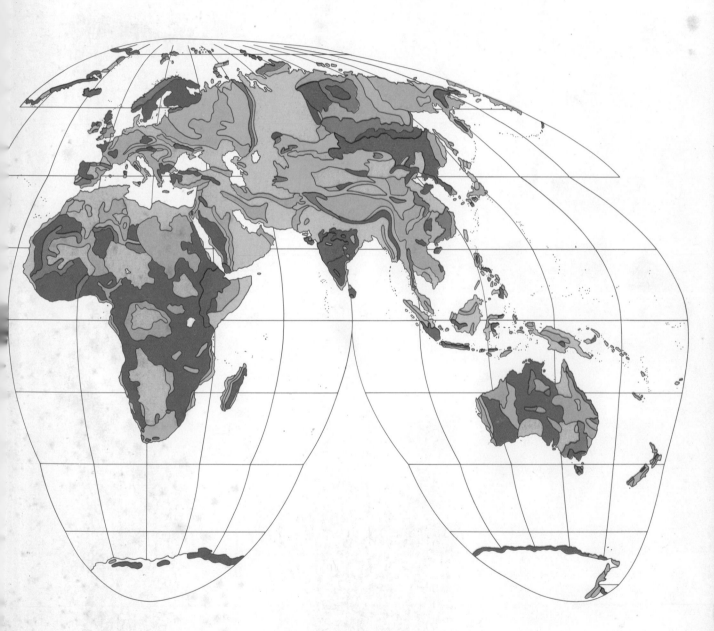

Scale

| 0 | 1000 | 2000 | 3000 | Miles |

| 0 | 1000 | 2000 | 3000 | 4000 | Kilometers |

Homolosine Equal-Area Projection
Copyright, The University of Chicago

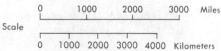

INTRODUCTION TO GEOLOGY

INTRODUCTION TO

Prentice-Hall, Inc., Englewood Cliffs, New Jersey

GEOLOGY

Physical and Historical

WILLIAM LEE STOKES

Chairman, Department of Geology
University of Utah

SHELDON JUDSON

Professor, Department of Geological
and Geophysical Sciences
Princeton University

PRENTICE-HALL INTERNATIONAL, INC., *London*

PRENTICE-HALL OF AUSTRALIA, PTY. LTD., *Sydney*

PRENTICE-HALL OF CANADA, LTD., *Toronto*

PRENTICE-HALL OF INDIA, PVT. LTD., *New Delhi*

PRENTICE-HALL OF JAPAN, INC., *Tokyo*

Current printing (last digit)

10 9 8 7 6 5 4 3 2

Preface

The range of subjects about which a modern college student should be informed has broadened greatly in the past decade. The pressure of new information dictates that former traditional courses be abbreviated or consolidated. Many faculties feel that the classical two-course approach to geology can no longer be maintained. For use in a comprehensive one-term course we have attempted to combine the material of our two previous texts: *Physical Geology* and *Essentials of Earth History*. The task of creating a unified text is not an easy one; there seems to be no ready formula for combining the cold facts of mineralogy and petrology with the history of life. Trilobites and quartz crystals tend to remain in their separate kingdoms.

But there exists a need and a challenge to depict the whole fabric of geology, to combine the essence of allied but dissimilar fields and to provide a unifying theme for understanding of the planet we inhabit. To neglect synthesis leads to fragmentation and ever-increasing gaps in understanding. Restrictions of space have forced us to abbreviate and eliminate many interesting and important topics and we have not been able to explain or illustrate concepts or processes to the extent that many of them deserve. Hopefully, instructors who use this book may fill the gaps as they find them.

Our over-all aim has been to bring to the student the essential knowledge of the earth and its past, to show how this information has been gathered and integrated and to focus attention on the still-unsolved problems confronting earth scientists.

New topics demand attention. Geologists have assumed the role of interpreting the physical features and past history of neighboring astronomical bodies. A chapter on the new science of astrogeology is included.

The long-debated subject of continental "drift" or displacement now seems to be approaching a solution favorable to the "drifters." We take the attitude that historical geology will have to be re-examined with continental drift as a strong possibility. Although a beginning textbook cannot be the place for a total examination of the subject, we have added a chapter pointing out the avenues of approach to this stimulating problem.

The list of persons who have assisted us in the preparation of this book should rightfully include all those who helped with previous editions of both parent volumes. Understandably the list is now so long that individual mention is not possible. To this list, however, we wish to add our colleagues at the University of Houston for many helpful comments. Credits for individual photographs reduce somewhat the anonymity of those to whom we are indebted. To our other professional colleagues who have given information, advice and friendly criticism, we can say only that we are indeed grateful. We reserve responsibility for all errors of fact or judgment.

Judson is indebted to Mrs. Helen Markham for assistance with technical aspects of the manuscript. The staff of the Project Planning Department of Prentice-Hall has been most helpful. We take particular pleasure in mentioning the assistance of Mr. Ronald Nelson, Miss Myra L. Forsythe and Mr. John J. Dunleavy whose patience and skill have brought the book through to publication.

W. L. S.   S. J.

Cover photograph courtesy Paul Hoffman and Geological Survey of Canada.

Contents

3

Igneous Rocks   32

The Three Rock Families. Description of Igneous Rocks. Classification of Igneous Rocks. Origin and Occurrence. Causes of Variation in Igneous Rocks.

4

Weathering   55

Types of Weathering. Rates of Weathering.

5

Sedimentary Rocks   70

Formation of Sedimentary Rocks. Classification of Sedimentary Rocks. Features of Sedimentary Rocks.

6

Metamorphic Rocks   91

A First Look at Metamorphic Rocks. Formation of Metamorphic Rocks. Types of Metamorphic Rocks. Origins of Granite.

7

Earthquakes and the Earth's Interior   105

Earthquakes. The Earth's Interior.

13

Early History of the Earth

The Cosmic Beginnings. Present Structure of the Earth. Heat and the Earth's Thermal History. The Core of the Earth. The Mantle. The Crust. The Oceans and Atmosphere. Continents and Ocean Basins. The Beginning of the Rock Record. Rocks of the Precambrian. North America as an Ideal Continent. Other Continents. Broad Features of the Precambrian.

14

The Origin of Life
and the Meaning of Fossils

Theories of Life. The Vital Synthesis. The Fossil Record. Metazoans Appear. What Is a Fossil? The Evolutionary Significance of Fossils. Patterns of Survival.

15

Keys to the Past

Uniformitarianism. Superposition. Reconstructing Past Events. Faunal Succession. Biotic Association. Recapitulation.

16

The Early Paleozoic Periods

Beginning of the Cambrian. Northwestern Europe and the Caledonian Revolution. The Tethys Seaway Takes Form. Eurasia North of Tethys. North America. The Southern Continents. Life of the Paleozoic. Economic Products of the Early Paleozoic Periods.

17

18

19

20

INTRODUCTION TO GEOLOGY

The Earth in Space

Geology is the science of the earth, its composition, structure, and history. Geology is partly descriptive and partly historical. The elements and compounds that compose the globe may be described in precise chemical and physical terms, or shown by accurate diagrams; this is the descriptive aspect of the subject. There is more to it than this, however, for the earth cannot be understood as a static body. It has a lengthy record of past and present change;

through time, all its features have been extensively altered by the interplay of external and internal forces. These changes can be traced backward in time until the history of the earth merges with that of the galaxy and the universe.

Not the least important of past events has been the gradual development of life, a phenomenon made possible by the peculiar and special conditions prevailing on the earth's surface. Past physical changes have dictated in large measure the sequence of biological events. Physical and historical geology, then, are related in complex and significant ways which we hope to make clear in this textbook.

EARTH AS A PLANET

The earth has been weighed and measured, its movements have been determined, its component parts have been analyzed, and its relations to other bodies in space have been examined in detail. The research that has been expended in the study of the planet is so prodigious that we cannot hope to delve deeply into all aspects of how our factual knowledge has been obtained. The following statistical figures will serve merely as an introduction to the subject.

Table 1-1   Facts and Figures concerning the Earth

Size

Polar radius	3,950 miles (6,357 kilometers)
Equatorial radius	3,964 miles (6,378 kilometers)
Mean radius	3,956 miles (6,371 kilometers)
Circumference around the poles, approx.	24,857 miles (40,009 kilometers)
Circumference around the equator, approx.	24,900 miles (40,079 kilometers)
Ellipticity $\left(\dfrac{\text{equatorial radius} - \text{polar radius}}{\text{equatorial radius}}\right) = \dfrac{1}{283}$	

Volumes

Volume of total earth	260 billion cubic miles $(1.08 \times 10^{12}\ \text{km}^3)$
Volume of water	330 million cubic miles $(1,370 \times 10^6\ \text{km}^3)$
Volume of crust	2 billion cubic miles $(6,210 \times 10^6\ \text{km}^3)$
Volume of mantle	216 billion cubic miles $(898,000 \times 10^6\ \text{km}^3)$
Volume of core	41 billion cubic miles $(175,500 \times 10^6\ \text{km}^3)$

Densities (Water = 1)

Density of entire earth	5.52
Density of crust, approx.	2.85
Density of mantle, approx.	4.53
Density of core, approx.	10.7

Shape

Oblate spheroid—a sphere flattened slightly at the poles. In nontechnical terms, the earth is also slightly pear-shaped, with the narrow end in the Arctic and the broader base in the Antarctic. The equator is egg-shaped and not circular. There are four high points arranged roughly like the corners of a pyramid.

Surface and Areas

Total surface area, approx.	198 million sq. miles $(510 \times 10^6\ \text{km}^2)$
Land area (29.22% of total)	57.5 million sq. miles $(149 \times 10^6\ \text{km}^2)$
Water area (70.78% of total)	139.4 million sq. miles $(361 \times 10^6\ \text{km}^2)$
Oceans and seas less continental shelves	128.4 million sq. miles $(322.6 \times 10^6\ \text{km}^2)$
Land area plus continental shelves	68.5 million sq. miles $(177.4 \times 10^6\ \text{km}^2)$

Relief

Greatest height of land, Mt. Everest	29,028 feet (8,848 m.)
Greatest known depth of ocean, Marianas Trench	36,198 feet (11,033 m.)
Average height of land	2,757 feet (840 m.)
Average depth of ocean	12,460 feet (3,808 m.)

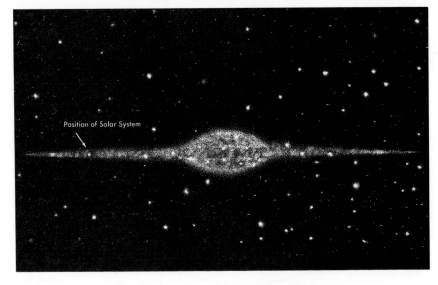

Figure 1-1 Edge view of the Milky Way galaxy showing its general shape and the position of the solar system.

Position of Solar System

THE EARTH'S PLACE IN THE UNIVERSE

The earth is a member of a small local group of celestial bodies known as the solar system. This group is part of a much larger system called the Milky Way galaxy, which in turn belongs to the vast aggregation of space and matter that is the universe. We cannot know how many earthlike planets there may be in space, but there are by recent calculations at least 100 billion stars in the local galaxy and at least a billion galaxies in the universe.

Obviously, the earth possesses an insignificant portion of the total mass and energy of the universe. Its importance as an abode of life, including mankind, cannot yet be assessed. What we think about these matters depends largely on what we know or infer about the origin of things, and for this reason the history of the universe is a matter of interest and importance.

As we would expect, the early history of the earth is difficult to decipher, but we are not without significant clues, for this reason: The organization of the "past" is being revealed to us on a much-delayed basis. Light that started its journey from distant sources hundreds, thousands, millions, or even billions of years ago is only now being received on earth. There is every reason to believe that the messages now arriving tell us about conditions that existed when the universe was younger and when our galaxy and solar system were forming from an unorganized mass of chaotic elements. What is seen causes us to believe that physical laws and processes have been operating on a timeless and universal scale and that we can indeed know something about the remote beginnings of our surroundings.

MODERN THEORIES OF THE UNIVERSE

The Evolutionary Theory

Many recent discoveries point to the conclusion that the universe is evolving—that it had a definite beginning at some finite time in the past and has progressed through definite stages to the present. The idea that the universe has evolved gains strong support philosophically from the success of the idea of organic evolution.

The evolutionary concept may be traced to the Belgian cosmologist Georges Lemaître, who published a comprehensive theory in 1931. The theory was expanded and modified in 1946 by the Russian-born American astrophysicist George Gamow. According to both Lemaître and Gamow, all the matter of the universe was at one time contained in a tightly packed, extremely dense region of space with a radius about equal to the distance from the earth to the sun. This state did not last for long, for the initial mass was shattered by a cataclysmic explosion that hurled matter and radiant energy into space and brought about the creation of

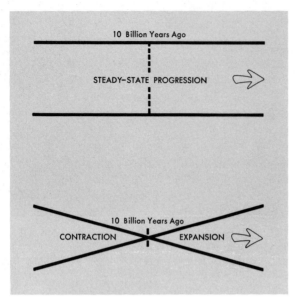

Figure 1-2 Simplified diagrams illustrating the concept of the steady-state universe (above) and the expansion-contraction universe (below).

the present chemical elements. According to the observed rate of expansion of the universe and to other methods of calculation, this event happened about 10 to 13 billion years ago.

The initial mass consisted of elementary particles not yet organized into elements. The elements formed when various numbers of neutrons combined with protons and appropriate numbers of electrons. Conditions for the uniting of the elementary particles were right for only a very short period following the explosion. During an interval between five minutes and half an hour long, according to Gamow, all the chemical elements were born. In that brief time, neutrons and protons were able to join and composite nuclei were formed. The rate of expansion was crucial. If it had been more rapid, only hydrogen could have formed; if less rapid, more complex units would have had time to associate, and the universe today would consist mostly of heavier elements.

Impelled by the initial explosion, matter and its attendant energy sped outward for many millions of years. During this interval, the initial radiant energy was so powerful that aggregations of matter were broken up and dispersed

as fast as they were formed. At length, however, gravity became an effective force, and matter began to segregate into the primordial, gaseous galaxies. Condensation is supposed to have begun about 250 million years after the initial explosion. The formation of gas clouds (**proto-galaxies**—at first, cold, dark, chaotic, and without stars) did not halt the headlong flight of matter through space. As a matter of fact, this flight or expansion is apparently still going on.

This is the concept of the beginning of the galaxies according to the evolutionary theory and, indeed, most other theories of the universe.

The Theory of Continuous Creation

A second hypothesis of the origin of the galaxies makes no mention of a specific initiating event in time or space. There is neither beginning nor end because matter is being continually formed and destroyed. The universe, according to this hypothesis, displays at present every stage in the creation, growth, and decay of stars and galaxies. Matter first appears as extremely rarefied masses of hydrogen gas in regions of space where stars are few and far between. Whether hydrogen is created literally from nothing is a debatable point, for there is a possibility that it marks the reappearance of the radiation lost from stars in other portions of space. That the new condensations should appear between existing masses of matter is explained by the pressure of light or other forms of radiation, which pushes particles of matter forward until they reach a position where pressure is balanced from all sides. Once an aggregation of hydrogen gas of sufficient total mass has accumulated, the influence of gravity begins to be felt, the mass contracts, and rotation begins. A typical galaxy, therefore, begins its evolution as a rotating mass of gas without stars, as we said before, and without light. The flattened shape and spiral form are direct consequences of its rotation.

According to the steady-state hypothesis of the universe, the heavier elements are not the products of an initial cataclysm. Rather, they

Figure 1-3 Supernova in distant galaxy Messier 101. Photo on the left, taken June 9, 1950, shows no nova; photo on the right, taken Feb. 7, 1951, shows nova at position indicated by arrow. (*Courtesy Mount Wilson and Palomar Observatories.*)

are being created continuously as normal products of events that can be observed and measured. Under conditions of heat and pressure that exist in the central regions of certain stars called red giants, elements as heavy as lead and bismuth may be built up from elemental hydrogen. Heavier elements can probably be created during the sudden explosion of a certain type of star called a **nova** or **supernova.** An explosion of this kind is the end result of a chain of events that start when a star runs out of hydrogen, its essential fuel. At this stage, it commences to shrink and collapse, thus causing a sudden increase in its rate of rotation. The faster it shrinks the faster it rotates, until it reaches a critical stage at which most of its mass is showered into space in a fiery burst of matter and energy. During this short interval, conditions are such that heavy elements can be formed in abundance.

The debris from nova and supernova explosions pours into space, where it mixes with the

Figure 1-4 The "Crab" Nebula in Taurus. This nebula is the remains of a supernova that appeared in 1054 A.D. (*Courtesy Mount Wilson and Palomar Observatories.*)

elemental hydrogen already there and becomes available for the construction of new galaxies and stars. Explosions of novae and supernovae are continually taking place and can be seen flaring up in our own galaxy as well as others. Several examples (1054 A.D., 1572 A.D., and 1604 A.D.) have been observed in our galaxy and each was, for a time, much brighter than any planet. Unfortunately, no similar eruptions have occurred in the Milky Way since the development of the telescope. The rate of production of novae and supernovae appears, however, to be high enough to provide a suitable source of heavy elements for the universe.

Contraction-Expansion Theory

At the time of writing (1967) the evolutionary, or "big-bang," theory seems to be supported by more facts than the steady-state theory. The distant objects called quasars, although not fully understood, seem to offer evidence of an early explosive state of the universe. If we are now witnessing a phase of expansion and started from a state of contraction, it is only natural to suspect that the universe might again contract and thus be in a state of endless pulsation. This is not to deny that many of the observations brought forth in support of the steady-state universe are true. There could be many minor steady-state processes within the general framework of an evolutionary universe.

THE BIRTH OF STARS

Most theories of the origin of the universe point to the formation of individual masses of gaseous material, each a potential galaxy. The appearance of individual stars within these masses follows a fairly well-defined pattern. **Gravitational instability** causes progressive segregations of gaseous material into smaller units, each having the mass and material of individual stars or solar systems. As gravity continues more and more to compress the central matter of such a gaseous mass, colliding atoms and molecules

gradually increase the temperature of the interior. At first, only heat is produced, but as the pressure increases, nuclear energies are released and the body becomes a self-luminous star. At the time of its formation, a normal star consists of about 1 per cent of oxygen, nitrogen, and carbon combined; about 1 per cent of the heavy elements such as iron; perhaps up to 5 per cent of helium; and the rest of hydrogen. The behavior of this combination of elements, by which a star remains active, involves nuclear reactions that are set off when the internal temperature reaches about 20 million°C. Disregarding details, we can say that the nuclear reactions that supply most stellar energy involve the transformation of hydrogen into helium through the catalytic action of carbon and nitrogen. Another important nuclear reaction involves only hydrogen and helium. Both these processes feed on hydrogen; but since this element makes up more than half of all matter, the stars are able to continue emitting energy for extremely long periods. That living organisms appear to have existed uninterruptedly on earth for at least 3,000 million years shows that our sun has not changed greatly, at least not during that length of time.

THE MILKY WAY GALAXY

All the stars visible without the aid of a telescope and most of those visible with a telescope are in our Milky Way galaxy. This group of at least 100 billion stars seems to be distributed about a center in the vicinity of the constellation Sagittarius, the Archer, which is visible from northern latitudes as it hangs low in the southeastern sky in summer. Our galaxy is shaped like a discus of truly Olympian proportions: about 20,000 light-years thick at the center, thinner at the edges, and 100,000 light-years in diameter. Our solar system is located in the principal plane of the galaxy, about 30,000 light-years from the center, a position that makes it difficult for us to work out the details of star distribution. It seems probable, however, that from a distance of 1,500,000

Figure 1-5 The Great Nebula in Andromeda. It is a spiral nebula similar in shape to our galaxy.

Figure 1-6 A globular cluster. At 22,000 light-years, this is one of the clusters nearest to us. (*Photo by Harvard University's Boyden Station, Bloemfontein, South Africa.*)

light-years the galaxy looks not unlike one of the nearest of our neighboring galaxies (see Figure 1-5). Such external galaxies are sometimes called **nebulae** because of their filmy, nebulous appearance in the telescopes through which they were first seen. Those known to have the spiral structure of Figure 1-5 are called **spiral nebulae.** The Milky Way is one of these.

Distributed fairly uniformly around the edge of our galaxy are about 100 globular clusters of stars (see Figure 1-6). Each cluster contains from 50,000 to 100,000 stars within a diameter of about 100 light-years. Since these stars are about one light-year apart, they are more closely crowded together than in any other region of the galaxy.

All the stars in our galaxy move around the galactic center. Our solar system, for instance, travels at a speed of about 150 miles per second and requires 200 million years to complete a circuit.

Figure 1-7 Horsehead Nebula in Orion, where some parts of the sky are blacked out while other areas glow with light reflected by interstellar matter. Photographed in red light by 200-inch telescope, Mt. Wilson and Palomar Observatories.

Our sun is a very ordinary star compared to others in the galaxy. Some stars are so large that they would encompass the orbit of sun and earth. They are 5 times as hot as the sun, 10,000 times as bright, and have 400 times its mass. Others are diminutive in comparison, having only one-fifth of the sun's mass, one-ten-thousandth of its brilliance, one-third of its heat.

Matter in Interstellar Space

Distributed irregularly in interstellar space throughout the universe are myriads of tiny pieces of dust and molecules of gas. Yet despite their small size these entities add up impressively. For instance, the dust and gas in the neighborhood of the sun, it has been estimated, account for half the total matter of our entire solar system. The bits of dust are larger than molecules and atoms, but so small that they could not be seen without the aid of the most powerful microscopes. They appear to be dusty grains of silica, or even frozen gases, or some other common substances converted to an unknown form by the low temperature, close to absolute zero, that prevails in interstellar space.

Light that has passed through this interstellar matter in certain directions becomes polarized—that is, it ends up vibrating in only one plane, in contrast to the random pattern of vibration common to most light. This polarizing effect is interpreted as evidence that the pieces are not spherical, but are rather elongated bodies aligned either by a gigantic magnetic field or by "winds" from moving gas.

The presence of interstellar matter is strikingly demonstrated in areas like the Horsehead Nebula in Orion, where some parts of the sky are blacked out by the material, while other areas glow with light that it reflects (see Figure 1-7).

It is now believed that most of the common elements found on earth can be found in interstellar space. The density of this material is very low—about what we would get by pulverizing an ordinary marble and spreading the dust uniformly throughout the volume of a sphere 1,000 miles in diameter. Yet the presence of interstellar matter is significant. There appears to be too much of it to have been blown out of occasional exploding stars or to have escaped from others. Theorists believe this matter to be left over from the creation of the universe—to be pieces of the very stuff from which the stars and planets were compounded.

ORIGIN OF THE SOLAR SYSTEM

FACTS TO BE EXPLAINED Any acceptable theory of cosmogony must account for the present constitution and mechanics of the solar system. The central sun appears to be a typical star composed chiefly of hydrogen and helium and a small proportion of other elements. Its outer surface temperature is 6,000°C, and the estimated temperature at its center is 20 million°C. It has a density of 1.4 and holds matter equivalent to 333,000 earths. The sun is representative of a great class of ordinary stars and is certainly no oddity in the universe, but the minor bodies that attend it are somewhat more difficult to account for. However, if a planet is defined as "a cold body shining by reflected light," there is now direct evidence that planets do exist in other solar systems.

Our solar family consists of 9 large planets, with 31 satellites attending 6 of them. There are also more than 1,600 named asteroids and countless comets and meteors in the system. The planets are all moving in the same direction and in essentially the same plane. The sun also rotates in the same direction, and its equator is only slightly inclined to the planetary plane.

The distribution and spacing of the individual bodies in the planetary system are also regular. In general, the distance of each member from the sun is approximately twice the distance of the preceding one (considering the asteroids to represent a planet). The mathematical expression of this relationship is called the Titus-Bode Law. Some astronomers regard this regular spacing as strictly accidental; others have developed elaborate hypotheses to explain it. Another feature that demands explanation is the fact that the inner, earth-like planets (Mercury, Venus, Earth, and Mars) are separated not only in space but also according to physical properties from the outer, or major, planets

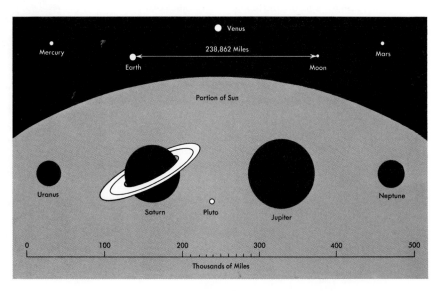

Figure 1-8 The size of the planets compared with a portion of the sun.

(Jupiter, Saturn, Uranus, and Neptune). The inner planets are comparatively small, with high specific densities, low rotational velocities, and few satellites. The outer planets are large, their specific densities are low, they rotate rapidly, and they have extensive moon systems.

The last, and in many ways most difficult, feature to explain is the distribution of the **angular momentum.** The angular momentum is the force with which a body moves, or the product of its mass and its velocity. The sun possesses about 99 per cent of the total mass of the solar system but only $\frac{1}{13}$ of the total angular momentum because of its slow rotation. Jupiter possesses .1 per cent of the mass but has about 59 per cent of the total angular momentum. It is interesting that planets should have such high angular momentums and that the sun should rotate so slowly. Just how the planetary material could have acquired so much momentum is a problem that any acceptable theory must explain.

Theories of Origin

In general, the various hypotheses that have been proposed to explain the origin of the solar system fall into two classes, according to whether or not a catastrophic event is involved. Theories that require no intervention from forces outside the solar system are called **single-body theories.** Theories that are based on the accidental intervention of outside influences are called **second-body theories,** since they acknowledge the influence of an object other than the sun in the creation of the solar system (see Figure 1-9).

The most widely accepted idea of planet formation is the **dust-cloud hypothesis.** According to this hypothesis, the planets formed from the same dust cloud as the sun and at approximately the same time. The whole mass not only was rotating slowly about the central proto-sun, but also contained a system of internal eddies in which dust and gas flowed in complicated turbulent patterns.

We are uncertain whether or not the central sun had become large and sufficiently com-

pressed for thermonuclear reactions to have commenced before the planets had become independent bodies. In other words, the sun as a luminous body may have developed either before or after the planets. In any event, the central mass was large enough to have a profound influence upon the proto-planets during the early stages of their formation.

In a mixed dust-gas nebula of the size appropriate for the parent of the solar system, the gaseous constituents would either tend to dissipate outward into space or fall into the sun.

Figure 1-9 Diagrammatic sketches illustrating the two chief theories of the origin of the earth. At the top is an interpretation of the nebular, or single-body, hypothesis showing the planets forming from dust or gas with the sun also gathering material in the center. Illustrated at the bottom is the planetesimal, or second-body, theory. The star in the distance has passed near enough to the sun to cause massive tides of matter to rise on both sides. The planets are forming from larger aggregations drawn from the sun.

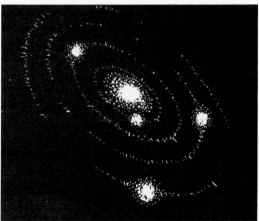
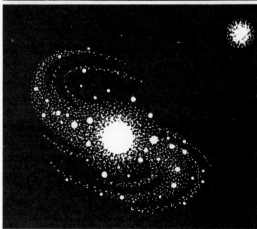

The dust particles, on the other hand, would tend to take up various elliptical orbits around the sun. Countless collisions between these particles would cause the smaller pieces to cling together to form large chunks of matter, which would in time begin to develop real gravitational attraction. The larger masses would grow at the expense of the smaller ones that they were able to sweep up as they traveled through space. The size and composition of the present-day planets were therefore determined by the total amount of material present in the regions they traversed. The larger planets would reflect an environment in which the relationship between space and matter would yield a maximum amount of mass. Near the sun, matter was abundant, but there was little space from which to gather matter; far from the sun there was more space but very little matter. This line of reasoning also explains the differences in composition between the outer and inner groups of planets. By the time the inner planets were formed, there was very little gas left in space from which atmospheres could arise. The larger planets collected thick atmospheres at an earlier stage when gas in the areas they traversed was plentiful.

A complex aspect of the nebular theory is its treatment of motions within the rotating mass of gas and dust. It is deduced that a number of complicated "whirlpools" or giant eddies would form, with the smaller whirls clustering near the sun and succeeding, larger ones developing farther out in space. These rotating systems would cause dust aggregations to collect more rapidly along certain zones where the planets eventually formed. The theory provides a reasonable explanation for the Titus-Bode Law, one of the most puzzling features of the solar system. It answers the question of angular momentum by assuming that the rotation of the dust eddies was governed by the rotation of the sun, which spins in the center and transmits energy to the remainder of the system. This variation of the nebular theory, in many ways the most complex to appear, seems to explain more features of the solar system than any other hypothesis yet proposed.

SUMMARY

The earth is a relatively small, dense, nonluminous member of a local group of celestial bodies called the solar system. This system is a part of the Milky Way galaxy, which is, in turn, a typical unit of the universe. Of the various hypotheses presenting a unified explanation of the cosmos, the **evolutionary,** or **"big bang," theory** is currently the most acceptable. According to this idea all matter of the universe was once highly compressed in a limited region of space. The "beginning" was a sudden explosion of this mass which initiated the expansion of the universe and brought about the creation of the presently existing elements. The galaxies came from aggregation of chiefly hydrogen gas brought together by gravity. Self-luminous stars appeared in the galaxies as nuclear reactions began to operate in compacting masses of gas.

More is known about the evolution of stars than about planets because the local solar system is the only clearly known example of the latter. It is supposed, however, that planet-formation is a normal process attending stars such as the sun. The most-favored current theory is that the planets appeared by the clumping together of matter within the cloud of gas and dust attending the sun in its early period of formation. A system of complicated eddies within this cloud is proposed as an explanation for the orbital relations of the planets and for the distribution of the angular momentum.

The inner, earth-like planets may have become more dense through the dissipation of light elements by powerful radiation and heat from the sun.

ADDITIONAL READING

Abell, G., *Exploring the Universe*. New York: Holt, Rinehart and Winston, 1964.

Broms, Allan, *Our Emerging Universe*. New York: Doubleday, 1961.

Coleman, James A., *Modern Theories of the Universe*. New York: New American Library of World Literature, 1963.

Gamow, George, *The Creation of the Universe*. New York: The Viking Press, Compass Books, 1956.

Hoyle, Fred, *Of Men and Galaxies*. Seattle: The University of Washington Press, 1964.

King, H. C., *Exploration of the Universe*. New York: The New American Library (Signet Science Library original), 1964.

Messel, H., and Butler, S. T., editors, *The Universe and its Origin*. New York: St. Martin's Press, 1964.

————, editors, *The Universe of Time and Space*. New York: Macmillan, 1963.

Urey, H. C., *The Planets, Their Origin and Development*. New Haven: Yale University Press, 1952.

Whipple, F. L., *Earth, Moon, and Planets*. Cambridge: Harvard University Press, 1963.

2

Matter and Minerals

In the preceding chapter we examined the position of the earth in space. Now let us come back to earth and look at space and matter on a much smaller scale. What is the earth made of?

To begin with, we can say that the fundamental building blocks of the rocks of the earth's crust are chemical elements and chemical compounds called minerals. Because geologic history is recorded in the rocks, we will want to know something about the minerals that make up these rocks. But if we look further we find that minerals themselves contain smaller units—**atoms**—and these in turn are made up of still smaller units, of which protons, neutrons, and electrons are the most important to us here. So before we begin our study of minerals, it would be wise to review briefly the nature of matter, specifically as it applies to minerals. Later in this chapter we will find out what constitutes a mineral and examine a handful of the most important mineral types.

MATTER

All matter seems to be essentially electrical in nature, either negative or positive. This electrical nature was early illustrated by a simple experiment—a piece of fur and a piece of amber were rubbed together, and afterwards they could pick up light objects such as wool or feathers. But the material picked up by the fur was repelled by the amber. In the 16th century, William Gilbert, personal physician to Queen Elizabeth I, proposed that the power responsible for this phenomenon be called electricity, from the Greek word *elecktron,* meaning amber.

We say that **like electric charges repel each other and unlike charges attract each other.** You have seen this principle in action in the poles of two adjacent magnets. The so-

called north poles repel each other but are attracted by the south poles, and vice versa.

Electron, Proton, and Neutron

When we rub fur and amber together, particles are said to pass from the fur to the amber. The fur, then, has a deficiency of particles and is positively charged. Therefore, the particles that moved to the amber to cause the condition must be negatively charged. These particles are called **electrons.**

Atoms are built up in part of the electrons. But because electrons are negatively charged there must be some positively charged particles to attract them if they are to be built into an atom. Scientists believe that there is such a particle, which they call the **proton.** Many additional particles of subatomic size have since been identified, but the only other one of importance to us here is the **neutron,** a particle with no electric charge.

The Atomic Model

The electron, the proton, and the neutron gather together into what we call the atom. Our concept of the atom derives from a series of indirect observations which come from the physicist's laboratory. As a result of these observations, we now believe that an atom is composed of a cloud of electrons that revolve about a central core of protons or of protons plus neutrons. Repeated experiments show that every atom has the same number of electrons as it has protons. The positively charged protons form the nucleus of the atom, and around it orbit an equal number of electrons whose negative charges balance the positive charges of the protons in the core of the atom.

The neutrons are also found in the nucleus of the atom, but because they are electrically neutral they are not matched by the negatively charged electrons outside the nucleus. These electrons, which move very rapidly around the nucleus at speeds of hundreds of miles per second, remind us of planets swinging around a sun.

Figure 2-1 Like charges of electricity repel each other; unlike charges attract each other. A: A small, positively charged sphere. B: This sphere is repelled by the approach of another positive charge. C: The positive charge is attracted by a negative charge.

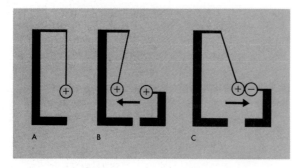

Table 2-1 Fundamental Particles

	Electric Charge	Mass
Electron	−1	0.00055
Proton	+1	1.00760
Neutron	0	1.00890

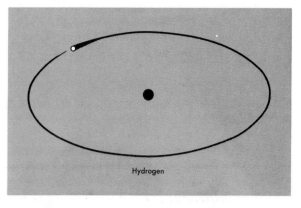

Figure 2-2 Schematic sketch of hydrogen atom, which consists of 1 proton and 1 electron. This is the simplest atom.

ATOMIC SIZE AND MASS The electrons form a protective shield around the nucleus and give size to the atom. In describing atomic dimensions we use a unit of length called the **angstrom** (abbreviated Å), which is one hundred-millionth of a centimeter (0.00000001 cm), usually written 1×10^{-8} cm.

Diameters of atomic nuclei range from a ten-thousandth to a hundred-thousandth of an angstrom—that is from 10^{-4} to 10^{-5} Å, which is from 10^{-12} to 10^{-13} cm. Atoms of the most common elements have diameters of 2 Å, which is roughly 20,000 to 200,000 times the diameter of their nuclei. On another scale, if the sun were the nucleus of our atomic model then the diameter of the atom would be greater than the diameter of the entire solar system.

The atom has not only size but **mass**. Within the atom the nucleus, which occupies only a thousandth of a billionth of the volume of the atom, contains 99.95 per cent of the atomic mass (see Table 2-1).

Elements

An atom is the smallest unit of an element. Ninety-two elements are known to occur in nature and a number of others have been made by man in the laboratory. Every element is a special combination of protons, neutrons, and electrons. Each element is identified by the number of protons in its nucleus and is designated by a name and a symbol.

Element Number 1 is a combination of one proton and one electron (see Figure 2-2). Long before its atomic structure was known, this element was named hydrogen, or "water-former" (from Greek roots *hydro* and *gen* meaning "water" and "to be born"), because water is

formed when hydrogen burns in air. Its symbol is H. Hydrogen has first place in the list of elements because it has one proton in its nucleus.

Element Number 2 consists of two protons (plus two neutrons in the most common form) and two electrons (see Figure 2-3). It was named helium, with the symbol He, from the Greek *helios*, "the sun," because it was first identified in the solar spectrum before it was isolated on the earth. Helium's place in the list of elements is Number 2, because it has two protons in its nucleus.

Figure 2-3 Diagrammatic representation of an atom of helium. The nucleus consists of 2 protons and 2 neutrons, and accordingly has a mass number of 4. There are 2 electrons (negative charges) to balance the positive charges on the 2 protons. Since there are 2 protons in the nucleus, this atom is number 2 in the table of elements. The symbol $_2\text{He}^4$ indicates number 2 in the table of elements, He for the name helium, and a mass number of 4. The nucleus of helium (2 protons + 2 neutrons) without any accompanying electrons is sometimes called an alpha particle.

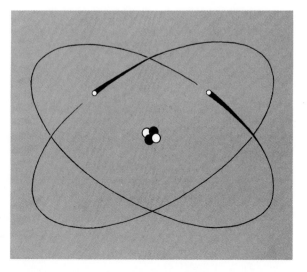

Figure 2-4 Electron shells around a nucleus. In true scale, the diameter of the shells is 20,000 to 200,000 times the diameter of the nucleus. If the sun were the nucleus, the electron shells would embrace more space than the entire solar system. Yet, the nucleus contains 99.95 per cent of the mass of the entire atom.

Each addition of a proton, with a matching electron to maintain electrical balance, produces another element. Neutrons seem to be included more or less indiscriminately, though there are about as many neutrons as protons in the common form of many of the elements. The list of elements appears in Appendix A.

Each electron swings around the nucleus in a definite path of travel, called its energy-

Figure 2-5 Schematic sketch of deuterium, an isotope of hydrogen formed by the addition of a neutron to the nucleus. It has a mass number of 2.

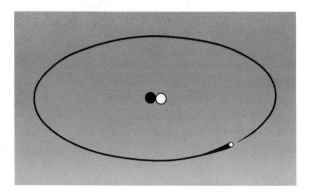

level orbital. These orbitals are arranged systematically at different distances from the nucleus (see Figure 2-4), and a specific amount of energy is required to maintain an electron at a given distance from its nucleus. For convenient reference, these orbitals are sometimes referred to as **energy-level shells.**

If you examine the list of elements in Appendix A, you will see that as electrons are added to match the increasing numbers of protons, they follow a simple pattern for the first 18 elements. After that, the system changes somewhat, but in the entire list there is **no atom with more than 8 electrons in its outermost shell.** The elements that have that maximum number are the inert gases neon, argon, krypton, xenon, and radon, which rarely combine with other elements. The number of electrons in the outer shell of an atom determines the manner and ease with which it can join with other atoms to form more complex structures (see "Compounds" below).

ISOTOPES Every element has alternate forms which, though essentially identical chemically and physically, have different masses (see Appendix A). Such forms are called **isotopes** (pronounced eye'-so-tope), from the Greek *iso,* "equal" or "the same," and *topos,* "place," since they occupy the same place in the table of elements, based on the number of protons in the nuclei. Isotopes show differences in mass as a result of differences in the number of neutrons in their nuclei. For example, hydrogen with 1 proton and no neutrons in its nucleus has a mass number of 1. When a neutron is present, however, the atom is an isotope of hydrogen with a mass number of 2, called *deuterium* (see Figure 2-5).

IONS **An ion is an electrically unbalanced form of an atom** or group of atoms. An atom is electrically neutral. But if it loses an electron from its outermost shell, the portion that remains behind has an extra unmatched positive charge. This unit is known as a positively charged ion. If the outermost shell gains an electron, the ion has an extra negative charge,

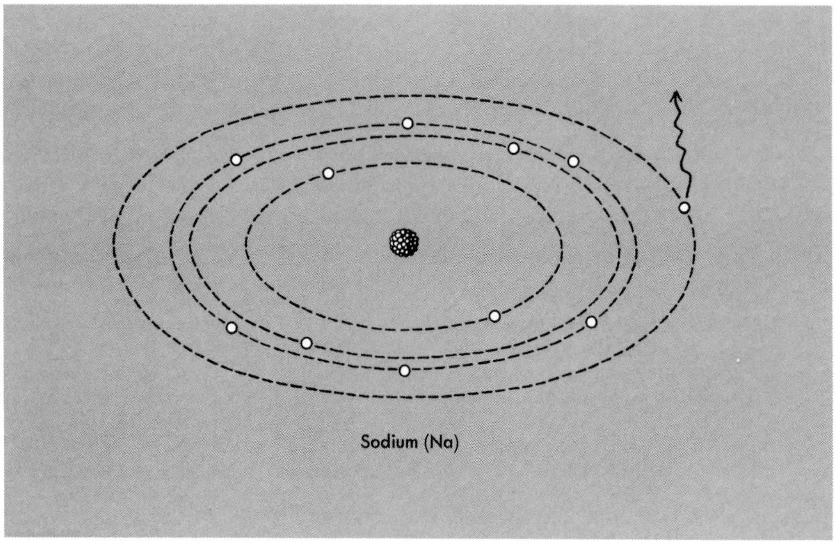

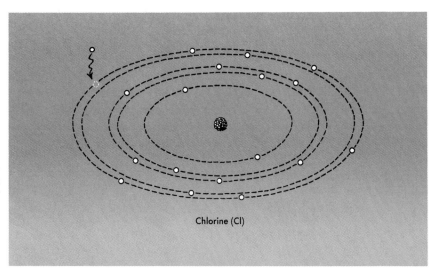

Figure 2-6 Formation of the sodium Na$^+$ results when the sodium atom loses the only electron in its outermost shell.

Sodium (Na)

and is known as a negatively charged ion. More than 1 electron may be lost or gained, as we shall see later, leading to the formation of ions with 2 or more units of electrical charge.

Compounds

Compounds are combinations of elements, effected mostly through the joining of ions. Those formed by life processes are called **organic compounds.** Others are known as **inorganic compounds.**

As we have just seen, elements with 8 electrons in their outermost shell do not combine readily with other elements. On the other hand, elements that have fewer than 8 electrons in their outermost shell readily shed or pick up electrons in an effort to achieve that magic number.

For example, an atom of sodium has only 1 electron in its outer shell, but 8 in the next shell (see Appendix A). By losing that outside electron, it becomes a positively charged ion (represented by the symbol Na$^+$), with 8 electrons in its outer shell (see Figure 2-6). Chlorine, on the other hand, has 7 electrons in its outer shell. By picking up 1 more, it becomes a negatively charged ion (represented by the symbol Cl$^-$), with 8 electrons in its outer shell (see Figure 2-7).

If a positive sodium ion and a negative chlorine ion approach each other, the electrical attraction of their opposite charges brings them firmly together, with what is called an **ionic bond,** to form a new product with properties unlike those of either sodium or chlorine. This product is the mineral halite (hay'-light), or common table salt. The chemical designation

Figure 2-7 Formation of the chlorine ion Cl$^-$ results when a chlorine atom gains an electron in its outermost shell, to make the total 8.

Chlorine (Cl)

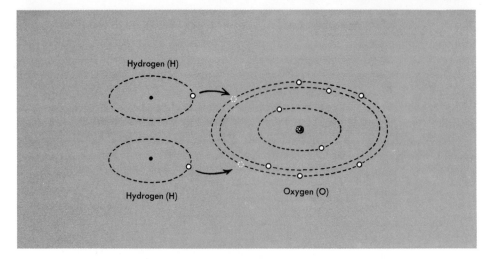

Figure 2-8 Two hydrogen atoms and 1 oxygen atom join to form water, H_2O, by a covalent bond. In this bond, the hydrogen electrons do double duty in a sense, filling the two empty places in the outer shell of oxygen, yet remaining at their normal distance from their hydrogen nuclei. The result is the formation of a molecule of water, the smallest unit that displays the properties of that compound.

for this compound is simply a combination of the symbols for the elements that compose it—NaCl.

The atoms of elements can combine in other ways to form compounds, as, for example, in the formation of a water molecule. Oxygen has 6 electrons in its outer shell (see Appendix A) and therefore needs 2 more to achieve 8. If 2 hydrogen atoms, each of which has only a single electron, approach an oxygen atom, the hydrogen electrons in effect slip into the vacant slots in the outer shell of the oxygen atom, but do not separate from their own protons. So the hydrogen nuclei are really *sharing* their electrons with the oxygen nucleus (see Figure 2-8). When this happens the atoms are said to be **covalently bonded.** Again, the result is a compound that is different in every way from the elements themselves. This compound is water,

whose symbol, H_2O, represents the elements that make it up and the proportions in which they are present. The combination of 2 atoms of hydrogen and 1 atom of oxygen forms the smallest unit that possesses the properties of water. This unit is called a **molecule** of water. **A molecule is the smallest unit of a compound which displays the characteristic properties of that compound.**

Since the oxygen atom has in effect gained 2 electrons, it takes on a negative charge. And each hydrogen atom, acting as though it had lost its electron, takes on a positive charge. As a result, a molecule of water acts like a small rod, with a positive charge on one end and a negative charge on the other (see Figure 2-9). These ends are referred to as a positive pole and a negative pole, because of the molecule's similarity to a bar magnet. The molecule, then,

Figure 2-9 The dipolar character of water. The oxygen has, in effect, gained 2 electrons, hence a double negative charge, whereas the hydrogen atoms have each lost the effective service of an electron and represent positive charges. Accordingly, the water molecule acts like a small rod with a positive charge on one end and a negative charge on the other, as suggested in B. Combinations of water molecules are suggested in C.

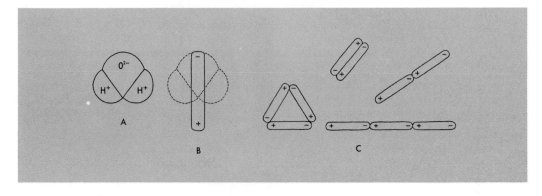

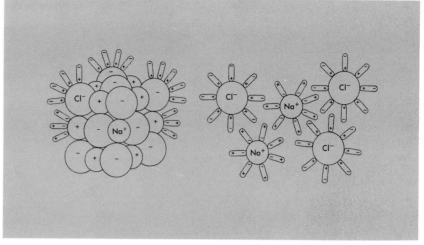

Figure 2-10 Mechanism by which water dissolves salt. Water dipoles attach themselves to the ions that compose the salt and overcome the ionic attractions that hold the salt together as a solid. Each Na^+ and Cl^- ion is then convoyed by a number of water dipoles into the body of the liquid.

is a **dipole** ("two-pole"), and water is known as a **dipolar compound.** This fact gives water special properties that make it an extremely important agent in geological processes. The mechanism by which water dissolves salt (see Figure 2-10) is an illustration of the ease with which water dissolves various substances and participates in weathering and other geological activities.

Organization of Matter

We have seen that matter is composed of fundamental particles (protons, neutrons, and electrons) combined into atoms. In nature there are 92 different combinations, each of which is an element. Elements, in turn, combine to form compounds (see Table 2-2).

Table 2-2 The Organization of Matter

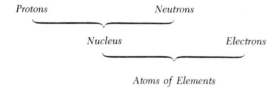

Protons   Neutrons

Nucleus   Electrons

Atoms of Elements

1 Proton	2 Protons (Neutrons)	3 Protons (Neutrons) — — — — — — — — — — — — — — — — — —	92 Protons (Neutrons)
1 Electron	2 Electrons	3 Electrons	92 Electrons
ELEMENT NO. 1	ELEMENT NO. 2	ELEMENT NO. 3 — — — — — — — — — — — — — — — —	ELEMENT NO. 92

Number of Protons + Number of Neutrons = *Mass Number*

Gain or Loss of Neutrons $\longrightarrow$ *Isotopes*

Gain or Loss of Electrons $\longrightarrow$ *Ions*

Element + Element (etc.) $\longrightarrow$ *Compounds*   (Smallest Unit of Compound = Molecule)

Note: This table is continued in Table 2-5.

19

Figure 2-11 A large, perfect crystal of diamond (uncut), which is the external expression of the orderly internal arrangement of atoms of carbon. Weight 84 carats. (*From Kimberley, South Africa. Harvard Mineralogical Collection. Photo by Harry Groom.*)

MINERALS

The word "mineral" has many different meanings in everyday usage. Some people use it to refer to anything that is nonliving, according to the old classification of all matter as animal, vegetable, or mineral. To prospectors and miners, mineral is an ore. And advertisers of pharmaceutical products associate the term with vitamins. But in our discussion, **"mineral"** will be used to refer to a **solid element or com-**

pound that has been formed by inorganic processes. Later on, we shall expand this definition to make it more comprehensive.

Mineral Composition

More than 2,000 minerals are known. Some are relatively simple compounds of elements in the solid state, others are complex. The diamond (Figure 2-11) is composed of only one element—carbon. Common table salt, really the mineral halite, is composed of two elements, sodium and chlorine, in equal amounts—every sodium ion present is accompanied by one chlorine ion. The mineral pyrite (pie'-right), sometimes known as "fool's gold," is also composed of two elements, iron and sulfur. But in this mineral there are two ions of sulfur for each ion of iron, a relationship expressed by the chemical symbol for pyrite, FeS_2.

Every mineral has a constant composition of elements in definite proportion. Later on, we shall see that a mineral's composition can vary slightly with an occasional substitution of other elements, but not enough to create a new mineral.

Figure 2-12 Cubic crystals of pyrite. Striations are clear on the large specimen. Note that those in adjacent faces are perpendicular to each other. The small specimen consists of three cubes intergrown. The reference grid of 2-inch squares in this picture and other photographs in the chapter supplies scale. (*Harvard Mineralogical Collection. Photo by Walter R. Fleischer.*)

Table 2-3 **Most Abundant Elements in the Earth's Crust***

Element Number	Name and Symbol	Volume Per Cent
8	Oxygen (O)	93.77
19	Potassium (K)	1.83
11	Sodium (Na)	1.32
20	Calcium (Ca)	1.03
14	Silicon (Si)	.86
13	Aluminum (Al)	.47
26	Iron (Fe)	.43
12	Magnesium (Mg)	.29

* Based on Brian Mason, *Principles of Geochemistry*, 2nd ed. (New York: John Wiley & Sons, Inc., 1960), p. 46.

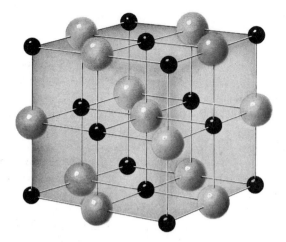

Figure 2-13 Schematic arrangement of sodium ions (*black*) with positive electrical charge, Na$^+$, and chlorine ions (*white*) with negative electrical charge, Cl$^-$, to form the ionic compound NaCl, common salt. The ions are held together by their unlike electrical charges. They are actually thought of as spheres (Na$^+$ with a radius of .98Å, and Cl$^-$ with a radius of 1.8Å) packed together as closely as possible. Here, the structure has been opened up to show the arrangement of ions in 3 dimensions.

Mineral Structure

The formation of a solid can be illustrated in the laboratory by preparing a white-hot liquid composed of sodium and chlorine. So long as the temperature of the liquid is kept at a high enough level, the activity of the ions is great enough to overcome their electrical attraction for one another. Even though they come into contact from time to time, the high temperature keeps them moving about freely. Then, as the temperature is reduced, they begin to lose their freedom of movement, and join together to form the compound sodium-chlorine. With further cooling, larger and larger clusters develop until finally all the ions are united in fixed positions. Now the sodium and chlorine appear as solid sodium chloride, the mineral halite.

The composition of the resulting solid is the same as that of the white-hot liquid; but in the solid state, the ions of sodium and chlorine are joined together in a definite pattern (see Figure 2-13). The pattern that the atoms of elements assume in a mineral is called its **crystalline structure,** the orderly arrangement of its atoms. In halite, the ions of sodium alternate with ions of chlorine.

Each mineral has a unique crystalline structure that will distinguish it from another mineral even if the two are composed of the same element or elements. Consider the minerals diamond and graphite, for example. Each is composed of one element, carbon (see Figure 2-14). In diamond, each atom of carbon is bonded to four neighboring carbon atoms. This complete joining of all its atoms produces a very strong bond and is the reason why diamond is so hard. In graphite, each atom of carbon is bonded in a plane to three neighboring atoms. This bonding forms sheets of layers of carbon

Figure 2-14 Different arrangements of atoms of carbon. The crystalline structure of diamond. The planar arrangement of graphite. (*Photos by Navias.*)

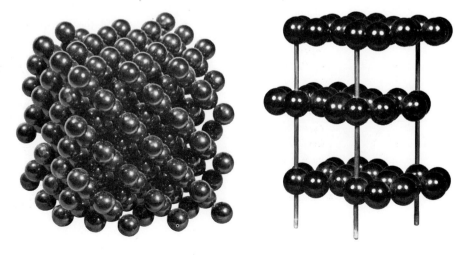

piled one on another, but the sheets can be separated easily. Thus graphite is a soft substance.

Pyrite and marcasite are two other minerals with identical composition, FeS_2, but with different crystalline structures. In pyrite, ions of iron are equally spaced in all directions. In marcasite, they are not equally spaced. The difference in spacing accounts for their being two different minerals (see Figure 2-15).

Other minerals may have more complicated crystalline structures: They may contain more elements and have these joined together in more complex patterns. The color, shape, and size of any given mineral may vary from one sample to another, but the **internal atomic arrangement of its component elements is identical in all specimens of a particular mineral.**

After taking all these factors into account, we find it necessary to include in our definition of a mineral not only the fact that it is an inorganic solid element or compound with a fixed chemical composition but also that it has **an orderly internal atomic arrangement of its elements.**

Identification of Minerals

All the properties of minerals are determined by the composition and internal atomic arrangement of their elements. So far, we have been talking about chemical properties—the factors that account for the existence of so many different minerals from such a limited number of elements. We can identify minerals on the basis of their chemical properties, but their physical properties are the ones most often used. Physical properties include such things as crystal form, hardness, specific gravity, cleavage, color, streak, and striations.

CRYSTAL FORM When any mineral grows without interference, it develops a characteristic **crystal form** that will be evident as soon as the mineral is large enough. If its development is constricted or impeded in any way, the characteristic form becomes distorted or modified.

The mineral quartz, for example, occurs in many rocks as irregular grains because its growth was constricted. Yet even in these irregular grains, the ions are arranged according to their typical crystalline structure. In some parts of the world, however, where conditions permitted the mineral to develop freely, crystals of quartz can be readily identified: They are always six-sided prisms. Whether an individual crystal of quartz is a quarter of an inch long or 10 inches long, the sides of the prism always come together at the same angle, and the basic crystal form is always the same (see Figure 2-16).

The crystal form of diamond is an eight-sided figure called an octahedron (see Figure 2-11); graphite exhibits a flat crystal with

Figure 2-15 Patterns of atoms under x-ray. *Top:* Pyrite shows orderly arrangement distinctive of crystalline structure. The mineral is composed of iron and sulfur, FeS_2. Large spots are atoms of iron; small ones are atoms of sulfur. Each atom of iron is bonded to 2 atoms of sulfur, and spacing of iron atoms is the same in both directions of the plane of the photograph. Magnification approximately 2.2 million diameters. *Bottom:* Marcasite, FeS_2. Note difference between horizontal and vertical spacing of iron atoms. Compare with pyrite. Magnification about 2.8 million diameters. *(Photos by Martin J. Buerger.)*

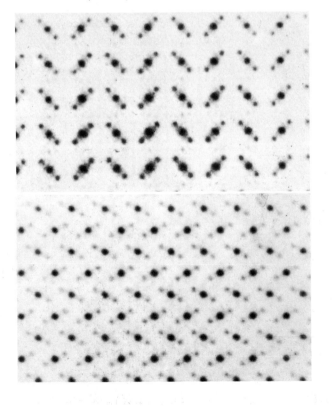

six sides. As we know, both minerals are composed of carbon. The difference in their crystal forms comes from the arrangement of carbon atoms—one pattern in diamond, another in graphite.

The crystal form of the mineral pyrite is a cube; that of marcasite is a flattened or tubular shape. Here, again, the reason for the difference in crystal form lies in the internal arrangement of their atoms.

Every mineral has one or more characteristic crystal shapes—the external form produced by its crystalline structure.

HARDNESS   Hardness is another property governed by the internal atomic arrangement of the elements of minerals. Again, graphite and diamond come to mind as contrasting examples. Their difference results from the ways in which the atoms of carbons are joined.

Hardness is a measure of the resistance that a smooth surface of a mineral offers to being scratched. It might be called the mineral's "scratchability." For example, if you pick up a piece of granite and try to scratch one of its light-colored grains with a steel knife blade, the granite simply refuses to be scratched. But if you drag one of its light-colored grains across a piece of glass, a scratch is easily made in the glass. Clearly, then, these particular mineral grains in granite are harder than either steel or glass. But if you have a piece of topaz handy, you can reveal the vulnerability of these light-colored mineral grains. For although they are harder than either steel or glass, they are not as hard as topaz.

Minerals differ widely in hardness (see Appendix D). Some are so soft that they can be scratched with a fingernail. Some are so hard that a steel knife is required to scratch them. But diamond, which is the hardest mineral known, cannot be scratched by any other substance.

SPECIFIC GRAVITY   Every mineral has a definite weight per cubic inch. This characteristic weight is usually described by comparing it with the weight of the same volume of water. The number that represents this comparison is called the **specific gravity** of the mineral.

The specific gravity of a mineral increases with the mass numbers of its constituent elements and with how closely these elements are packed together in their crystalline structure. Most rock-forming minerals have a specific gravity of around 2.7, although the average specific gravity of metallic minerals is about 5. Pure gold has the highest specific gravity, 19.3.

It is not difficult to acquire a sense of relative weight by which to compare specific gravities. We can all learn to tell the difference between two bags of equal size, one filled with

Figure 2-16 Quartz crystals. Regardless of the shape or size of crystals, the angles between true crystal faces remain the same. Transverse striations on prism faces are most clearly seen on the faces of the two large crystals, which also carry blotches of foreign matter, but striations are present on faces of the other crystals, too. The large, stubby crystal came from Dauphine, France; the others from Brazil. (*Harvard Mineralogical Collection. Photo by Walter R. Fleischer.*)

feathers and one filled with lead, and experience in hefting stones has given most geologists a sense of the "normal" weight of rocks.

CLEAVAGE **Cleavage** is the tendency of a mineral to break in certain preferred directions along smooth plane surfaces. Cleavage planes are governed by the internal arrangement of the atoms. They represent the directions in which the atomic bonds are relatively weak. Cleavage, then, is a **direction** of weakness, and a mineral sample tends to break along planes parallel to this direction.

COLOR Although color is not a very reliable property in identifying most minerals, it is useful in making certain general distinctions. For example, minerals containing iron are usually "dark-colored." In geologic usage, "dark" includes dark gray, dark green, and black. Minerals that contain aluminum as a predominate element are usually "light-colored," a term that includes purples, deep red, and some browns.

STREAK The **streak** of a mineral is the color it displays in finely powdered form. The streak may be quite different from the color of a hand specimen. For example, specimens of the mineral hematite may be brown, green, or black in color, but they always have a distinctive red-brown streak. One of the simplest ways of determining the streak of a mineral is to rub a specimen across a piece of unglazed porcelain known as a streak plate. The color of the powder left behind on the streak plate helps to identify the mineral.

STRIATIONS A few common minerals have parallel, thread-like lines or narrow bands called **striations** running across their surfaces. These can be seen clearly on crystals of quartz and pyrite, for example (see Figures 2-12 and 2-16). Once again, this property is a reflection of the internal arrangement of the atoms of the crystals.

Rock-Forming Minerals

Though there are more than 2,000 minerals known, only a few of these are **rock-forming minerals,** the minerals that constitute most of the rocks of the earth's crust.

SILICATES More than 90 per cent of the rock-forming minerals are silicates, compounds containing silicon and oxygen and one or more metals. Each silicate mineral has as its basic compound a complex ion called the **silicon-oxygen tetrahedron** (see Figure 2-17), one of the first compounds to form as the molten earth cooled. It is a combination of one "small" silicon ion with a radius of .42 Å surrounded as closely as geometrically possible by four "large" oxygen ions with a radius of 1.32 Å (forming a tetrahedron). The oxygen ions contribute an electric charge of -8 to the tetrahedron, and the silicon ion contributes $+4$. So the tetrahedron is a complex ion with a net charge of -4. Its symbol is $(SiO_4)^{4-}$.

Some silicates consist of single tetrahedra alternating with positive metal ions. In others, tetrahedra are joined together into chains, sheets, or three-dimensional structures.

The most common of the silicate minerals are olivine, augite, hornblende, biotite, muscovite, feldspars, and quartz. Each one of these common rock-forming silicate minerals has a skeleton of silicon-oxygen tetrahedra.

FERROMAGNESIANS In the first four of these rock-forming silicates—olivine, augite, hornblende, and biotite—the silicon-oxygen

Figure 2-17 The silicon-oxygen tetrahedron $(SiO_4)^{4-}$. The upper view is from above and the lower from the side. This is the most important complex ion in geology, since it is the central building unit of nearly 90 per cent of the minerals of the earth's crust.

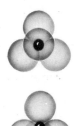

tetrahedra are joined by ions of iron and magnesium. Iron is interchangeable with magnesium in the crystalline structure of these silicates, because the ions of both elements are approximately the same size and have the same positive electric charge. These silicate minerals are known as ferromagnesians, from the joining of the Latin *ferum*, "iron," with magnesium. All four ferromagnesians are very dark or black in color and have a higher specific gravity than the other rock-forming silicate minerals.

Olivine. Silicon-oxygen tetrahedra joined with positive ions of iron or magnesium or both form olivine; thus, its formula is best written $(Mg, Fe)_2SiO_4$. Its specific gravity ranges from

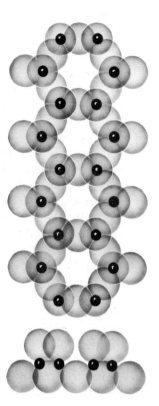

Figure 2-19 *Top:* Double chain of tetrahedra viewed from above. *Bottom:* Viewed from an end. The doubling of the augite chain is accomplished by the sharing of oxygen atoms by adjacent chains.

Figure 2-18 *Top:* Single chain of tetrahedra viewed from above. *Bottom:* Viewed from an end. Each silicon ion (*small black sphere*) has 2 of the 4 oxygen ions of its tetrahedron bonded exclusively to itself, and it shares the other 2 with neighboring tetrahedra fore and aft. The resulting individual chains are in turn bonded to one another by positive metallic ions. Since these bonds are weaker than the silicon-oxygen bonds that form each chain, cleavage develops parallel to the chains.

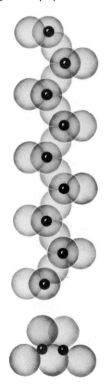

3.27 to 3.37, increasing with the amount of iron present. This mineral, named for its characteristic olive color, usually occurs in grains or granular masses without well-developed cleavage.

Augite. The crystalline structure of **augite** is based on single chains of tetrahedra,[1] as shown in Figure 2-18, joined together by ions of iron, magnesium, and calcium. Color range is very dark green to black; its streak is colorless; its specific gravity ranges from 3.2 to 3.4, and its cleavage is along two planes almost at *right* angles to each other. This cleavage angle is important in distinguishing augite from hornblende. A good way to remember it is to recall that augite rhymes with "right."

Hornblende. The crystalline structure of the mineral **hornblende** is based on double chains of tetrahedra, as shown in Figure 2-19,

---

[1] The term "tetrahedra" will be used throughout this chapter to refer to silicon-oxygen tetrahedra.

Figure 2-20 Cleavage of hornblende (*left*) compared with that of augite (*right*). The top "roof" of the hornblende specimen and the top and perpendicular left-hand faces of the augite are cleavage surfaces. Throughout each specimen, easiest breaking is parallel to these surfaces. On the front face of the augite are some "steps" outlined by cleavage planes. Such steps are the most common manifestation of cleavage, which seldom produces pieces as large as those shown here. (*Harvard Mineralogical Collection. Photo by Walter R. Fleischer.*)

Figure 2-21 Tetrahedral sheets. Each tetrahedron is surrounded by 3 others, and each silicon ion has 1 of the 4 oxygen ions to itself, while sharing the other 3 with its neighbors.

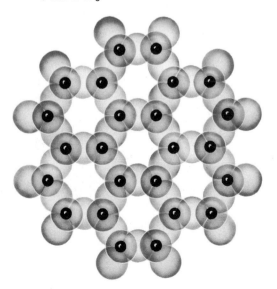

joined together by the iron and magnesium ions common to all ferromagnesians, and also by ions of calcium, sodium, and aluminum. Hornblende's color range is dark green to black, like that of augite; its streak is colorless; its specific gravity is 3.2. Two directions of cleavage meet at angles of approximately 56° and 124°, which helps distinguish hornblende from augite (see Figure 2-20).

Biotite. Named in honor of the French physicist J. B. Biot, **biotite** (buy'-oh-tight) is a mica (my'-ka, from the Latin *micare,* "to shine"). Like all the other micas, it is constructed of tetrahedra in sheets, as shown in Figure 2-21. Each silicon ion shares three oxygen ions with adjacent silicon ions to form a pattern like wire netting. The fourth, unshared oxygen ion of each tetrahedron stands above the plane of all the others. The basic structural unit of mica consists of two of these sheets of tetrahedra, with their flat surfaces facing outward and

26

their inner surfaces held together by positive ions. In biotite, those ions are iron and magnesium. These basic double sheets of mica, in turn, are loosely joined together by positive ions of potassium.

Layers of biotite, or any of the other micas, can be peeled off easily (see Figure 2-22), because there is perfect cleavage along the surfaces of these weak potassium bonds. In thick blocks, biotite is usually dark green, brown, or black. Its specific gravity ranges from 2.8 to 3.2.

NONFERROMAGNESIANS The other common rock-forming silicate minerals are known as the **nonferromagnesians,** simply because they do *not* contain iron or magnesium. These minerals are muscovite, the feldspars, and quartz. They are all marked by their light colors and relatively low specific gravities ranging from 2.6 to 3.0.

Muscovite. This white mica was so named because it was once used as a substitute for glass in old Russia (Muscovy). It has the same basic crystalline structure as biotite, but in muscovite each pair of tetrahedra sheets is tightly cemented together by ions of aluminum rather than iron and magnesium. As in biotite, however, the double sheets are held together loosely by potassium ions, along which cleavage readily takes place. In thick blocks, the color of muscovite is light yellow, brown, green, or red. Its specific gravity ranges from 2.8 to 3.1.

Feldspars. The most abundant rock-forming silicates are the **feldspars.** The name comes from the German *feld,* "field," and *spar,* a term used by miners for various nonmetallic minerals. Its name reflects the abundance of these minerals. Feldspars make up nearly 54 per cent of the minerals that are found in the earth's crust.

Figure 2-22 Mica cleavage. The large block (or ''book'') is bounded on the sides by crystal faces. Cleavage fragments lying in front of the large block are of different thicknesses, as indicated by their degrees of transparency. (*Photo by Walter R. Fleischer.*)

In the feldspars, each tetrahedron shares its oxygen ions with adjoining tetrahedra ions in a three-dimensional network. However, in one-quarter to one-half of the tetrahedra, aluminum ions with a radius of .51 Å and an electric charge of +3 have replaced silicon (with its radius of .42 Å and electric charge of +4) in the centers of the tetrahedra. The negative electric charge resulting from such substitution in the tetrahedra is corrected by the entry into the crystalline structures of ions of potassium, sodium, or calcium—K^{+1}, Na^{+1}, or Ca^{+2}. The proportions of K, Na, and Ca that enter the structure are determined by the temperature at the time of crystallization. Since the feldspars contain these elements in different proportions, they grade continuously one into another.

The mineral names given the feldspars are **orthoclase** and **plagioclase.** Plagioclase is in turn subdivided into two minerals: albite and anorthite. Each one is classified in terms of the "end members" of the sequence. **Orthoclase** is the one with potassium; **albite** has sodium; **anorthite** has calcium. The feldspars are listed in Table 2-4. In this table, the column headed "Diagnostic Positive Ion" (from the Greek *diagnostikos,* "able to distinguish") indicates the ion that corrects the electrical unbalance caused by the substitution of aluminum for silicon.

Orthoclase is named from the Greek *orthos,* "straight," and *klasis,* "a breaking," because the two dominant cleavages intersect at a right angle when a piece of orthoclase is broken (see Figure 2-23). Aluminum replaces silicon in every fourth tetrahedron, and positive ions of potassium correct the electrical unbalance. The streak of orthoclase is white; its color is white, gray, or pinkish; and its specific gravity is 2.57.

Plagioclase ("oblique-breaking") feldspars are so named because they have cleavage planes that intersect at about 86°. One of the cleavage planes is marked by striations. As we mentioned, the two plagioclase feldspars are albite and anorthite. In albite, aluminum replaces silicon in every fourth tetrahedron, and positive ions of sodium correct the electrical unbalance. The specific gravity of albite is 2.62. In anorthite, aluminum replaces silicon in every second tetrahedron, and positive ions of calcium correct the electrical unbalance. The specific gravity of anorthite is 2.76. Both plagioclase feldspars may be colorless, white, or gray, although some samples show a striking play of colors called opalescence.

Quartz. The very common mineral **quartz** is the only rock-forming silicate mineral that is composed exclusively of silicon-oxygen tetrahedra. Every oxygen ion is shared by adjacent silicon ions, which means that there are two ions of oxygen for every ion of silicon. This relationship is represented by the formula SiO_2. The specific gravity of quartz is 2.65.

Quartz usually appears smoky to clear in color, but many less common varieties include purple or violet **amethyst,** massive rose-red or pink **rose quartz,** smoky yellow to brown **smoky quartz,** and **milky quartz.** These color differences are caused by other elements that

Table 2-4 **Feldspars (Aluminosilicates)**

Diagnostic Positive Ion	Name	Symbol	Descriptive Name		Formula°
K^+	Orthoclase	Or	Potassic feldspar		$K(AlSi_3O_8)$
Na^+	Albite	Ab	Sodic feldspar	plagioclase	$Na(AlSi_3O_8)$
Ca^{+2}	Anorthite	An	Calcic feldspar	feldspars	$Ca(Al_2Si_2O_8)$

° In these formulas, the symbols *inside* the parentheses indicate the tetrahedra. The symbols *outside* the parentheses indicate the diagnostic ions—that is, the ions that are worked in among the tetrahedra.

are present as impurities. They are not caused by, and do not affect, the crystalline structure of the quartz.

OXIDE MINERALS Oxide minerals are formed by the direct union of an element with oxygen. These are relatively simple minerals compared to the complicated silicates. The oxide minerals are usually harder than any other class of minerals except the silicates, and they are heavier than others except the sulfides. Within the oxide class are the chief ores of iron, chromium, manganese, tin, and aluminum. Some common oxide minerals are ice (H_2O), corundum (Al_2O_3), hematite (Fe_2O_3), magnetite (Fe_3O_4), and cassiterite (SnO_2).

SULFIDE MINERALS Sulfide minerals are formed by the direct union of an element with sulfur. The elements that occur most commonly in combination with sulfur are iron, silver, copper, lead, zinc, and mercury. Some of these sulfide minerals occur as commercially valuable ores, such as pyrite (FeS_2), chalcocite (Cu_2S), galena (PbS), and sphalerite (ZnS).

CARBONATE AND SULFATE MINERALS We found that silicates are built around the complex ion $(SiO_4)^{4-}$—the silicon-oxygen tetrahedron. But two other complex ions also are of great importance in geology. One of these consists of a single carbon ion with three oxygen ions packed around it—$(CO_3)^{2-}$. Compounds in which this complex ion appears are called carbonates. For example, the combination of a calcium ion with a carbon-oxygen ion produces calcium carbonate, $CaCO_3$, known in its mineral form as **calcite.** This mineral is the principal component of the common sedimentary rock limestone. The other complex ion is

Figure 2-23 Feldspar cleavage in specimens of orthoclase. The large block on the right and the small fragment on the black box show the cleavage planes at nearly 90°, a characteristic of feldspars. (*Photo by Walter R. Fleischer.*)

$(SO_4)^{2-}$, a combination of one sulfur ion and four oxygen ions. This complex ion combines with other ions to form sulfates; for example, it joins with a calcium ion to form calcium sulfate, $CaSO_4$, the mineral anhydrite.

Definition of Minerals

We know that minerals are special combinations of elements or compounds in the solid state, and now we can complete our definition of a mineral: (1) It is a naturally occurring element or inorganic compound in the solid state; (2) it has a chemical composition which is fixed or which varies within narrow limits; (3) it has a crystalline structure; and (4) it exhibits certain physical properties as a result of its composition and crystalline structure. The organization of the common minerals is shown in Table 2-5.

Table 2-5 The Organization of Common Minerals (Continuation of Table 2-2)

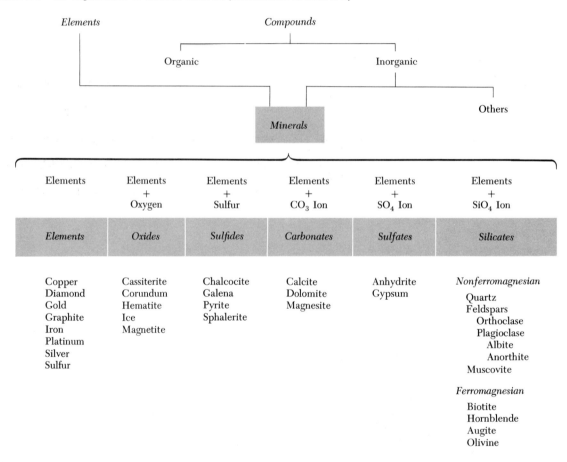

Elements	Elements + Oxygen	Elements + Sulfur	Elements + CO_3 Ion	Elements + SO_4 Ion	Elements + SiO_4 Ion
Elements	*Oxides*	*Sulfides*	*Carbonates*	*Sulfates*	*Silicates*
Copper	Cassiterite	Chalcocite	Calcite	Anhydrite	*Nonferromagnesian*
Diamond	Corundum	Galena	Dolomite	Gypsum	Quartz
Gold	Hematite	Pyrite	Magnesite		Feldspars
Graphite	Ice	Sphalerite			Orthoclase
Iron	Magnetite				Plagioclase
Platinum					Albite
Silver					Anorthite
Sulfur					Muscovite
					Ferromagnesian
					Biotite
					Hornblende
					Augite
					Olivine

SUMMARY

Rocks are composed of minerals, minerals of atoms, and atoms of protons, neutrons, and electrons. Ions are electrically unbalanced forms of atoms or groups of atoms produced by the gain or loss of electrons. Atoms of the 92 elements found in nature combine in various ways to form compounds called minerals, which make up the rocks of the earth.

Minerals are naturally occurring elements or compounds in the solid state and are inorganic in character. Each mineral has a chemical composition fixed within narrow limits and displays a crystalline structure. The composition and structure give rise to characteristic physical properties for each mineral type.

ADDITIONAL READING

Dennen, William, *Principles of Mineralogy* (rev. ed.). New York: Ronald Press Co., 1960.

Frey, Paul R., *College Chemistry* (3rd ed.). Englewood Cliffs, N.J.: Prentice-Hall, 1965.

Hurlbut, Cornelius, Jr., *Dana's Manual of Mineralogy* (17th ed.). New York: John Wiley & Sons, 1961.

Mason, Brian, *Principles of Geochemistry* (2nd ed.). New York: John Wiley & Sons, 1960.

Physical Science Study Committee, *Physics* (2nd ed.). Boston: D.C. Heath and Co., 1965.

3

Igneous Rocks

As we have seen, minerals are the units from which the rocks of the earth's crust are built. These rocks are divided into three main groups —igneous, sedimentary, and metamorphic. In this chapter we are concerned with the igneous rocks, but before we proceed with a detailed examination of this group, it will be useful to look at the general relationships of the three major rock types.

THE THREE ROCK FAMILIES

Igneous rocks, the ancestors of all other rocks, take their name from the Latin *ignis*, "fire." These "fire-formed" rocks were once a hot, molten, liquid-like mass known as a **magma,** which subsequently cooled into firm, hard rock. Thus, the lava flowing across the earth's surface from an erupting volcano soon cools and hardens into an igneous rock. But there are other igneous rocks now exposed at the surface that actually cooled some distance beneath the surface. We see such rocks today only because erosion has stripped away the rocks that covered them during their formation.

Most **sedimentary** rocks (from the Latin *sedimentum*, "settling") are made up of particles derived from the breakdown of pre-existing rocks. Usually these particles are transported by water, wind, or ice to new locations where they are deposited in new arrangements. For example, waves beating against a rocky shore may provide the sand grains and pebbles for a nearby beach. If these beach deposits were to be hardened, we would have sedimentary rock. One of the most characteristic features of sedimentary rocks is the layering of the deposits that make them up.

Metamorphic rocks compose the third large family of rocks. Metamorphic, meaning "changed form," refers to the fact that the original rock has been changed from its primary form to a new one. Earth pressures, heat, and chemically active fluids beneath the surface may all be involved in changing an originally sedimentary rock into a new metamorphic rock.

The Rock Cycle

We have suggested that there are definite relationships among sedimentary, igneous and metamorphic rocks. With time and changing conditions, any one of these rock types may be changed into some other form. These relationships form a cycle, as shown in Figure 3-2.

Figure 3-1 Igneous rocks form when molten rock material solidifies. Here a 900-foot fountain of lava spouts into the crater of Kilauea Iki, Hawaii. (*Photo by U.S. Geological Survey.*)

Figure 3-2 The rock cycle, shown diagramatically. If uninterrupted, the cycle will continue completely around the outer margin of the diagram from magma through igneous rocks, sediments, sedimentary rocks, metamorphic rocks, and back again to magma. The cycle may be interrupted, however, at various points along its course and follow the path of one of the arrows crossing through the interior of the diagram.

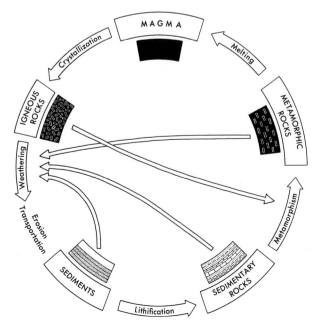

Figure 3-3 Many concepts of present-day geology stem directly from observations of the Scotsman James Hutton (1726–1797). (*From F. D. Adams, Birth and Development of the Geological Sciences. Reprinted by permission of Dover Publications, Inc., New York.*)

This is simply a way of tracing out the various paths that earth materials follow. The outer circle represents the complete cycle; the arrows within the circle represent shortcuts in the system that can be, and often are, taken. Notice that the igneous rocks are shown as having formed from a magma, and as providing one link in a continuous chain. From these parent rocks, through a variety of processes, all other rocks can be derived.

First, weathering attacks the solid rock, which either has been formed by the cooling of a lava flow at the surface, or is an igneous rock that was formed deep beneath the earth's surface and then was exposed by erosion. The products of weathering are the materials that will eventually go into the creation of new rocks—sedimentary, metamorphic, and even igneous. Landslides, wind, running water, and glacier ice all help to move the materials from one place to another. In the ideal cycle, this material seeks the ocean floors, where layers of soft mud, sand, and gravel are consolidated into sedimentary rocks. If the cycle continues without interruption, these new rocks may in

turn be deeply buried and subjected to heat, to pressures caused by overlying rocks, and to forces developed by earth movements. The sedimentary rocks may then change in response to these new conditions and become metamorphic rocks. If these metamorphic rocks undergo continued and increased heat and pressure, they may eventually lose their identity and melt into a magma. When this magma cools, we have an igneous rock again, and we have come full cycle.

But notice, too, that the complete rock cycle may be interrupted. An igneous rock, for example, may never be exposed at the surface and hence may never be converted to sediments by weathering. Instead, it may be subjected to pressure and heat and converted directly into a metamorphic rock without passing through the intermediate sedimentary stage. Other interruptions may take place if sediments, or sedimentary rocks, or metamorphic rocks are attacked by weathering before they continue to the next stage in the outer, complete cycle.

This concept of the rock cycle was probably first stated in the late 18th century by James Hutton:

> We are thus led to see a circulation in the matter of this globe, and a system of beautiful economy in the works of nature. This earth, like the body of an animal, is wasted at the same time that it is repaired. It has a state of growth and augmentation; it has another state, which is that of diminution and decay. This world is thus destroyed in one part, but it is renewed in another; and the operations by which this world is thus constantly renewed are as evident to the scientific eye, as are those in which it is necessarily destroyed.[1]

We can consider the rock cycle to be an outline of physical history. Each step has its

[1] James Hutton, *Theory of the Earth* (Edinburgh, 1795), II, 562. Hutton's theory of the earth was first presented as a series of lectures before the Royal Society of Edinburgh in 1785. These lectures were published in book form in 1795. Seven years later, Hutton's concepts were given new impetus through a more readable treatment called *Illustrations of the Huttonian Theory* by John Playfair.

place; each is a part of the whole picture. But we must remember that in a more fundamental sense the rock cycle represents a response of earth materials to various forms of energy. We must realize that matter and energy are inseparable, that earth materials change and features of the earth's face are altered in response to changes in energy.

DESCRIPTION OF IGNEOUS ROCKS

We have already seen that three groups of rocks—igneous, sedimentary, and metamorphic—record the history of the earth. In the course of this book, we will want to look at all of them in detail. Because igneous rocks seem to be the source of the other two types we shall begin our study with them, starting with a description and then developing a classification that stems from the description.

Let us assume that we are faced with a whole binful of specimens of igneous rocks, one that contains representatives of the most important types. Hopefully, if we could determine the characteristics of these rocks, we would find perhaps a way of bringing order to our jumbled pile of chaos. What characteristics

might we pick out? Here are some immediately obvious ones. First, color; second, specific gravity; third, texture; fourth, mineral composition.

Color

Color is the characteristic that we probably notice first, without even touching the rocks. We immediately detect that there is a group of very light-colored, almost white rocks and a group of dark green, almost black types. In between we see rocks of varying tones of gray, as well as some of pink and even red cast. If we select the lightest- and darkest-colored rocks and let them stand at either end of our color scale, we can arrange the rest of the rocks in all tones between the two end members. For example, because of their tone, we will want to arrange the pinkish and reddish rocks on the light gray side of our scale. This is a very simple—indeed, too simple—way of classifying rocks. Yet it can be important, as we shall see.

Specific Gravity

Now let's mix our rocks up and start our sorting over again. This time we will arrange our specimens according to their specific grav-

Figure 3-4 Igneous rocks range from very dark, almost black in color to very light almost white. Here, at Cohasset, Massachusetts, a dark basalt cuts across a light granite. (*Photo by John A. Shimer.*)

ity. At first we heft individual rock specimens by hand. We find that we can tell the difference between some of the rocks on the basis of their apparent specific gravity. Volume for volume some of them feel somewhat heavier than do others. Now if we use a simple balance we discover that the specific gravities range from approximately 2.3 to approximately 3.3. Furthermore, within this range, we find that the greatest number of rocks falls somewhere around 2.6 or 2.7. Another group has a density of about 3.0. We may even find a third peak half way between 2.6 and the 3.0. Looking at our pile of rocks, now separated by specific gravity, we will find that again we have arranged them more or less by color. The heaviest rocks are the darkest rocks. The light-colored rocks also have the lowest specific gravity. The rocks intermediate in color are intermediate in specific gravity. Still, there are one or two exceptions. For instance, there is one glassy rock (we know it as volcanic glass or **obsidian**) that is dark-colored, but has a specific gravity of only about 2.4. (Later, we can return to the problem of why it doesn't seem to follow the rule of dark color/high specific gravity.) We note, too, that the pink- and reddish-colored rocks generally group with the light-colored ones in having specific gravities that hover around 2.6.

Having sorted our rocks by color and by specific gravity, we find that we get approximately the same order of rocks whichever method we use. We are tempted to feel, then, that there is some relationship between color and specific gravity and that these characteristics represent something important in terms of the origin and classification of igneous rocks. Let us go on and look at some of the other characteristics.

Texture

In handling and sorting our igneous rocks, we very possibly noted another difference: Some of the rocks seem to be made up of smaller units, others seem to be homogeneous throughout. Let's try sorting on this basis now. If we look at the rocks more carefully, we will see that we can further subdivide these two groups. For instance, take the homogeneous group. Some of the rocks are very glassy, reflecting light and breaking as if they were the thick bottoms of milk bottles. This type would include obsidian. Others of this homogeneous group tend to have duller surfaces, or a matte

Figure 3-5 Obsidian, a rock with a glassy texture. (*Photo by Navias.*)

Figure 3-6 Basalt, a dark, fine-grained rock. (*Photo by Navias.*)

finish. So let's divide the homogeneous rocks on the basis of surface, **glassy** or **matte.**

Turning to the other pile of rocks, those with specimens made up of smaller units, we find that here, too, we can subdivide into at least two groups. In one, the individual particles that we can see with the naked eye are more or less the same size. In the second, the large crystals visible to the naked eye are set

Figure 3-7 Granite, a coarse-grained rock. (*Photo by Navias.*)

in a matrix, or **groundmass,** in which finer crystals may or may not be discerned; the effect is rather like plums in a plum pudding, or raisins in a piece of raisin bread.

Now if we look at our four new piles of rocks (the glassy, the matte, the coarse-grained, and the plum pudding groups) we find that each pile includes rocks of different color and specific gravity. If the characteristics described in these four piles are significant, they don't relate to color or to specific gravity.

In this third sorting of our rock pile, we have been grouping on the basis of **texture,** a term derived from the Latin *texere,* "to weave." Texture has many meanings. For instance, a cake has "texture," sometimes light and fluffy, sometimes heavy and sodden. A shirt has texture. A jacket has texture. Texture is a matter of the size of the individual components of a specimen (whether it be cake, shirt, or jacket) and how these components are arranged. In reference to rocks, texture means the shape, size, arrangement, and distribution of the minerals that make up the rocks. Now, let us give formal definitions to the four textures we used to sort our rocks.

COARSE-GRAINED TEXTURE   When the particles in a rock can be seen with the naked eye, we call the texture **coarse-grained.** If we look carefully at this rock's minerals, with a hand lense or a microscope, we will see that the minerals interlock, one with the next. The actual size of the mineral may vary from perhaps a sixteenth of an inch to several inches, usually on the smaller side. In speaking of coarse-grained textures, geologists usually refer only to those rocks with more or less equigranular texture, that is, one in which most of the particles are all of the same general size. When some of the particles are larger than the groundmass in which they rest, we use another term, "porphyritic," which will be explained below.

FINE-GRAINED TEXTURE   When we are unable to see the individual particles with the naked eye but must instead use a microscope

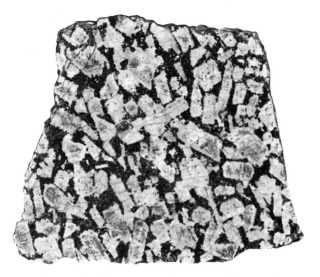

Figure 3-8　A granite porphyry. (*Photo by Navias.*)

to identify them, we call the texture **fine-grained.** In our piles of rocks, the fine-grained igneous rocks are those with a matte surface. What we actually see are the little pinpoints of minerals that give the specimen a rather rough surface. Although we cannot see the individual particles, we could, with a microscope, make out the interlocking pattern of the individual mineral grains.

GLASSY TEXTURE　Among our homogeneous rocks, we found several which showed a very shiny, glassy aspect, ranging from red to black in color. Indeed, they are made of **volcanic glass.** Appropriately, we call the texture glassy. Were we to put this rock under a microscope, we would find that in fact it con-

tains no, or very few, individual mineral particles. The great bulk of the rock is made up of unorganized, or noncrystalline, material.

PORPHYRITIC TEXTURE　When larger crystals are set in a groundmass of finer crystals, we refer to the texture as **porphyritic.** These larger crystals are called "phenocrysts," from the Greek *phainein,* "to show." The term porphyry, which comes from the Greek word for "purple," was originally applied to rocks containing phenocrysts set in a dark red or purple groundmass. This original porphyry is the well-known material from which some statues of ancient Rome were made.

PRELIMINARY CLASSIFICATION　On the basis of the observations we have made so far—color, specific gravity, and texture—we can construct a classification system, as suggested in Figure 3-9. Notice that in this figure the textures grade upward from glassy through fine-grained and prophyritic to coarse. The other axis is devoted to an increase in specific gravity from low to high, as well as a change in color from light to dark. Into this classification system, we can fit most of our rocks. For instance, a light gray, coarse-grained rock with a specific gravity of about 2.6 is what we generally refer to as a granite. But in actual practice, we use a somewhat more sophisticated classification than that in Figure 3-9. And although texture is used as indicated, for specific gravity and color we will substitute mineral composition.

Figure 3-9　A preliminary classification system for igneous rocks based on texture (*vertical axis*) and color and density (*horizontal axis*).

TEXTURE	LIGHT COLOR	INTERMEDIATE COLOR	DARK COLOR
Coarse-grained			
Porphyritic			
Fine-grained			
Glassy			
	Low Density	Intermediate Density	High Density

Composition

The material from which things are made is very often fundamental to our classification of objects. We can begin determining the material of our igneous rocks by identifying the minerals present in the coarse-grained rocks. We will see that the light-colored rocks are generally very low in ferromagnesian minerals, those that are present being usually the micas and amphiboles. Furthermore, there is a recognizable amount of quartz. And there is a great deal of feldspar, both orthoclase and plagioclase, the latter tending more toward the albite side than the anorthite side. In very dark-colored, coarse-grained rocks, we find that there is no quartz, and no orthoclase. But there are considerable amounts of dark-colored anorthite plagioclase, and of ferromagnesian minerals, primarily augite and olivines. Coarse-grained rocks of intermediate color will have little or no orthoclase, little or no quartz, a great deal of plagioclase (intermediate in composition between albite and anorthite) and a goodly amount of ferromagnesian minerals, mostly hornblende with some augite. If we were to identify the major constituents for all the coarse-grained rocks, we would find that there is a complete gradation in mineral composition from light to dark, as shown in Figure 3-10.

We cannot identify with the naked eye, or even with the hand lens, the mineral components of the fine-grained igneous rocks. Use of the microscope, however, has demonstrated that the same gradation holds for the fine-grained as for the coarse-grained rocks. Turning to the porphyritic rocks, we find that if the mineral constituents are all coarse enough to be identified by the naked eye, then these rocks, too, follow the same compositional order as the fine-grained and the coarse-grained rocks. For those porphyritic rocks whose groundmass is too fine to be identified with the naked eye, the microscope again demonstrates the same pattern as found in the other types.

CLASSIFICATION OF IGNEOUS ROCKS

No classification is any more than an attempt to bring order out of a series of observations. Since our observations have been directed toward color, specific gravity, texture, and mineral composition, our classification will be

Figure 3-10 As a coarse-grained rock varies from a light to dark color and from a lower to higher density, so also does the mineral composition change.

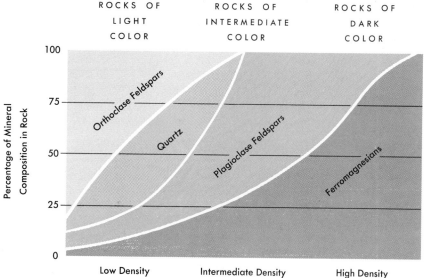

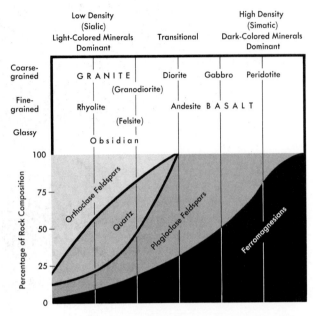

Low Density (Sialic) Light-Colored Minerals Dominant — Transitional — High Density (Simatic) Dark-Colored Minerals Dominant

Coarse-grained: G R A N I T E (Granodiorite) · Diorite · Gabbro · Peridotite

Fine-grained: Rhyolite (Felsite) · Andesite · B A S A L T

Glassy: O b s i d i a n

Percentage of Rock Composition: 100, 75, 50, 25, 0

Orthoclase Feldspars · Quartz · Plagioclase Feldspars · Ferromagnesians

Figure 3-11 General composition is indicated by a line from the name to the composition chart: Granite and rhyolite consist of about 50 per cent orthoclase, 25 per cent quartz, and 25 per cent divided among plagioclase feldspars and ferromagnesian minerals. Relative importance is stressed by the size of the lettering for rock names: Granite is the most important coarse-grained rock, basalt the most important fine-grained rock. (Composition chart modified after Pirsson and Knopf, Rocks and Rock Minerals. New York: John Wiley & Sons, 1926, p. 144.)

based on these characteristics. The classification is presented in Figure 3-11, which is nothing more than a combination of Figures 3-9 and 3-10. The names of rocks are arbitrarily assigned on the basis of average mineral compositions. Actually, there are many more names in use than are shown in Figure 3-11. Sometimes intermediate types are indicated by such names as granodiorite, a composition between that of granite and that of diorite.

Light-Colored Igneous Rocks

The igneous rocks on the light side of the classification chart are light in both color and specific gravity. They are sometimes referred to as **sialic** rocks. The term "sial," coined from the chemical symbols for silicon and aluminum,

is generally used in speaking of the composition typical of the continental areas of the earth. The composition is dominated by granites and granodiorites.

It has been estimated that granites and granodiorites together constitute 95 per cent of all rocks that have solidified from magma trapped in the outer few miles of the earth's continental surface. The origin and history of some of these are still under debate, but we shall use the terms here only to indicate composition and texture, not origin.

Granite is a coarse-grained rock. Its mineral composition is approximately as follows: orthoclase feldspar 45 per cent, quartz 25 per cent, plagioclase feldspars 25 per cent, small amounts of ferromagnesian minerals 5 per cent. Rocks with the same mineral composition as granite, but with a fine-grained texture, are called **rhyolite.**

The glassy equivalent of granite is called **obsidian.** Although this rock is listed near the light side of the composition chart, it is usually pitch black in appearance. Actually, though, pieces of obsidian thin enough to be translucent turn out to be smoky white against a light background. If we were to grind up obsidian and granite separately, each would produce a powder that would be very light in color and essentially indistinguishable from the other.

Dark-Colored Igneous Rocks

The darker, heavier rocks are sometimes designated collectively as **sima.** This name, was coined from *Si* for silicon and *Ma* for magnesium, and is generally used in speaking of the shell of dark, heavy rock that underlies the ocean basins and the sialic rocks of the continents.

Of the total volume of rock formed from molten material that has poured out onto the earth's surface, by far the greatest amount is **basalt.** A popular synonym for basalt is "trap rock," from a Swedish word meaning "step." This name refers to the tendency of certain basalts to weather or break down into masses that look like giant stairways. Basalt is a fine-grained rock. Its mineral composition is as follows: plagioclase feldspars 50 per cent, ferromagnesian minerals including pyroxene and olivine 50 per cent. The coarse-grained equivalent of basalt is **gabbro. Peridotite,** named from "peridotit," another word for olivine, is a coarse-grained rock that is composed largely of the mineral olivine.

Transitional Igneous Rocks

COMPOSITION Rock compositions blend continuously from one to another as we go from the light to the dark side of the classification chart. **Andesite** is the name given to the fine-grained rocks that are intermediate in composition between granite and basalt. These rocks were first identified in the Andes Mountains of South America, hence the name "andesite." They seem to have been derived from magmas from which the heavier minerals had settled out before crystallization, leaving a rich concentration of the lighter minerals. Andesites are almost always found in areas around the Pacific Ocean where active mountain-making has taken place. The coarse-grained equivalent of andesite is **diorite.** The mineral composition of these rocks is typically as follows: orthoclase and quartz, very small or missing; plagioclase feldspars 75 per cent, mostly midway between albite and anorthite; ferromagnesian minerals, largely hornblende, with some pyroxene and some micas, approximately 25 per cent.

TEXTURE As we go from the top to the bottom of the chart in Figure 3-11, we find that the rock textures grade continuously from coarse-grained to fine-grained, whereas the composition remains the same. For example, as we read down along the first vertical rule, we find that granite, rhyolite, and obsidian are progressively finer-grained types, although all three have essentially the same composition. The same is true of gabbro and basalt.

Any of the rocks may have porphyritic texture. Essentially, this texture means that a given rock has grains of two distinctly different sizes, conspicuously large phenocrysts em-

Figure 3-12 Dark-basalt flows, Idaho, as seen from a low-flying plane. (*Photo by U.S. Army Air Corps.*)

bedded in a finer-grained groundmass. When the phenocrysts constitute less than one-quarter of the total, the adjective porphyritic is used to modify the rock name, as in porphyritic granite or porphyritic andesite. When the phenocrysts constitute more than one-quarter, the rock is called a porphyry. The composition of a porphyry and the texture of its groundmass are indicated by using rock names as modifiers, for example, granite porphyry or andesite porphyry. These relationships are summarized for the most common rocks in Table 3-1.

Table 3-1 Porphyritic Rock and Rock Porphyry

Less than 25% Phenocrysts	More than 25% Phenocrysts
Porphyritic granite	Granite porphyry
Porphyritic rhyolite	Rhyolite porphyry
Porphyritic diorite	Diorite porphyry
Porphyritic andesite	Andesite porphyry

ORIGIN AND OCCURRENCE

Having established some of the characteristics and regularities of igneous rocks and having devised a classification system, now let us examine the origin and occurrence of these rocks in the earth's crust. This study should also lead us to some explanation for the regularities behind our classification.

Volcanoes are surface expressions of processes at work far beneath the surface. The material erupted from a volcano must have been prepared at some place below the surface. This material, which arrives in a molten, very viscous state, flows out or is thrown out across the earth's surface when an eruption takes place. Volcanic rocks, then, are those igneous rocks which form by the cooling of igneous material that has been extruded through the upper layers of the earth's crust onto the surface. Therefore, we speak of volcanic rocks as extrusive rocks.

We never see the actual process of igneous activity that goes on beneath the surface. Our evidence for it is, first, that volcanic rocks are being formed today, and second, that we now find certain other igneous rocks which are not forming in volcanoes today and, we therefore assume, do not form under such exterior conditions. These rocks, which must have cooled deep beneath the surface, are exposed to our view now only because long, continued erosion has stripped away the overlying layers. These rocks, such as granite, are referred to as intrusive rocks because the molten material, the magma from which they were cooled, was intruded into pre-existing rocks within the earth's crust.

Extrusive Igneous Rocks

ROCK TYPES   Actual observation has shown that the rock types produced by modern volcanoes include rhyolite, andesite, basalt, felsite, and obsidian, all rocks with fine-grained or glassy textures already described. Other prod-

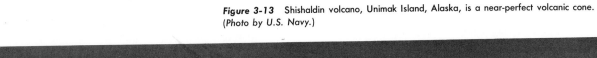

Figure 3-13 Shishaldin volcano, Unimak Island, Alaska, is a near-perfect volcanic cone. (*Photo by U.S. Navy.*)

Figure 3-14 The Teton Mountains, Wyoming, are cored with the igneous rock, granite. The rock crystallized from a molten state at some depth beneath the surface. Later erosion of overlying material has exposed the rock to our view.

ucts that also result from volcanic eruptions include volcanic ash, cinders, and dust, as well as two rocks, one called pumice and the other tuff.

Pumice is a very light-weight rock. In fact it is so light-weight that it has a lower specific gravity than does water and as a result has been known to float on water. Perhaps the nearest analogy to pumice is stiffly whipped egg whites, for pumice is actually a froth of volcanic material that has chilled with the bubbles still intact. It is this collection of cells of rock-enclosed air that gives pumice its light weight. In composition, pumice is actually on the granitic or rhyolitic side of our igneous rock classification. In texture, although it does not look like obsidian, it is in fact a volcanic glass. Close observation with a hand lens reveals that the little dividing walls between adjacent cells of air are actually glassy, and further examination with a microscope substantiates this conclusion.

Tuff is a type of volcanic ash that has been partly consolidated. Sometimes the ash that forms the tuff is deposited from a very hot and glowing cloud of material erupted by a volcano, and the actual ash is welded into an even more coherent rock than is the ordinary volcanic tuff.

DISTRIBUTION During the period from 1800 to 1914 an estimated total of 393 cubic kilometers of volcanic material was ejected at the earth's surface. But these modern-day volcanoes are not randomly scattered across the face of the earth. On the contrary, they are

Figure 3-15 Pumice.

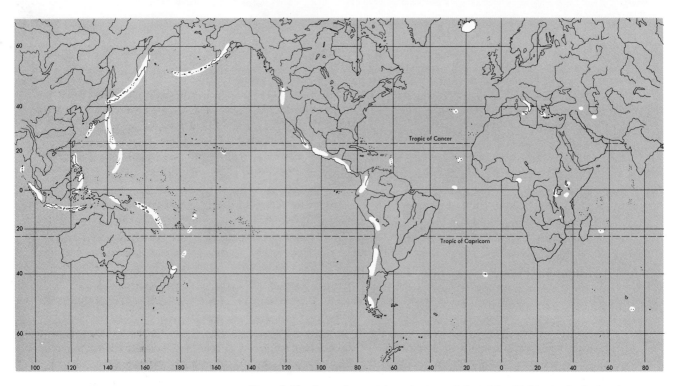

Figure 3-16 Areas of present-day volcanism as indicated (in white) by the distribution of active volcanoes. The location of submarine volcanic eruptions is not indicated.

concentrated in certain narrow bands. An examination of the map presented in Figure 3-16 indicates immediately that the greatest concentration of volcanoes still active today, or only recently extinct, runs around the rim of the Pacific Ocean. One can begin at the far southern tip of South America at Tierra del Fuego and travel northward along the western flanks of the Andean Mountain Belt on the South American continent, then through the mountains of Central America, up through Mexico and the western United States (California, Washington, and Oregon) into southern Canada, and thence past some recently extinct volcanoes until we come to Alaska. Continue out from the mainland of Alaska, westward along the long, looping arc of the Aleutian Islands, and across to Russia's Kamchatka Peninsula, which points like a long, straggily finger southward, through the Kurilian Islands to the home islands of Japan. Here the chain breaks into two parts, one swinging westward toward the Asiatic continent and down into the Philippines, the other eastward into the Pacific Ocean and toward the islands of Guam and

Yap. Through the East Indies lie a whole series of volcanoes, beginning with New Zealand on the far east and swinging northward and westward through the Solomon Islands, through New Guinea, and over to the Malayan Islands and to Malay itself. This ring of fire that circumscribes the Pacific Ocean is not the only locus for active volcanoes. In addition, the Mediterranean Basin has long been known for its active volcanoes, from modern Turkey through Greece into Italy and the islands of the Central Mediterranean. In Africa we trace a string of modern volcanoes from the rift country of central Africa south of the equator toward the Red Sea. Iceland is really itself a volcanic center. And, in truth, whole series of oceanic islands are expressions of volcanoes. Not the least familiar of these are the Hawaiian Islands. In the Atlantic a sprinkling of small, relatively unknown islands is marked by volcanic activity. General distribution is shown in Figure 3-16 and Table 3-2.

In addition to these volcanoes which are revealed at the surface of the land or above the surface of the ocean, many are now submerged

Table 3-2 **Relative Percentage of Active Volcanoes by Area**

Area	Percentage
CIRCUM PACIFIC ZONE	
Indonesian Island Arc	14
Western Pacific Island Arcs	42
Pacific Margin of North and South America	16
	72
OTHERS	
Atlantic Ocean	13
Mediterranean Basin	7
Northern Asia Minor and African Rift	4
Central Pacific Islands	3
Indian Ocean	1
	28

TYPES OF VOLCANIC ERUPTION   Igneous activity as we see it at the surface often appears to be intermittent, and in some cases it seems to repeat itself at regular intervals. Actually, however, this activity is the result of a continuous series of events that are connected with the cooling of magma.

There are two principal types of volcanic activity: explosive and quiet flows of lava. At any given time in its history a volcano shows a persistent tendency towards one of the types. Even so, it may occasionally exhibit the other type of behavior just for variety. A long-lived volcano may shift from one type to the other for long periods of time.

The explosiveness of a volcano depends on the amount of gas trapped in its lava and on the viscosity of the lava. If the gases, mostly steam, are held firmly within the lava and prohibited from escaping to the surface, large pressures build up. These pressures are relieved suddenly in a great explosion. The ease with which gases are retained within a lava depends on its viscosity, and its viscosity, in turn, usually depends on the amount of silica in the melt. Turning back to our classification of igneous rocks, we find that those magmas and lavas with the highest amount of silica produce rocks high in quartz content; these are the silicic or sialic rock types. The explosive volcanoes, then, are on the sialic side of our composition chart; therefore, the rock types most commonly found in conjunction with explosive volcanoes are rhyolite, obsidian, volcanic tuff, pumice,

beneath the oceans and are, apparently, inactive. This group of drowned volcanoes, or **sea mounts,** are most characteristic of the Pacific Ocean, particularly of the western and northwestern Pacific Ocean, but they are also found in all the other major oceans of the world. Their origin, description, and significance are treated in our discussion of ocean basins (see Chapter 11).

Figure 3-17 Mount Vesuvius throwing out still-molten blobs of lava and clouds of ash-laden steam.

ashes, and cinders. Less explosive volcanoes produce andesites, and the least explosive volcanoes produce basalts.

The volcanoes of the Pacific border are by far the most violent. The quiet eruptions are found in the Atlantic and Indian Oceans as well as in the mid-Pacific. Southern Italy, Iceland, and the African Rift system have eruptions intermediate between the two extremes.

VOLCANIC FORM   No single volcano has the precise shape of any other volcano. Yet, despite the individual differences among volcanoes, they can be grouped into the following major subdivisions: **basaltic flows, shield volcanoes,** and **composite cones.** These forms reflect the nature of the magma and type of the volcanic activity.

Figure 3-18 The "ropy" surface of a lava flow on Mt. Vesuvius. (*Photo by Sheldon Judson.*)

Figure 3-19 In 79 A.D. the Roman towns of Pompeii and Herculaneum were buried in volcanic ash from Mount Vesuvius. Here archaeological excavations have exposed portions of ancient Herculaneum. In the middle distance, modern Herculaneum stands on volcanic deposits that still cover portions of the old town. On the skyline a white plume of steam issues from Mount Vesuvius. (*Photo by Ewing Galloway.*)

Figure 3-20 Mount Hood, Oregon. (Photo by U.S. Army Air Corps.)

Basaltic lavas, which in general give rise to quieter eruptions than any other lava type, are highly fluid. They originally contain less gas than the silicate types, and what gas they do have escapes more easily to the air than does the gas in other lavas. Because of their fluidity, basalts may flood out as great sheets across the countryside. The Columbia and Snake River plateaus of the northwestern United States are of this type. These eruptions began tens of millions of years ago and continued down to a few thousand years ago. The flows, which covered 400,000 square kilometers of area, range from a few feet to tens of feet in thickness.

When basaltic lavas erupt from a single central vent, they build up a mound similar to the broad, low cones of Iceland or to the much larger cone of the Island of Hawaii. Slopes are gentle, perhaps 3 to 6 degrees, and the height is low compared with the diameter. Such volcanoes, which are made up largely of lava flows with only a few beds of cinders and ash, are referred to as "shield" volcanoes because in plan they take on very nearly the aspects of a large circular shield with a central boss.

In contrast to the forms produced during the quiet eruptions of basalt are the steep-sided volcanoes that result from highly explosive eruptions. Such eruptions are fed by magma of higher silica content than the basaltic magma. It is this difference in composition which accounts for the differences in both form and activity. The gases imprisoned in the more viscous silicic magmas build up pressures of great magnitude. The sudden release of this pressure causes an explosive eruption of the sort that throws up great quantities of fragmental material, including pulverized pieces of rock from the solid cone or from the base of the volcano along with bits of magma suddenly chilled by contact with air. We have already seen that the greatest concentration of explosive activity is in the volcanoes that surround the Pacific Basin. If we look at the form of these volcanoes, we find that their slopes are considerably steeper than those we met on the shield volcanoes, approaching in their upper portions 30° or more. Since most volcanoes of the explosive variety extrude at least some lavas, the cone is really a composite of a great

47

deal of fragmental material and a smaller amount of lava. Because of this combination, such a cone is called a "composite cone."

A single volcano may develop as a shield volcano during part of its history and as a composite one later. Mount Etna, on the island of Sicily, is an example of such a volcano.

Intrusive Igneous Rocks

As soon as a volcano has become extinct, erosion begins to wear it away and eventually exposes its internal construction to view. Often we can identify the plug that was formed when the magma solidified in the central vent, the reservoirs from which the magmas came, and the channels through which it flowed. All the rock masses that were produced when the magma solidified below the surface are called **plutons.** Furthermore, because these rocks are intruded into older pre-existing rocks, we also refer to them as **intrusive igneous** rocks. If the rocks invaded by magma are layered, a pluton that is parallel to the layering is said to be **concordant.** A pluton that cuts across the layering is said to be **discordant.** Plutons are classified according to their size and their shape in relationship to surrounding rocks. The two major subdivisions are tabular and massive plutons.

TABULAR PLUTONS A pluton whose thickness is small relative to its other dimensions is called a **tabular pluton.** There are two types: sills and dikes.

Sills. A tabular concordant pluton is called a **sill.** It may be horizontal, inclined, or vertical depending on the rock structure with which it is concordant.

Sills range in size from sheets less than an inch in thickness to tabular masses hundreds of feet thick. A sill must not be confused with an ordinary lava flow that has been buried by other rocks later on. Since a sill is an intrusive form—that is, it has forced its way into already existing rocks—it is always younger than the rocks that surround it. There are fairly reliable ways of distinguishing between the two occurrences: Most important, a buried lava flow usually has a rolling or wavy-shaped top, pocked by the scars of vanished gas bubbles, whereas a sill has a more even surface. Also, a sill may contain fragments of rock that were broken off when the magma forced its way into the surrounding structures.

The composition of most sills is basaltic. The Palisades along the west bank of the Hudson River opposite New York City, for example, are the remnants of a basalt sill that was several hundred feet thick. Here the magma was originally intruded into sediments that are now inclined at a low angle toward the west.

Dikes. A tabular pluton that has cut across the structure of the surrounding rock formation is called a **dike.** Most dikes are also composed of basalt. Apparently many dikes were formed

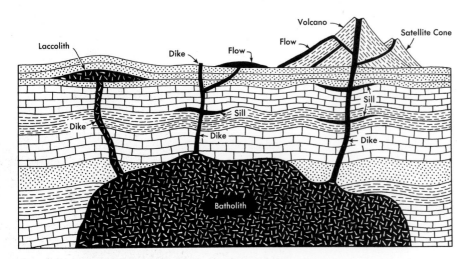

Figure 3-21 Intrusive and extrusive occurrences of igneous rocks.

Figure 3-22 The Palisades of the Hudson River are vertical cliffs of a sill intruded during the Triassic period about 200 million years ago. The rock type is a diabase, a variety of *gabbro*. The vertical patterns result from columnar jointing which developed at right angles to the upper and lower boundaries of the igneous mass as it cooled. (*Photo by Ewing Galloway.*)

when magma forced its way out of a reservoir through fractures in the adjoining rock. Often we find dikes radiating outward from a central area where the magma was presumably subjected to concentrated pressures. Others have formed in fractures that outline an inverted cone, with the apex pointing down toward the magma reservoir. Dikes of this sort are called **cone sheets.** In Scotland, for example, the angles of certain cone sheets suggest that their apex is approximately 3 miles below the present surface of the earth.

When a body of magma forces its way upward into the crust, it sometimes exerts enough pressure to lift up a plug of solid rock. Later on, when some of the magma escapes by way of dikes, sills, or flows, the plug may settle back again into the remaining magma. As a result, we find plugs that are surrounded by roughly vertical, cylindrical bands which mark the areas where the magma has subsequently solidified. These plutons are called **ring dikes.** Patterns of ring dikes have been mapped with diameters ranging from 1 to 15 miles. The width of individual dikes ranges from a few inches to several feet. The Medford dike near Boston, Massachusetts, is 500 feet wide in places, but this is a rare extreme.

Just how far we can trace the course of a dike across the countryside depends in part on how much it has been exposed by erosion. In Iceland dikes 10 miles long are common and many can be traced for 30 miles, and at least one is known to be 65 miles long.

MASSIVE PLUTONS   Any pluton that is not tabular in shape is classified as a **massive pluton.** The two types are laccoliths and batholiths.

Laccoliths. A massive concordant pluton that has pushed up the overlying rock structures into a dome is called a **laccolith** (from

Figure 3-23 Bear Butte, near Sturgis, S. D., is a laccolith. Around the base are the remnants of the sedimentary rocks which once extended up over the core of the intrusion which forms the main mass of the hill. (*Photo by Darton, U.S. Geological Survey.*)

Figure 3-24 Weathering has exposed this portion of the Sierra Nevada batholith in Yosemite National Park, California. (*Photo by William C. Bradley.*)

the Greek *lakkos,* "a cistern," and *lithos,* "stone"). A laccolith may be a blister on the surface of a sill or it may be a local body of magma that is fed from a channel cutting up from the underlying rocks. If the ratio of width to thickness is less than 10 to 1, the pluton is arbitrarily classed as a laccolith. If this ratio is more than 10 to 1, the pluton is classed as a sill. Obviously, since it is extremely difficult to establish the lateral limits of a pluton, in many cases it is best to use the term "concordant pluton" and supplement it by whatever dimensional details we can observe.

In composition, laccoliths are commonly granitic. A classic development of laccoliths occurs in the Henry, La Sal, and Abajo Mountains of southeastern Utah, where these features are exposed on the Colorado plateau, a famous geological showplace.

Batholiths. A large discordant pluton that increases in size as it extends downward and that has no determinable floor is called a **batholith** (from the Greek *bathos,* "deep," and *lithos,* "stone"). "Large" in this connection is generally taken to mean a surface exposure of more than 40 square miles. A pluton that has a smaller surface exposure but that exhibits the other features of a batholith is called a **stock.** Actually, a stock is probably an offshoot from an underlying batholith.

Batholiths are solidified reservoirs of magma that once in the molten state presumably fed volcanoes and supplied materials for all igneous activity. Today these great masses of solid igneous rock lie exposed thousands of feet above sea level where they have been lifted by forces operating in the earth's crust. The miles of rock that covered them, when they were still reservoirs of molten lava, have been stripped away by the erosion of millions of years. We can see these remnants of the roots of vanished volcanoes in the White Mountains of New Hampshire and the Sierra Nevada of California. Although batholiths provide us with many valuable facts on igneous activity, they also raise a host of unsolved problems, all of which bear directly on our understanding of igneous processes and the complex events that accompany the folding, rupture, and eventual elevation of sediments to form mountains. (We shall discuss these mountain-forming processes in Chapter 8.)

We can summarize what we do know about batholiths as follows:

(1) They are usually located in mountainous belts that have been deformed by severe crumpling and folding. Although in some mountain ranges we find no batholiths at all, we never find batholiths that are not associated with mountain ranges both in location and time of development. In any given mountain range the number and size of the batholiths are directly related to the folding and crumpling that

has taken place. This does not mean, however, that the batholiths caused the folding and the crumpling. Actually, there is convincing evidence to the contrary, as you will see in some of the following features.

(2) Batholiths usually run parallel to the axis of the mountain ranges.

(3) The intrusions have taken place only after the folding of the mountains had begun, although the folding may have continued after the batholiths were formed.

(4) Batholiths have an irregular dome-shaped roof, which is related to stoping, one of the mechanisms by which batholiths move upward into the crust, at least in the final stages. **Stoping** (a mining term that refers to removal of rock and ore from the ceiling above the miner's head) means that as the magma moves upward, blocks of rock are broken off from the structures into which the magma is intruding. At low levels, when the magma is still very hot, stoped blocks may be melted and assimilated by the magma reservoir. Higher in the crust, as the magma approaches stability, and when its heat has nearly vanished, stoped blocks are frozen in the intrusion as **xenoliths**—that is, "strange rocks."

(5) The composition of batholiths is usually granitic or granodioritic and is relatively homogenous, at least as far down as we have been able to observe.

(6) Batholiths give the impression of having replaced the formation into which they have intruded, instead of having pushed them aside or upward. But if that is what really took place, what happened to the great volumes of rock that the batholiths appear to have replaced? Here we come up against the problem of the origins of batholiths, in fact against the whole mystery of igneous activity. Some observers have even been led to question whether granitic batholiths originated from true magmas at all. The suggestion has been made that batholiths may have been formed through a process, called **granitization,** in which the solutions from magmas move into solid rocks, exchange ions with them and convert them into the rocks that have the characteristics of gran-

ite but have never actually existed as magma. We shall return to this highly controversial proposal in Chapter 6.

(7) The great volume of batholiths means that the original magma must have persisted for a long time, cooling only very slowly. There must have been considerable contraction during this cooling period and a gradual readjustment with the rocks into which it intruded. The Coast Range batholith of Alaska and British Columbia, for example, is roughly 1,100 miles by 80 to 120 miles; the Sierra Nevada batholith of California is 400 by 40 to 70 miles; and a partially exposed batholith in Southern California and Baja California is probably about 1,000 by 70 miles.

CAUSES OF VARIATION
IN IGNEOUS ROCKS

We have found that there is a wide variation in igneous rocks, both in composition and texture, as well as in occurrence. In the following paragraphs we will examine some of the reasons for these variations.

Variations in Texture

Earlier we discovered that there is a wide variation in the texture of igneous rocks, from the glassy obsidians on down to the very coarse-grained porphyrys and pegmatites. Later we found that the volcanic rocks are in large part either very fine-grained or glassy and that the deep-seated, or plutonic, rocks are coarse-grained or porphyritic. This rightfully leads us to the conclusion that there is some relationship between the rate at which an igneous melt cools and the texture that results.

Indeed, the rate at which a magma crystallizes influences the size to which crystals grow. This is so because the cooling rate controls the time that ions have to move about and enter into combinations. If a magma cools rapidly, there is no time for the ions to move into the orderly arrangement of crystals. But if a magma cools slowly, there is every possibility that the

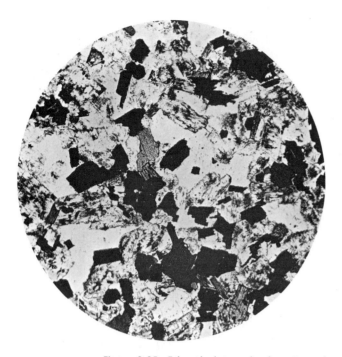

Figure 3-25 Enlarged photograph of a piece of coarse-grained igneous rock, taken through a slice that has been ground to translucent thinness (known as a thin section). The photo shows the rock to be compounded of interlocking crystals of different minerals.

Figure 3-26 Enlarged photograph of a thin section of a porphyritic igneous rock.

individual ions will seek out the pattern of crystal structures they are best adapted to.

The rate of crystallization varies with depth. For example, a molten mixture consisting largely of nonferromagnesians at 1100°C (2000°F), exposed to the air on top, and ranging in thickness from 3 to 30,000 feet would cool down to 750°C (1400°F) as follows:[2]

Thickness (in Feet)	Time Required
3	12 days
30	3 years
300	300 years
3000	30,000 years
30,000	3,000,000 years

We can demonstrate both by experiment and by direct observation in the field that the very glassy and fine-grained rocks are those which cool the quickest. In addition, experimentally we can show that slow cooling produces large crystals. But now we must explain that texture which is half-way between coarse and fine, the porphyritic texture, which has large crystals set in a gound mass of smaller crystals. What can this texture mean?

The explanation lies in two different generations of cooling. The large crystals cooled first and at a slower rate than did the smaller crystals. The smaller crystals cooled later and more rapidly, and engulfed the already formed original crystals. The way in which this double cooling takes place may vary. One way is as follows: A melt cooling at some depth beneath the surface begins to precipitate crystals of a particular type. Then this same melt becomes part of a volcanic eruption, and is forced upward rapidly toward the surface and spewed out across the ground surface as a lava flow. As it moves upward, it carries with it in suspension the already formed crystals, which then become congealed within the groundmass of the cooling lava; in this groundmass are the small crystals produced by fast cooling at the surface. The resulting texture is porphyritic.

[2]R. A. Daly, *Igneous Rocks and the Depths of the Earth* (New York: McGraw-Hill Book Co., 1933), p. 63.

Variation in Composition

The original magma is actually a liquid solution of ions at high temperature, called a **melt.** Once the heat that keeps the magma molten begins to decrease, the melt starts to crystallize. Bit by bit, solids with crystalline structure grow, and gases are released. Now we no longer have a pure liquid, but rather a liquid with solid and gaseous materials mixed in with it. As the temperature continues to drop, the mixture solidifies completely, to form an igneous rock. Exactly what sort of igneous rock is formed depends on the composition of the original magma and the conditions under which it has crystallized as suggested below.

ORDER OF CRYSTALLIZATION   Even when a magma contains all the ions necessary to yield the nine silicate minerals, these minerals do not all form at once. There is a definite temperature or temperature range at which each mineral crystallizes.

The complex ions of the silicon-oxygen tetrahedra develop first. And as the mixture continues to cool, the other ions join with these tetrahedra in various ways to form the silicate minerals. The ferromagnesians form, beginning with olivine and progressing in order through augite, hornblende, and biotite. At the same time, the plagioclase feldspars form, starting with anorthite and progressing through albite. After all these minerals have crystallized, orthoclase, muscovite, and then quartz are formed.

N. L. Bowen found that the silicates could be arranged in two series of crystallization. Each mineral in each series is derived from the preceding mineral as the result of a reaction (that is, a chemical change) with the remaining liquid of the magma. For this reason, these series are called the **Bowen reaction series.**

In the ferromagnesian series, olivine is the first to form because it has the simplest structure: Its tetrahedra are merely piled together, but are not joined to one another. Augite is built around single chains of tetrahedra; horn-blende is built around double chains; and bio-tite, the most complex of this series, consists of sheets of tetrahedra. Since each new ferromag-nesian to form has a different crystalline structure and different composition from the one that preceded it, Bowen called this a **discontinuous reaction series.**

The first feldspar to form is anorthite. This mineral crystallizes at about the same temperature as olivine. As the anorthite grows, the remaining liquid becomes impoverished in calcium, and sodium begins to substitute for it in the growing feldspar crystal. The outer rind of the crystal may thus develop a progressively more albitic composition. Because of this continuous replacement of calcium ions by sodium ions in the same silicate structure, Bowen referred to the crystallization of the plagioclase feldspars as a **continuous reaction series.**

This gradual progressive change does not occur, however, between albite and orthoclase. There is no ion-by-ion replacement of sodium by potassium because, as indicated in Table 3-3, the radius of the potassium ion is so much greater than that of the sodium ion.

In spite of the orderly manner in which the minerals crystallize, a single magma can produce a great variety of rocks as a result of interruptions in the reaction series. For instance, an interruption occurs when crystals settle out of the magma, for they are then separated from the liquid and cannot enter into further reactions with it. This process is **fractionation.**

If all the crystals of olivine remain in the magma left after their formation, they will eventually be transformed into crystals of au-

Table 3-3   Ionic Radii and Electric Charges for Positive Ions of the Feldspars*

		Electric Charge	Radius (Angstroms)
Calcium	Ca²⁺	+2	0.99
Sodium	Na⁺	+1	0.97
Potassium	K⁺	+1	1.33

° After Brian Mason, *Principles of Geochemistry*, 2nd ed. (New York: John Wiley & Sons, 1960), pp. 287–88.

gite. But if some of the olivine crystals settle out of the magma, they are effectively isolated from further chemical changes. Now only the olivine left in the liquid will be changed into augite. Similarly, only the augite remaining in

the magma will be transformed into hornblende, and so on through the entire reaction series. A single parent magma may produce any of the rocks shown in Figure 3-11 depending on the degree of fractionation.

SUMMARY

Igneous, sedimentary, and metamorphic rocks are the three types of rocks recognized in the earth's crust. Of these, we consider the igneous rocks to be the parents from which the others are eventually derived. We can relate the three rock types to each other by means of the rock cycle.

The chief characteristics of igneous rocks are color, density, mineral composition, and texture. Of these, color, density, and mineral composition tend to go together, whereas texture is generally independent. We classify igneous rocks on the basis of textures (coarse-grained, fine-grained, glassy, and porphyritic) and mineral compositions. Among the light-colored types are granite, and rhyolite. Dark-colored rocks include gabbro, basalt, and peridotite, and intermediate between these two groups are diorite and andesite. Igneous rocks either solidify at the surface (the extrusive igneous rocks) or they crystallize beneath the surface (the intrusive igneous rocks).

Volcanic eruptions vary with the composition of the magma as do the volcanic forms. Basaltic eruptions are relatively quiet and the volcanic forms have gentle slopes. Rhyolitic eruptions are more explosive and the forms have steeper slopes.

Intrusive igneous bodies are concordant (injected in conformity with the structure of the rock which encloses them) or discordant (injected across the structure of the enclosing rock). Concordant rocks include sills and laccoliths; discordant bodies, batholiths and dikes.

Rapid cooling produces glassy or fine-grained textures. Slow cooling means coarse-grained textures. Porphyritic textures suggest a period of slow cooling followed by a period of more rapid cooling. Bowen's reaction series explains how a magma of a given composition can give rise to igneous rocks of different compositions.

ADDITIONAL READING

Barth, Tom F. W., *Theoretical Petrology* (2nd ed.). New York: John Wiley & Sons, 1962.

Bullard, Fred M., *Volcanoes.* Austin, Texas: University of Texas Press, 1962.

Rittmann, A., *Volcanoes and Their Activity.* New York: John Wiley & Sons, 1962.

Turner, J. Francis, and John Verhoogen, *Igneous and Metamorphic Petrology* (2nd ed.). New York: McGraw-Hill Book Co., 1960.

Weathering

4

Shattered rock on a mountain slope, the crumbling foundations of an old building, the blurred inscription of a gravestone—all remind us that rocks are subject to constant change and destruction. Changes of temperature, moisture soaking into the ground, the ceaseless activity of living things—all work to alter rock material. This process of alteration we call weathering, and we can define it as the changes that take place in minerals and rocks at or near the

Figure 4-1 Differential weathering of horizontally bedded and vertically jointed sedimentary rock has helped to produce towering turrets of Bryce Temple in Bryce National Park, Utah. Both bedding and jointing planes provide zones where weathering can proceed more rapidly. (*Photo by National Park Service.*)

surface of the earth in response to the atmosphere, to water, and to plant and animal life. Later on, we will extend this definition slightly, but it will serve our purpose for the time being.

Weathering leaves its mark everywhere about us. The process is so common, in fact, that we tend to overlook the way in which it functions and the significance of its results. It plays a vital role in the rock cycle (see pp. 33–35, and Figure 3-2), for by attacking the exposed material of the earth's crust—both solid rock and unconsolidated deposits—it produces new material for new rocks.

The products of weathering are usually moved by water and the influence of gravity, less commonly by wind and glacier ice. When dropped by the carriers, they settle down and accumulate in new places. The mud in a flooding river, for example, is really weathered material that is being moved from the land to some settling basin, usually the ocean. Sometimes, however, the products of weathering remain right where they are formed and so are incorporated into the rock record. Certain ores, for example, such as those of aluminum, are actually old zones of weathering.

TYPES OF WEATHERING

There are two general types of weathering: **mechanical** and **chemical.** It is hard to separate these two types in nature for they often go hand in hand, though in some environments one or the other predominates. Still, for our purposes here it is more convenient to discuss them separately.

Mechanical Weathering

Mechanical weathering, which is also called **disintegration,** is the process by which rock is broken down into smaller and smaller fragments as the result of the energy developed by physical forces. For example, when water freezes in a fractured rock, enough energy may develop to pry off pieces of rock. Or a boulder moved by gravity down a rocky slope may be shattered into smaller fragments. Note that in mechanical weathering the size of the material changes from large to small, but the composition remains unchanged.

56

EXPANSION AND CONTRACTION RESULTING FROM HEAT   Changes in temperature, if they are rapid enough and great enough, may bring about the mechanical weathering of rock. For instance, in areas where bare rock is exposed at the surface, unprotected by a cloak of soil, forest or brush fires can generate enough heat to break up the rock. The rapid and violent heating of the exterior zone of the rock causes it to expand, and if the expansion is great enough, flakes and larger fragments of rock are split off. Lightning often starts such forest fires, and in rare instances, may even shatter exposed rock by means of a direct strike.

Variations in temperature from day to night and from winter to summer cause expansion and contraction of rock material. Occasionally these changes are known to cause mechanical failure of rock, as suggested in Figure 4-2. But it still seems unlikely that temperature changes are great enough to cause extensive mechanical weathering. Theoretically, such changes in temperature should cause disintegration. For instance, we know that the different minerals which form a granite expand and contract at different rates as they react to rising and falling temperatures. We would expect,

then, that even minor expansion and contraction of adjacent minerals would, over long periods of time, weaken the bonds between mineral grains, and that it would be thus possible for disintegration to occur along these boundaries. But evidence from the laboratory to support these speculations is inconclusive. In one laboratory experiment, coarse-grained granite was subjected to temperatures ranging from 58°F to 256°F every 15 minutes. This alternate heating and cooling was carried on long enough to simulate 244 years of daily heating and cooling. Yet the granite showed no signs of disintegration. Perhaps experiments extended over longer periods of time would produce observable results. In any event, we are still uncertain of the mechanical effect of daily or seasonal temperature changes. If these fluctuations do bring about the disintegration of rock, they must do so very slowly.

FROST ACTION   Frost is much more effective than heat in producing mechanical weathering. When water freezes, its volume increases about 9 per cent. So when water that trickles down into the cracks, crevices, and pores of a rock expands as it passes from the liquid to

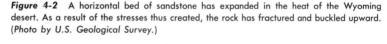

Figure **4-2** A horizontal bed of sandstone has expanded in the heat of the Wyoming desert. As a result of the stresses thus created, the rock has fractured and buckled upward. (*Photo by U.S. Geological Survey.*)

the solid state, it sets up pressures that are directed outward from the inside of the rock. And these pressures are great enough to dislodge fragments from the rock's surface. In fact, by the time the temperature has fallen to about −7.6°F, the resulting pressures may be as great as 30,000 pounds per square inch, equivalent to the pressure produced by a 15-ton granite block. This temperature is not unusually low and is experienced several times a year even in temperate latitudes.

Under actual conditions, however, pressures like this are probably never produced by frost action, at least close to the earth's surface. For an internal pressure of 30,000 pounds per square inch to build up, a rock crevice would have to be completely filled with water and completely sealed off, and the containing block would have to be strong enough to withstand the pressures at least up to that point. But most crevices contain some air in addition to water and are open either to the surface or to other crevices. Furthermore, no rock can withstand a pressure of 30,000 pounds per square inch directed from within toward the outside.

And yet frost action is responsible for a great deal of mechanical weathering. Water that soaks into the crevices and pores of a rock usually starts to freeze at its upper surface, where it is in contact with the cooling air. This means that in time the water below is confined by an ice plug. Then, as the freezing continues, the trapped water expands, and pressure is exerted outward. Rock may be subjected to this action several times a year. In high mountains, for example, the temperature may move back and forth across the freezing line almost daily.

Dislodged fragments of mechanically weathered rock are angular in shape, and their size depends largely on the nature of the bedrock from which they have been displaced. Usually the fragments are only a few inches in maximum dimension, but in some places— along the cliffs bordering Devil's Lake, Wisconsin, for instance—they reach sizes of up to 10 feet.

A second type of mechanical weathering produced by freezing water is **frost-heaving.** This action usually occurs in fine-grained, unconsolidated deposits rather than in solid rock. Much of the water that falls as rain or snow soaks into the ground, where it freezes during the winter months. If conditions are right, more and more ice accumulates in the zone of freezing as water is added from the atmosphere above and drawn upward from the unfrozen ground below, much as a blotter soaks up moisture. In time, lense-shaped masses of ice are built up, and the soil above them is heaved

Figure 4-3 Strong frost action high in the Medicine Bow Range, Wyoming, has produced this field of angular boulders. Alternate freezing and thawing of water in the crevices of the bedrock has dislodged these large fragments from the solid rock beneath. (*Photo by E. N. Cameron.*)

Figure 4-4 North Dome, Yosemite National Park, California, is an example of an exfoliation dome. The massive granite in this dome has developed a series of partings or joints more or less parallel to the surface. Rock slabs spall off the dome giving it its rounded aspect. The jointing probably originated as the granite expanded after the erosion of overlying material. (*Photo by William C. Bradley.*)

upward. Frost-heaving of this sort is common on poorly constructed roads. And lawns and gardens are often soft and spongy in the springtime as a result of the heaving up of the soil during the winter.

Certain conditions must exist before either type of frost action can take place: (1) There must be an adequate supply of moisture; (2) the moisture must be able to enter the rock or soil; and (3) temperatures must move back and forth across the freezing line. As we would expect, frost action is most pronounced in high mountains and in moist regions where temperatures fluctuate across the freezing line, either daily or seasonally.

EXFOLIATION Exfoliation is a mechanical weathering process in which curved plates of rock are stripped from the larger rock mass by the action of physical forces. This process produces two features that are fairly common in the landscape: large dome-like hills called **exfoliation domes,** and rounded boulders usually referred to as **spheroidally weathered boulders.** It seems likely that the forces that produce these two forms originate in different ways.

Let us look first at the manner in which exfoliation domes develop. Fractures or parting planes, called **joints,** occur in many massive rocks. These joints are broadly curved and run more or less parallel to the rock surface. The distance between these joints is only a few inches near the surface, but it increases to several feet as we move deeper into the rock. Under certain conditions, one after another of the curved slabs between the joints is spalled or sloughed off the rock mass. Finally, a broadly curved hill of bedrock develops as shown in Figure 4-4.

Just how these slabs of rock come into being in the first place is still a matter of dispute. Most observers believe that as erosion strips away the surface cover, the downward pressure on the underlying rock is reduced. Then, as the rock mass begins to expand upward, lines of fracture develop, marking off the slabs that later fall away. Precise measurements made on granite blocks in New England quarries provide some support for this theory. Selected blocks were accurately measured and then removed from the quarry face, away from the confining pressure of the enclosing rock mass. When the free-standing blocks were measured again, it was found that they had increased in size a small, but measurable, amount. Massive rock does expand, then, as confining pressures are reduced, and this slight degree of expansion may be enough to initiate the process of exfoliation.

Among the better-known examples of exfoliation domes are Stone Mountain, Georgia; the

Figure 4-5 Spheroidal weathering in an exposure of granite, Great Smoky Mountains, North Carolina. The granite has been fractured and the rounding by spheroidal weathering has worked inward from the fracture planes. (*Photo by L. B. Gillett.*)

Figure 4-6 This cross section through a spheroidally weathered boulder suggests the stresses set up within the rock. The stress is thought to develop as a result of the change in volume as feldspar is converted to clay. Note that the shells become thinner toward the surface.

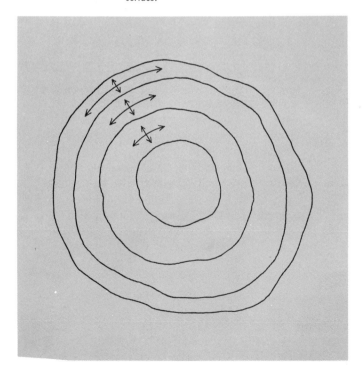

domes of Yosemite Park, California; and Sugar Loaf in the harbor of Rio de Janeiro, Brazil.

Now let us look at a smaller instance of exfoliation—spheroidally weathered boulders. These boulders have been rounded by the spalling off of a series of concentric shells of rock (see Figures 4-5 and 4-6). But here the shells develop as a result of pressures set up within the rock by chemical weathering, rather than the lessening of pressure from above by erosion. We shall see later on that, when certain minerals are chemically weathered, the resulting products occupy a greater volume than the original material. And it is this increase in volume that creates the pressures responsible for spheroidal weathering. Since most chemical weathering takes place in the exposed portions of the rock, it is there that we find the most expansion and hence the greatest number of shells.

Spheroidally weathered boulders are sometimes produced by the crumbling off of concentric shells. If the cohesive strength of the rock is low, individual grains are partially weathered and dissociated, and the rock simply crumbles away. The underlying process is the same in both these cases, however.

60

Certain types of rock are more vulnerable to spheroidal weathering than others. Igneous rocks such as granite, diorite, and gabbro are particularly susceptible, for they contain large amounts of the mineral feldspar, which, when weathered chemically, produces new minerals of greater volume.

OTHER TYPES OF MECHANICAL WEATHERING Plants also play a role in mechanical weathering. The roots of trees and shrubs growing in rock crevices sometimes exert enough pressure to dislodge previously loosened fragments of rock, much as tree roots heave and crack sidewalk pavements (Figure 4-7).

More important, though, is the mechanical mixing of the soil by ants, worms, and rodents. Constant activity of this sort makes the soil particles more susceptible to chemical weathering (see below) and may even assist in the mechanical breakdown of the particles.

Finally, such agents as running water, glacier ice, wind, and ocean waves all help to reduce rock material to smaller and smaller fragments. The role of these agents in mechanical weathering will be discussed in later chapters.

Chemical Weathering

Chemical weathering, sometimes called **decomposition,** is a more complex process than mechanical weathering. As we have seen, mechanical weathering merely breaks rock material down into smaller and smaller particles, without changing the composition of the rock. Chemical weathering, however, actually transforms the original material into something different. The chemical weathering of the mineral feldspar, for example, produces the clay minerals, which have a different composition and different physical characteristics from those of the original feldspar. Sometimes the products of chemical weathering have no mineral form at all, as when the mineral halite is transformed into a salty solution.

Figure 4-7 The roots of two pine trees pry loose large rocks in the Sierra Nevada Mountains, California. (*Photo by U.S. Geological Survey.*)

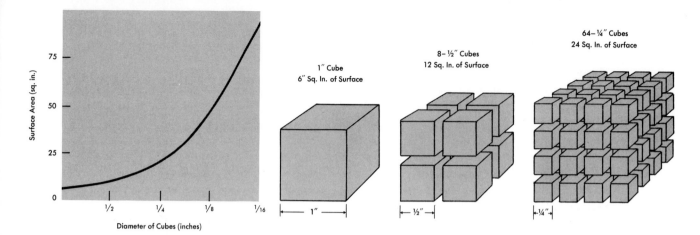

Surface Area (sq. in.)

75

50

25

0

½   ¼   ⅛   1/16

Diameter of Cubes (inches)

1" Cube
6" Sq. In. of Surface

8 – ½" Cubes
12 Sq. In. of Surface

64 – ¼" Cubes
24 Sq. In. of Surface

1"   ½"   ¼"

Figure 4-8 Relation of volume, particle size, and surface area. In this illustration, a cube one inch square is divided into smaller and smaller units. The volume remains unchanged, but as the particle size decreases, the surface area increases. Because chemical weathering is confined to surfaces, the more finely a given volume of material is divided, the greater is the surface area exposed to chemical activity, and the more rapid is the process of chemical weathering.

PARTICLE SIZE AND CHEMICAL WEATHERING
The size of individual particles of rock is an extremely important factor in chemical weathering, since substances can react chemically only when they come in contact with one another. The greater the surface area of a particle, the more vulnerable it is to chemical attack. If we were to take a pebble, for example, and grind it up into a fine powder, the total surface area exposed would be greatly increased. And, as a result, the materials that make up the pebble would undergo more rapid chemical weathering.

OTHER FACTORS IN CHEMICAL WEATHERING
The rate of chemical weathering is affected by other factors as well—the composition of the original material, for example. As we shall see later on, a mineral like quartz (SiO_2) responds much more slowly to chemical weathering than does a mineral like olivine ($FeMg_2SiO_4$). And to take a more familiar example, copper water pipes last longer than iron water pipes, for copper weathers more slowly than iron.

Climate also plays a key role in chemical weathering. Moisture, particularly when it is accompanied by warmth, speeds up the rate of chemical weathering; conversely, dryness and cold slow it down. Finally, plants and animals contribute directly or indirectly to chemi-

cal weathering, since their life processes produce oxygen, carbon dioxide, and certain acids that enter into chemical reactions with earth materials.

Chemical Weathering of Igneous Rocks

In Chapter 3, we found that the most common minerals in igneous rocks are silicates, and that the most important silicates are quartz, the feldspars, and certain ferromagnesian minerals. Let us see how chemical weathering acts on each of these three types of silicate.

WEATHERING OF QUARTZ Chemical weathering affects quartz very slowly, and for this reason we speak of quartz as a relatively stable mineral. When a rock such as granite, which contains a high percentage of quartz, decomposes, a great deal of unaltered quartz is left behind. The quartz particles (commonly called **sand grains**) found in the weathered debris of granite are the same as those that appeared in the unweathered granite.

When these quartz grains are first set free from the mother rock, they are sharp and angular. But since even quartz responds slowly to chemical weathering, the grains become more or less rounded as time passes. After many years of weathering, they look as though they had been abraded and worn by the water action along a stream bed or a beach. And yet the change may have come about solely through chemical action.

WEATHERING OF FELDSPARS   In the reaction series on p. 53, we saw that when a magma cools to form an igneous rock like granite, the feldspars crystallize before the quartz. When granite is exposed to weathering at the earth's surface, the feldspars are also the first to be broken down. Mineralogists and soil scientists still do not understand the precise process by which the feldspars weather, and some of the

Figure 4-9 Deep chemical weathering has decomposed this simatic igneous rock almost beyond recognition. Wadesborough, North Carolina. (*Photo by U.S. Geological Survey.*)

end products of this action—the clay minerals—offer many puzzles. But the general direction and results of the process seem fairly clear.

Aluminum silicate, derived from the chemical breakdown of the original feldspar combines with water to form hydrous aluminum silicate, which is the basis for another group of silicate minerals, the clays.

The decomposition of the feldspar orthoclase is a good example of the chemical weathering of the feldspar group of silicates. Two substances are essential to the weathering of orthoclase: carbon dioxide and water. The atmosphere contains small amounts of carbon dioxide and the soil contains much greater amounts. Since carbon dioxide is extremely soluble in water, it unites with rain water and water in the soil to form a weak acid, H_2CO_3, called carbonic acid. Now, when orthoclase comes into contact with water containing carbonic acid, several products are formed as shown in the following equation:

2 parts orthoclase	plus	1 part carbonic acid	plus	1 part water	
$2K(AlSi_3O_8)$	$+$	H_2CO_3	$+$	H_2O	$\xrightarrow{\text{yield}}$

clay	plus	1 part potassium carbonate	plus	4 parts silica
$Al_2Si_2O_5(OH)_4$	$+$	K_2CO_3	$+$	$4SiO_2$

In this reaction, the hydrogen ion formed from the water forces the potassium out of the orthoclase, disrupting its crystal structure. Then the hydrogen ion combines with the aluminum silicate to form the new clay mineral. (The process by which water combines chemically with other molecules is called hydrolosis.) A second product of the original orthoclase crystal is a soluble salt, potassium carbonate, which is formed when the potassium ejected from the orthoclase combines with the carbonate ion of the carbonic acid. The third product, silica, is formed by the silicon and oxygen that are left over after the hydrogen has been combined with the aluminum silicate to form the clay mineral.

Now, let us look more closely at each of the three products of the decomposition of

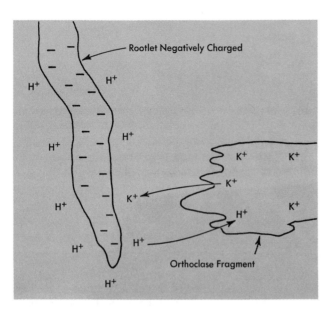

Figure 4-10 The conversion of orthoclase to a clay mineral by plant roots. In this diagram, a swarm of hydrogen ions (*positive*) is shown surrounding a negatively charged plant rootlet. The suggestion has been made that a hydrogen ion from the rootlet may replace a potassium ion in a nearby orthoclase fragment and there bond with the oxygen within the original mineral to begin the conversion of the orthoclase to clay. The potassium ion thus ejected replaces the hydrogen ion along the negatively charged rootlet and is eventually utilized in plant growth. (*Redrawn from W. D. Keller and A. F. Frederickson, "Role of Plants and Colloidal Acids in the Mechanism of Weathering," Am. J. Sci., CCL (1952), p. 603.*)

orthoclase. First, the **clay.** At the start, the clay is very finely divided. In fact, it is sometimes of colloidal size, variously estimated as between .2 micron and 1 micron.

Immediately after it is formed, the aluminum silicate may be amorphous—that is, the atoms that make it up may not be arranged in any orderly pattern. It seems more probable, however, that even at this stage the atoms are arranged according to the definite patterns of a true crystal. In any event, as time passes, the small individual particles join together to form larger particles which, when analyzed by such means as X-rays, exhibit the crystalline pattern of true minerals.

In Chapter 2, we found that the mica minerals are composed of sheets of silicon-oxygen tetrahedra. The clay minerals, too, are built up of silicon-oxygen tetrahedra linked together in sheets. These sheets combine in different ways

with sheets composed of aluminum atoms and hydroxyl molecules. For this reason we refer to the clay minerals as hydrous aluminum silicates.

Let us look back for a minute to the equation for the decomposition of orthoclase on p. 63. Notice that the second product is **potassium carbonate,** which is soluble in water. We might expect that a soluble salt like this would be dissolved and carried off by the water percolating through the ground, so that all of it would eventually find its way to the rivers and finally to the sea. Yet analyses show that not nearly as much potassium is present in river and ocean water as we would expect. What happens to the rest of the potassium? Some of it is used by growing plants before it can be carried away in solution, and some of it is absorbed by clay minerals or even taken into their crystal structure.

The third product resulting from the decomposition of orthoclase is **silica,** which appears either in solution (for even silica is slightly soluble in water), or as very finely divided quartz in the size range of the colloids. In the colloidal state, silica may exhibit some of the properties of silica in solution.

So far, we have been talking only about the weathering of orthoclase feldspar. But the products of the chemical weathering of plagioclase feldspars are very much the same. Instead of potassium carbonate, however, either sodium or calcium carbonate is produced, depending on whether the feldspar is the sodic albite or the calcic anorthite (see Table 4-1). As we found in Chapter 2, plagioclase feldspar almost always contains both sodium and calcium. The carbonates of sodium and calcium are soluble in water and may eventually reach the sea. We should note here, however, that calcium carbonate also forms the mineral calcite (see p. 29), which in turn forms the greater part of the sedimentary rock limestone, and the metamorphic rock marble, both of which are discussed in subsequent chapters.

WEATHERING OF FERROMAGNESIANS Now let us turn to the chemical weathering of the third group of the common minerals in igneous rocks—the ferromagnesian silicates. This process yields the same products as the weathering of the feldspars: clay, soluble salts, and finely divided silica. But the presence of iron and magnesium in the ferromagnesian minerals makes possible certain other products as well.

The iron may be incorporated into one of the clay minerals or into an iron carbonate mineral. Usually, however, it unites with oxygen to form **hematite**, Fe_2O_3, which is one of the most common of the iron oxides. Hematite commonly has a deep red color, and in powdered form it is always red; this characteristic gives it its name from the Greek *haimatites*, "blood-like." Sometimes the iron unites with oxygen to form another iron oxide, goethite, FeO(OH), which is generally brownish in color. (Goethite was named after the German poet Goethe, in honor of his lively scientific interests.) Chemical weathering of the ferromagnesian minerals often produces a substance called **limonite**, which has a yellowish to brownish color and is referred to in everyday language as just plain "rust." Limonite is not a true mineral, however, because its composition is not fixed within narrow limits. But the term is universally applied to the iron oxides of uncertain composition which contain

a variable amount of water. It is limonite and some of the other iron oxides that give the characteristic colors to most of our soils.

What happens to the magnesium produced by the weathering of the ferromagnesian minerals? Some of it may be removed in solution as a carbonate, but most of it tends to stay behind as newly formed minerals, particularly in the clays.

SUMMARY OF WEATHERING PRODUCTS If we know the mineral composition of an igneous rock, we can determine in a general way the products that the chemical weathering will probably yield. The chemical weathering products of the common rock-forming minerals are listed in Table 4-1. These include the minerals that make up most of our sedimentary rocks, and we shall meet them again in a subsequent chapter.

RATES OF WEATHERING

Some rocks weather very rapidly, others only slowly. This difference in rate of weathering is caused by a variety of factors, including the

Table 4-1 **Chemical Weathering Products of Common Rock-Forming Silicate Minerals**

Mineral	Composition	Important Decomposition Products	
		Minerals	Others
QUARTZ	SiO_2	Quartz grains	Some silica in solution
FELDSPARS Orthoclase	$K(AlSi_3O_8)$	Clay Quartz (finely divided)	Some silica in solution Potassium carbonate (soluble)
Albite (sodic plagioclase) Anorthite (calcic plagioclase)	$Na(AlSi_3O_8)$ $Ca(Al_2Si_2O_8)$	Clay Quartz (finely divided) Calcite (from Ca)	Some silica in solution Sodium and calcium carbonates (soluble)
FERROMAGNESIANS Biotite Augite Hornblende	Fe, Mg, Ca silicates of Al	Clay Calcite Limonite Hematite Quartz (finely divided)	Some silica in solution Carbonates of calcium and magnesium (soluble)
Olivine	$(Fe,Mg)_2SiO_4$	Limonite Hematite Quartz (finely divided)	Some silica in solution Carbonates of iron and magnesium (soluble)

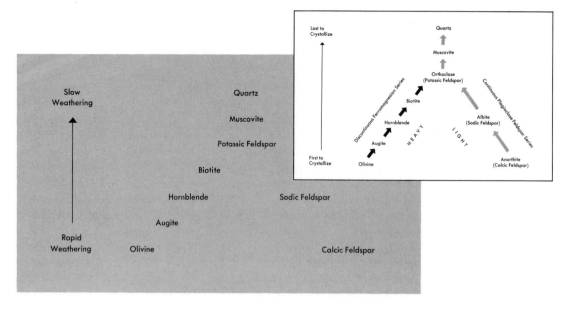

Figure 4-11 Relative rapidity of chemical weathering of the common igneous rock-forming minerals. The rate of weathering is most rapid at the bottom and decreases toward the top. Note that this table is in the same order as Bowen's reaction series (*inset*). The discrepancy in the rate of chemical weathering between, for instance, olivine and quartz, is explained by the fact that, in the zone of weathering, olivine is farther from its environment of formation than is quartz. It therefore reacts more rapidly than quartz to its new environment and thus weathers more rapidly.

type of rock and mineral involved, the temperature and amount of moisture present, the topography of the land, and the degree of plant and animal activity.

Rate of Mineral Weathering

On the basis of field observations and laboratory experiments, the minerals commonly found in igneous rocks can be ranged according to the order in which they are chemically decomposed at the surface. We are not sure of all the details, and different investigators report different conclusions. But we can make the following general observations:

1. Quartz is highly resistant to chemical weathering.
2. The plagioclase feldspars weather more rapidly than orthoclase feldspar.
3. Calcic plagioclase (anorthite) tends to weather more rapidly than sodic plagioclase (albite).
4. Olivine is less resistant than augite, and in many instances augite seems to weather more rapidly than hornblende.
5. Biotite mica weathers more slowly than the other dark minerals, and muscovite mica is more resistant than biotite.

Notice that these points suggest a pattern (Figure 4-11) similar to that of the reaction series for crystallization from magma, which was discussed in Chapter 3. But there is one important difference between these two patterns: In weathering, the successive minerals formed do not react with one another as they do in a continuous reaction series.

The relative resistance of these minerals to decomposition reflects the difference between the surface conditions under which they undergo weathering and the conditions that existed when they were originally formed. Olivine, for example, forms at high temperatures and pressures early in the crystallization of a melt. Consequently, as we might expect, it is extremely unstable under low temperatures and pressures that prevail at the earth's surface, and it weathers quite rapidly. On the other hand, quartz forms late in the reaction series, under considerably lower temperatures and pressures. Since these conditions are more similar to those at the surface, quartz is relatively stable and is very resistant to weathering.

Now we can qualify slightly the definition of weathering that we gave at the beginning of this chapter. We have found that weathering disrupts the equilibrium that existed while the minerals were still buried in the earth's crust, and that this disruption converts them into new minerals. We may revise our definition as follows: **Weathering is the response of materials that were once in equilibrium within the earth's crust to new conditions at or near contact with water, air, and living matter.**

Depth and Rapidity of Weathering

Most weathering takes place in the upper few feet or tens of feet of the earth's crust, where rock is in closest contact with air, moisture, and organic matter. But some factors operate well below the surface and permit weathering to penetrate to great depths. For instance, when erosion strips away great quantities of material from the surface, the underlying rocks are free to expand. As a result, parting planes or fractures, called joints, develop hundreds of feet below the surface.

Then, too, great quantities of water move through the soil and down into the underground, transforming some of the materials there long before they are ever exposed at the surface. This is just what happens to much of the rock salt that is distributed as a sedimentary rock in various places on the earth. If there is enough underground water present, the salt is dissolved and carried off long before it can be exposed by erosion.

Weathering is sometimes so rapid that it can actually be recorded. The eruption of the volcano Krakatoa in August, 1883, threw great quantities of volcanic ash into the air. A deposit of this ash over 100 feet deep fell on the nearby island of Long-Eiland. By 1928, 45 years later, a soil nearly 14 inches deep had developed on top of this deposit, and laboratory analyses showed that a significant change had taken place in the original materials. Chemical weathering had removed a measurable amount of the original potassium and sodium. Furthermore, either mechanical weathering or chemical weathering, or both, had broken down the original particles so that they were generally smaller than the particles in the unweathered ash beneath.

Graveyards provide many fine examples of weathering that has occurred within historic time. Figure 4-12 shows a pair of marble headstones in a small cemetery near the Welsh-founded community of Remsen in central New York. The calcite which composes the two stones has weathered so rapidly that the inscriptions to the memories of Richard and Robert James were only partially legible about a century later.

Undoubtedly the rate of weathering has increased with time, for two reasons: First, continued weathering roughens the marble surface, exposing more and more of it to chemical attack and quickening the rate of decomposition. Second, the amount of carbon dioxide in the atmosphere has increased with increasing industrialization since 1900. Consequently, rain water in the 20th century carries more carbonic acid than it did in the 19th, and it attacks calcite more rapidly.

In contrast to the badly weathered marble is a headstone of red slate erected in the same

Figure 4-12 Weathering of marble headstones in a cemetery near Remsen, New York, has nearly obliterated the original inscriptions. Inscription on left-hand stone: "Richard James/Died/Feb. 6, 1862/Aged/17 yrs. and 2 mos." Inscription on the right-hand stone: "Robert B. James/born/Sept. 4, 1845/died/Jan. 29, 1870." The stones illustrate the instability and rapid weathering of calcite (predominant mineral in marble) in a humid climate. Compare with Figures 4-13 and 4-14. (*Photo by Sheldon Judson, 1965.*)

Figure 4-13 Weathering of slate headstone in cemetery near Remsen, New York. Note that the inscription is still sharp and clear although it was cut at about the same time as those on the two marble stones shown in Figure 4-12. The slate is composed largely of clay minerals formed in the zone of weathering and therefore relatively stable when exposed to additional chemical weathering. (*Photo by Sheldon Judson, 1965.*)

cemetery and at about the same time (Figure 4-13). A century later the inscription was still sharp and plainly visible. Slate is usually a metamorphosed shale, which, in turn, is composed largely of clay minerals formed by the weathering of feldspars. Because these clay minerals were originally formed in the zone of weathering, they are relatively stable when exposed to additional chemical weathering. The slate headstone shows little sign of decomposition after a hundred years of exposure because most of the minerals of which it is composed are still in an environment similar to that in which they were formed.

Those rocks which weather very slowly chemically may weather much more rapidly mechanically. Again we can use a slate headstone, this one near Madison, Connecticut (see Figure 4-14). Although the inscription is still sharp 250 years after it was carved, mechanical weathering has begun to take its toll, as shown by a comparison of the two photographs taken a year apart.

These examples show, then, that weathering takes place at a measurable rate, which is often rapid enough to be observed within a single

Figure 4-14 A slate headstone in the West Cemetery, Madison, Connecticut. Chemical weathering has been slight in the 250 years since the stone was erected and the inscription is still clear. But mechanical weathering has begun to pry away pieces of the face of the stone. In the view on the left (taken in 1965), the angel's head is still complete. Close observation, however, shows some cracks, and a year later, in 1966, a portion of the head had been broken off, presumably by frost action during the winter. (*Photos by Sheldon Judson.*)

Figure 4-15 Differential weathering in a sandstone monument, Burying Ground of Christ Church, Cambridge, Massachusetts. Mechanical weathering has been concentrated along the inner faces of the vertically fluted columns. The more rapid disintegration here is due to differential exposure. Moisture remains longer on the inner faces, which are less accessible to the sun, and consequently frost action has been more effective here than on the outer faces. (*Photo by Sheldon Judson.*)

lifetime. Yet, although precise measurements can be made for isolated and specific situations, the factors of weathering are so numerous and so variable that exact rates of weathering are usually difficult, if not impossible, to determine.

DIFFERENTIAL WEATHERING

Differential weathering is the process by which different sections of a rock mass weather at different rates. Almost all rock masses of any size weather in this manner. The results vary from the boldly sculptured forms in Bryce Canyon, Utah, to the slightly uneven surface of a marble tombstone. Unequal rates of weathering are caused chiefly by variations in the composition of the rock itself. The more resistant zones stand out as ridges or ribs above the more rapidly weathered rock on either side.

On the other hand, a second cause of differential weathering is simply that the intensity of weathering varies from one section to another in the same rock.

SUMMARY

Weathering is the response of surface or near-surface material to contact with water, air, and living matter. Mechanical weathering (disintegration) is marked by a reduction in the size of fragments but by no change in composition. Chemical weathering (decomposition) involves a change in composition of the material weathered.

Chemical weathering is hastened by a reduction in particle size and by an increase in temperature and moisture. Certain minerals weather chemically more rapidly than others: For example, olivine weathers more rapidly than orthoclase and orthoclase more rapidly than quartz.

Weathering provides the sediments which form sedimentary rocks. The chemical weathering of an igneous rock containing quartz, feldspar, and ferromagnesian minerals will produce the common minerals of sedimentary rocks—quartz, clay, and the iron oxides—in addition to soluble salts, some of which may be precipitated into minerals such as calcite and halite.

ADDITIONAL READING

Keller, Walter D., *The Principles of Chemical Weathering* (rev. ed.). Columbia, Mo.: Lucas Brothers, 1959.
Reiche, Parry, *A Survey of Weathering Processes and Products.* Albuquerque, N.M.: University of New Mexico Press, 1950.

5

Sedimentary Rocks

River gravel, marsh mud, beach sand—all are common enough materials. They do not remind us immediately, however, of hard, firm rock. Yet deposits of these substances, or of materials very similar to them, are the stuff from which the great bulk of the rocks exposed at the earth's surface were formed.

The story of these rocks, called sedimentary rocks, begins with the weathering processes discussed in Chapter 4, for the products of chemical and mechanical weathering provide the basic raw materials. Streams, glaciers, wind, and ocean currents then move the weathered materials to new localities and deposit them as sand, or gravel, or mud. The transformation of these sediments into rock is the final step.

Some sediments, particularly sand and gravel, are consolidated into rock by a process in which the individual grains are actually cemented together. Subsurface water trickling through the open spaces leaves behind a mineral residue that serves to bind the grains firmly together, giving the entire deposit the strength we associate with rock. Other sediments, such as fine mud, are transformed into rock by the weight of overlying deposits, which press or compact them into smaller and smaller spaces.

The sedimentary rock that results from either of these processes may eventually be exposed at the earth's surface. If the rock was formed at the bottom of the ocean, it may be exposed either by the slow withdrawal of the seas or by the upward motion of the sea floor forming new areas of dry land.

It is extremely difficult to work out a concise, comprehensive definition of sedimentary rocks. The adjective **sedimentary**, from the Latin *sedimentum,* means "settling." So we might expect sedimentary rocks to be formed when individual particles settle out of a fluid, like the water of a lake or an ocean. And many sedimentary rocks are formed in just that way. Fragments of minerals derived from the breakdown of rocks are swept into bodies of water where they settle out as unconsolidated sediments, to be hardened later into true rocks. But others, such as rock salt, are made up of minerals that have been left behind after the evaporation of large bodies of water. And these are as truly sedimentary rocks as those formed from particles that have settled on an ocean floor. Still other sedimentary rocks are made up largely of the shells and hard parts of animals, particularly of invertebrate marine organisms.

Sedimentary rocks are often layered, or stratified. Unlike massive igneous rocks such as granite, most sedimentary rocks are laid down in a series of individual beds, one on top of another. The surface of each bed is essentially parallel to the horizon at the time of deposition, and in cross section, the beds expose a series of layers like those of a giant cake. True, some igneous rocks, such as those formed from lava flows, are also layered. By and large, however, the **stratification** is the most characteristic single feature of sedimentary rocks.

About 75 per cent of the rocks exposed at the earth's surface are sedimentary rocks, or metamorphic rocks derived from them (see

Figure 5-1 Erosion has exposed flat-lying beds of sedimentary rocks along this small side canyon of the Grand Canyon of the Colorado, Arizona. Height of cliffs about 250 feet. (*Photo by U.S. Army Air Corps.*)

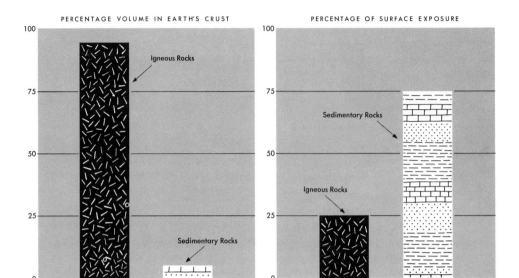

PERCENTAGE VOLUME IN EARTH'S CRUST   PERCENTAGE OF SURFACE EXPOSURE

Figure 5-2 Graphs showing relative abundance of sedimentary rocks and igneous rocks. *Graph A* shows that the great bulk (95 per cent) of the outer 10 miles of the earth is made up of igneous rocks and that only a small percentage (5 per cent) is sedimentary. In contrast, *Graph B* shows that the areal extent of sedimentary rocks at the earth's surface is three times that of igneous rocks. Metamorphic rocks are considered with either igneous or sedimentary rocks, depending on their origin.

Chapter 6). Yet sedimentary rocks make up only about 5 per cent by volume of the outer 10 miles of the globe. The other 95 per cent of the rocks in this 10-mile zone are, or once were, igneous rocks. The sedimentary cover is only as thick as a feather edge where it laps around the igneous rocks of the Adirondacks, of southern Canada, and of the Rockies. In other places, it is thousands of feet thick. In the delta region of the Mississippi River, oil-drilling operations have cut into the crust more than 22,000 feet and have encountered nothing but sedimentary rocks. In the Ganges basin of India, the thickness of the sedimentary deposits has been estimated at between 45,000 and 60,000 feet.

FORMATION OF SEDIMENTARY ROCKS

We found in Chapter 3 that igneous rock hardens from molten material which originates some place beneath the surface, under the high temperatures and pressures that prevail there. In contrast, sedimentary rocks form at the much lower temperatures and pressures that prevail at or near the earth's surface.

Origin of the Material

The material from which sedimentary rocks are fashioned originates in two ways. First, the deposits may be accumulations of minerals and rocks derived either from the erosion of existing rock or from the weathered products of these rocks. Deposits of this type are called detrital deposits (from the Latin for "worn down"), and sedimentary rocks formed from them are called **detrital sedimentary rocks.** Second, the deposits may be produced by chemical processes. We refer to these as chemical deposits and to the rocks formed from them as **chemical sedimentary rocks.**

Gravel, sand, silt, and clay derived from the weathering and erosion of a land area are examples of detrital sediments. Let us take a specific example. The quartz grains freed by the weathering of a granite may be winnowed out by the running water of a stream and swept into the ocean. There they settle out as beds of sand, a detrital deposit. Later, when this deposit is cemented to form a hard rock, we have a sandstone, a detrital rock.

72

Chemically formed deposits are usually laid down by the precipitation of material dissolved in water. This process may take place either directly, through inorganic processes, or indirectly, through the intervention of plants or animals. The salt left behind after a salty body of water has evaporated is an example of a deposit laid down by inorganic chemical processes. On the other hand, certain organisms, such as the corals, extract calcium carbonate from sea water and use it to build up skeletons of calcite. When the animals die, their skeletons collect as a biochemical (from the Greek for "life," plus "chemical") deposit, and the rock that subsequently forms is one example of a **biochemical rock**—in this case, limestone.

Although detrital rocks and chemical rocks are the main divisions of sedimentary rocks based on the origin of material—indeed, as we shall see later, they form the two major divisions in the classification of sedimentary rocks—we commonly find that a chemically formed rock contains a certain amount of detrital material. In similar fashion, predominately detrital rocks include some material that has been chemically deposited.

Sedimentation

The general process by which rock-forming material is laid down is called **sedimentation,** or **deposition.** The factors controlling sedimentation are easy to visualize. To have any

Figure 5-3 The environment of this Lake Michigan beach in Wisconsin favors the deposition of fine-grained sand. Compare with Figure 5-4. (*Photo by Wisconsin Conservation Department.*)

deposition at all, there must be something to deposit; that is, a source of sediments must exist. We also need some process to transport this sediment. And, finally, there must be some place and some process for the deposition of the sedimentary material.

SOURCE OF THE MATERIAL   In talking about the rock cycle (Chapter 3), we mentioned that igneous rocks are the ultimate source of the sedi-

Figure 5-4 Exposed to the direct attack of ocean waves the environment of this rocky headland on the coast of Maine favors the deposition of coarse gravel. Compare with Figure 5-3. (*Photo by Edward A. Schmitz.*)

ments in sedimentary rocks, but that metamorphic rocks or other sedimentary rocks may serve as the immediate source.

In either case, after the rock material has been weathered, it is ready to be transported to some place of accumulation. Its movement is usually from a higher to a lower level. The energy for this movement is provided by gravity, which makes possible not only the process of mass movement itself, but also the activity of such agents of transportation as running water and glacier ice. If gravity were free to go about its work without opposition, it would long ago have reduced the continents to smooth, low-lying land masses. But working against the leveling action of gravity are energies within the earth that elevate the continents and portions of the sea floor (see Chapter 8). By constantly exposing new areas of the earth's surface to weathering, movements of this sort insure a continuing supply of material for the formation of sedimentary rocks.

METHODS OF TRANSPORTATION Water—in streams and glaciers, underground, and in ocean currents—is the principal means of transporting material from one place to another. Landslides and other movements induced by gravity also play a role, as does the wind, but we shall look more closely at these processes in Chapters 9, 10 and 11.

PROCESSES OF SEDIMENTATION Detrital material consisting of minerals and rock fragments is deposited when its agent of transportation no longer has enough energy to move it farther. For example, a stream flowing along at a certain velocity possesses enough energy to move particles up to a certain maximum size. If the stream loses velocity, it also loses energy, and it is no longer able to transport all the material that it has been carrying along at the higher velocity. The solid particles, beginning with the heaviest, start to settle to the bottom. The effect is much the same when a wind that has been driving sand across a desert suddenly dies. A loss of energy accompanies the loss in velocity.

Material that has been carried along in solution is deposited in a different way: by precipitation, a chemical process through which dissolved material is converted into a solid and separated from the liquid solvent. As we have already noted, the precipitant may be either biochemical or inorganic.

Although at first glance the whole process of sedimentation seems quite simple, actually it is as complex as nature itself. Many factors are involved, and they can interact in a variety of ways. Consequently, the manner in which sedimentation takes place and the sediments that result from it differ greatly from one situation to another (see Figures 5-3, 5-4).

Mineral Composition of Sedimentary Rocks

Sedimentary rocks, like igneous and metamorphic rocks, are accumulations of minerals. In sedimentary rocks, the three most common minerals are clay, quartz, and calcite, although, as we shall see, a few others are important in certain localities.

Rarely is a sedimentary rock made up of only a single mineral, although one mineral may predominate. Limestone, for example, is composed mostly of calcite, but even the purest limestone contains small amounts of other minerals, such as clay or quartz. The grains of many sandstones are predominantly quartz, but the cementing material that holds these grains together may be calcite, dolomite, or iron oxide. In general, we may say that most sedimentary rocks are mixtures of two or more minerals.

CLAY Chapter 4 described how clay minerals develop from the weathering of the silicates, particularly the feldspars. These clays subsequently may be incorporated into sedimentary rocks: They may, for example, form an important constituent of mudstone and shale.

QUARTZ Another important component of sedimentary rocks is silica, including the very common mineral quartz as well as a number of other forms such as chert, flint, and opal.

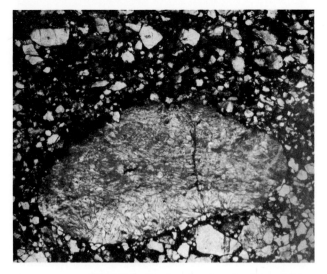

Figure 5-5 Quartz grains of varying sizes and shapes are cemented together by hematite. The large quartz fragment is about half an inch long. (*Photo by Willard Starks.*)

is similar to flint but tends to be lighter in color, and **jasper** is a red variety of the granular cryptocrystalline form of silica.

The general term **chalcedony** is often applied to the fibrous types of cryptocrystalline silica, which have a higher, more waxy luster than the granular varieties. Sometimes the term is also used to describe a specific variety of brown, translucent cryptocrystalline silica.

Agate is a variegated form of silica, its bands of chalcedony alternating with bands of either opal or some variety of granular cryptocrystalline silica, such as jasper.

CALCITE   The chief constituent of the sedimentary rock limestone, **calcite** ($CaCO_3$) is also the most common cementing material in the

Figure 5-6 Viewed under the microscope some limestones are seen to have a clastic texture (see p. 77), as does this example. Pellets of calcite are cemented together by clear (dark) calcite. Note how particles of varying size are segregated into layers. (*Photo by A. G. Fischer.*)

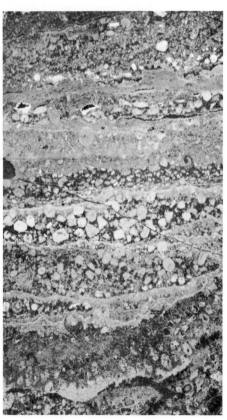

1/4 inch

The mechanical and chemical weathering of an igneous rock such as granite sets free individual grains of quartz that eventually may be incorporated into sediments. These quartz grains produce the detrital forms of silica and account for most of the volume of the sedimentary rock sandstone. But silica in solution or in particles of colloidal size is also produced by the weathering of an igneous rock. This silica may be precipitated or deposited in the form of quartz, particularly as a cementing agent in certain coarse-grained sedimentary rocks. Silica may also be precipitated in other forms, such as opal, generally regarded as a hydrous silica ($SiO_2.nH_2O$). Opal is slightly softer than quartz and has no true crystal structure.

Silica also occurs in sedimentary rocks in a form called **cryptocrystalline.** This term (from the Greek *kryptos*, "hidden," plus crystalline) indicates that the crystalline structure of this type of silica is so fine that it cannot be seen under most ordinary microscopes. The microscope does reveal, however, that some cryptocrystalline silica has a granular pattern and that some has a fibrous pattern. To the naked eye, the surface of the granular form is somewhat duller than that of the fibrous form. Among the dull-surfaced or granular varieties is **flint,** which is usually dark in color. Flint is commonly found in certain limestone beds—the chalk beds of southern England, for example. **Chert**

coarse-grained sedimentary rocks. The calcium is derived from igneous rocks that contain calcium-bearing minerals, such as calcic plagioclase and some of the ferromagnesian minerals. Calcium is carried from the zone of weathering as calcium bicarbonate, $Ca(HCO_3)_2$, and is eventually precipitated as calcite, $CaCO_3$, through the intervention of plants, animals, or inorganic processes. The carbonate is derived from water and carbon dioxide.

Figure 5-7 Microscopic examination reveals several facts about the formation of this limestone. The dark, curved forms are cross-sections through small clam shells. On top of these shells, zones with mottled aspects represent deposition of small calcite fragments, some of them pieces of shell. The uniform white zones above these deposits are very fine-grained calcareous sediments deposited subsequent to the mottled zones with their somewhat coarser sediments. (*Photo by A. G. Fischer.*)

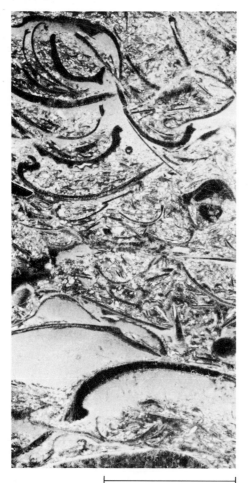

1/4 inch

OTHER MATERIALS IN SEDIMENTARY ROCKS Accumulations of clay, quartz, and calcite, either alone or in combination, account for all but a very small percentage of the sedimentary rocks. But certain other materials occur in quantities large enough to form distinct strata. The mineral **dolomite**, $CaMg(CO_3)_2$, for example, usually is intimately associated with calcite, though it is far less abundant. It is named after an eighteenth-century French geologist, Dolomieu. When the mineral is present in large amounts in a rock, the rock itself is also known as dolomite. The mineral dolomite is easily confused with calcite, and since they often occur together, distinguishing them is important. We can do so through this chemical test: Calcite effervesces freely in dilute hydrochloric acid; dolomite effervesces very slowly or not at all, unless it is finely ground or powdered. In the latter instance, the more rapid chemical activity results from the increase in surface area, an example of the general principle discussed under "Chemical Weathering" in Chapter 4.

The feldspars and micas are abundant in some sedimentary rocks. In Chapter 4, we found that chemical weathering converts these minerals into new minerals at a relatively rapid rate. Therefore, when we find mica and feldspar in a sedimentary rock, chances are that it was mechanical, rather than chemical, weathering that originally made them available for incorporation in the rock.

Iron produced by chemical weathering of the ferromagnesian minerals in igneous rocks may be caught up again in new minerals and incorporated into sedimentary deposits. The iron-bearing minerals that occur most frequently in sedimentary rocks are hematite, goethite, and limonite. In some deposits, these minerals predominate, but more commonly they act simply as coloring matter or as a cementing material.

Halite (NaCl) and gypsum ($CaSO_4 2H_2O$) are minerals precipitated from solution by evaporation of the water in which they were dissolved. The salinity of the water—that is, the proportion of the dissolved material to the water —determines the type of mineral that will precipitate out. The gypsum begins to separate from sea water when the salinity (at 30°C) reaches a little over 3 times its normal value. Then, when the salinity of the sea water has increased to about 10 times its normal value, halite begins to precipitate.

Volcanic ash and cinders, mentioned in Chapter 3, are sedimentary rocks composed mostly of fragments blown from volcanoes. The fragments may be large pieces that have fallen close to the volcano, or extremely fine ash that has been carried by the wind and deposited hundreds of miles away.

Finally, organic matter may be present in sedimentary rocks. In the sedimentary rock known as coal, plant materials are almost the only components. More commonly, organic matter is very sparsely disseminated through sedimentary deposits and the resulting rocks.

Texture

Texture refers to the general physical appearance of a rock—to the size, shape, and arrangement of the particles that make it up. There are two major types of texture in sedimentary rocks: clastic and nonclastic.

CLASTIC TEXTURE   The term **clastic** is derived from the Greek for "broken" or "fragmental," and rocks that have been formed from deposits of mineral and rock fragments are said to have clastic texture. The size and shape of the original particles have a direct influence on the nature of the resulting texture. A rock formed from a bed of gravel and sand has a coarse, rubble-like texture that is very different from the sugary texture of a rock developed from a deposit of rounded, uniform sand grains. Furthermore, the process by which a sediment is deposited also affects the texture of the sedimentary rock that develops from it. Thus, the debris dumped by a glacier is composed of a jumbled assortment of rock material ranging from particles of colloidal size to large boulders. A rock that develops from such a deposit has a very different texture from one that develops from, for instance, a deposit of wind-blown sand, in which all the particles are approximately 0.15 to 0.30 mm in diameter.

Chemical sedimentary rocks may also show a clastic texture. A rock made up predominantly of shell fragments from a biochemical deposit has a clastic texture which is as recognizable as that of a rock formed from sand deposits.

One of the most useful factors in classifying sedimentary rocks is the size of the individual particles. In practice, we usually express the size of a particle in terms of its diameter, rather than in terms of volume, weight, or surface area. When we speak of "diameter," we imply that the particle is a sphere, but it is very unlikely that any fragment in a sedimentary rock is a true sphere. In geological measurements, the term simply means the diameter that an irregularly shaped particle would have if it were a sphere of equivalent volume. Obviously, it would be a time-consuming, if not impossible, task to determine the volume of each sand grain or pebble in a rock, and then to convert these measurements into appropriate diameters. So the diameters we use for particles are only approximations of their actual sizes. They are accurate enough, however, for our needs.

Several scales have been proposed to describe particles that range in size from large boulders to minerals of microscopic dimensions. The Wentworth scale, presented in Table 5-1, is used widely, though not universally, by American and Canadian geologists. Notice that

Table 5-1 Wentworth Scale of Particle Sizes for Clastic Sediments

Wentworth Scale SIZE	FRAGMENT	To Get Next Larger Size, Multiply by	Approximate Equivalent
	Boulder		
256 mm			10 in.
	Cobble	4	
64 mm			$2\frac{1}{2}$ in.
	Pebble	16	
4 mm			$\frac{5}{32}$ in.
	Granule	2	
2 mm			$\frac{5}{64}$ in.
	Sand	32	
$\frac{1}{16}$ mm			.0025 in. (.06 mm)
	Silt	} Dust 16	
$\frac{1}{256}$ mm			.00015 in. (.004 mm)
	Clay		

Modified after C. K. Wentworth, "A Scale of Grade and Class Terms for Clastic Sediments," *J. Geol.*, XXX (1922), 381.

although the term "clay" is used in the table to designate all particles below $\frac{1}{256}$ mm in diameter, the same term is used to describe certain minerals. To avoid confusion, we must always refer specifically to either "clay size" or "clay mineral," unless meaning is clear in context.

Since determining the size of particles calls for the use of special equipment, the procedure is normally carried out only in the laboratory. In examining specimens in the field, geologists make an educated guess based on careful examination, which usually suffices.

NONCLASTIC TEXTURE   Some, but not all, sedimentary rocks formed by chemical processes have a nonclastic texture in which the grains are interlocked. These rocks have somewhat the same appearance as igneous rocks with crystalline texture. Actually, most of the sedimentary rocks with nonclastic texture do have a crystalline structure, although a few of them, such as opal, do not.

The mineral crystals that precipitate from an aqueous solution are usually very small in size. Because the fluid in which they form has a very low density, they usually settle out rapidly and accumulate on the bottom as mud. Eventually, under the weight of additional sediments, the mud is compacted more and more. Now the size of the individual crystals may begin to increase. Their growth may be induced by added pressure causing the favorably oriented grains to grow at the expense of less favorably oriented neighboring grains. Or crystals may grow as more and more mineral matter is added to them from the saturated solutions trapped in the original mud. In any event, the resulting rock is made up of interlocking crystals. Depending on the size of the crystals, we refer to these nonclastic textures as fine-grained, medium-grained, or coarse-grained. A coarse-grained texture has grains larger than 5 mm in diameter, a fine-grained one, less than 1 mm in diameter.

Lithification

The process of **lithification** converts unconsolidated rock-forming materials into consolidated, coherent rock. The term is derived from the Greek for "rock" and the Latin for "to make." In the following section, we shall discuss the various ways in which sedimentary deposits are lithified.

CEMENTATION   In cementation, the spaces between the individual particles of an unconsolidated deposit are filled up by some binding agent. Of the many minerals that serve as cementing agents, the most common are calcite, dolomite, and quartz. Others include iron oxide, opal, chalcedony, anhydrite, and pyrite. Apparently, the cementing material is carried in solution by water that percolates through the open spaces between the particles of the deposit. Then some factor in the new environment causes the mineral to be deposited, and what was formerly an unconsolidated deposit is cemented into a sedimentary rock.

In coarse-grained deposits, there are relatively large interconnecting spaces between the particles. As we would expect, these deposits are very susceptible to cementation, because the percolating water can move through them with great ease. Deposits of sand and gravel are transformed by cementation into the sedimentary rocks sandstone and conglomerate.

COMPACTION AND DESICCATION   In a fine-grained clastic deposit of silt-sized and clay-sized particles, the pore spaces are usually so small that water cannot freely circulate through them. Consequently, very little cementing material manages to find its way between the particles. But deposits of this sort are lithified by two other processes: compaction and desiccation.

In **compaction,** the pore space between individual grains is gradually reduced by the pressure of overlying sediments or by the pressures resulting from earth movement. Coarse deposits of sand and gravel undergo some compaction, but fine-grained deposits of silt and clay respond much more readily. As the individual particles are pressed closer and closer together, the thickness of the deposit is reduced and its coherence is increased. It has been estimated that deposits of clay-sized particles, buried to depths of 3,000 feet, have been compacted to about 60 percent of their original volume.

In **desiccation,** the water that originally filled the pore spaces of water-laid clay and silt deposits is forced out. Sometimes this process is the direct result of compaction. But desiccation also takes place when a deposit is simply exposed to the air and the water evaporates.

CRYSTALLIZATION The crystallization of certain chemical deposits is in itself a form of lithification. Crystallization also serves to harden deposits that have been laid down by mechanical processes of sedimentation. For example, new minerals may crystallize within a deposit, or the crystals of existing minerals may increase in size. New minerals sometimes are produced by chemical reactions among amorphous, colloidal materials in fine-grained muds. Exactly how and when these reactions occur is not yet generally understood. But the fact that new crystals *have* formed after the deposit was initially laid down becomes increasingly apparent as we make ever more detailed studies of sedimentary rocks. Furthermore, it seems clear that crystallization promotes the process of lithification, particularly in the finer sediments.

CLASSIFICATION OF SEDIMENTARY ROCKS

Having examined some of the factors involved in the formation of sedimentary rocks, we are in a better position to consider a classification for this rock family. The classification presented in Table 5-2 represents only one of many possible schemes, but it will serve our purposes adequately. Notice that there are two main groups—detrital and chemical—based on the origin of the rocks, and that the chemical category is further split into inorganic and biochemical. All the detrital rocks have clastic texture, whereas the chemical rocks have either clastic or nonclastic texture. We use particle size to subdivide the detrital rocks, and composition to subdivide the chemical rocks.

Detrital Sedimentary Rocks

CONGLOMERATE A **conglomerate** is a detrital rock made up of more or less rounded fragments, an appreciable percentage of which are of granule size (2 to 4 mm in diameter) or larger. If the fragments are more angular than rounded, the rock is called a **breccia.**

Table 5-2 Classification of Sedimentary Rocks

Origin		Texture	Particle Size or Composition	Rock Name
Detrital		Clastic	Granule or larger	Conglomerate
			Sand	SANDSTONE
			Silt and clay	MUDSTONE and SHALE
Chemical	Inorganic	Clastic and Nonclastic	Calcite, $CaCO_3$	Limestone
			Dolomite, $CaMg(CO_3)_2$	Dolomite
			Halite, $NaCl$	Salt
			Gypsum, $CaSO_4 \cdot 2H_2O$	Gypsum
	Biochemical		Calcite, $CaCO_3$	LIMESTONE
			Plant remains	Coal

Figure 5-8 A conglomerate is a lithified gravel composed of rounded pebbles, as shown in this example from the Mud Springs Mountains, New Mexico. (*Photo by L. M. Cline.*)

Another type of conglomerate is **tillite,** a rock formed from deposits laid down directly by glacier ice. The large particles in a conglomerate are usually rock fragments, and the finer particles are usually minerals derived from pre-existing rocks (see Figures 5-8 and 5-9).

SANDSTONE A **sandstone** forms from an accumulation of mineral grains the size of sand (between $\frac{1}{16}$ mm and 2 mm in diameter). Sandstone is thus intermediate between coarse-grained conglomerate and fine-grained mudstone. Since the size of the grains varies from one sandstone to another, we speak of coarse-grained, medium-grained, and fine-grained sandstone.

Very often, but not always, the grains in a sandstone are composed of the mineral quartz. If the minerals are predominantly quartz and feldspar, the sandstone is called an **arkose,** a French word for the rock formed by the consolidation of debris from a mechanically weathered granite. Another variety of sandstone, called **graywacke,** is characterized by its hardness and dark color, and by angular grains of quartz, feldspar, and small fragments of rock set in a matrix of clay-sized particles.

MUDSTONE AND SHALE Fine-grained detrital rocks composed of clay and silt-sized particles (less than $\frac{1}{16}$ mm in diameter) are termed either mudstone or shale. **Mudstones** are fine-grained rocks with a massive or blocky aspect, whereas **shales** are fine-grained rocks that split into platy slabs more or less parallel to the bedding (see Figure 5-11). The particles in these rocks are so small that it is difficult to determine the precise mineral composition of mudstone and shale. We do know, however, that they contain not only clay minerals but also clay-sized and silt-sized particles of quartz, feldspar, calcite, and dolomite, to mention but a few.

Chemical Rocks

LIMESTONE Limestone is a sedimentary rock that is made up chiefly of the mineral calcite, $CaCO_3$, that has been deposited by either inorganic or organic chemical processes. Most limestones have a clastic texture; but nonclastic, particularly crystalline, textures are common as well.

Biochemically formed limestones are created by the action of plants and animals that extract calcium carbonate from the water in which they live. The calcium may be either incorporated into the skeleton of the organism or precipitated directly. In any event, when the organism dies, it leaves behind a quantity of calcium carbonate, and over a long period of time thick deposits of this material may be

Figure 5-9 A breccia is a lithified gravel containing many angular fragments. This is an example near Highgate Falls, Vermont. (*Photo by Walcott, U.S. Geological Survey.*)

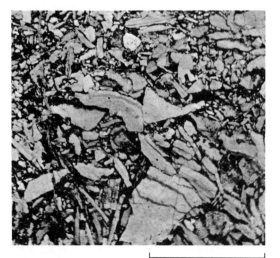

6 inches

Figure 5-10 Alternating beds of sandstone and conglomerate dip inland from the sea cliff at Lobos State Park, near Carmel, California. (Photo by Sheldon Judson.)

built up. Reefs, ancient and modern, are well-known examples of such accumulations. The most important builders of modern reefs are algae, molluscs, corals, and one-celled animals. The ancestors of the same animals built up the reefs of ancient seas, the reefs, now old and deeply buried, that are often valuable reservoirs of petroleum.

Chalk (from the Latin *calx*, "lime") is made up in part of biochemically derived calcite in the form of the skeletons or skeletal fragments of microscopic oceanic plants and animals. These organic remains are found mixed with very fine-grained calcite deposits of either biochemical or inorganic chemical origin. A much coarser type of limestone composed of organic remains is known as **coquina,** from the Spanish for "shellfish" or "cockle," and is characterized by the accumulation of many large fragments of shells.

Inorganically formed limestone is made up of calcite that has been precipitated from solution by inorganic processes. Some calcite is precipitated from the fresh water of streams, springs, and caves, although the total amount of rock formed in this way is negligible. When calcium-bearing rocks undergo chemical weathering, calcium bicarbonate, $Ca(HCO_3)_2$, is produced in solution. If enough of the water evaporates, or if the temperature rises, or if the pressure falls, calcite is precipitated from this solution. For example, most **dripstone,** or **travertine,** is formed in caves by the evaporation of water that has carried calcium carbonate in solution.

And **tufa** (from the Italian for "soft rock") is a spongy, porous limestone formed by the precipitation of calcite from the water of streams and springs.

DOLOMITE In discussing the mineral dolomite, $CaMg(CO_3)_2$, we mentioned that when it occurs in large enough concentration it forms a rock that is also called dolomite. Most dolomite rocks are probably formed from limestone through the replacement of some of the calcium by magnesium.

Figure 5-11 Exposure of essentially flat-lying Pierre shale of Cretaceous age (which ended about 65 million years ago) on the Fort Totten Indian Reservation in east-central North Dakota. The shale splits into small, thin slabs parallel to the bedding, a characteristic known as fissility. The fracture planes (approximately at right angles to the bedding) and the fissility give the exposure a blocky appearance. The shovel is approximately $2\frac{1}{2}$ feet long. (Photo by Aronow, U.S. Geological Survey.)

EVAPORITES   An **evaporite** is a sedimentary rock composed of minerals that were precipitated from solution during the evaporation of the liquid in which they were dissolved. **Rock salt** (composed of the mineral halite, NaCl), and **gypsum** (composed of the mineral of the same name, $CaSO_4 \cdot 2H_2O$), are the most abundant evaporites. **Anhydrite** (from the Greek, *anydros*, "waterless") is an evaporite composed of the mineral of the same name, which is simply gypsum without the water, $CaSO_4$.

Most evaporite deposits seem to have been precipitated from sea water, according to a definite sequence. The less soluble minerals are the first to drop out of solution. Thus, gypsum and anhydrite, both less soluble than halite, are deposited first. Then, as evaporation progresses, the more soluble halite is precipitated.

In the United States, the most extensive deposits of evaporites are found in Texas and New Mexico. Here, gypsum, anhydrite, and rock salt make up over 90 per cent of the Castile formation, which has a maximum thickness of nearly 4,000 feet. In central New York State there are layers of rock salt, and in central Michigan there are layers of rock salt and gypsum. Some evaporite deposits are mined for their mineral content, and in certain areas, particularly in the Gulf Coast states, deposits of rock salt have pushed upward toward the surface to form salt domes containing commercially important reservoirs of petroleum (see Chapter 22).

COAL   Coal is a rock composed of combustible matter derived from the partial decomposition of plants. We shall consider coal as a biochemically formed sedimentary rock, although some geologists prefer to think of it as a metamorphic rock because it passes through various stages (see "Anthracite," in Chapter 22).

The process of coal formation begins with an accumulation in a swamp of the plants' remains. This accumulation is known as **peat,** a soft, spongy, brownish deposit in which plant structures are easily recognizable. Time, coupled with the pressure produced by deep burial and sometimes by earth movement, gradually trans-

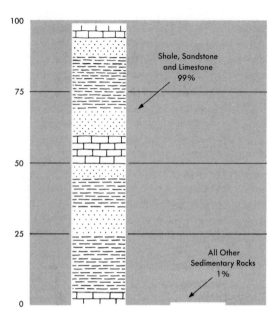

Figure 5-12 Shale, sandstone and limestone make up about 99 per cent of all the sedimentary rocks. All other sedimentary rocks total only about 1 per cent.

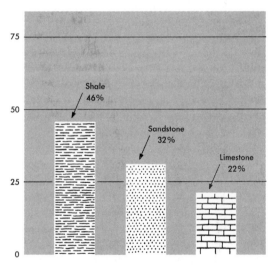

Figure 5-13 Of shale, sandstone, and limestone, shale is relatively the most abundant and limestone the least abundant.

forms the organic matter into coal. During this process, the percentage of carbon increases as the volatile hydrocarbons and water are forced out of the deposit. Coals are ranked according to the percentage of carbon they contain. Peat,

Figure 5-14 Layers of limestone separated from each other by parallel bedding planes. Originally horizontal, these beds have been gently arched by later earth movements. (*Photo by E. N. Cameron.*)

with the least amount of carbon, is the lowest-ranking; then come lignite, or brown coal; bituminous, or soft coal; and finally anthracite, or hard coal, the highest in percentage of carbon.

Relative Abundance of Sedimentary Rocks

Sandstone, mudstone and shale, and limestone constitute about 99 per cent of all sedimentary rocks. Of these, mudstone and shale are the most abundant; limestone is the least abundant. Although various estimates have been made of the abundance of each type, actual observations of rocks exposed on the continents suggest that mudstone and shale represent about 46 per cent of the total, sandstone about 32 per cent, and limestone about 22 per cent (see Figures 5-12 and 5-13).

FEATURES OF SEDIMENTARY ROCKS

We have mentioned that the stratification, or bedding, of sedimentary rocks is their most characteristic feature. Now we shall look more closely at this quality, along with certain other characteristics of sedimentary rocks, including mud cracks and ripple marks, nodules, concretions, geodes, fossils, and color.

Figure 5-15 Thinly bedded limestone in Hastings County, Ontario, Canada. The beds have been tilted to a vertical position from the original horizontal position. (*Photo by Canadian Geological Survey.*)

Bedding

The beds or layers of sedimentary rocks are separated by parallel bedding planes, along which the rocks tend to separate or break. The varying thickness of the layers in a given sedimentary rock reflects the changing conditions that prevailed when each deposit was laid down.

Figure 5-16 Some sedimentary beds are deposited at a noticeable angle from the horizontal, as were the sandstone layers exposed in this cliff face. They record ancient sand dunes in what is now Zion National Park, Utah. (*Photo by Hillers, U.S. Geological Survey.*)

In general, each bedding plane marks the termination of one deposit and the beginning of another. For example, let us imagine the bay of an ocean into which rivers normally carry fine silt from the nearby land. This silt settles out from the sea water to form a layer of mud. Now, heavy rains or melting snows may cause the rivers suddenly to flood and thereby pick up coarser material, such as sand, from the river bed. This material will be carried along and dumped into the bay. There it settles to the bottom and blankets the silt that was deposited earlier. The plane of contact between the mud and the sand represents a bedding plane. If, later on, the silt and the sand are lithified into shale and sandstone, respectively, the bedding plane persists in the sedimentary rock. In fact, it marks a plane of weakness along which the rock tends to break.

Although deposits are usually laid down in horizontal beds, some are created at angles to the horizontal. For example, beds laid down on the surface of sand dunes are inclined, as are some of the beds that build up on deltas. A special type of inclined bedding is created by the alternate scouring and filling of a stream bed. If the velocity of a stream increases at some point along its course, it scours the sand

Figure 5-17 Sequence in the formation of inclined bedding by alternate scouring and filling. A turbulent current first scours a depression in unconsolidated deposits. With a decrease in the velocity of the water, the stream begins to fill up the depression with inclined layers. (*Redrawn by permission from Robert R. Schrock, Sequence in Layered Rocks, New York: McGraw-Hill Book Co., 1948, p. 280.*)

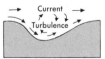

Erosion Stage

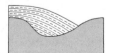

Back-Filling Stage

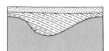

Truncation Stage

84

and gravel from the bottom and carries them away. Then, if the velocity subsequently decreases, the depression is filled up again by sediments that tend to be laid down in inclined layers (for a schematic representation, see Figure 5-17).

Mud Cracks and Ripple Marks

Ripple marks are the little waves of sand that commonly develop on the surface of a sand dune, or along a beach, or on the bottom of a stream. Mud cracks are familiar on the dried surface of mud left exposed by the subsiding waters of a river. These features are often preserved in solid rock and provide us with clues to the history of the rock.

Mud cracks make their appearance when a deposit of silt or clay dries out and shrinks (see Figure 5-18). The cracks outline roughly polygonal areas, making the surface of the deposit look like a section cut through a large honeycomb. Eventually, another deposit may come along to bury the first. If the deposits are later lithified, the outlines of the cracks may be accurately preserved for millions of years. Then, when the rock is split along the bedding plane between the two deposits, the cracks will be found much as they appeared when they were first formed, providing evidence that the original deposit underwent alternate flooding and drying.

Ripple marks preserved in sedimentary rocks also furnish clues to the conditions that prevailed when a sediment was originally deposited. For instance, if the ripple marks are symmetrical, with sharp or slightly rounded ridges separated by more gently rounded troughs, we are fairly safe in assuming that they were formed by the back-and-forth movement of water such as we find along a sea coast outside the surf zone. These marks are called **ripple marks of oscillation.** If, on the other hand, the ripple marks are asymmetric, we can assume that they were formed by air or water moving more or less continuously in one direction. These marks are called **current ripple marks** (see Figure 5-19).

Nodules, Concretions, and Geodes

Many sedimentary rocks contain structures that were formed only *after* the original sediment was deposited. Among these are nodules, concretions, and geodes.

Figure 5-18 Polygonal pattern of mudcracks resulting from dessication of modern fine-grained sediments on the delta of the Colorado River. Maximum dimension of polygons about 12 inches. (*Photo by Gilbert, U.S. Geological Survey.*)

Figure 5-19 Current ripple marks from the Baraboo Hills, Wisconsin, are seen on the bedding plane of this quartzite, a metamorphic rock derived from sandstone. The asymmetric nature of the ripples indicate that the current which formed them (about 700 million years ago) moved from left to right. Distance from crest to crest of the ripples averages about 3 inches. (*Photo by Sheldon Judson.*)

Figure 5-20 Two geodes broken open to show their internal structure. The dark outer layer of chalcedony is lined with milky-to-clear quartz crystals that project inward toward a hollow center. These structures are most commonly found in limestone, where they apparently form by the modification and enlargement of an original void. Scale given by 2-inch squares in background. (*Specimen from the Geological Museum, Harvard University. Photo by Walter R. Fleischer.*)

A **nodule** is an irregular, knobby-surfaced body of mineral matter that differs in composition from the sedimentary rock in which it has formed. It usually lies parallel to the bedding planes of the enclosing rock, and sometimes adjoining nodules coalesce to form a continuous bed. Nodules average about one foot in maximum dimension. Silica, in the form of chert or flint, is the major component of these bodies. Most nodules are thought to have formed when silica replaced some of the materials of the original deposit; some, however, may consist of silica that was deposited at the same time as the main beds were laid down.

A **concretion** is a local concentration of the cementing material that has lithified a deposit into a sedimentary rock. Concretions range in size from a fraction of an inch to several feet in maximum dimension. Most are shaped like simple spheres or disks, although some have fantastic and complex forms. For some reason, when the cementing material entered the unconsolidated sediment, it tended to concentrate by spreading outward from a common center point or along a common center line. The particles of the resulting concretion are cemented together more firmly than the particles of the host rock that surrounds it. The cementing material usually consists of calcite, dolomite, iron oxide, or silica—in other words, the same cementing materials that we find in the sedimentary rocks themselves.

Geodes, more eye-catching than either concretions or nodules, are roughly spherical, hollow structures that vary in diameter from a few inches to more than a foot (see Figure 5-20). An outer layer of chalcedony is lined with crystals that project inward toward the hollow center. The crystals, often perfectly formed, are usually quartz, although crystals of calcite and dolomite have also been found and, more rarely, crystals of other minerals. Geodes are most commonly found in limestone, but they also occur in shale.

How does a geode form? First, a water-filled pocket develops in a sedimentary deposit, probably as a result of the decay of some plant or animal that was buried in the sediments. As the deposit begins to consolidate into a sedimentary rock, a wall of silica with a jelly-like consistency forms around the water, isolating it from the surrounding material. As time passes, fresh water may enter the sediments. The water inside the pocket has a higher salt concentration than the water outside. In order to equalize the concentrations, there is a slow mixing of two liquids through the silica wall or membrane that separates them. This process of mixing is called **osmosis.** So long as the osmotic action continues, pressure is exerted outward toward the surrounding rock. The original pocket expands bit by bit, until the salt concentrations of the liquids inside and outside are equalized. At this point, osmosis stops, the outward pressure ceases, and the pocket stops growing. Now the silica wall dries, crystallizes to form chalcedony, contracts, and cracks.

If, at some later time, mineral-bearing water finds its way into the deposit, it may seep in through the cracks in the wall of chalcedony. There the minerals are precipitated, and crystals begin to grow inward, toward the center, from the interior walls. Finally, we have a crystal-lined geode imbedded in the surrounding rock. Notice that the crystals in a geode grow inward, whereas in a concretion they grow outward.

Fossils

The word **fossil** (derived from the Latin *fodere*, "to dig up") originally referred to anything that was dug from the ground, particularly a mineral or some inexplicable form. It is still used in that sense occasionally, as in the term "fossil fuel" (see Chapter 22). But today the term "fossil" generally means any direct evidence of past life—for example, the bones of a dinosaur, the shell of an ancient clam, the footprints of a long-extinct animal, or the delicate impression of a leaf.

Fossils are usually found in sedimentary rocks, although they sometimes turn up in igneous and metamorphic rocks. They are most abundant in mudstone, shale, and limestone, but are also found in sandstone, dolomite, and conglomerate. Fossils account for almost the entire volume of certain rocks, such as coquina and limestones formed from ancient reefs.

The remains of plants and animals are completely destroyed if they are left exposed on the earth's surface; but if they are somehow protected from destructive forces, they may become incorporated in a sedimentary deposit where they will be preserved for millions of years. In the quiet water of the ocean, for example, the remains of starfish, snails, and fish may be buried by sediments as they settle slowly to the bottom. If these sediments are subsequently lithified, the remains of the animals are preserved as fossils that tell us about the sort of life that existed when the sediments were laid down.

Fossils are also preserved in deposits that have settled out of fresh water. Countless re-

mains of land animals, large and small, have been dug from the beds of extinct lakes, flood plains, and swamps.

In Chapter 12 we shall find that fossils are extremely useful in subdividing geologic time and constructing the geologic calendar. The detailed story of the development of life through geologic time is recorded by the fossils found for the most part in sedimentary rocks. We will consider this story in Chapters 14 through 20.

Sedimentary Facies

If we examine the environments of deposition that exist at any one time over a wide area, we find that they differ from place to place. Thus, the fresh-water environment of a river changes to a brackish-water environment as the river nears the ocean. In the ocean itself, marine conditions prevail. But even here, the marine environment changes—from shallow water to deep water, for example. And as the

Figure 5-21 Some sedimentary rocks are made up of extremely fine particles. This photo by electron microscope shows the structure of a limestone of Paleocene age from Zumaya, Spain. The magnification is about 10,000X. The geometric markings represent coccoliths, interlocking, overlapping plates of calcite that are developed by certain one-celled flagellate animals. (*Photo by S. Honjo.*)

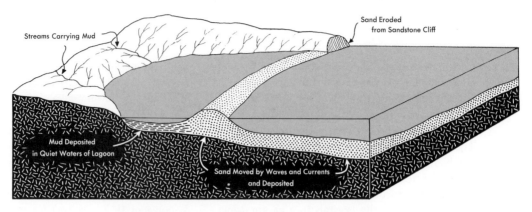

Figure 5-22 Diagram illustrating a change in sedimentary facies. Here, the fine-grained muds are deposited in a lagoon close to shore. A sand bar separates them from sand deposits farther away from shore. The sand in this instance has been derived from a sea cliff and transported by waves and currents.

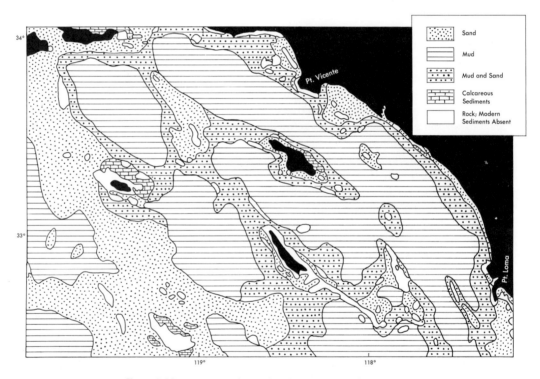

Figure 5-23 Variation in facies of modern sediments off the coast of southern California. (*After Revelle and Shepard, in* Recent Marine Sediments, *Am. Assoc. Petroleum Geol., 1939, p. 246.*)

environment changes, the nature of the sediments that are laid down also changes. The deposits in one environment show characteristics that are different from the characteristics of deposits laid down at the same time in another environment. This change in the "look" of the sediments is called a change in **sedimentary facies;** the latter word derives from the Latin for "aspect" or "form."

We may define sedimentary facies as an accumulation of deposits that exhibits specific characteristics and grades laterally into other sedimentary accumulations formed at the same time but exhibiting different characteristics. The concept of facies is widely used in studying sedimentary rocks and the conditions that gave rise to metamorphic rocks (see Chapter 6). The concept is not generally used in referring to igneous rocks, though there is no valid reason why it should not be used.

Let us consider a specific example of facies. Figure 5-22 shows a coastline where rivers from the land empty into a lagoon. The lagoon is separated from the open ocean by a sandbar. The fine silts and clays dumped into the quiet waters of the lagoon settle to the bottom as a layer of mud. At the same time, waves are eroding coarse sand from a nearby headland outside the lagoon. This sand is transported by currents and waves and deposited as a sandy layer seaward of the sandbar. Different environments exist inside and outside the lagoon; therefore different deposits are being laid down simultaneously. Notice that the mud and the sand grade into each other along the sandbar. Now, imagine that these deposits were consolidated into rocks and then exposed to view at the earth's surface. We would find a shale layer grading into sandstone—that is, one sedimentary facies grading into another.

Color of Sedimentary Rocks

Throughout the western and southwestern areas of the United States, bare cliffs and steep-walled canyons provide a brilliant display of the great variety of colors exhibited by sedimentary rocks. The Grand Canyon of the Colorado River in Arizona cuts through rocks that range in color from gray, through purple and red, to brown, buff, and green. Bryce Canyon in southern Utah is fashioned of rocks tinted a delicate pink, and the Painted Desert, farther south in Arizona, exhibits a wide range of colors, including red, gray, purple, and pink.

The most important sources of color in sedimentary rocks are the iron oxides. Hematite (Fe_2O_3), for example, gives rocks a red or pink color, and limonite and goethite produce tones of yellow and brown. Some of the green, purple, and black colors may be caused by iron, but exactly what form of iron is not completely understood. Only a very small amount of iron oxide is needed to color a rock. In fact, few sedimentary rocks contain more than 6 per cent of iron, and most contain much less.

Organic matter, when present, may also contribute to the coloring of sedimentary rocks, usually in a range from gray to black. Generally, but not always, the higher the organic content, the darker the rock.

The size of the individual particles in a rock also influences the color, or at least the intensity of the color. For example, fine-grained clastic rocks are usually somewhat darker than coarse-grained rocks of the same mineral composition.

Figure 5-24 Variation in facies of ancient sediments constituting the Maquoketa formation in Illinois. (*After E. P. DuBois, Illinois Geol. Survey*, Report of Investigations #105, 1945, p. 10.)

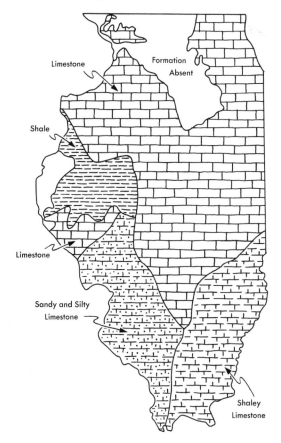

SUMMARY

Sedimentary rocks cover 75 per cent of the worlds' land surface but make up only 5 per cent of the volume of rock in the outer 10 miles of the earth's crust.

Material for sedimentary rocks includes the detrital material (fragments of pre-existing rocks) eroded from the land masses of the world, and also of material precipitated (chemically or biochemically) from solution. Three minerals—clay, quartz and calcite—are the most important rock-forming constituents of the sedimentary rocks.

The texture of sedimentary rocks depends on the size, shape, and arrangement of particles. The textures are clastic (made up of particles cemented together) or nonclastic (usually crystalline and formed by the precipitation of mineral matter from solution).

Soft sediments are turned to rock (lithified) by the processes of compaction, cementation, dessication, and crystallization.

Sedimentary rocks can be classified as detrital or chemical. Detrital rocks have clastic textures and include conglomerate, sandstone, mudstone, and shale. Chemical rocks may have either clastic or nonclastic textures and include limestone, dolomite, rock salt, gypsum, anhydrite, chert, flint, and coal. Mudstone and shale, sandstone, and limestone constitute 99 per cent of the sedimentary rocks. Of these, mudstone and shale are most abundant and limestone least abundant.

Bedding or stratification is the most characteristic feature of sedimentary rock. Other features include ripple marks, mudcracks, fossils, nodules, concretions, geodes, and color. Iron oxide is the most important coloring matter.

A sedimentary facies is an accumulation of deposits with specific characteristics grading laterally into other sedimentary deposits with different characteristics.

ADDITIONAL READING

Degens, Egon T., *Geochemistry of Sediments—A Brief Survey*. Englewood Cliffs, N.J.: Prentice-Hall, 1965.

Krumbein, W. C., and L. L. Sloss, *Stratigraphy and Sedimentation* (2nd ed.). San Francisco: W. H. Freeman and Co., 1963.

Pettijohn, F. J., *Sedimentary Rocks* (2nd ed.). New York: Harper & Row, 1957.

Shrock, Robert R., *Sequence in Layered Rocks*. New York: McGraw-Hill Book Co., 1948.

6

Metamorphic Rocks

Having examined in some detail the nature and origin of igneous rocks (Chapter 3) and sedimentary rocks (Chapter 5), let us now turn to an examination of the classification, composition, and formation of the third major family, the metamorphic rocks.

In our study of the metamorphic rocks, two difficulties confront us. The first is their great variety. In Figure 3-2 we can see that any igneous or sedimentary rock can be changed into

Figure 6-1 Contorted gneiss. Dark bands of ferromagnesian minerals trace out the pattern of distortion to which this rock was subjected by the processes of metamorphism. Two-inch squares form the background reference grid to give scale. From Bedford, Westchester County, New York. (*Photo by Walter R. Fleischer.*)

a metamorphic rock; thus there can be at least as many metamorphic rocks as there are igneous and sedimentary rocks. We will see that there can be even more, because a single sedimentary or igneous type can give rise to a number of metamorphic rocks depending on the conditions to which the rock is subjected. Furthermore, an existing metamorphic rock may itself be turned into a new one. Therefore, the number of individual rock types in the metamorphic family is potentially greater than in the igneous and sedimentary rock groups combined.

The second problem in our study of metamorphic rocks is that we cannot observe their formation directly. Virtually all metamorphic rocks now exposed at the surface of the earth were formed at some depth beneath the surface. Therefore, we are dependent on erosion to expose the metamorphic rocks to view. In contrast, the processes of sedimentation can be observed, albeit with difficulty, as can the formation of volcanic or extrusive igneous rocks, though witnessing the formation of deep-seated igneous rocks is denied us. Thus, our information concerning the origin of metamorphic rocks must

come either by inference drawn from their composition, structure, and occurrence or by analogy with artificial conditions set up in the laboratory.

A FIRST LOOK AT METAMORPHIC ROCKS

In Chapter 3, we began our study of igneous rocks by arranging a representative assemblage in several ways. We tried color, density, texture and composition. Eventually we arrived at a classification based on texture and mineral composition, to which color and specific gravity were related. Now, let us similarly assume that we have an undifferentiated collection of representative metamorphic rocks.

Separating first by color, we can arrange our samples on a scale that varies from pure white to black with various tones of gray, green, and red in between. Each of our final groupings, however, contains rocks that differ in composition, specific gravity, and texture. We find, thus, that our classification has little relation to any observable characteristics other than color. We meet much the same problem when we classify according to density.

Turning to composition, we discover almost as many categories as individual specimens. We are forced, therefore, to abandon composition as a primary basis of classification. We will see later, however, how composition can be used as a secondary characteristic in classification.

We are left, then, at least for our initial separation of the metamorphic rocks, with texture, which was so important in both the igneous and the sedimentary families.

Texture

A number of textural characteristics become evident as we examine our pile of metamorphic rocks. Many of our samples, for instance, are coarse; with the naked eye we can see individual mineral grains, which may range in largest dimension from about 1 to 10 mm, and sometimes more. These crystals are interlocking, even as they are in coarse-grained igneous rocks and in some of the sedimentary rocks. We find, also, that many of the metamorphic rocks are very fine-grained; in these we cannot identify by eye the constituent minerals, only flashing points of light from individual crystals or from cleavage planes. And again, as we found in some igneous rocks, there can be a mixture of both small and large crystals in the same specimen. We called this characteristic porphyritic in the igneous rocks, but the term is not generally used in describing the metamorphic rocks.

How does the texture of these metamorphic rocks differ from that of the sedimentary and igneous rocks we have already studied? It turns out that we can divide metamorphic rocks into two groups according to texture. But the decisive quality is not the size or uniformity of the grains, rather it is the arrangement of the grains.

In the larger of the two groups the texture is characterized by a preferred orientation of individual grains, or by parallel layers of minerals of different composition. In size the minerals may be large or small or "mixed," but their arrangement gives the rocks a distinctive aspect which is properly called **foliation** (from the

Latin *foliatus*, "leaved or leafy," hence, consisting of leaves or thin sheets).

Foliation imparts a characteristic called **rock cleavage.** You will remember that we used the term cleavage to describe the relative ease with which a mineral breaks along parallel planes. Here we use the modifier "rock" to distinguish rock cleavage from mineral cleavage. All foliated rocks tend to break or cleave most easily along planes parallel to their foliation.

In the second, smaller group, of metamorphic rocks we find that there seems to be no preferred orientation of breakage. We generally refer to these rocks as **unfoliated.**

Figure 6-2 Metamorphic rock (a gneiss) showing alignment of previously unoriented minerals. The light-colored bands are mainly orthoclase and quartz; the dark streaks are biotite and other ferromagnesian minerals. The bulk composition is that of granite; but in contrast to the random mixing in granite, the minerals are here distributed in relatively systematic patterns. *(Photo by Navias.)*

Figure 6-4 Blocks for building stones are sawed out of this marble quarry. This monomineralic rock does not have a preferred direction of breakage as does the foliated slate shown in Figure 6-3. (*Photo by Benjamin M. Shaub.*)

TYPES OF FOLIATED ROCKS We can further subdivide the foliated rocks into groups based on the coarseness or fineness of the foliation. These divisions are as follows:

1. *Slaty* (from the French *éclat*, "fragment or splinter"). In this type the cleavage occurs along planes separated by distances of microscopic dimensions. The planes of cleavage are very smooth and regular.

2. *Phyllitic* (from the Greek *phyllon*, "leaf"). Here the cleavage produces cleavage fragments barely visible to the unaided eye. The fragments are thicker than those of rocks with slaty cleavage, and the surface of cleavage planes are somewhat more irregular.

3. *Schistose* (from the Greek *schistos*, "divided, divisible"). This type of cleavage produces flakes that are clearly visible. Cleavage surfaces are rougher than in the slaty or phyllitic types.

4. *Gneissic* (from the German *gneiss*, a term originally used to refer to the country rock containing the mineral deposits of the Erzgebirge region of southern Germany). The term gneiss is now given to a metamorphic rock and sometimes an igneous rock characterized by coarse foliation or banding, in which the bands of differing mineral composition are usually a few millimeters or centimeters thick. Cleavage planes are very irregular and rough.

Composition

The composition of metamorphic rocks is extremely diverse. But we can make two very simple observations and refine them later in this

94

Table 6-1 Simplified Classification of Metamorphic Rocks Based on Texture and Composition

Texture	Monomineralic	Multimineralic
Unfoliated	Quartzite, marble	Hornfels
Foliated		Slate, phyllite, schist, gneiss

chapter. First, some metamorphic rocks are made up exclusively or predominantly of a single mineral type. They are, therefore, **monomineralic.** Examples are marble (made up of calcite) and quartzite (composed of quartz). Monomineralic rocks are either unfoliated or weakly foliated.

Second, most metamorphic rocks are composed of two or more minerals, and so are called **multimineralic.** Usually (but not always), these multimineralic rocks are foliated.[1] An example is *gneiss*. Gneisses have differing compositions, but if one has the mineral assemblage characteristic of a granite (quartz, orthoclase, plagioclase, and a few ferromagnesian minerals), we call it a granite gneiss. Like the granite, it is coarse-grained, and has interlocking crystals. It differs from granite in possessing a foliated texture defined by a coarse banding of the various minerals.

Table 6-1 gives a simplified classification of metamorphic rocks based on texture (foliated and unfoliated) and composition (monomineralic and multimineralic).

Many of the minerals of sedimentary and igneous rocks are found in the metamorphic group as well. These include the familiar minerals of quartz, calcite, orthoclase and plagioclase feldspars, muscovite and biotite, amphibole, and augite. But the processes of metamorphism also create minerals uncommon in the sedimentary and igneous rocks. These include diopside, tremolite, sillimanite, kyanite, andalusite, staurolite, garnet, epidote, and chlorite, which are discussed beginning on page 97, later in this chapter.

[1]Hornfels (see p. 162), usually unfoliated, are commonly multimineralic.

FORMATION OF METAMORPHIC ROCKS

Thus far we have confined our study to a general examination and ordering of the metamorphic rocks. Now let us consider the ways in which metamorphic rocks might form. Inference and analogy have led to the universal opinion that metamorphic rocks come into being as existing rocks in the solid state respond to alterations in temperature, pressure, and chemical environment. These changes are thought to be the same as those that fold, fault, inject magma into, and elevate or depress large masses of rock. What is distinctive is that the process of metamorphism occurs within the earth's crust, below the zone of weathering and cementation and above the zone of remelting. In this environment rocks undergo chemical and structural changes in response to conditions that differ from those under which they originally formed.

Agents of Metamorphism

We limit the term metamorphism to changes that take place in the texture and composition of solid rocks. Metamorphism can occur only while the rock is solid, because when the rock reaches its melting point, a magma forms and igneous activity begins. We should recognize, however, that a rock can exist in the plastic state, a condition transitional between the brittle character of rocks at or near the earth's surface and the molten state of subterranean magma.

In this zone of change, the agents producing metamorphic rocks are **heat, deforming processes (or pressure),** and **chemically active fluids.**

HEAT Various lines of evidence suggest that metamorphism takes place within a temperature range of about 300°F to 1470°F (150°C to 800°C). Many believe that temperature may be the single most important agent of metamorphism. Nevertheless, it is most certainly accompanied and abetted by changes in pressure and the presence of chemically active fluids.

PRESSURE Drilling for oil has revealed that sedimentary rocks 20,000 to 30,000 feet deep do not undergo metamorphic change. Somewhere below this depth, however, where pressures begin to approach 40,000 pounds per square inch, most rocks become plastic. The high confining pressures combine with differential pressures to produce two general results. First, pressure reduces the space occupied by the rock mass, thereby leading to recrystallization and the formation of new minerals with closer atomic packing. Second, differential pressures combine with confining pressures to produce a flow of rock material. This flow results in intergranular motion, the formation of minute shear planes within the rock, changes in texture, the reorientation of grains, and the growth of crystals. It is from these processes that most of the foliation in metamorphic rock derives.

CHEMICALLY ACTIVE FLUIDS The magma from which igneous rocks crystallize contains water, most of which does not become a part

Figure 6-6 Chemically active fluids probably helped to form these bands of mica, amphibole and some quartz, which define the foliation in a gneiss on Pemaquid Point, Maine. The light band which cuts across the foliation at a low angle and parallel to the pen is a thin dike of granitic material. (*Photo by Sheldon Judson.*)

of the minerals forming from the magma but is driven off. In a volcanic eruption, for instance, much of the "smoke" from the vent is water in the form of steam. If the water is released below the surface, it moves through the surrounding rock as a **hydrothermal solution.** This solution transports ions from the igneous body into the rock, where it may deposit ions, pick up others, and generally alter the original rock. When a chemical reaction within the rock or the introduction of ions from an external source cause one mineral to grow or change into another of different composition, the process is called **metasomatism.** The term describes all ionic transfers, not just those that involve gases or solutions from magma.

Some of the chemically active fluid in the process of metamorphism is already present as liquid in the pores of a rock subjected to agents of metamorphism. It is believed that such pore liquid may often act as a catalyst; that is, it expedites changes without itself undergoing change.

Types of Metamorphism

Several types of metamorphism occur, but we shall concern ourselves here with the two basic ones: contact metamorphism and regional metamorphism.

Figure 6-5 The light-colored, elongate patches in this rock represent pebbles that have been deformed and stretched out as a conglomerate went through the initial stages of metamorphism. This "stretched-pebble conglomerate" is in the Panamint Range, California. (*Photo by Sheldon Judson.*)

96

CONTACT METAMORPHISM The alteration of rocks by ionic transfer brought about by high temperatures and by the introduction of magmatic solutions at or near their contact with a body of magma is called **contact metamorphism.** At the actual surface of contact, all the elements of a rock may be replaced by other elements introduced by hot gases and solutions escaping from the magma. Farther away, the replacement may be only partial.

Contact metamorphism occurs in restricted zones called **aureoles** ("halos"), which seldom measure more than a few hundred feet in width and may be only a fraction of an inch. Aureoles are found bordering laccoliths, stocks, and batholiths. During contact metamorphism, temperatures range from 570°F to 1470°F (300°C to 800°C) and load pressures from 1,500 to 45,000 pounds per square inch.

Contact metamorphism develops late in the mountain-building sequence (discussed in Chapter 8) and at relatively shallow depths. It is only late in the cooling of a magma that large quantities of hydrothermal solutions are released, then only as the body of magma approaches the surface.

A great deal of recrystallization is caused by the heat of contact metamorphism. Contact metamorphic minerals include **diopside** and **tremolite,** which are silicates of calcium and magnesium. The most important materials brought in by hydrothermal solutions involved in contact metamorphism in many situations help to form economically important ore minerals.

REGIONAL METAMORPHISM Regional metamorphism develops over extensive areas, often involving thousands of square miles of rock thousands of feet thick. It is commonly believed that the huge reservoirs of melted rock associated with the formation of some mountain ranges is an expression of regional metamorphism, but the assumption has not been proved. The effects of regional metamorphism are best seen, however, in the root regions of old fold mountains and in the Precambrian continental shields (see Chapters 8 and 13). Thousands of feet of rock have had to be eroded in order to expose these metamorphic rocks to view.

During regional metamorphism, many new minerals are developed as rocks respond to increases in temperature and pressure. These include some new silicate minerals not found in igneous and sedimentary rocks, such as sillimanite, kyanite, andalusite, staurolite, various garnets, brown biotite, epidote, and chlorite.

The first three of these are silicates with the formula Al_2SiO_5. Their independent SiO_4 tetrahedra are bound together by positive ions of aluminum. **Sillimanite** (in honor of Benjamin

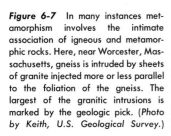
Figure 6-7 In many instances metamorphism involves the intimate association of igneous and metamorphic rocks. Here, near Worcester, Massachusetts, gneiss is intruded by sheets of granite injected more or less parallel to the foliation of the gneiss. The largest of the granitic intrusions is marked by the geologic pick. (*Photo by Keith, U.S. Geological Survey.*)

Figure 6-8 Crystals of staurolite from Farmington, Georgia. (*Photo by Benjamin M. Shaub.*)

Silliman, a 19th-century professor of chemistry at Yale) develops in long, slender crystals that are brown, green, or white in color. **Kyanite** (from the Greek *kyanos*, "blue") forms blade-like blue crystals. **Andalusite** (from *Andalusia*, a province of Spain) forms coarse, nearly square prisms.

Staurolite (from the Greek *stauros*, "cross") is a silicate composed of independent tetrahedra bound together by positive ions of iron and aluminum. Staurolite has a unique crystal habit that is striking and easy to recognize: It develops 6-sided prisms that intersect either at 90°,

forming a cross (see Figure 6-8), or at 60°, forming an X.

Garnets (from the Latin *granatus*, "a grain") are a group of metamorphic silicate minerals. All have the same atomic structure of independent SiO_4 tetrahedra, but a wide variety of chemical compositions is produced by the many positive ions that bind the tetrahedra together. These ions may be iron, magnesium, aluminum, calcium, manganese, or chromium. But whatever the chemical composition, garnets appear as distinctive 12-sided or 24-sided fully developed crystals (see Figure 6-9). Actually, it is difficult to distinguish one kind of garnet from another without resorting to chemical analysis. A common deep red garnet of iron and aluminum is called **almandite.**

Epidote is a silicate of calcium, aluminum, and iron in which the tetrahedra are in pairs that are independent of each other. On a freshly broken surface, this mineral is pistachio green in color; otherwise it is black or blackish-green.

Chlorite is a sheet-structure silicate of calcium, magnesium, aluminum, and iron. The characteristic green color of chlorite was the basis for its name, from the Greek *chloros*, "green" (as in chlorophyll). Chlorite exhibits a cleavage similar to that of mica, but the small scales produced by the cleavage do not, when bent, snap back to their original position as do these flakes of mica. Chlorite occurs either as aggregates of minute scales or as individual scales scattered throughout a rock.

REGIONAL METAMORPHIC ZONES Regional metamorphism may be divided into zones: high-grade, middle-grade, and low-grade. Each

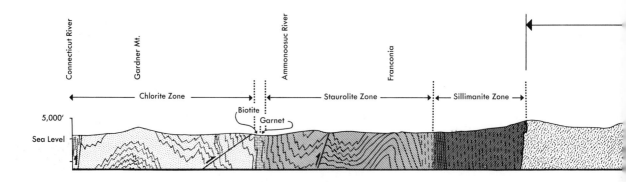

Figure 6-9 Garnet crystal in mica schist. The mold once occupied by another crystal can also be seen. Ruled 2-inch squares give scale for size. (*Photo by Walter R. Fleischer.*)

an indication of the conditions at the time of its formation.

The first appearance of chlorite, for example, tells us that we are at the beginning of a low-grade metamorphic zone. The first appearance of the garnet, almandite, is evidence of the beginning of a middle-grade metamorphic zone. And the first appearance of sillimanite marks a high-grade zone. Other minerals sometimes occur in association with each of these index minerals, but they are usually of little help in determining the degree of metamorphism of a given zone.

By noting the appearance of the minerals that are characteristic of each metamorphic zone, it is possible to draw a map of the regional metamorphism of an entire area. Of course, the rocks must have the proper chemical composition to allow these minerals to form.

grade is related to the temperature and pressure reached during metamorphism. Thus, low-grade metamorphism is found farthest away from the reservoir and blends into unchanged sedimentary rock.

Metamorphic zones are identified by using certain **index minerals** as diagnostic keys. Zones of regional metamorphism reflect the varied mineralogical response of chemically similar rocks to different physical conditions, especially temperatures. And each index mineral gives

TYPES OF METAMORPHIC ROCKS

Metamorphic rocks are usually named on the basis of texture. A few of these rocks may also be further classified by including the name of a mineral present in them, such as chlorite schist, mica schist, and hornblende schist.

SLATE **Slate** is a metamorphic rock that has been produced from the low-grade metamorphism of shale. It is fine-grained with a characteristic cleavage caused by the alignment of flat, flaky minerals under the pressures of

Figure 6-10 Cross section of New Hampshire showing metamorphic zones around the White Mountain batholith of the Older Appalachians. Length of section approximately 50 miles. (*After Marland P. Billings.*)

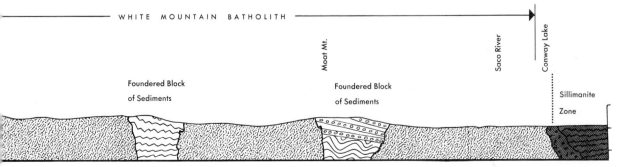

metamorphism (see Figure 6-11). Some of the clay minerals in the original shale have been transformed by heat into chlorite and mica. In fact, slate is composed predominantly of small, colorless mica flakes, with smaller quantities of chlorite. It occurs in a wide variety of colors. Dark-colored slate owes its color to the presence of carbonaceous material or iron sulfides.

PHYLLITE   **Phyllite** is a metamorphic rock with much the same composition as slate, but with minerals in larger units. Phyllite is actually slate that has undergone further metamorphism. When slate is subjected to heat greater than 500° or 600°F (250° or 300°C), the chlorite and mica minerals of which it is composed develop large flakes, giving the resulting rock its characteristic phyllitic cleavage and a silky sheen on freshly broken surfaces. The predominant minerals in phyllite are chlorite and muscovite. This rock usually contains the same impurities as slate but sometimes a new metamorphic mineral such as tourmaline or magnesium garnet makes its appearance.

SCHIST   Of the metamorphic rocks formed by regional metamorphism, **schist** is the most abundant. There are many varieties of schist, for it can be derived from many igneous, sedimentary, or lower-grade metamorphic rocks. But all schists are dominated by clearly visible flakes of some mineral, such as mica, talc, chlorite, or hematite. Fibrous minerals are commonly present as well. Schist tends to break between the platy or fibrous minerals, giving the rock its characteristic schistose cleavage.

Table 6-2 lists some of the more common varieties of schist, together with the names of the rocks from which they were derived.

Table 6-2   **Common Schists**

Variety	Rock from Which Derived
Chlorite schist	Shale
Mica schist	
Hornblende schist	Basalt or gabbro
Biotite schist	
Quartz schist	Impure sandstone
Calc-schist	Impure limestone

Schists often contain large quantities of quartz and feldspar as well as lesser amounts of minerals such as augite, hornblende, garnet, epidote, and magnetite. A green schistose rock produced by low-grade metamorphism, sometimes called a **greenschist**, owes its color to the presence of the minerals chlorite and epidote.

AMPHIBOLITE   **Amphibolite** is composed mainly of hornblende and plagioclase. There is some foliation due to the alignment of hornblende grains, but it is less conspicuous than in schists. Amphibolites, which may be green, gray, or black, sometimes contain such minerals as epidote, green augite, biotite, and almandite.

Figure 6-11 Slate in Cornwall, England, shows both cleavage and bedding. The bands of dark and light rock running diagonally across the exposure from upper left to lower right mark bedding which was horizontal when the sediments were deposited. Earth pressures have tilted the rock and imposed a rock cleavage on it which dips in the same direction as the original bedding but at a lower angle. The resulting rock is a slate which breaks most easily parallel to the cleavage rather than to the original bedding. (*Photo by British Geological Survey.*)

Figure 6-12 Folded gneiss, Pemaquid Point, Maine. Figures in upper right give scale. (*Photo by Sheldon Judson.*)

They are products of medium-grade to high-grade regional metamorphism of ferromagnesian igneous rocks and of some impure calcareous sediments.

GNEISS The coarse-grained metamorphic rock **gneiss** is most commonly formed during high-grade regional metamorphism. A banded appearance makes it easy to recognize in the field. Although gneiss does exhibit rock cleavage, it is far less pronounced than in the schists.

In gneiss derived from igneous rocks such as granite, gabbro, or diorite, the component minerals are arranged in parallel layers: The quartz and the feldspars alternate with the ferromagnesians. In gneiss formed from the metamorphism of clayey sedimentary rocks such as graywackes, bands of quartz or feldspar usually alternate with layers of platy or fibrous minerals such as chlorite, mica, graphite, hornblende, kyanite, staurolite, sillimanite, and wollastonite.

MARBLE This familiar metamorphic rock, composed essentially of calcite or dolomite, was derived during the contact or regional metamorphism of limestone or dolomite. It does not exhibit rock cleavage. Marble differs

from the original rock in having larger mineral grains. In most marble, the crystallographic direction of its calcite is nearly parallel in response to the metamorphic pressures to which it was subjected. The rock exhibits no foliation, however, because the grains have the same color, and the mineral orientation does not show up.

Although the purest variety of marble is snow-white, many marbles contain small percentages of other minerals that were formed during metamorphism from impurities in the original sedimentary rock. These impurities account for the wide variety of color in marble. **Black marbles** are colored by bituminous matter; **green marbles** by diopside, hornblende, serpentine, or talc; **red marbles** by an iron oxide, hematite; and **brown marbles** by another iron oxide, limonite. Garnets have often been found in marble and, on rare occasion, rubies.

Figure 6-13 Deformation and recrystallization of marble at 500° C. (868° F.) and pressure of 5 kilobars (about 70,000 pounds per square inch). Large, deformed crystals on right are extruded through an opening 1.5 mm. in diameter. The calcite recrystallizes into smaller grains oriented parallel to direction of extrusion. (*Photo by Hugh C. Heard.*)

The beautiful patterns of some marbles are often produced by the presence of fossilized corals in the original limestone.

Marble occurs most commonly in areas that have undergone regional metamorphism, where it is often found in layers between mica schists or phyllites.

QUARTZITE The metamorphism of quartz-rich sandstone forms the rock **quartzite.** The grains of quartz in the original have become firmly bonded together by the entry of silica into the pore spaces. Quartzite is unfoliated and is distinguishable from sandstone in two ways: There are no pore spaces in the quartzite, and the rock breaks right through the sand grains that make it up, rather than around them.

On rare occasions, limited amounts of quartzite may have been formed by percolating water under the temperatures and pressures of ordinary sedimentary processes working near the surface of the earth. Most quartzites, however, are true metamorphic rocks and may have been formed by metamorphism of any grade.

The structure of quartzite cannot be recognized without a microscope. But when we cut it into thin sections, we can identify both the original rounded sand grains and the silica that has filled the old pore spaces.

Pure quartzite is white, but iron or other impurities sometimes give the rock a reddish or dark color. Among the minerals that often occur in small quantities in quartzite are feldspar, muscovite, chlorite, zircon, tourmaline, garnet, biotite, epidote, hornblende, and sillimanite.

HORNFELS A **hornfels** is a rock produced by the contact metamorphism of a rock such as shale, limestone, sandstone, or basalt. Generally fine-grained and unfoliated, it may often contain larger crystals scattered through it. Since the process involves the high temperature attendant on igneous intrusions, the zone of hornfels defines a halo surrounding an intrusion. The temperature of metamorphism is typically higher than that of regional metamorphism and, therefore, in excess of 1470°F (700°C).

ANTHRACITE Back in Chapter 5, we discussed the formation of coal as a sedimentary rock, a process that starts with the accumulation of plant and tree remains in a swamp or a bog. There the organic matter is attacked by bacteria, and gradually decays beneath the water, out of reach of the air. As the decayed material builds up greater and greater thicknesses, the growing pressure of the overlying deposits compresses it and drives out the water. The cellulose and lignin of the original plant tissues are slowly altered, producing certain volatile compounds. Among these are the common methane ("marsh gas") and oxides of carbon.

Now if this compacted material is subjected to increased heat and pressure, many of the volatile substances are driven off and the sedimentary rock is transformed into a metamorphic rock. The volatiles carry away with them greater amounts of oxygen and hydrogen than of carbon, leaving the mass relatively richer in carbon. The names by which the coal is known at successive stages are listed in Table 6-3.

Table 6-3 Classification of Coals and Antecedent Material

Name	Percentage of Carbon	Percentage of Oxygen
Dry plant materials	50	40
Peat	60	30
Lignite	70	20
Bituminous coal	80	10
Anthracite	95	2

Notice that the percentage of carbon increases as the percentage of oxygen decreases. The amount of hydrogen and nitrogen also decreases, but the effect of these elements on the formation of coal is of no importance. Sulfur, silica (SiO_2), and aluminum oxide (Al_2O_3) may also be present as impurities. These are the substances that produce most of the ashes that remain after coal has been burned.

ORIGINS OF GRANITE

The 18th-century geologist James Hutton once stated that granite was produced by the crystallization of minerals from a molten mass. Ever since, most geologists have accepted the magmatic origin of granite. But several investigators have questioned this conclusion, suggesting instead that granite is a metamorphic rock produced from pre-existing rocks by a process called **granitization.**

In discussing batholiths, we mentioned that one of the reasons for questioning the magmatic origin of granite was the mystery of what happened to the great mass of rock that must have been displaced by the intrusion of the granite batholiths. This so-called "space problem" has led some geologists to conclude that batholiths actually represent pre-existing rocks transformed into granite by metasomatic processes.

Certain rock formations support this theory; these sedimentary rocks were originally formed in a continuous layer, but now grade into schists and then into **migmatites** ("mixed rocks"), apparently formed when magma squeezed in between the layers of schist. The migmatites in turn grade into rocks containing the large, abundant feldspars characteristic of granite, but also seem to show shadowy remnants of schistose structure. Finally, these rocks grade into pure granite. The proponents of the granitization theory say that the granite is the result of extreme metasomatism, and that the schists, migmatites, and granite-like rocks with schistose structure are intermediate steps in the transformation of sedimentary rocks into granite.

What mechanism could have brought about granitization? Perhaps ions migrated through the original solid rock, building up the elements characteristic of granite, such as sodium and potassium, and removing superfluous elements, such as calcium, iron, and magnesium. The limit to which the migrating ions are supposed to have carried the calcium, iron, and magnesium is called the **simatic front.** The limit to which the migrating ions are supposed to have deposited the sodium and potassium is called the **granitic front.**

In the mid-20th century, geologists are still carrying on an enthusiastic debate over the origin of granite. But they have reached agreement on one fundamental point—namely, that various rocks with the composition and structure of granite may have different histories. In other words, some may be igneous (see Figure 6-14) and others metasomatic. So the debate between "magmatists" and "granitizationists" has been reduced to the question of percentages. Those who favor magmatic origin admit that perhaps 15 per cent of the granite exposed at the earth's surface is metasomatic. But the granitizationists reverse the percentages and insist that about 85 per cent is metasomatic and only 15 per cent of magmatic origin.

While the battle rages, the magmatists are still seeking an adequate explanation for the origin of magma, particularly magma of sialic composition. And the granitizationists are trying to unravel an equally knotty problem—the mechanism by which pre-existing rocks have been converted to granite.

Figure 6-14 Xenolith ("strange rock") in Mt. Airy granite, North Carolina, is evidence in support of magmatic origin of this granite, because the inclusion could not have retained its sharp edges and separate identity during granitization. (*Photo by T. M. Gathright, II.*)

SUMMARY

We divide metamorphic rocks on the basis of texture into two main groups: foliated and unfoliated. The foliated group—which is the largest— is characterized by rock cleavage which parallels a preferred orientation of mineral grains or layers of minerals of differing composition. The unfoliated rocks lack rock cleavage. Textures of foliated rocks are: slaty, phyllitic, schistose, and gneissic.

A few metamorphic rocks such as marble and quartzite are dominated by a single mineral and are called monomineralic. Most metamorphic rocks, however, are multimineralic.

Agents of metamorphism include heat, pressure, and chemically active fluids. Metamorphism may be contact metamorphism near the edge of an igneous mass or it may be regional metamorphism.

Metamorphic rocks include slate, phyllite, schist, amphibolite, gneiss, marble, quartzite, hornfels, and anthracite.

Some geologists believe that granite is a metamorphic rock produced by extreme metamorphism of pre-existing rocks, a process called "granit- ization."

ADDITIONAL READING

Barth, Tom F. W., *Theoretical Petrology* (2nd ed.). New York: John Wiley & Sons, 1962.

Hurlbut, Cornelius, Jr., *Dana's Manual of Mineralogy* (17th ed.). New York: John Wiley & Sons, 1961.

Turner, Francis J., and J. Verhoogen, *Igneous and Metamorphic Petrology* (2nd ed.). New York: McGraw-Hill Book Co., 1960.

7

Earthquakes and the Earth's Interior

In the last several chapters we have investigated the nature of the materials that we can see at the earth's surface—the igneous, sedimentary, and metamorphic rocks and the minerals that compose them. But what about the nature of the earth deep beneath the surface? What is its composition? What would the globe look like were we to slice it in half?

Much of the information gathered in the search for answers to these questions has come

Figure 7-1 A section of the San Adreas fault in the Indio Hills, California; view looks northwest. Total horizontal displacements along this fault have been estimated at 350 miles. An abrupt movement of 20 feet along this same fault caused the San Francisco earthquake of 1906. (*Spence Air Photos.*)

from the study of earthquakes. So let us look first at earthquakes and then later in this chapter return to the problem of the earth's interior.

EARTHQUAKES

During the next 24 hours after you have read this, you can expect that about 400 earthquakes will shake our earth. The chances are that you won't feel any of these, either because you live in a comparatively stable area, or because the quake will be too small to be sensed over a large area. You probably have, however, felt the earth tremble at one or more times in your life, and probably will again in the future. The 150,000 earthquakes that occur on the average each year remind us of the restless nature of our earth, and of the forces within it that are constantly operating to wrinkle and crack the outer few tens of miles of its crust and mantle. They are evidence of rock deformation, and reveal the regions in which the earth's crust is now undergoing active change.

Cause of Earthquakes

The immediate cause of an earthquake is the sudden break in rocks that have been distorted beyond the limit of their strength in a process called **faulting.** Our assurance that earthquakes are caused by faulting is based by actual observations of effects that can be seen directly on the surface. It is also based on our knowledge of how rocks behave when they are subjected to pressures that are equivalent to the pressures at various depths in the earth's crust down to 100 miles. Under these pressures the rocks gradually change shape, but they resist more and more as the pressure builds up until finally they reach the breaking point. Then they tear apart and snap back into unstrained positions. This snapping back is called **elastic rebound.** Just before the rocks reach the rupture point, small shocks sometimes announce that the stress has become critical. In actual earthquakes, these shocks are often felt as **fore-shocks.** Minor adjustments occur after the break, too; these are called **aftershocks.**

SAN ANDREAS FAULT Events along the San Andreas Fault in California provided an unusual opportunity to study elastic rebound. Surveys of part of the fault had been made by the U.S. Coast and Geodetic Survey at various intervals during the years preceding the great quake of 1906. H. F. Reid of Johns Hopkins University later analyzed the events in three groups, 1851–1865, 1874–1892, and

Figure 7-2 Sequence of deformation leading to fracture along the San Andreas fault, which caused the California earthquake of 1906.

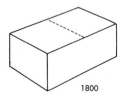

1800

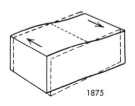

1875

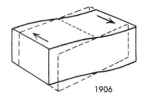

1906

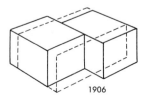

1906

1906–1907. From the displacements revealed by those surveys and from the displacements that occurred at the time of the actual quake, Reid reconstructed a history of the movement (Figure 7-2). Though there was no direct evidence, he assumed that the elastic energy had been stored at a uniform rate over the entire interval, and that the region had started from an unstrained condition approximately a century before the earthquake. As the years passed, a hypothetical line which in 1800 would have cut straight across the fault at right angles became progressively more and more warped. When the relative movement of the blocks on either side of the fault became as great as 20 feet in places, the strength of the rock was exceeded and fracture occurred. The blocks snapped back toward an unstrained position, driven by the stored elastic energy.

The fault zone runs roughly from northwest to southeast. Land on the western, or Pacific Ocean, side of the fault moved northwest relative to land on the eastern side. The strains and adjustments were greatest within a zone extending 6 miles each side of the fault. Imagine a straight line 12 miles long crossing this zone at right angles to the fault which, of course, was in the center of the zone. After the earthquake, this line was broken by the fault, and was shifted into two curves. The broken ends were separated by 20 feet at the break, but the other ends were unmoved. Actually, fences, roads, and rows of vegetation provided short sections of line by which the displacement at the fault could be gauged.

Surveys conducted at intervals since the 1906 earthquake indicate that the region around the San Andreas Fault is still warping and storing up energy that may be released in future quakes.

Distribution of Earthquakes

DEPTH OF FOCUS   In seismology, the scientific study of earthquakes, the term **focus** is used to designate the source of a given set of earthquake waves. Just what is this source? As we know, the waves that constitute an earthquake are generated by the rupture of rock masses. When these waves are recorded by an instrument at some distant point, the pattern indicates that they originated in a single simple source. Of course, this source can not be just a pinpoint; it must have dimensions. Most sources are probably closer to 30 miles in length and breadth than to 3 miles or 300 miles. But trying to fix these dimensions more accurately offers a real problem, still unsolved.

In any event, the focus of an earthquake is usually at some depth below the surface of the earth. The area on the surface directly above the focus is called the epicentral area, or **epicenter** (Greek *epi,* "above").

Foci are classed as shallow, intermediate, and deep. Shallow foci are those within 40 miles of the surface; intermediate foci are 40 to 200 miles down; deep foci are at depths greater than 200 miles. Foci have been located at all depths down to 435 miles, which is more than a tenth of the earth's radius (Figure 7-3).

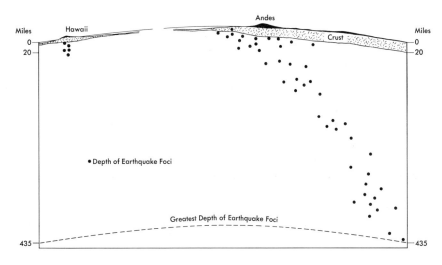

Figure 7-3 Earthquake foci under Hawaii and South America.

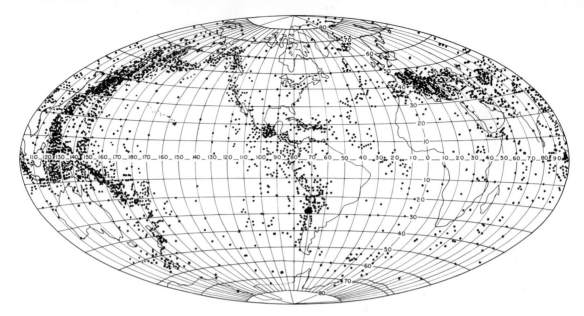

Figure 7-4 Locations of 3,737 earthquakes that occurred in 30 years (1899–1910; 1913–1930, inclusive) on Aitoff's equal area projection. This map stresses the importance of regions of relatively little earthquake activity, since it does not show the number of repetitions at active centers such as Japan. (*Prepared by L. Don Leet.*)

Between 1904 and 1946, 85 per cent of the earthquake energy released was from shallow, 12 per cent from intermediate, and 3 per cent from deep foci.

EARTHQUAKE BELTS   Earthquakes tend to occur in belts or zones surrounding stable, relatively inactive areas as suggested in Figure 7-4. The earthquakes that occur in the most active zone, around the border of the Pacific Ocean, account for a little more than 80 per

Figure 7-5 Push-pull wave, sometimes called compressional wave. In the top row, the balls connected by springs are all at rest. The second row shows conditions after the ball on the left-hand end has been pushed against its neighbor and the compression has started down the line. As each ball responds to this push, it compresses the next spring and pushes against the next ball. A wave of compression moves down the line, followed by a wave of pulling, or rarefaction. In this type of wave, each particle in the path of the wave moves back and forth about its starting position, along the line of the wave's advance.

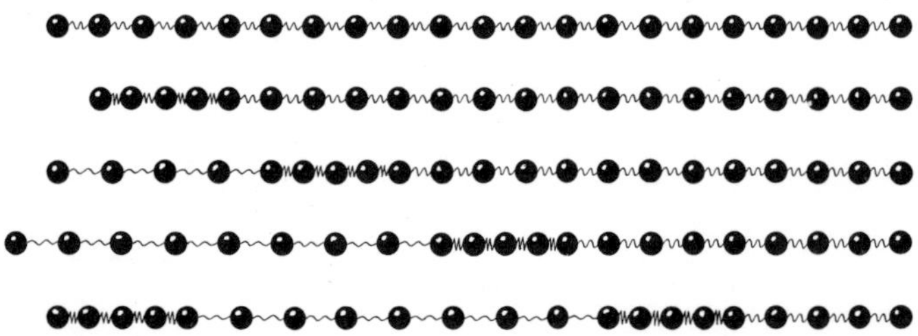

cent of the total earthquake energy released throughout the world. The greatest earthquake activity is in Japan, western Mexico, Melanesia, and the Philippines. The loop of islands bordering the Pacific has a high proportion of great shocks at all focal depths.

Fifteen per cent of the total energy released by all earthquakes is released in a zone which extends from Burma through the Himalaya Mountains into Baluchistan, across Iran, and westward through the alpine structures of Mediterranean Europe. This is sometimes called the Mediterranean and Trans-Asiatic Zone. The earthquakes that occur in the zone are of shallow and intermediate depth with foci aligned along mountain chains.

With 80 per cent of the total earthquake energy released around the Pacific and 15 per cent along the Mediterranean and Trans-Asiatic Zone, 5 per cent must be released through the rest of the world. Narrow belts of shallow-focus activity follow the Mid-Atlantic Ridge and the ridges in the Indian and Arctic Oceans.

Wave Types

When rocks break and cause an earthquake, the energy released travels away by means of waves. The manner in which waves

108

transmit energy can be illustrated by the behavior of waves on the surface of water.

When we drop a pebble into a quiet pool, we set up ripples that travel outward over the water's surface in concentric circles. These ripples carry away part of the energy that the pebble possessed as it struck the water. Now, if we place a listening device at some distant point beneath the surface we can detect the noise produced by the pebble striking the water. The noise is transmitted through the body of the water by sound waves which differ greatly from the surface waves and cannot be seen by ordinary means.

Just as with the water-born waves, there are two general classes of earth-born waves: (1) **body waves**, which travel through the interior of the mass in which they are generated and (2) **surface waves**, which travel only along the surface.

BODY WAVES   Body waves are of two general types: compressional and transverse. We may also refer to them as push-pull and shake waves, respectively. Each is defined by the manner in which it moves particles as it travels along.

Compressional, or **push-pull**, **waves**, more commonly known as sound waves, can travel through any material—solid, liquid, or gas. These waves move the particles forward and backward; consequently the materials in the path of these waves are alternately compressed and rarefied (Figure 7-5). For example, when we strike a tuning fork sharply, the prongs vibrate back and forth, first pushing then pulling the molecules of air with which they come in contact. Each molecule bumps the next one, and a wave of pressure is set in motion through the air. If the molecules next to your ear drum are compressed at the rate of 440 times a second, you hear a note that is called Middle A.

Transverse waves, or **shake waves**, can travel only through solids. These waves shake the particles in their path at right angles to the direction of their advance. Imagine that you are holding one end of a rope fastened to a wall (Figure 7-6). If you move your hand up

and down regularly, a series of waves will travel along the rope to the wall. As each wave moves along, the particles in the rope move up and down just as the particles in your hand did. In other words, the particles move at right angles to the direction of the wave's advance. The same is true when you move your hand from side to side instead of up and down.

SURFACE WAVES   Surface waves can travel along any material. Let us look again at the manner in which waves transmit energy along the surface of water. If you stand on the shore and throw a pebble into a quiet pool, setting up surface waves, some of the water seems to be moving toward you. Actually, though, what is coming toward you is energy in the form of waves. The particles of water move in a definite

Figure 7-6   Shake wave, sometimes called shear wave. If the hand is moved up and down rhythmically, adjacent particles are displaced, as shown in the sequence of diagrams, and a wave form moves along the rope. As the wave form moves forward, particles in its path move up and down. A similar result could be obtained by moving the hand from side to side or in any intermediate direction.

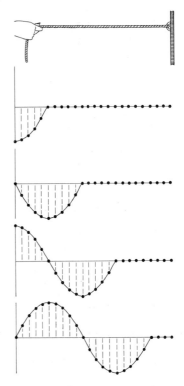

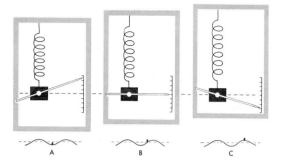

Figure 7-7 The principle of a seismograph. The weight on its spring can bounce up and down, requiring a certain length of time (called the period) to complete each oscillation. But as long as the ground under the instrument moves up and down with a shorter period (taking less time for each oscillation than the weight does if it is bouncing freely), the weight hangs still in space, or nearly so. It can then become the fulcrum of a simple lever. Sketch B shows the seismograph in its neutral position. Sketch A shows that as the seismograph's case dips into the through of an earth wave and the weight remains at the original level, the short arm of the lever goes down while the long arm goes up a greater amount. A record is obtained at the long arm of the lever (it is usually magnified optically or electronically, to make it large enough to be seen). Sketch C shows the opposite happening, when the case rides up onto the crest of an earth wave. The seismograph in the example records vertical movements, but the same general principle can be applied to the design of a seismograph that records horizontal movements.

pattern as each wave advances, up, forward, down, and back in a small circle. We can observe this pattern by dropping a small cork into the path of waves. When the surface waves are generated in a rock, one common type of particle motion is just the reverse of what we find in water—forward, up, back, and down.

Recording Earthquake Waves

THE SEISMOGRAPH AND THE SEISMOGRAM The waves that constitute an earthquake travel into and through the earth, as well as around its surface. They are now recorded by instruments called **seismographs** (from *seismos,* "a shaking," and *graphein* "to write"). The record itself is called a **seismogram.**

A seismograph is designed to measure and record displacements of the ground. It does so by means of a mass that is either suspended on a spring to record vertical movements, or attached to the end of a rod to record horizontal ones. A stylus or other device attached to

the mass will record the motion of the earth relative to the virtually unmoving mass. A special device marks off minutes and hours on the recording sheet. Most earthquake recording stations have seismographs designed to respond to both horizontal (east-west and north-south) motion and vertical motion.

Seismographs are so designed that if the earth moves quickly their mass remains at rest. For instance, a mass suspended on a spring so that it moves freely up and down, but not sideways, requires a certain length of time to complete one up-and-down cycle. This time is called the **period.** If the ground under the mass moves up and down with a shorter period (taking less time for each oscillation than the weight does if bouncing freely), the weight hangs still in space, or nearly so, as the ground moves up and down (see Figure 7-7). It then serves as a point of reference from which to measure the earth's motion—so small that it must be magnified in order to be recorded.

One way we can make a record of the earth's motion is to bounce a beam of light off the steady mass to a recorder that moves with the earth and records the relative motion between the mass and the light. The farther the light is bounced, the greater the magnification.

To obtain recordings of most earth waves generated by earthquakes, we need seismographs capable of responding to short-and long-period waves. Short periods are from 1 to 5 seconds; long periods are from 5 to 60 seconds or more.

There are many kinds of seismographs. Some weigh hundreds of pounds, or even several tons, and are set up in underground vaults. They can record anything from the vibrations of railroad trains miles away to the tremors of an earthquake any place in the world (if the earthquake is large enough). Other seismographs are small enough to be slipped into a vest pocket, or carried several in a hand, and are used to record waves generated by small dynamite charges in prospecting for minerals.

TRAVEL TIMES A seismogram demonstrates that a series of three different waves are recorded after any one earthquake (see Figure 7-8).

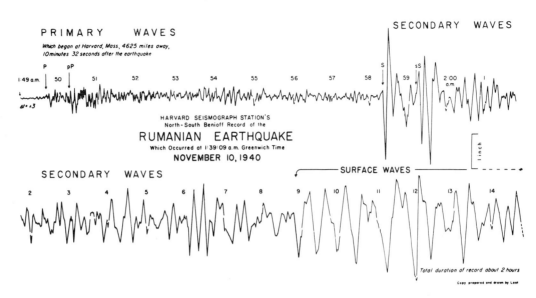

Figure 7-8 A modern seismogram. All waves started in Rumania at the same instant. They arrived as indicated above because of different speeds and paths. Experience has shown that when the Secondary waves begin 8 min 41 sec after the start of the Primary waves, as here, and each group includes a special wave (marked pP and sS), they are 4,625 miles from their places of origin at a depth of 80 miles below the earth's surface.

The first waves to arrive at the recording station are named the **primary waves,** the second are called **secondary waves,** and the last are **long waves.** The abbreviations P, S, and L are commonly used for these three types. Close study reveals that the P waves are push-pull, or compressional, waves, and that they travel with a speed determined by the rigidity and density of the rocks as well as their resistance to change in volume. S waves are found to be shake waves, or transverse waves, and they travel with a speed determined by the rigidity and the density of rocks.

The primary and secondary waves travel from the focus of an earthquake through the interior of the earth to the recording station.

The L waves, which are generated by S and P waves, are surface waves that travel from the area directly above the focus, along the crust's surface, and finally to the station.

Remember that the P waves arrive at a station before the S waves. The reason is that, although these two sets of waves follow the same general path, they travel at different speeds. The push-pull pattern by which the P waves travel produces more rapid speed than does the shake style of the S waves. S waves travel at about two-thirds the speed of P waves in any given earth material. The L waves are the last to arrive because they travel at a slower speed and over a longer route.

If we know where a major earthquake has taken place, we can measure the distance from the point of origin to the various seismograph stations that have recorded its waves. The records at these stations indicate the exact time at which the various waves arrived.

Less than 7,000 Miles. From thousands of measurements the world over, we have learned that P, S, and L waves have regular travel schedules for surface distances up to 7,000 miles. From an earthquake in San Francisco, for example, we can predict the arrival times of P and S waves at the following places:

El Paso, 1,000 miles away; P in 3 minutes 22 seconds; S in 6 minutes, 3 seconds.

Table 7-1 **Sample Timetable for P and S Waves**

| Miles from Source | Travel Time | | | | Interval between P and S (S − P) | |
| | for P | | for S | | | |
	(Min)	(Sec)	(Min)	(Sec)	(Min)	(Sec)
1,000	3	22	6	03	2	41
2,000	5	56	10	48	4	52
3,000	8	01	14	28	6	27
4,000	9	50	17	50	8	00
5,000	11	26	20	51	9	25
6,000	12	43	23	27	10	44
7,000	13	50	25	39	11	49

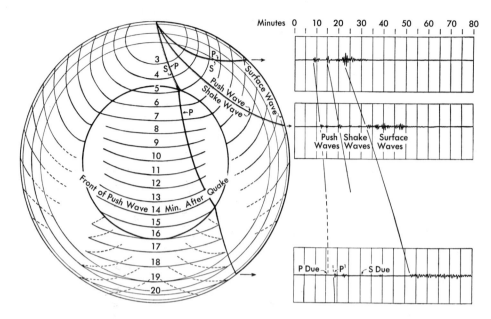

Indianapolis, 2,000 miles away; P in 5 minutes, 56 seconds; S in 10 minutes, 48 seconds.

Costa Rica, 3,000 miles away; P in 8 minutes, 1 second; S in 14 minutes, 28 seconds.

The travel schedules move along systematically out to a distance of 7,000 miles, as shown in Table 7-1, p. 111.

Beyond 7,000 Miles. Beyond 7,000 miles, however, something happens to the schedule and the P waves are delayed. By 10,000 miles they are 3 minutes late. When we consider that up to 7,000 miles, we could predict their arrival time within seconds, a 3-minute delay becomes significant.

The fate of the S waves is even more spectacular: They disappear altogether, never to be heard from again (Figure 7-9).

When the strange case of the late P and the missing S was first recognized, seismologists realized they were not just recording earthquakes, but were developing a picture of the interior of the globe. This subject we will consider in greater detail later in the chapter.

Earthquake Magnitude and Energy

How to specify the size of an earthquake has always posed a problem. Before the modern development of instrumental seismology, some of the early investigations of earthquakes led to various attempts to describe the intensity of the shaking. A missionary in some remote region would keep a diary in which he listed earthquakes as weak, strong, or very strong. This was, at best, a personal scale. Then in Italy in 1874 and in Switzerland in 1878, arbitrary scales were developed which culminated soon afterward in the Rossi-Forel Scale, a combination of the efforts of M. S. di Rossi, Direc-

Table 7-2 Rossi-Forel Scale of Earthquake Intensity

I.   Recorded by instruments; felt only by experienced observers at rest.

II.   Felt by small number of persons at rest.

III.   Felt by several persons at rest; strong enough for the duration or direction to be appreciable.

IV.   Felt by several persons in motion; disturbance of movable objects, doors, windows; creaking of floors.

V.   Felt generally by everyone; disturbance of furniture and beds; ringing of some bells.

VI.   General awakening of those asleep; general ringing of bells; oscillation of chandeliers; stopping of clocks; visible disturbance of trees and shrubs; some startled persons leave their dwellings.

VII.   Overthrow of movable objects, fall of plaster, ringing of church bells, general panic, without damage to buildings.

VIII.   Fall of chimneys, cracks in the walls of buildings.

IX.   Partial or total destruction of some buildings.

X.   Great disaster, ruins, disturbance of strata, fissures in the earth's crust, rock-falls from mountains.

tor of the Geodynamic Observatory at Rocca di Pappa, near Rome, and F. A. Forel at Lausanne, a member of a committee appointed by the Helvitic Society of Natural Sciences to study earthquakes in Switzerland in the last quarter of the 19th century. For half a century the Rossi-Forel Scale of earthquake intensity was widely used throughout the world (Table 7-2).

But since having to rely on the impressions of many people is a very unsatisfactory way of compiling accurate information, a scale was finally devised in 1935 that was based on instrumental records. This system ascribes to each earthquake a number, called the earthquake's **magnitude,** which is an index of the quake's energy at its source. According to this scale, an earthquake of magnitude 2.5 is just strong enough to be felt nearby. One of magnitude 4.5 or over is capable of causing some very local damage. One of 6 or over is potentially destructive. A magnitude of 7 or over represents a major earthquake. The largest magnitude observed in the first half of the 20th century was 8.6.

An earthquake of magnitude 5 releases approximately the same amount of energy as the first atomic bomb did on July 16, 1945. Of course, the energy is applied in quite different ways, being highly concentrated in the bomb and widely dispersed in the earthquake. The results, therefore, are correspondingly different. The energy released by an earthquake of magnitude 8.6 is 3,000,000 times as great as that of an earthquake of magnitude 5, or of the first atomic bomb.

The statistics of earthquake occurrences make one fact very clear: Most of the energy released is concentrated in a relatively small number of very large earthquakes. A single earthquake of magnitude 8.4 releases just about as much energy as was released on the average each year during the first half of the 20th century. It is not unusual for the energy of one great earthquake to exceed that of all the others in a given year, or in several years put together. Seven great shallow-focus earthquakes accounted for nearly 25 per cent of the total energy released by quakes from 1906 to 1964 (Table 7-3).

The maximum energy released by earthquakes becomes progressively less as depth of focus increases. The seven largest shallow focus earthquakes had magnitudes of 8.6, 8.4, 8.4, 8.5, 8.5, 8.6, 8.5. The five largest intermediate shocks over the same interval had magnitudes of 8.1, 8.2, 8.1, 7.9 and 8.0; the three largest deep-focus shocks had magnitudes of only 8.0, 7.5, and 7.75. This trend suggests that the force required to rupture rocks decreases as depth increases.

Locating Earthquakes

We now have timetables for P, S, and L in all possible distances from an earthquake. These are represented in the graph of Figure 7-10, p. 114.

Table 7-3   **Great Shallow-focus Earthquakes (1906–1964)**

Date	Place	Location	Magnitude
Jan. 31, 1906	Colombia	1°N., 82°W.	8.6
Aug. 17, 1906	Chile	33°S., 72°W.	8.4
Jan. 3, 1911	U.S.S.R.	44°N., 78°E.	8.4
Dec. 16, 1920	China	36°N., 105°E.	8.5
Mar. 2, 1933	Japan	39°N., 145°E.	8.5
Aug. 15, 1950	Chinese-Indian border	29°N., 97°E.	8.6
Mar. 28, 1964	Alaska	61°N., 147°W.	8.5

When the records of a station give clear evidence of the P, S, and L waves from an earthquake, the observer first determines the intervals between them. By using an interval table, such as that of Table 7-1, he can immediately translate the intervals into actual distances. For example, if he observes that S arrived 8 minutes after P, he knows that the earthquake must have been 4,000 miles away. He then notes that P arrived at 4 hours, 12 minutes, 22 seconds that morning. From the travel time

table, he can then find that P requires 9 minutes, 50 seconds to travel 4,000 miles. The earthquake, therefore, occurred at 4 hours, 02 minutes, 32 seconds.

Since this process is carried out at all the seismograph stations that have recorded the quake, an arc can be drawn on a globe to represent the computed distance from each station. The point at which all the arcs intersect indicates the center of the disturbance.

Effects of Earthquakes

Of all the earthquakes that occur every year, only one or two are likely to produce such spectacular effects as landslides or the elevation or depression of large land masses, and a hundred or so may be strong enough, near their sources, to destroy human life and property. But the rest are too small to have any serious effects.

FIRE   When an earthquake occurs near a modern city, fire is a greater hazard than the actual shaking of the ground. In fact, fire has caused an estimated 95 per cent of the total loss caused by some earthquakes.

On September 1, 1923, an earthquake occurred underneath Sagami Bay, 50 miles from Yokohama, and 70 miles from Tokyo. The rupture produced vibrations that spread outward with such energy that they caused serious damage to an area 90 miles long and 60 miles wide along the coast. Within 30 minutes after the beginning of the earthquake, fire had broken out in 136 places in Tokyo. In all, 252 started and only 40 were extinguished. Authorities estimated that at least 44 were started by chemicals. A 12-mile-an-hour wind from the south spread the flames rapidly. The wind shifted to the west in the evening, and increased to 25 miles an hour, and then shifted to the north. These changes in wind direction added greatly to the extent of the area burned. Within 18 hours, 64 per cent of the houses in Tokyo had burned. The fires died away after 56 hours with 71 per cent of the houses consumed, a total of over 366,000. The spread of fire in Yokohama,

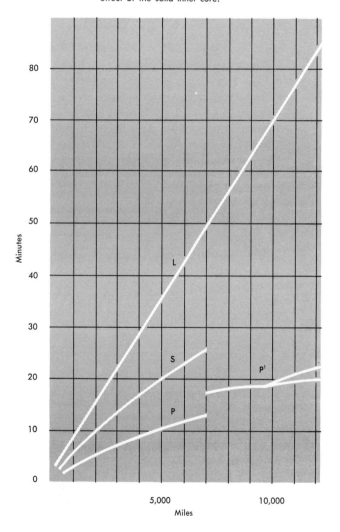

Figure 7-10 Time-distance graph for earthquake waves. P^1 is a push-pull wave that has traversed the core. The line P^1 is split beyond 10,000 miles by the effect of the solid inner core.

a city of half a million population, was even more rapid. Within 12 hours, 65 per cent of the structures in the city had burned. Eventually the city was completely destroyed (Figure 7-11). Fire was also a great killer in this Japanese earthquake. Final government statistics for this particular catastrophe were 99,000 killed and 43,000 missing.

TIDAL WAVES   Tidal waves are more correctly referred to by the term **seismic sea waves** or by the Japanese word **tsunami**, which has the same form in both the singular and the plural.

Any earthquake that causes an abrupt change in the level of the sea bottom or produces submarine landslides may generate a tsunami. Tsunami travel across the open ocean at speeds ranging between 300 and 500 miles an hour depending on the depth of water. For example, on April 1, 1946, a severe earthquake occurred at 53.5° north, 16° west, about 80 miles southeast of Unimak Island, Alaska, where the ocean is about 12,000 feet deep on the steepest slope of the Aleutian trench. Four hours and 35 minutes later a tsunami reached Honolulu. It had traveled 2,240 miles at a speed of 490 miles per hour (Figure 7-12).

When a tidal wave strikes a coastal area, it can effect great damage and loss of life. The impending approach of a seismic sea wave is heralded by a quiet withdrawal of the sea from the shore line with a speed and to a distance that exceeds any low tide. Then, the water returns in a great surging sweep, piling higher and higher as it approaches the shore, until

Figure 7-11   Yokohama, Japan, showing devastation caused by earthquake and fire of September 1, 1923. (*Photo by L. Don Leet.*)

in some places it has been known to form a wall 75 to 100 feet high. In deep water the seismic sea wave is hardly noticed, if at all, for there the wave is only 2 or 3 feet high, and the distance between crests is measured in scores of miles.

DAMAGE TO STRUCTURES   One reason for the rapid spread of fire after an earthquake is that the vibrations often disrupt the water system of the area. In San Francisco, for example, some 23,000 service pipes were broken by the great earthquake of 1906. Water pressure throughout the city fell so sharply that, when the hoses were attached to fire hydrants, only a small stream of water trickled out. Since that time, a system of valves has been installed to isolate any affected area so as to keep the water pressure at a high level in the rest of the city.

Modern, well-designed buildings of steel-frame construction can withstand the shaking of even the most severe earthquakes. In the Tokyo earthquake of 1923, the Mitsubishi Bank

Figure 7-12   Seismic sea wave at Hilo, Hawaii, April 1, 1946. The wave is smashing a warehouse. Seconds later it will sweep the man to his death. (*Photo taken from a ship's deck by Corps of Engineers, U.S. Army.*)

Figure 7-13 A few minutes after midnight on August 17, 1959, an earthquake of shallow focus struck southwestern Montana. The quake triggered this landslide which carried an estimated 2 million tons of rock into the valley of the Madison River. Scores of individuals, most of them occupants of a now-buried campsite, lost their lives, and the debris backed up the Madison River into a 100-foot-deep lake. (*Photo by Lloyd Skinner.*)

Building was surrounded by many badly damaged structures of an older type of construction, but it escaped comparatively unharmed. In the July 28, 1957, earthquake, the 43-story Latino-Americano Tower in Mexico City rode the shock waves undamaged, while surrounding buildings suffered greatly.

Chimneys are particularly sensitive to earthquake vibrations, since they tend to shake in one direction while the buildings on which they stand shake in another. Consequently, chimneys often break off at the roof line. Two small earthquakes in New Hampshire in 1940 severed dozens of chimneys but caused no other damage. In contrast, tunnels and other underground structures are little affected by even the largest earthquakes, since they move as a unit with the surrounding rock.

The extent to which a building is affected by the waves of an earthquake depends, in part, on the type of ground on which it stands. In the 1906 San Francisco earthquake, for instance, buildings on water-soaked sand, gravel, or clay suffered up to 12 times as much damage as similar structures standing on solid rock nearby. This factor accounts for some of the seemingly erratic pattern of damage that is caused by earthquakes.

CHANGES IN LAND LEVEL Along a coast not far from Tokyo, a marine animal known as *Lithophea nasuta* (the rock eater first described by a man named Nasuta) lives in a cigar-shaped pair of shells about 2 inches long, drilling his home in the rocky shores at mean sea level, and subsisting on organisms brought to its abode by ocean currents. At one place on the coast, abandoned sets of bore holes have been found at four different levels above the sea. Historical records suggest that each of these rises of the land coincides with a major earthquake, in the years 33, 818, 1703, and 1923, respectively. The total rise over the 1,890 year period was 45 feet (see Figure 8-2). This may not seem like much of a change, but if it were to continue at the same rate for 200,000 years, the land would rise nearly a mile. And in geological terms that is remarkably rapid movement.

Even more rapid movement was evidenced by changes in Alaska after 3 major earthquakes between the third and twenty-ninth of September, 1899, in the vicinity of Yakugat Bay, at about 60° north, 139° west. These earthquakes were recorded on the relatively insensitive instruments then in operation around the world. Investigators who journeyed to that remote region 6 years later found recently deceased barnacles in great profusion, still clinging to elevated sections of a former shore line. Not far away, whole forests had been drowned beneath the sea. Geologists found changes in the level of the land over an area of 30 square miles, ranging from depressions of 5 feet to elevations of 50.

LANDSLIDES In regions where there are many hills and steep slopes, large earthquakes are often accompanied by landslides. These slides occur within a zone seldom exceeding 20 to 30 miles in radius, though the very largest earthquakes have affected areas within as much as a 50-mile radius. In the Province of Kansu, China, in deposits of loess (see Chapter 10), an earthquake on December 16, 1920 caused some of the most spectacular landslides on record. The death toll was 100,000. Great masses of surface material moved for more than a mile. Some of the blocks carried roads, trees, and houses along undamaged.

CRACKS IN THE GROUND One of man's most persistent fears about earthquakes is that the earth is likely to open up and swallow everyone and everything in the vicinity. Such fears have been nourished by a great many tall tales. One account of the Lisbon earthquake of November 1, 1755 claimed that, about 25 miles from Lisbon, the earth opened up and swallowed a village's 10,000 inhabitants with all their cattle and belongings, and then closed again. The story probably got its start when a landslide buried some village in the area.

It is true that landslides and slumps do bury people and buildings, and under special conditions may even open up small shallow cracks. In California in 1906, a cow did fall into such a crack and was buried with only her tail protruding. But there is no authenticated case in which solid rock has yawned open and swallowed anything.

SOUND When an earthquake occurs, the vibrations in the ground often disturb the air and produce sound waves that are within the range of the human ear. These are known as

Figure 7-14 Cracks in pavement caused by an earthquake in Tokyo, Japan, 1923. (*Photo by L. Don Leet.*)

earthquake sounds. They have been variously described, but usually as low, booming noises. Very near the source of an earthquake, sharp snaps that are sometimes audible suggest the tearing apart of great blocks of rock. Farther away, the sounds have been likened to heavy vehicles passing rapidly over hard ground— the dragging of heavy boxes of furniture over the floor—a loud, distinct clap of thunder— an explosion—the boom of a distant cannon— or the fall of heavy bodies or great loads of stone. The true earthquake sound, of course, is quite distinct from the rumble and roar of shaking buildings. In some cases, however, the sounds are probably confused.

THE EARTH'S INTERIOR

So far in this chapter we have been concerned with earthquakes—phenomena which occur in the outer one-tenth of the globe. Now let us turn to the interior of the earth down to its very center and see what we can reasonably deduce, not only from our knowledge of the behavior of the waves generated by earthquakes but also from the mass, shape, and behavior of the earth and from the nature of meteorites.

The Mass of the Earth

The earth has a mass of 5.97×10^{27} grams, and a volume of 1.08×10^{12} km^3. The density then, is approximately 5.5 grams per cubic centimeter. In sharp contrast to this figure for the earth as a whole are the values for the rocks which we can sample at or near the earth's surface. For instance, granite has a density of approximately 2.6, basalt an average of a little less than 3. Sedimentary rocks such as sandstone, limestone, and shale are perhaps 2.4 or 2.5. The density of the continents as a whole is generally taken as 2.8.

We must obviously ask where the extra mass is in the earth. Why is the earth so much heavier than the rocks which we can actually sample at the surface?

As a first approximation, we might say that the light-weight skin with a specific gravity of around 2.8 completely encircles an inner zone having a specific gravity of approximately 6 or a little more. If the volume of these two zones were averaged out, we might get a density of 5.5 for the entire earth.

But if we turn to the rotation of the earth, we will find that the axis of rotation changes slowly under the combined influence of sun and moon. This wobble, like that of a giant top, is known precisely and is best explained by assuming that a very large part of the earth's mass is concentrated near its center. This suggestion is in part substantiated by the shape of the earth. The extent of the equatorial bulge of the earth indicates that the mass of the earth is greatest toward its center, and that a moderately dense material extends to a considerable depth beneath the surface. Were the mass of the earth more evenly distributed through its body, the equatorial bulge would be considerably greater.

From these facts, we can conclude that there is some sort of stratification within the earth, going from lightweight material at and near the surface toward heavier material at the core. More specific deductions can be made from the use of earthquake data and from the nature of meteorites.

The Evidence of Earthquakes

Having studied the causes, effects, and recording of earthquakes, we wish to use our knowledge to extend our senses and probe be-

yond the deepest mine and oil well, down toward the interior of the earth.

Studies of the travel habits of earthquake waves through the earth and of surface waves around the earth, have given us information about the structure of the globe from its surface to its center. These studies have been made possible by our knowledge of the speed at which these waves travel and of their behavior in different materials. For example, waves travel at greater speeds through simatic materials than through sialic materials. When they move from one kind of material to another across a discontinuity, they are deflected, as light waves are deflected by a lens. Part of the energy of the waves is bounced back to the surface where it can be recorded. The rest of the energy travels on into the new material.

In order to reach greater and greater distances on the surface, body waves have to penetrate deeper and deeper into the earth's interior. In traveling from an earthquake in San Francisco to a station at Dallas, for example, a surface distance of 1,500 miles, the waves have penetrated 300 miles below the surface. This would also be true for any other 1,500-mile surface distance. To reach a station 7,000 miles away, the waves dip into the interior to a maximum depth of 1,800 miles, and bring us information from that depth.

On the basis of the data assembled from studies of the travel habits of waves, the earth has been divided into three zones: the **crust,** the **mantle,** and the **core.**

THE CRUST Information on the earth's crust comes primarily from seismological observations. These include P and S waves from local earthquakes (within 700 miles), dynamite, and nuclear blasts. One of the first things revealed is that the earth's crust is solid rock. Early in the history of crustal studies a seismologist in Yugoslavia, A. Mohorovičić (Moho-ro-vee-cheech), made a special study of records of the earth waves from an earthquake on October 8, 1909, in the Kulpa Valley, Croatia. He concluded that velocities of P and

S increased abruptly below a depth of about 30 miles. This abrupt change in the speed of P and S indicated a change in material and became known as the **Mohorovičić discontinuity.** For convenience, it is now referred to as the **Moho.** The Moho marks the bottom of the earth's crust and separates it from the mantle.

The Crust of Continents. The depth to the Moho varies in different parts of the continents. In the United States, data collected up to the present time show that the thinnest portion of the crust is approximately 22 miles, the thickest 35 miles.

It has been difficult to get precise data on the earth's crust from the waves of earthquakes. Waves from dynamite blasts, however, with precisely known locations on the surface and times of detonation, have filled in some of the details. In 1941, the Harvard Seismograph Station determined the structure of the continental crust in New England, which has turned out to be fairly representative of other sections of continents. Analysis of many blast records revealed that in New England the continental crust has three layers, each one with different elastic properties, indicating different rock types. Table 7-4 summarizes the data. The first layer is sialic in composition and has been called the granitic layer. The second and third layers are more and more simatic in composition. The third is believed to be composed of basalt.

Table 7-4 Earth's Crust under New England

Thickness (miles)		Velocity (mi/sec) P	S	Rock Type
10	Layer 1	3.8	2.1	Sialic
8	Layer 2	4.2	2.4	Intermediate
4	Layer 3	4.5	2.7	Simatic
– – – – – – – – MOHO – – – – – – – –				
Top of Mantle		5.2	2.9	

L. D. Leet, "Trial Travel Times for Northeastern America," *Bull. Seis. Soc. Am.* XXXI (1941), 325–34.

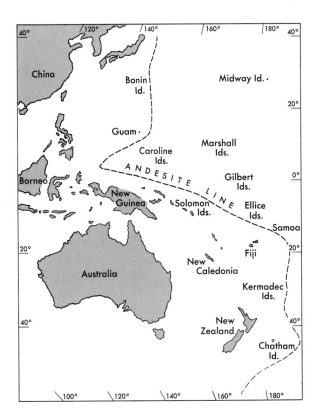

Figure 7-15 Position of the andesite line in the southwestern Pacific Ocean. This line marks the border of the true Pacific basin in a geological sense. On the Pacific side of the line, young eruptive rocks are basaltic; on the other side, they are principally andesitic. Islands east of the line are isolated or grouped volcanic peaks; west of the line they have the characteristic structure of folded continental mountain ranges. (*After R. A. Daly.*)

The crust under the United States is thickest—more than 35 miles—under the eastern front of the Rocky Mountain Ranges and the adjacent plateau. It thins from there toward each ocean, with the exception of a local thicker pocket under the part of Nevada popularly known as the Great Basin.

The Crust under Oceans. Our knowledge of the structure of the crust beneath the oceans is based on observations of rocks exposed on volcanic islands and on studies of the velocities of L waves from earthquakes. These are now being supplemented in a few places by dynamite-wave profiles.

The rock types found on islands help to determine the edges of the Pacific Basin. The andesite line (see Figure 7-15) has on its ocean

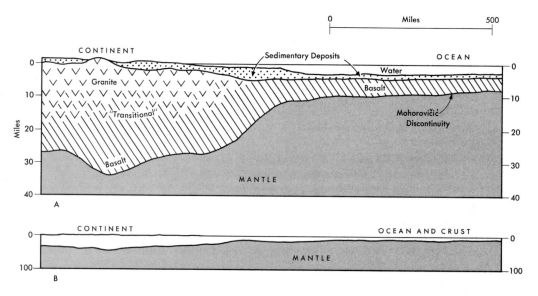

Figure 7-16 Relation of oceanic and continental crust to each other and to the upper mantle. In diagram A the vertical scale is about 10 times the horizontal scale. Diagram B is drawn to scale.

side younger, extrusive rocks composed of basalt, while on the other side they are principally andesite. This has been viewed as the dividing line between oceanic and continental crusts.

On the basis of seismic wave velocities, it appears that the crust under the Pacific is not layered and is appreciably thinner than the crust of continents. Thicknesses as little as 3 miles have been measured in the northeast Pacific.

The crust under the Pacific Ocean is made up of simatic rocks and so, apparently, is that beneath the Atlantic and Indian oceans. In all these basins, the sialic layer is missing.

THE MANTLE Below the earth's crust is a second major zone, the mantle, which extends to a depth of approximately 1,800 miles into the interior of the earth. Our knowledge of the mantle is based in part on evidence supplied by the behavior of P and S waves recorded between 700 and 7,000 miles.

At the Moho, the speeds of P and S increase sharply, an indication that the com-

position of the material suddenly changes. We have no direct evidence of the new material's nature, but the change in speed suggests that it may contain more ferromagnesian minerals than the crust.

We know that the mantle is solid, because it is capable of transmitting S waves. In an attempt to explain mountain-building processes and the tendency of the earth's crust toward isostasy (see Chapter 8), some observers have emphasized that the mantle material may undergo slow flow as it adapts to changing conditions on the surface. Some have suggested that at least the upper portion of the mantle may consist of elements arranged in a random pattern. They feel that a disorderly atomic arrangement might permit the material of the mantle to flow more readily than it would if it were crystalline.

The S waves travel through the outer part of the mantle with a velocity of 2.9 miles per second, and the speed increases with depth. As a result of these observations, geophysicists have concluded that the rigidity of the mantle increases with depth.

There is a worldwide discontinuity in the mantle at a depth of about 300 miles. There, the velocities of P and S waves increase sharply, thus producing the **20° discontinuity,** so-called because it becomes apparent on earth-wave records at stations 20° (1,400 miles) from an earthquake focus. What produces this change in the mantle? It may be a rearrangement of atoms under pressure or a change in the kinds of atoms present. We do not know exactly; yet, whatever the new material is that produces the change, it seems to be substantially uniform down to 1,800 miles, the inner limit of the mantle.

THE CORE   We come now to the core, a zone that extends from the 1,800-mile inner limit of the mantle to the center of the earth, at a depth of 3,950 miles. An analysis of seismographic records from earthquakes 7,000 miles or more distant reveals that the core has two parts: an outer zone 1,360 miles thick, and an inner core with a radius of 790 miles (see Figure 7-17).

In traveling between two points 7,000 surface miles apart, we know that P and S waves penetrate 1,800 miles into the interior. But once they go deeper than that, they enter a material that delays P and eliminates S

altogether. Since S waves are capable of traveling through only solids, we can conclude that the outer zone of the core is not solid. It is generally believed to be liquid rather than gas, for it is unlikely that any gas could support the terrific pressures existing at that depth.

The P waves travel on through the outer zone of the core, though at a lower speed. Then, at a depth of 3,160 miles, they suddenly speed up again, an indication that the inner core is solid.

The Evidence of Meteorites

For clues to the composition of the innermost core of the earth, we turn to evidence that comes to us from outer space in the form of meteorites. Meteorites are of two major types, stony and iron. By far the most common are the **stony meteorites.** They constitute over 90 per cent of all falls. (A "fall" is a meteorite which has been picked up after it has been actually seen to descend to the earth.) Stony meteorites, which have a density of between 3 and 4, are made up largely of olivine and orthopyroxene with odd mixtures of some accessory minerals, some of which occur only in meteorites.

Figure 7-17   Two earthquake records showing the effect of the earth's core on wave propagation. H on each record is the time of the earthquake's occurrence. The first P-wave reached 76.4° (5,276 miles) about 11.5 minutes after leaving the source. On the travel schedule that this represents, this P-wave was due to arrive at 134.1° (9,315 miles) about 3 minutes before the first waves were actually recorded there. No S-waves reached 9,315 miles. P-waves and S-waves reaching 5,275 miles do not travel deeply enough into the earth to reach the core. But those that enter the earth at an angle that would return them to the surface 9,315 miles from their source do encounter the core en route. If travel schedules out to 7,000 miles are extended to 9,315 miles, they show that P and S are due at the times indicated by arrows on the more distant record. But P is delayed and arrives as P[1], and no S or delayed equivalent of S ever arrives.

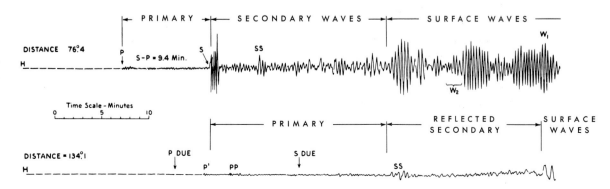

Figure 7-18 Small metallic meteorite from Meteor Crater, Arizona. (Photo by Willard Starks.)

The **iron meteorites,** in contrast, are made up largely of a crystalline iron mixed with some nickel, and have a density of about 8. Assuming that the meteorites are fragments of a now-disintegrated planetary body, it may be that we can draw an analogy between the composition of these meteorites and that of the earth's mantle and core. This, in fact, has been done by many observers. Thus, the composition of the mantle is suggested to be largely iron-magnesian silicate, which is the general composition of the olivines and the pyroxenes; the composition of the core may be an iron-nickel alloy. This compositional

Figure 7-19 Structure of the mantle and the core.

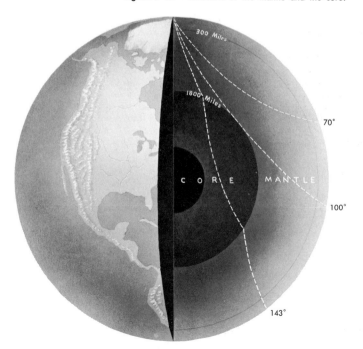

difference would account for the abrupt change between the mantle and the core.

A Model of the Earth

Combining the various lines of evidence and reasoning in the foregoing paragraphs, we may arrive at a generalized picture of the earth, from center to surface. A core which begins 1,800 miles below the surface is liquid in nature. Its composition, probably, is largely iron mixed with small amounts of nickel. Within this liquid zone, beginning 3,160 miles below the surface, is a solid inner core, thought by many to be of the same composition. The density of the core increases with depth, from 9 in the outer core to approximately 15 at the center. This increase in density is in all probability due to the increase in pressure of the overlying material.

Outside the core lies the solid mantle. Its composition, most probably an iron-magnesium silicate, is fairly constant almost to the outer part of the mantle. The top of the mantle is defined by the Mohorovočić discontinuity. Above it lies an earth-encircling layer of basalt or basaltic-like rock, which underlies oceans and continents alike. But on the continents, overlying and grading down into the basalt, we find thicknesses of sialic or granitic material, which is absent from the deep sea basins. Over both these crystalline materials lie sedimentary rocks of varying ages and varying thicknesses. They are thickest on the continents, thinnest on the ocean bottoms.

122

SUMMARY

Earthquakes are our most valuable tool for probing the deep interior of the earth. They occur in narrow zones, or belts, and to depths of 435 miles below the surface. Quakes generate various types of waves, of which two are called the P and the S waves. These penetrate into the body of the earth and serve to map the globe's interior. The faster P wave is a compressional wave and is transmitted through both liquid and solid material. The slower S waves are transverse waves and pass through solids only. It is the behavior of these waves which leads to many of our deductions about the earth's interior. Their interpretation allows us to divide the earth into core, mantle, and crust, and to further subdivide these three major units of the earth. Thus, the difference in composition and thickness between the crust beneath the oceans and the continents is inferred from these earthquake waves.

Our model of the earth pictures a solid inner core at a depth of 3,160 miles, surrounded by a liquid to depth of 1,800 miles below the surface. This core is thought to be a mixture of iron and nickel. The mantle outside the core is composed of iron-magnesium silicate material and is separated from the crust by the Mohorovočić discontinuity.

ADDITIONAL READING

Bullen, K. E., *An Introduction to the Theory of Seismology*. London: Cambridge University Press, 1963.

Gutenberg, B., and C. F. Richter, *Seismistry of the Earth* (2nd ed.). Princeton: Princeton University Press, 1954.

Hodgson, John H., *Earthquakes and Earth Structure*, Englewood Cliffs, N.J.: Prentice-Hall, 1964 (paperback).

Mason, Brian, *Meteorites*. New York: John Wiley & Sons, 1962.

Leet, L. Don, *Earthquake—Discoveries in Seismology*. New York: Dell Publishing Co., 1964 (paperback).

8

Crustal Deformation
and Mountain Building

The earth's crust which seems so solid to our feet, is, in reality, restless and everchanging. For the solid rock bends and breaks, yielding to forces, still incompletely understood, that build mountains and raise the land masses above the sea. In the previous chapter we examined one manifestation of these forces—earthquakes. Here we will look not only at the nature of rock deformation, but also at the way in which mountains are built.

EVIDENCE OF EARTH MOVEMENT

Wherever we can see the rocks of the earth's crust, we see the evidence of rock movement. Sometimes, this movement happens in a few brief moments, and can actually be observed by man. Other movements are recorded in the longer scale of man's life span or of human history. But most of our evidence for rock deformation comes from the geologic record and stretches backward toward the dim origins of the earth.

Rapid Movements

During earthquakes, rapid motion of the land has been observed in many different places. The motion may be vertical or horizontal or some combination thereof. During the earthquake of August 17, 1959, west of Yellowstone National Park near the Hebgen Reservoir in Montana, vertical movements up to 20 feet were recorded (see Figure 8-1). During the 1923 earthquake in Tokyo, Japan, a cliff along Sagami bay moved upward by some 15 feet (Figure 8-2). And as a result of the Good Friday earthquakes of 1964 in Alaska, changes in land level of tens of feet occurred over a wide area. Horizontal movements were recorded during the San Francisco earthquake

Figure 8-1 A cliff about 5 feet high formed as a result of the Hebgen, Montana, earthquake on August 17, 1959. (*Photo by Lloyd Skinner.*)

of 1906. In this instance, roads and fences were offset across a fracture in the earth's crust by distances of up to 15 or 20 feet.

Slow Movements

Some cases of crustal deformation involve almost instantaneous displacements of several feet. Other movements of the crust, however, are going on slowly and more or less continuously. The coast of California, it is calculated, is moving northwestward an average of about 2 inches a year. In one place this slow creep has been noticeable even without engineering surveys: In Tres Pinos, a winery constructed a building across two portions of the crust that are moving relative to each other; now the building is gradually being twisted apart.

Figure 8-2 Drawing showing elevated cliff on Sagami Bay, Japan. Lower right, Lithophaga shells.

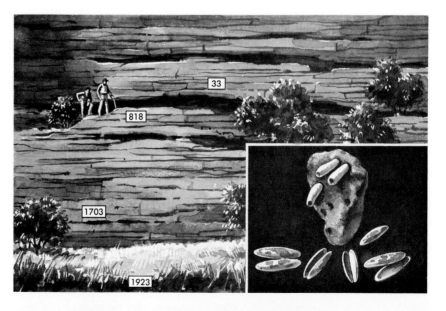

Figure 8-3 These beds in the Great Smoky Mountains were laid down as horizontal beds of sandstone. They have since been rotated into their present vertical position and metamorphosed into quartzite. (*Photo by L. B. Gillett.*)

powerful forces are at work, and the resulting changes in the earth's crust are by no means superficial.

Geologic Evidence

In Chapter 5, we found that sedimentary rocks are characterized by beds separated by surfaces called bedding planes. These bedding planes are generally horizontal or nearly so when the sedimentary rocks are first formed. Today we find that many ancient sedimentary rocks are arranged at various angles to the horizontal. Some are even vertical (Figure 8-3) and others are turned upside down. We must conclude that, since the rocks were originally formed, some force has tilted them out of their normal position. As we shall see later in this chapter, this force has deformed once flat-lying rocks into folds measuring from a few inches to scores of miles in breadth. At the same time it has broken once-continuous layers and moved the sections thus formed into new positions.

In Japan, surveys have shown that the crust is composed of a mosaic of blocks, tens of miles across, that are milling about and tilting one way or another like icecakes on a stormy sea. The amount of movement in a year is minuscule, but it is there, and it involves the entire thickness of the crust. Undeniably

Figure 8-4 In the geologic past stresses in the earth created this fault in the rocks north of Great Bear Lake, Canada. (*Photo by Royal Canadian Air Force.*)

Many of the mountain ranges of the world contain sedimentary rocks that enclose the fossils of marine organisms. The presence of these marine fossils high above the ocean bottoms testifies to the extensive differential movement of the mountain masses and ocean basins since the rocks and fossils were laid down on an ancient sea floor. The amount of this motion is measured in tens of thousands of feet in some places.

The rate at which differential movement progresses is difficult to measure, but we do know that it varies considerably. Evidence indicates that a mountainous mass such as the Himalayas may move upward at a rate of 5 to 6 meters (about 16 to 20 feet) per thousand years. Other rates appear to have been much smaller, perhaps 0.1 meter (about 4 inches) per thousand years.

BEHAVIOR OF ROCK MATERIAL IN RESPONSE TO STRESS

The force that produces rock movement is called **stress,** and it is usually measured in pounds per square inch or kilograms per square centimeter. As rock reacts to stress, it undergoes change in shape or volume or both. Such deformation is called **strain.**

Rocks respond to stress in three ways: 1) by **elastic deformation,** 2) by **plastic deformation,** and 3) by **rupturing.**

An elastic solid is a substance that, after undergoing a change in shape or volume when stress is applied returns to its original condition when the stress is removed. The deformation is usually proportional to the stress (see Figure 8-5).

In plastic deformation a substance undergoes a continuous change of shape. In this case the rock does not recover its original volume or shape after the stress is removed. In most instances, the deformation is elastic up to a certain critical point (called the **yield point** of a rock) after which it becomes plastic, continuing as a "flow" so long as stress is applied (Figure 8-6).

A rock may also respond by "rupturing." In this type of deformation, stresses are relieved by the actual breaking of the rock at the rupture point. Rocks which are being elastically deformed may eventually reach a point of stress in which the accumulated pressures are relieved by breaking, or rupturing. Again, if rocks are being plastically deformed at a relatively rapid rate, stress may also be

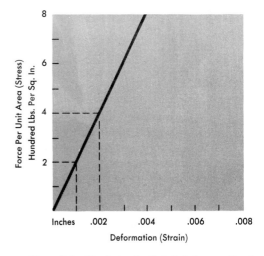

Figure 8-5 Graph showing that strain is proportional to the stress causing it, and that it vanishes when the stress is removed. Any material that behaves in this way is being deformed elastically.

Figure 8-6 Graph showing that as stress increases, for a while strain is proportional to stress. This is the range of elastic deformation. Then, when the stress reaches the yield point, or elastic limit, deformation may become plastic. If the stress is removed after the material has begun to behave plastically, the material will not return to its original shape.

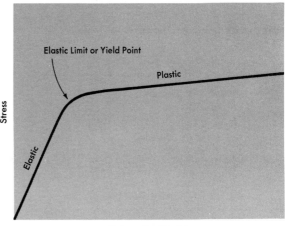

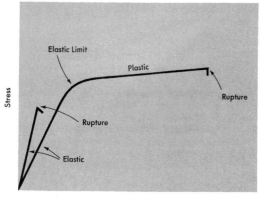

Figure 8-7 This graph shows the behavior of two different substances under stress. One responds elastically only, and then, when stress reaches a critical point, it deforms by rupturing. The second substance behaves elastically for a while, passes its elastic limit, and then deforms plastically. Eventually, however, this material, too, may deform by rupture.

relieved by rupturing (Figure 8-7). It is this rupture, or breakage, in a rock which probably causes the earthquakes discussed in Chapter 7.

The study of rocks in the laboratory under varying conditions of pressure and temperature and the observation of the deformation of rocks in nature lead to the conclusion that at the surface rocks respond to stress first by undergoing elastic deformation, and then by rupturing. At great depths, however, they undergo elastic deformation and then plastic flow. Deep rocks rupture only if the movement is great enough and fast enough. We now know that an increase in the confining pressure of a rock increases its elastic limit and therefore the strength of the rock. At the same time, an increase in temperature weakens a rock. Long-continued stress, even if not very great, also weakens a rock's resistance to deformation. And within the earth, solutions contained within a rock also tend to weaken it.

ISOSTASY

The earth's surface is irregular, the primary irregularities being those that separate the ocean basins from the continents. In Chapter 7 we found that the continents are really large islands of light-weight substance standing above basins underlain by material of greater specific gravity. Smaller irregularities are found both in the ocean basins and on the continents. On the continents we know that the large mountain chains and high plateaus are made of the same types of materials which we find immediately underlying the continental lowlands. One of the problems of geology is to explain why such masses—whether continents or mountain ranges—do not seek a common level.

One possible explanation is that the earth's crust is strong enough to support these masses as dead loads. But since laboratory experiments have shown that no rock is strong enough to support the weight of even comparatively low hills, we must conclude that the crust by itself is not capable of supporting the dead weight of mountains, much less of the continents.

Another explanation is that the elevations of continents and mountain ranges are being actively pushed upward by the forces deep within the earth. In areas where active mountain-making forces (see below) still reveal their pressure through earthquakes, changes of level, and the breaking and folding of rocks, it is quite reasonable to assume that they are in fact contributing to the continued elevations of mountains. But in many mountainous areas of the world there is no evidence that these forces are still actively at work. Furthermore, modern deformation of the earth's crust is not uniformly distributed across the continents of the world. Therefore, we must look elsewhere for an explanation of the persistent elevation of mountains and of continents.

A third explanation, one that has proved to be more acceptable to geologists, proposes that high-standing masses of land, both mountains and the continents themselves, are actually supported by deep roots. That is, these land masses float in an underlying high-density rock that is under tremendous pressure and is in a plastic state. The high portions of the earth's surface, then, are said to be in balance with the rock in which they rest. This condition of balance is called **isostasy** (from the Greek

Figure 8-8 An iceberg floating near the Grand Banks off Newfoundland. An estimated 3 to 4 million cubic feet of ice towers above the Coast Guard cutter "Evergreen." Nine times this amount of ice lies beneath the water level. As the exposed mass of ice is reduced, then the "root" of the iceberg will rise proportionately so that throughout the life of the iceberg a constant proportion of ice above and below the surface of the sea is preserved. (*Photo by U.S. Coast Guard.*)

words meaning "equal standing"). A familar analogy would be that of a piece of ice floating in water: Having a somewhat lower density than the water, the ice has approximately $\frac{1}{10}$ of its volume above water and $\frac{9}{10}$ below (see Figure 8-8).

The principle of isostasy suggests that if gravity were the only force acting on the earth's surface, all masses of surface rock would be standing today at heights determined by their thickness and the ratio of their specific gravity to that of the rocks supporting them. We would expect that the blocks would move up or down as materials are removed from them by erosion or added to them by sedimentation. We would expect also that forces other than gravity might depress areas of the earth's crust or raise them up, thus operating to disrupt the balance demanded by isostasy.

STRUCTURAL FEATURES

When rocks are deformed out of their original shape, they assume new patterns which we refer to as **structural features.** These features are joints, folds, faults, and unconformities.

To describe the position in space of the rocks making up such structural features, geologists have found it convenient to use two special measurements: **dip** and **strike.** These are most easily described with reference to sedimentary or layered rocks. The dip and strike of a rock layer provide a description of its orientation in relation to a horizontal plane.

The dip is the acute angle that a tilted rock layer makes with an imaginary horizontal plane. The direction of strike is always at right angles to the direction of dip. Thus, a bed that has a dip either to the east or to the west has a strike north-south, usually designated simply as north (see Figure 8-9).

Figure 8-9 Dip and strike. *Top:* Photo showing outcropping edges of tilted beds in southwestern Colorado, a few miles east of Durango. *Bottom:* Sketch illustrating terms used to describe the attitude of these beds. The beds strike north and dip 30° east. (*Photo by Soil Conservation Service, U.S. Department of Agriculture.*)

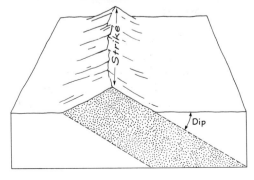

Figure 8-10 Joint planes vertical to the surface and to each other cut this limestone rock on Drummond Island, Michigan. The horizontal bedding planes of the rock combine with the joint planes to produce cubic patterns on the quarry face. (*Photo by Russell, U.S. Geological Survey.*)

Figure 8-11 In this quarry near Washington, D.C., joint planes produce rhombic-shaped blocks in gneiss. (*Photo by Diller, U.S. Geological Survey.*)

Figure 8-12 Joints more or less parallel to the surface cut this granite cliff. These joints probably develop when the rock expands upward as erosion removes material from above and thus reduces the pressure on that which remains. (*Photo by Dale, U.S. Geological Survey.*)

Figure 8-13 A small syncline about 10 feet across near Upton, Pennsylvania. (*Photo by Stose, U.S. Geological Survey.*)

Figure 8-14 An anticline and a syncline on St. Anne's Head, Pembroke, Wales. Width of exposure about 150 feet. (*Photo by Geological Survey of Great Britain.*)

Joints

The most common structural feature of rocks exposed at the surface is a **joint.** This is simply a break in the rock material, without any relative movement of the rock on either side. Joints may have almost any orientation—vertical, horizontal, or at some angle—but in any given rock mass, joints tend to occur in sets, with the fractures more or less parallel to one another (see Figures 8-10, 8-11, 8-12).

Although joints are an extremely common feature, their causes are not completely understood. Some, those that are parallel to the earth's surface, seem to be caused by the upward expansion of the rock as the weight of overlying material is removed by erosion. Others must be caused by the stresses that deform the earth's crust. In some lava flows the contraction of molten lava as it cools tends to create a series of joints that lie vertical to the surface of the flow. This "columnar jointing" has produced the spectacular columns of the Devil's Causeway of Ireland and of the Devil's Tower of Wyoming.

Folds

When layered rocks are subject to compressive stress, they may be thrown into a series of wrinkles, or **folds.** These folds may range from a few inches to hundreds of miles across. The two most common types are called **anticlines** and **synclines** (Figures 8-13, 8-14, 8-15). In the anticline the beds dip downward away from a central axis or ridge. In the syncline the direction is just the opposite. At the earth's surface most synclines and anticlines have been breached to a greater or lesser extent, so that rocks of differing ages are met as one crosses the fold. In an eroded anticline the oldest beds are in the center, in a syncline the youngest beds are in the center. The

Figure 8-15 A large syncline marks the crest of Mt. Perdrix, Alberta, Canada. (*Photo by Geological Survey of Canada.*)

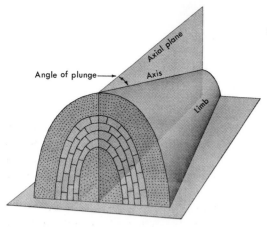

Figure 8-16 Nomenclature of a fold, shown on a plunging anticline, but applicable to a syncline, also. *Axis* is line joining places of sharpest folding. *Axial plane* includes axis and divides fold as symmetrically as possible. If axis is not horizontal, fold is said to be *plunging*, and angle between axis and horizontal is *angle of plunge*. Sides of a fold are called the *limbs*.

Figure 8-17 Types of folds. A: Symmetrical fold. Axial plane (Ap) vertical, limbs dip in opposite directions at same angles. B: Asymmetrical fold. Axial plane inclined, limbs dip in opposite directions at different angles. C: Overturned fold. Axial plane inclined, limbs dip in same direction, usually at different angles. D: Recumbent fold. Axial plane horizontal. (After Marland P. Billings, Structural Geology, 2nd ed. Englewood Cliffs, N.J.: Prentice-Hall, Inc., 1954.)

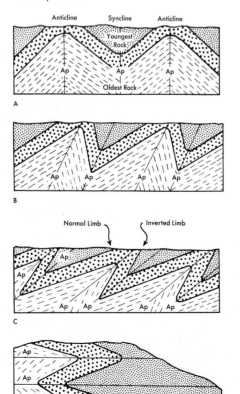

nomenclature for a fold is given in Figure 8-16, and some of the various types of folds are illustrated in Figure 8-17.

Faults

When the rupture point is exceeded, rocks break and separate sections may be displaced. Such a structural feature is a **fault.** Earthquakes, as we have noted, are caused by movements along faults. Seldom, however, do we see the results of such movement at the surface of the earth until after millions of years of erosion have exposed the old break.

TYPES OF FAULTS   If the movement along the break has been horizontal, the fault is called a **strike-slip fault,** because the slipping has been parallel to the strike of the fault. Strike-slip faults can be further designated right-hand or left-hand. The one sketched in Figure 8-18 is right-hand: If you were walking along the road shown, and came to the offset caused by the fault, you would have to go to the right to get onto the other section of the road.

Faults have been classified in other ways. One of the most useful systems is based on the relative movement of the two rock masses affected by the fracture. The fracture, or **fault plane,** usually dips at some angle from the vertical. The mass of rock above the fault plane is called the **hanging wall.** The one beneath it the **foot wall.** (These names, which come from mining, refer to the position of masses of rock relative to miners.) Faults may be described on the basis of the relative movement of the foot wall to the hanging wall. A **normal fault,** for instance, is one in which the hanging wall has moved downward in relation to the foot wall (Figure 8-19).

A **thrust fault,** sometimes called a **reverse fault,** is one in which the hanging wall moves upward as against the foot wall (Figure 8-20).

The direction of movement is relative along faults. It is not possible to designate which way or how much either wall has moved except in relation to the other.

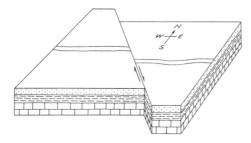

Figure 8-18 Sketch of right-hand strike-slip fault, depicting movement along San Andreas fault, California, in 1906.

Figure 8-19 A normal fault in sandstone beds, New Mexico. (*Photo by Sheldon Judson.*)

Unconformities

In many places younger rocks are separated from older rocks by surfaces of erosion or of nondeposition. Such surfaces are called **unconformities.** They represent events in earth history, but events which are not preserved as rock material. The time span may run from a few hundred or thousands of years up to tens and even hundreds of millions of years.

Geologists recognize unconformities of various types: (1) angular unconformity, (2) disconformity, (3) nonconformity.

An **angular unconformity** may form in the following way. Sedimentary rocks laid down on a sea floor may be tilted and raised above sea level, where they are partially destroyed by agents of erosion. If this surface of erosion, underlain by partially beveled and deformed sedimentary rocks, is flooded again by the sea and if new sedimentary rocks are laid down on top of the surface, then an angular unconformity has been created. If we were to look at a section through this sequence of rocks, we would see a series of tilted rock layers overlaid at some angle by younger rocks. The surface which separates the two groups of rocks represents the period

Figure 8-20 Thrust fault, 25 miles northwest of San Salvador on the Pan American Highway. (*Photo by Thos. F. Thompson.*)

Figure 8-21 A striking angular unconformity between Precambrian sedimentary rocks that were twisted from their original horizontal attitude into a vertical position before deposition of overlying Devonian beds. In Box Canyon, near Ouray, Colorado. (*Photo by Kirtley F. Mather.*)

of erosion and nondeposition (Figure 8-21).

Sometimes sedimentary rocks that have been exposed to erosion undergo further sedimentation without being folded. An unconformity between parallel beds formed in this way is called a **disconformity** (Figure 8-22).

A **nonconformity** is an unconformity that develops when massive igneous rocks that are exposed to erosion are then covered by sedimentary rocks (Figure 8-23).

GEOSYNCLINES

All the major rock types—igneous, metamorphic, and sedimentary—can be found in the mountains of the world. In many mountains the sedimentary rocks represent thick accumulations of deposits which originally reached as much as 30,000 or 40,000 feet in thickness, and were laid down close to sea level. Reconstruction of the events surrounding the accumulation of these sedimentary rocks shows that they were laid down in a slowly subsiding trough in which subsidence and deposition were concurrent. Such a subsiding trough is referred to as a **geosyncline,** and the muds, silts, and sands accumulated in it are called **geosynclinal sediments.**

Geosynclines are usually linear, extending for hundreds of miles in length and tens or scores of miles in breadth. The evidence indicates that the waters in a geosyncline are seldom more than 1,000 feet in depth and very often far more shallow. We can judge the rate at which geosynclines must have subsided in the past in two ways. First, we can consider the age and thickness of sedimentary rocks known to have been deposited in geosynclinal troughs, and second, we can extrapolate from the present rates of deposition in modern seas backward to the geosynclinal troughs of the past. Both of these methods are subject to a large possible error, but both indicate that a geosynclinal trough sinks at a rate of somewhere between 500 and 1,000 feet per million years.

Figure 8-22 A disconformity in the walls of the Grand Canyon. Line traces buried erosion surface. (*Photo by U.S. Geological Survey, courtesy Robt. M. Garrels.*)

Figure 8-23 A nonconformity between light-colored granite and dark overlying Table Mountain sandstone on the Cape of Good Hope, South Africa. The cave, about 20 feet above sea level, was cut into the granite by wave action when sea level was higher than it is now. (*Photo by R. A. Daly.*)

The formation of a geosyncline is obviously not a simple process. It is true that the growing weight of sediments tends to deepen the trough, but this cannot be the entire answer. We must remember that the sediments in a geosyncline eventually sink to levels where they become surrounded by denser rock and their buoyancy sets a limit to the depth to which they can sink under their own weight. For example, assume that we begin with a trough 1,000 feet deep and that we pour sediments into it. These sediments will push the bottom of the trough down into the denser substratum until it is 2,500 feet below sea level, but by that time the sediments will have filled the trough to sea level and there will be no room to add any more. The whole system has become isostatic, or in balance, and the thickness of the sediments cannot be increased just by load. Therefore, in order to account for the tens of thousands of feet of shallow-water sediments within a geosyncline, we must look to a force or forces other than sediment load to help in the downbowing of the geosyncline.

A consideration, then, of geosynclines leads us to a picture of a rising land mass that provides vast amounts of sediments side by side with a slowly sinking trough. Portions of this movement may be attributed to isostasy as sediments are moved from one position on the earth's crust to another. But another portion of the motion can be attributed only to deep-seated forces that tend to crumple the earth's crust and to create mountain ranges.

MOUNTAINS AND THEIR ORIGIN

Mountains are the dominant landscape feature of the continents. In general, they occur in long chains, following curving or straight lines, and are concentrated largely toward the margins of the continents. In contrast, the interiors seem relatively lower and are devoid of extensive mountain-building activity. This apparent lack of mountains toward the interior of continents, however, is belied if we look far enough back into geologic time. For there we find that, as the continents evolved,

Figure 8-24 Possible conditions in Appalachian geosynclines across New York, Vermont, and New Hampshire at the close of Ordovician time. (*After reconstruction by Kay.*)

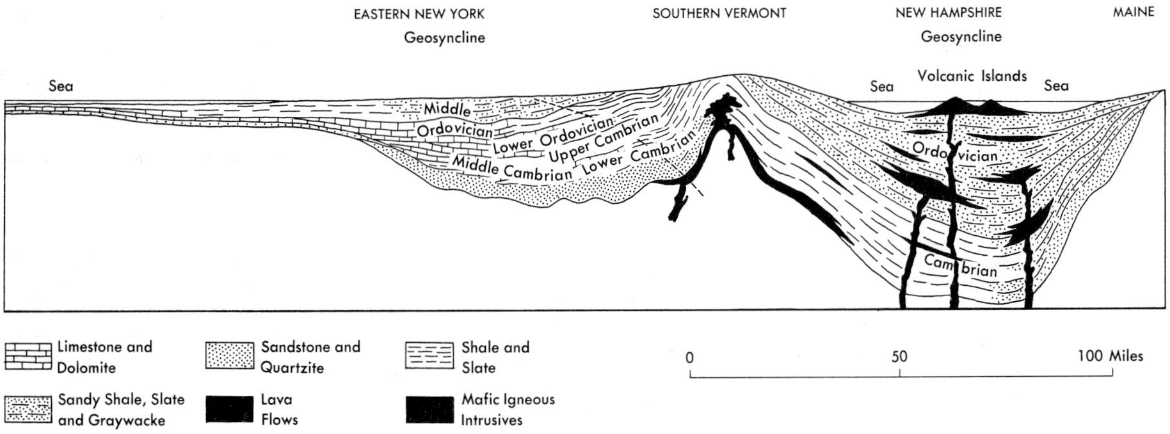

EASTERN NEW YORK
Geosyncline

SOUTHERN VERMONT

NEW HAMPSHIRE
Geosyncline

MAINE

Sea

Middle Ordovician
Lower Ordovician
Upper Cambrian
Middle Cambrian Lower Cambrian

Sea Volcanic Islands Sea

Ordovician

Cambrian

Limestone and Dolomite

Sandstone and Quartzite

Shale and Slate

Sandy Shale, Slate and Graywacke

Lava Flows

Mafic Igneous Intrusives

0   50   100 Miles

Figure 8-25 The major mountains of the land areas of the world occur in long chains, following curving or straight lines as suggested by this relief globe. (*Photo by Charles Kulick.*)

these heartlands were also marked by mountains, mountains which now have ceased to exist as topographic features. Erosion has long since removed all but their roots.

Mountainous masses are not restricted only to the continents. The ocean basins are crossed by a remarkable series of ridges towering above the general elevation of the ocean floors. Thus, under the Atlantic Ocean, from Iceland to the Antarctic, there is a belt of mountains, called the Atlantic Ridge or Mid-Atlantic Ridge, which roughly parallels the outlines of the continents and is nearly midway between them. It stands as much as 6,000 feet above the ocean bottom and is covered in places by 9,000 feet of water. In a few places its peaks protrude above the water to form islands, such as the Azores, St. Helena, and Tristan da Cunha. Similar ridges characterize the other oceans.

Types of Mountains

The origin and development of mountains is a complex and as yet incompletely under-

stood process. In the following paragraphs we will look at some of the types of mountains in the United States. Then we will briefly survey the various sources of energy which have caused the construction of these mountains. But the history and origin of various mountain chains is left for consideration in Chapters 16-19.

The Appalachian Mountains run from Alabama and Georgia on the south, northeastward through the eastern United States, and on into the Maritime Provinces of Canada. Let us look at a section through this feature in North Carolina and Tennessee (Figure 8-26). Traveling northwestward from the seaboard we cross first the Atlantic Coastal Plain, which is underlain by a series of gently dipping, relatively unconsolidated marine sediments of sand, silt, and clay. These sedimentary rocks lap up onto older igneous and metamorphic rocks that form the so-called Piedmont Plateau of the eastern United States. Folded and faulted, they represent the eroded roots of the ancestral Appalacian Mountains. Today they are marked in their eastern portion by low, gently rolling hills.

As we progress westward, the hills become higher and soon we come up against the escarpment of the Blue Ridge, which separates the plateau country from the highest mountains in the eastern United States. These mountains are also underlain by igneous and metamorphic rocks of the same general age as those of the Piedmont. Evidence exists to suggest that they have been thrust upward and outward over sedimentary rocks lying farther to the west.

These sedimentary rocks of sandstone, shale, and limestone form what is called the Valley and Ridge Province of the Appalachian Mountains. In this section of the Appalachians

Figure 8-26 A geologic cross-section through the Appalachian Mountains in North Carolina and Tennessee.

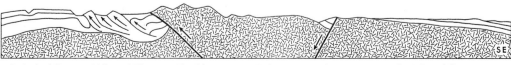

Cumberland Plateau   Valley and Ridge   Blue Ridge   Piedmont   Atlantic Coastal Plain

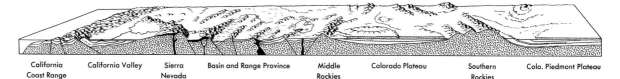

Figure 8-27 Section across western United States from the Pacific Ocean to the Great Plains. (*After A. K. Lobeck.*)

California
Coast Range

California Valley

Sierra
Nevada

Basin and Range Province

Middle
Rockies

Colorado Plateau

Southern
Rockies

Colo. Piedmont Plateau

they are marked by a series of thrust faults indicating pressures from the east. Farther to the north, in Pennsylvania, the pressures have not been as intense and the same rocks, instead of being thrust one over the other in great slices of material, now stand as folded mountains. But in both sections of the Valley and Ridge Province the topography is characterized by a series of nearly parallel ridges and valleys. The valleys were formed as the processes of erosion etched out areas of non-resistant rock, leaving behind as ridges the resistant rocks, which are usually composed of quartzite and sandstone. Still farther to the west the rocks which are faulted in the Valley and Ridge Province stand as relatively undeformed sedimentary rocks underlying plateau country. In parts of Pennsylvania and New York the plateaus are known as the Catskill Mountains. In the area of Tennessee and Virginia they form the Cumberland Plateau. Erosion has dissected these plateaus to a greater or lesser extent, creating low mountains or high hills depending on one's frame of reference.

Looking back, then, across the Appalachian Mountains, we find that in reality there are three distinct forms within this range. On the extreme western side are the hills or mountains carved in flat-lying rocks as are the Catskill Mountains. Next eastward lie the parallel features of the Valley and Ridge Province underlain by folded and thrust-faulted beds that alternate in their resistance to erosion. Still farther to the east lie the high mountains carved on the massive and resistant beds of crystalline rocks both metamorphic and igneous. Progressing toward the sea is the rolling Piedmont section, which is also underlain by igneous and metamorphic rocks. It passes under the gently dipping younger strata of the Coastal Plain.

Let us turn now to the West Coast of the United States and begin a traverse from central California eastward across the coastal ranges, through the Sierra Nevada, across Nevada and Utah, and into Colorado. The coastal ranges are underlain by a complexly folded and faulted series of sedimentary rocks and separated from the Sierra Nevada on the east by the Great Valley of California. The Sierra Nevada are asymmetric, with a gentle western slope and a steep eastern scarp. The mountains themselves are cored with granitic rocks. But characteristic is the great fault which bounds and defines the eastern scarp of the mountain. It is along this fault that the mountain mass of the Sierra Nevada has risen upward to its present height and now towers above the lower desert valleys and basins to the east.

If we were to continue eastward toward the Colorado Plateau, we would cross a series of ranges separated by broad basins, the Basin and Range Province. This area is characterized not only by great aridity, with dried lake basins and a few salt lakes, but also by a series of mountains we refer to as fault-block mountains. Even as the Sierra Nevada were thrown up along a long fault, so also have the various ranges in the Basin and Range Province been uplifted along bordering, generally north-south fault lines. While these blocks moved upward to expose igneous, metamorphic, and sedimentary rocks, the intervening basins moved downward to receive the sediments carried by desert and mountain streams from the nearby mountain masses.

To the east the Colorado Plateau stands as a great block of sedimentary rocks overlying older igneous and crystalline materials, forming not really mountains, but an interior plateau. Nonetheless, the Colorado Plateau will undoubtedly someday be carved into a series of hills or mountains not dissimilar to the Catskill Mountains, for instance, of eastern United States. The Rocky Mountains in Colorado are characterized by two long parallel ridges of igneous and metamorphic rock. The western ridge is called the Park Range, and the eastern ridge, the Front Range. Lapping up onto the flanks of these mountains are Paleozoic and Mesozoic sediments (see Chapters 16–18) that stretch from the Front Range eastward onto the Great Plains and from the Park Range westward toward the Colorado Plateau. Between these two ranges lie the somewhat lower areas, such as South Park and Estes Park, which are filled with sediments washed from the higher mountains. The two ranges are upbucklings of the granitic and other crystalline rocks which underlie much of the center of the continent.

Another type of mountain is the volcano. Northward from the Sierra Nevada in Oregon and Washington lie the Cascade Mountains, which support a series of high, towering peaks of volcanoes, extinct or dormant or only recently active.

This brief survey by no means exhausts the various mountains of the United States. But it does tell us that mountains have different forms. The rocks within them range from sedimentary through igneous to metamorphic. These rocks may be folded or faulted or merely flat-lying. The mountains may be lifted upward in great buckles or arches, or they may be thrust laterally from one place to another, or they may be bounded by fault scarps along which they have moved upward toward their present positions.

CAUSES OF MOUNTAIN–BUILDING MOVEMENTS

We know that motions take place in the earth's crust which bend, break, and metamorphose rocks. We know, too, that within the earth's crust occasional changes of state occur in which solid rock passes to molten rock and gives rise to the whole process of igneous activity. We are still far from having precise explanations of these events. But we can make some suggestions, some of which are sketched briefly below.

Gravity

In discussing the general process of isostasy, we found that blocks of the earth's crust move vertically—up or down—in response to differences in mass and specific gravity. These movements are, in actuality, a response to gravitational stress. They are important in the elevation or depression of portions of the earth's crust. They do not, however, explain the crumpling and thrusting so characteristic of many of our mountains. Nor is igneous activity explained by isostasy.

At the earth's surface, gravity affects the materials of the landscape by causing landslides and rock falls. In fact, in many ways gravity becomes one of the most important processes in wearing away the earth's crust and lowering its level, a subject which we will discuss in more detail in Chapter 10. Of recent years geologists have discovered, however, that gravity plays its role in the history of some mountain systems. There have been large-scale movements of immense volumes of rock material that, in many instances, can be best explained as movements under the influence of gravity. Thus, it is now well established that in the Apennine Mountains of central Italy, many of the characteristic folds and faults were created by the sliding of the earth materials under gravitational stress while they were beneath the ocean's surface. In the western United States, along the eastern boundary of the Yellowstone National Park, lie the Absoraka Mountains, a portion of which, many geologists now believe, is composed of the remnants of a vast sheet of rock material that moved eastward under the stress of gravity to its present position.

Although gravity plays its role in mountain building, it is not the most important factor. Probably more important are the effects of temperature within the earth.

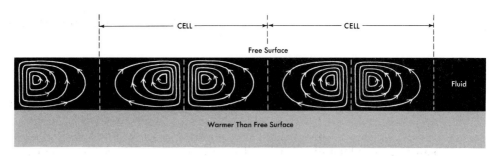

CELL —————————— CELL ——————————

Free Surface

Fluid

Warmer Than Free Surface

Figure 8-28   Convection currents and cells.

Heat

We know that energy in the form of heat flows from the earth and is lost at the surface. For the earth as a whole it is estimated that this rate of flow is about 1.5×10^{-6} calories per square centimeter per second. There isn't much difference between the heat flow in the ocean basins and on the continents, but there are local variations. Thus, measurements show that heat flow rises to several times the average over the large topographic ridges or rises which subdivide the ocean basins. In contrast the heat flow drops below average in the deep, arcuate trenches that crease the borders of some of the oceanic basins (see Chapter 10). On the continents, too, there are belts of higher heat flow, particularly in areas of geologically recent or active mountain building. There are two sources of this interior energy: The heat left over from the original formation of the earth, and the heat that derives from the decay of radioactive minerals within the earth. Although geophysicists are uncertain about the planet's early thermal history, most now feel that very little of the heat flow observed at the surface comes from the original heat of the earth. Most is produced by the decay of radioactive elements in the earth's crust. The most radioactive rocks are in the family of granites. The simatic rocks, such as basalt and gabbro and peridotite, are considerably less so. Thus, in general, the continents are more radioactive than the rocks underlying the ocean basins.

Because little or no granitic materials underlie the ocean basins we would expect the heat flow there to be less than on the continents, assuming that radioactivity is the dominant source of heat. But we have found that this is not the case and that continents and ocean basins have about the same heat flow. There must, therefore, be differences in the thermal regimes of the earth beneath the oceans and the continents.

Whatever the origin and distribution of earth heat, however, it is estimated that the amount of thermal energy lost at the earth's surface each year is nearly 1,000 times greater than the energy released annually by earthquakes and volcanoes combined. It is not surprising, therefore, that thermal energy should be appealed to in the search for an explanation of mountain-building. Indeed, there are several different theories based on heat. We shall consider two of these: 1) the convection-current theory, and 2) the thermal-contraction theory.

CONVECTION-CURRENT THEORY Convection currents within the earth have been suggested as an explanation of mountain-building. Convection is a process whereby heat is transferred from one place to another by the movement of particles. We can see how it works by heating a pan of water on a stove: The water at the bottom heats fastest, rises (because it becomes lighter), and is replaced by cooler water sinking to the bottom. Under proper conditions a pattern of circulation called a **convection current** is established. Convection currents normally occur in pairs, each called a **convection cell.**

It has been proposed that convection currents originating at the core-mantle boundary may be circulating in the mantle. The materials of the mantle do not behave like water, of course, but they do flow plastically if subjected to enough force. Since these materials have some cohesive strength, to establish convection currents, the heat and expansion in the core must build up until the upward push is greater than the strength of the overlying mantle. Assuming that the mantle is in equilibrium, it has been computed that, when heating in the core has finally expanded nearby mantle material until it starts to move upward, then for about 25 million years the movement would gradually "speed up" until it reached the rate of about 5 inches a year. After these currents reach the base of the crust, they may bulge the crust upward and then be deflected horizontally, move along the base of the crust, eventually to plunge back toward the core again. Their downward movement would drag the crust downward, thus forming geosynclines. After the geosynclines had deepened to 50,000 feet, the currents would crumple and fold the sediments that were by now softened by immersion in the hot mantle rocks. At the same time, the convection currents would lose their drive and slow to a stop. Meanwhile, melting in the geosynclines would have caused local expansion, thereby producing the uplift to form mountains. A quiescent period would follow while heat at the core again built up; when the strength of the overlying rocks was exceeded, another cycle could start.

This theory uses heat as the source of the energy. Its supporters offer calculations that the temperature of the core is high enough to keep material liquid at pressures of 25 to 50 million pounds per square inch. If that is the case, then heat is presumably present in adequate supply to drive the convection process. Further, since laboratory and field data show that folded and deformed rocks yield plastically under the right conditions of heat and pressure, it requires no great extrapolation from the evidence to establish that mantle materials are plastic enough to move according to the convection theory.

On the other hand, seismological evidence suggests that regardless of the plausibility of these arguments, the entire mantle has not been stirred by convection currents. Studies of the travel times in the mantle of earth waves generated by earthquakes and nuclear explosions have yielded increasingly precise data which establish that there are zones in the mantle structure. No such layering would be possible, however, if convection currents had stirred the mantle, mixing the materials between the core and the top. These data, then, have suggested to some observers that convection currents, if in fact they operate, occur only somewhere in the upper mantle.

THERMAL-CONTRACTION THEORY The thermal-contraction theory is based on the idea that heat is lost during the cooling of the earth. The loss of heat causes a decrease in the volume of the earth, and the crust adjusts itself to the earth's shrinking interior. In any event, regardless of the details of the earth's origin, there is strong evidence that at one stage it was a molten sphere. As it cooled, its radius decreased and its surface area shrank.

According to thermal-contraction theory, the original heat present in the earth at its formation has provided the source of energy for mountain-building. Harold Jeffreys, a world-renowned British geophysicist, supports this theory with computations based on seismological evidence and on the behavior of rocks subjected to heat and pressure in the laboratory. He has come to certain conclusions on the history of the earth's cooling: The earth is solid to a depth of 1,800 miles, but the temperature of this solid material varies. Near the surface, the rocks are undergoing no further cooling, but from a depth of a few miles to about 400 miles they still are. Below 400 miles, the rocks are still as hot as they were when they first solidified.

On the basis of these temperature conditions, we can picture three zones. The inner and outer zones are fixed in volume because they are not losing heat, but the middle zone is cooling, and shrinking as it cools. The outer zone attempts to adjust itself to the shrinking zone below and in this process becomes squeezed. The squeezing buckles it into low basins where sediments may accumulate, and high places that provide the sedimentary materials. When the buckling of the crust pushes the sediments in a geosyncline to the depth of melting temperatures, the melted sediments expand, producing the elevation of the geosyncline to form mountains.

Some geologists have criticized the thermal-contraction theory on the grounds that it fails to provide for enough shrinkage of the crust. Relying on seismological data that show the outer 400 miles of the mantle to be solid, some geologists conclude that the earth cannot have lost significant amounts of heat in the last 2 billion years—at least not enough heat to counterbalance the great volume of material we find in mountains. Another criticism involves the distribution of mountain ranges in time, in direction, and in place. Some feel that a contracting crust would shorten every circle around the globe the same amount, and that mountains should therefore be more evenly distributed than they are. Underlying this objection is the assumption that heat is lost uniformly through the earth's crust, though this criticism does not take into account the localized loss of heat and material from volcanic eruptions or from the oceanic rises.

STATUS OF THE PROBLEM In spite of the impressive lists of data being assembled about mountains, no theory proposed for the cause of mountain-building has been generally accepted. This is again one of those cases in which more data or better analyses of present data will apparently be needed before solution is reached.

SUMMARY

The earth's solid crust is subject to movement which varies in rate from tens of feet per second to a few inches per thousand years. The rocks in the crust behave both as elastic and as plastic substances.

Dip and strike are measurements that define the position of a rock in space. Stress on rocks produce features which include joints, anticlines, synclines, and normal and thrust faults. In many places younger rocks are separated from older rocks by surfaces of erosion or nondeposition. These are called unconformities.

Geosynclines are basins of deposition hundreds of miles in length and scores of miles in width. They collect up to tens of thousands of feet of sediments and many become the location of future mountains.

The stress that forms mountains may be gravitational in part, but thermal energy is probably the single most important factor in mountain building. The convection-current theory and the thermal-contraction theory both rely on heat as a source of energy.

ADDITIONAL READING

Billings, Marland P., *Structural Geology* (2nd ed.). Englewood Cliffs, N.J.: Prentice-Hall, 1954.

Eardley, A. J., *Structural Geology of North America.* New York: Harper & Row, 1951.

Goguel, Jean, *Tectonics,* trans. Hans E. Thalmann. San Francisco: W. H. Freeman and Co., 1962.

Jeffreys, Harold, *The Earth* (4th ed.). New York: Cambridge University Press, 1959.

King, Philip B., *The Evolution of North America.* Princeton: Princeton University Press, 1959.

Lee, William H. K. (ed.), *Terrestrial Heat Flow.* Geophysical Monograph Series, No. 8, Washington, D.C.: American Geophysical Union, 1965.

9

Running Water and Water Underground

Thus far in our study of the earth we have examined the rocks that compose it, how they are made, and how one type of rock can be transformed into another. Further, we have looked at the forces that have buckled and broken rocks, and raised mountains. Now we begin the study of the processes that erode earth material, transport it from one place, and deposit it in another. The agents of erosion include water at the surface and immediately below the surface (the subjects of this chapter), glaciers, gravity working on slopes, and wind (discussed in Chapter 10). Whenever and wherever rocks are raised above the sea's surface, one or more of these processes sets to work to wear down and reduce them again to sea level.

This constant **gradation,** or leveling, of the land involves weathering, which we considered in Chapter 4. Weathering helps to prepare material for erosion and for transport to new resting places. This movement, though slow, is constantly going on. Were it not for counteragents working to raise the land, erosion would long ago have reduced our continents to featureless pancakes. In fact, it has been calculated that, at the present rate of erosion and assuming no uplift of the land, the North American continent would be reduced to sea level in about 12 million years, a remarkably short span indeed when considered against the 4 to 5 billion years of earth history.

We can picture, then, a struggle between those forces that are building up the land above sea level, and those that are tearing it down and, particle by particle, moving it back toward the oceans. This has been going on for as far back as we can read the earth's record. As James Hutton, Scottish medical man, farmer, and geologist, put it so succinctly at the end of the 18th century:

> We are thus led to see a circulation of matter of the globe, and a system of beautiful economy in the works of nature.[1]

RUNNING WATER

Of all the agents at work leveling the earth's surface, running water is most important. Year after year, the streams of the earth move staggering amounts of debris and dissolved material through their valleys to the great settling basins, the oceans.

"All the rivers run into the sea, yet the sea is not full: unto the place from whence

[1] Hutton, James, *Theory of the Earth.* (Edinburgh, 1795.) Vol. II, p. 562.

the rivers come, thither they return again," reads *Ecclesiastes* 1:7. And thither they still return, for nearly all the water that runs off the slopes of the land in thin sheets, and then travels on in rills, streams, and rivers, is derived from the oceans. There is only one exception: Volcanic eruptions apparently bring water to the surface from deep beneath the earth. But once it has reached the surface, this water also follows the general pattern of water movement from sea to land and back again to the sea, a pattern that we call the **hydrologic cycle.**

Precipitation and Stream Flow

Once water has fallen on the land as precipitation, it follows one of the many paths that make up the hydrologic cycle. By far the greatest part is evaporated back to the air directly or is taken up by the plants and transpired (breathed back) by them to the atmosphere. A smaller amount follows the path of **runoff,** the water that flows off the land. And the smallest amount of precipitation soaks into the ground through **infiltration** (Figure 9-1, p. 144).

Figure 9-2 shows how infiltration, runoff, and evaporation-transpiration vary in 6 widely separated localities in the United States. In the examples given, between 54 and 97 per cent of the total precipitation travels back to the atmosphere through transpiration and evaporation. About 2 to 27 per cent drains into streams and oceans as runoff, and between 1 and 20 per cent finds its way into the ground through infiltration. Bearing in mind the ways in which water proceeds through the hydrologic cycle, we can express the amount of runoff by the following generalized formula:

$$\text{Runoff} = \text{Precipitation} - (\text{Infiltration} + \text{Evaporation and Transpiration})$$

LAMINAR AND TURBULENT FLOW   When water moves slowly along a smooth channel or through a tube with smooth walls, it follows

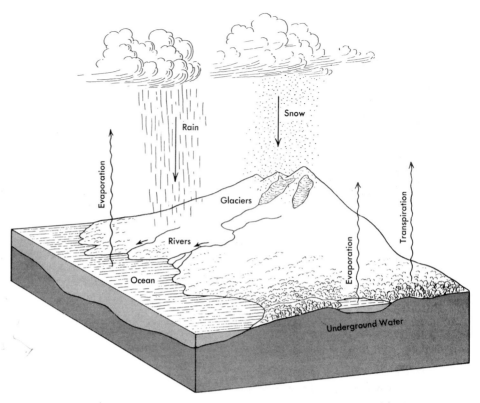

Figure 9-1 In the hydrologic cycle, water evaporated into the atmosphere reaches the land as rain or snow. Here it may be temporarily stored in glaciers, lakes, or the underground before returning by the rivers to the sea. Or some may be transpired or evaporated directly back into the atmosphere before reaching the sea.

straight-line paths that are parallel to the passage. This type of movement is called **laminar flow.**

If the rate of flow increases, however, or if the confining channel becomes rough and irregular, this smooth, streamline movement is disrupted. The water in contact with the channel is slowed down by friction, whereas the rest of the water tends to move along as before. As a result (see Figure 9-3), the water is deflected from its straight paths into a series of eddies and swirls. This type of movement is known as **turbulent flow.** It is highly effective both in eroding a stream's channel and in transporting materials. Water in streams usually flows in this way.

VELOCITY, GRADIENT, AND DISCHARGE   The velocity of a stream is measured in terms of the distance its water travels in a unit of time, usually in feet per second. A velocity of half a foot per second (about 0.3 miles per hour) is

relatively low, and a velocity of 25 to 30 feet per second (about 17 to 20 miles per hour) is relatively high.

A stream's velocity is determined by many factors, including the amount of water passing a given point, the nature of the stream banks, and the **gradient** or slope of the stream bed. In general, a stream's gradient decreases from its headwaters toward its mouth; as a result, a stream's longitudinal profile is more or less concave toward the sky (Figure 9-4). We usually express the gradient of a stream as the number of feet the stream descends during each mile of flow. The Mississippi River from Cairo, Illinois, to the mouth of the Red River in Arkansas has a low gradient, for along this stretch the drop varies between only one-tenth and one-half foot per mile. On the other hand, the Arkansas River in its upper reaches through the Rocky Mountains in central Colorado has a high gradient, for there the drop averages 40 feet per mile. The gradi-

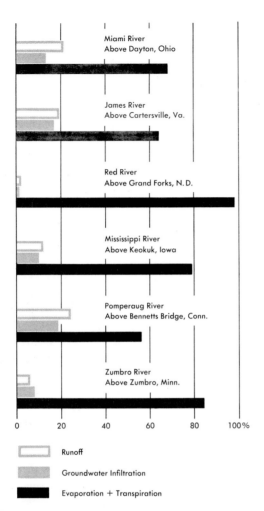

Miami River
Above Dayton, Ohio

James River
Above Cartersville, Va.

Red River
Above Grand Forks, N.D.

Mississippi River
Above Keokuk, Iowa

Pomperaug River
Above Bennetts Bridge, Conn.

Zumbro River
Above Zumbro, Minn.

0   20   40   60   80   100%

☐ Runoff

▒ Groundwater Infiltration

█ Evaporation + Transpiration

Figure 9-2 Distribution of precipitation in selected drainage basins. Notice that in all cases 50 per cent or more of all moisture that falls is returned to the atmosphere by evaporation and transpiration. Runoff from the surface is comparatively small, and infiltration of water in the underground is still less. (*Data from W. G. Hoyt and others*, Studies of Relation of Rainfall and Run-off in the United States. *Washington, D.C.: U.S. Geological Survey, Water Supply Paper 772, 1936.*)

ents of other rivers are even higher. The upper 12 miles of the Yuba River in California, for example, have an average gradient of 225 feet per mile; and in the upper 4 miles of the Uncompahgre River in Colorado, the gradient averages 350 feet per mile.

The velocity of a stream is checked by friction along the banks and bed of its channel and, to a much smaller extent, by friction with the air above. So if we were to study a cross section of a stream, we would find that the velocity would vary from point to point. Along a straight stretch of a channel, the greatest velocity is achieved toward the center of the stream at, or just below, the surface, as shown in Figure 9-5 (p. 146).

We have, then, two opposing forces: the **forward flow** of the water under the influence of gravity, and the **friction** developed along

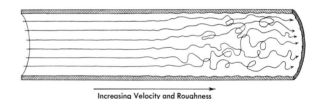

Increasing Velocity and Roughness

Figure 9-3 Diagram showing laminar and turbulent flow of water through a section of pipe. Individual water particles follow paths depicted by the black lines. In laminar flow, the particles follow paths parallel to the containing walls. With increasing velocity or increasing roughness of the confining walls, laminar flow gives way to turbulent flow. The water particles no longer follow straight lines but are deflected into eddies and swirls. Most water flow in streams is turbulent.

Figure 9-4 In longitudinal profile (from mouth to headwaters), a stream valley is concave to the sky. Irregularities along the profile indicate variations in rates of erosion. (*Redrawn from Henry Gannett*, Profiles of Rivers in the United States. *Washington, D.C.: U.S. Geological Survey, Water Supply Paper 44, 1901.*)

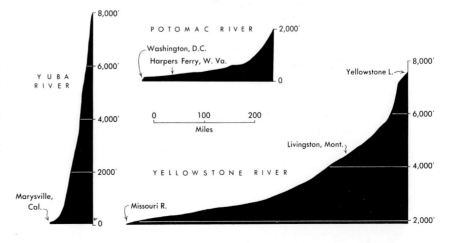

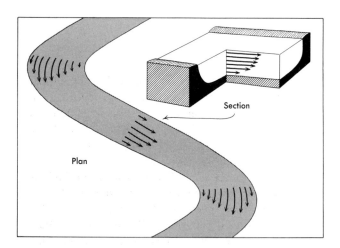

Figure 9-5 Velocity variations in a stream. Both in plan view and in cross section, the velocity is slowest along the stream channel, where the water is slowed by friction. On the surface, it is most rapid at the center in straight stretches and toward the outside of a bed where the river curves. Velocity increases upward from the river bottom.

Figure 9-6 Zones of maximum turbulence in a stream are shown by the shaded areas in the sections through a river bed. They occur where the change between the two opposing forces—the forward flow and the friction of the stream channel—is most marked. Note that the maximum turbulence along straight stretches of the river is located where the stream banks join the stream floor. On bends, the two zones have unequal intensity; the greater turbulence is located on the outside of a curve.

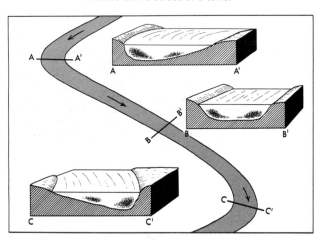

the walls and bed of the stream. These two forces create different velocities, and zones of maximum turbulence occur where the different velocities come into the closest contact (see Figure 9-6).

There is one more term that will be helpful in our discussion of running water—**discharge**, or the **quantity** of water that passes a given point in a unit of time. It is usually measured in cubic feet per second, abbreviated **c.f.s.** Discharge varies not only from one stream to another, but also within a single stream from time to time and from place to place along its course.

The Economy of a Stream

Elsewhere, we have seen that earth processes tend to seek a balance, to establish an equilibrium, and that there is, in the words of James Hutton, "a system of beautiful economy in the works of nature." We found, for example, that weathering is a response of earth materials to the new and changing conditions they meet as they are exposed at or near the earth's surface. On a larger scale, the major rock groups—igneous, sedimentary, and metamorphic—reflect certain environments and as these environments change, members of one group may be transformed into members of another group. These changes were traced in what we called the rock cycle (Figure 3-2). Water running off the land in streams and rivers is no exception to this universal tendency of nature to seek equilibrium.

ADJUSTMENTS OF DISCHARGE, VELOCITY, AND CHANNEL We can relate the discharge of a river to its width, depth, and velocity as follows:

$$\text{Discharge (c.f.s.)} = \frac{\text{Channel width}}{\text{(ft)}} \times \frac{\text{Channel depth}}{\text{(ft)}} \times \frac{\text{Water velocity}}{\text{(ft/sec)}}$$

In other words, if the discharge at a given point along a river increases, then the width, depth, or velocity, or some combination of these factors must also increase. These variations in width, depth, and velocity are neither

146

random nor unpredictable. In most streams, if the discharge increases, then the width, depth, and velocity each increase at a definite rate. The stream maintains a balance between the amount of water it carries on the one hand, and its depth, width, and velocity on the other. Moreover, it does so in an orderly fashion, as shown in Figure 9-7.

Let us turn now from the behavior of a stream at a single locality to the changes that take place along its entire length. From our own observations, we know that the discharge of a stream increases downstream as more and more tributaries contribute water to its main channel. We also know that the width and depth increase as we travel downstream. But if we go beyond casual observation and gather accurate data on the width, depth, velocity, and discharge of a stream from its headwaters to its mouth for a particular stage of flow— say, flood or low-water—we would find again that changes follow a definite pattern and that depth and width increase downstream as the discharge increases (Figure 9-8). And, surprisingly enough, we would also find that the stream's **velocity** increases toward its mouth. This is contrary to our expectations, for we know that the gradients are higher upstream, which suggests that the velocities in the steeper headwater areas would also be higher. But the explanation for this seeming anomaly is simple: In order to handle the greater discharge downstream, a stream not only must deepen and widen its channel, but must also increase its velocity.

Adjustments of Gradient

The gradient of a stream decreases along its course from headwaters to mouth, producing an over-all profile that is concave to the sky. If it were not for this gradual flattening of the profile, the increased discharge downstream would produce velocities fantastically higher than those observed in nature. A concave slope tends to decrease the rate at which stream velocity increases.

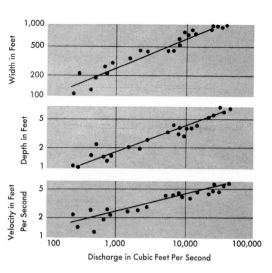

Figure 9-7 As the discharge of a stream increases at a given gauging station, so do its velocity, width, and depth. They increase in an orderly fashion, as shown by these graphs based on data from a gauging station in the Cheyenne River near Eagle Butte, South Dakota. (*Redrawn from Luna B. Leopold and Thomas Maddock, The Hydraulic Geometry of Stream Channels and Some Physiographic Implications. Washington, D.C.: U.S. Geological Survey, Professional Paper 252, 1953, p. 5.*)

Figure 9-8 Stream velocity and depth and width of a channel increase as the discharge of a stream increases downstream. Measurements in this example were made at mean annual discharge along a section of the Mississippi-Missouri river system. (*Ibid., p. 13.*)

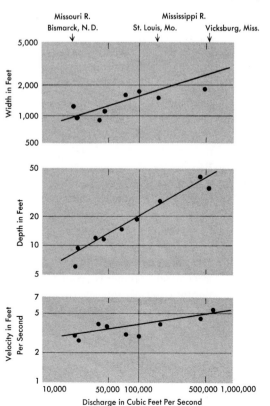

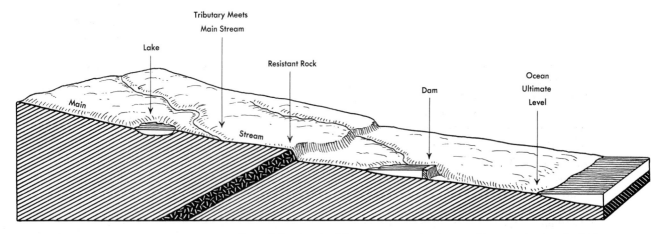

Figure 9-9 Base level for a stream may be determined by natural and artificial lakes, by a resistant rock stratum, by the point at which a tributary stream enters a main stream, and by the ocean. Of these, the ocean is considered ultimate base level; others are temporary base levels.

BASE LEVEL OF A STREAM   A key concept in the study of stream activity is the **base level,** or the lowest point to which a stream can erode its channel. Anything that prohibits the stream from lowering its channel serves to create a base level. For example, the velocity of a stream is checked when it enters the standing, quiet waters of a lake. Consequently, the stream loses its ability to erode, and it cannot cut below the level of the lake. Actually, the lake's control over the stream is effective along the entire course upstream, for no part of the stream can erode beneath the level of the lake—at least until the lake has been destroyed. But in a geologic sense, every lake is temporary. So when the lake has been destroyed, perhaps by the down-cutting of its outlet, it will no longer control the stream's base level, and the stream will be free to continue its downward erosion. Because of its impermanence, the base level formed by a lake is referred to as a **temporary base level.** But even after a stream has been freed from one temporary base level, it will be controlled by others farther downstream. And its erosive power is always influenced by the ocean, which is the **ultimate base level.** Yet, as we shall see in later chapters, the ocean itself is subject to changes in level, so even the ultimate base level is not fixed.

The base level of a stream may be controlled not only by lakes, but also by layers of resistant rock and the level of the main stream into which a tributary drains (see Figure 9-9).

Streams adjust the level of their channels to new situations. In general, a stream adjusts to a rise in base level by building up its channel through sedimentation, and it adjusts to a fall in base level by eroding its channel downward.

Work of Running Water

The water that flows along through river channels does several jobs: (1) It transports debris, (2) it erodes the river channel deeper into the land, and (3) it deposits sediments at various points along the valley or delivers them to lakes or oceans.

TRANSPORTATION   The material that a stream picks up directly from its own channel—or that is supplied to it by slope wash, tributaries, or mass movement—is carried downstream toward its eventual goal, the ocean. The amount of material that a stream carries at any one time, called its **load,** is usually less than its **capacity**—that is, the total amount it is capable of carrying under any given set of conditions (see Figure 9-10). The maximum size of particle that a stream can move measures the **competency** of a stream. Experiments have shown that the diameter

148

of a moveable particle varies approximately with the square of the stream's velocity. Thus, a stream with a velocity of one-quarter of a mile per hour can move coarse sand particles of about 0.02 inch diameter. If the velocity doubles to half a mile per hour, then the diameter of moveable particles increases to about 0.08 inch; a stream flowing at a velocity of 1 mile an hour can move a pebble about 0.32 inch in diameter.

There are three ways in which a stream can transport material: by (1) solution, (2) suspension, and (3) bed load.

Solution. In nature, no water is completely pure. When water falls and filters down into the ground, it dissolves some of the soil's compounds. Then the water may seep down through openings, pores, and crevices in the bedrock and dissolve additional matter as it moves along. Much of this water eventually finds its way to streams at lower levels. The amount of dissolved matter contained in water varies with climate, season, and geologic setting and is measured in terms of parts of dissolved matter per million parts of water. Sometimes the amount of dissolved material exceeds 1,000 parts per million, but usually it is much less. By far the most common compounds found in solution in running water, particularly in arid regions, are calcium and magnesium carbonates. In addition, streams carry small amounts of chlorides, nitrates, sulfates, and silica, with perhaps a trace of potassium. It has been estimated that the total load of dissolved material delivered to the seas every year by the streams of the United States is about 270,000,000 tons. All the rivers of the world are thought to dump about 3 billion tons of dissolved material into the oceans each year.

Suspension. Particles of solid matter that are swept along in the turbulent current of a stream are said to be in **suspension**. This process of transportation is controlled by two factors: (1) the turbulence of the water, and (2) a characteristic known as **terminal velocity** of each individual grain. Terminal velocity is the constant rate of fall that a particle eventually attains when the acceleration caused by gravity is balanced by the resistance of the fluid through which the grain is falling. If we drop a grain of sand into a quiet pond, it will settle toward the bottom at an ever-increasing rate until the friction of the water on the grain just balances this rate of increase. Thereafter, it will settle at a constant rate, its terminal velocity. If we can set up a force that will equal or exceed the terminal velocity of the grain, we can succeed in keeping it in suspension. Turbulence supplies such a force. The eddies of turbulent water move in a series of orbits, and grains caught in these eddies

Figure 9-10 These converging rivers in British Columbia illustrate the different loads carried by two streams. The Frazer River enters from the upper right, milky with suspended sediment derived largely from the melting of mountain glaciers. Its load is high but probably somewhat less than capacity. The Thompson River, entering from the lower right, is relatively clear and carries a very small load, much less than its capacity. (*Photo by Elliott A. Riggs.*)

will be buoyed up, or held in suspension, so long as the velocity of the turbulent water is equal to, or greater than, the terminal velocity of the grains.

Terminal velocity increases with particle size, given the same general shape and density. The bigger a particle, the more turbulent the flow needed to keep it in suspension. And since turbulence increases when the velocity of stream flow increases, it follows that the greatest amount of material is moved during flood time when velocities and turbulence are highest. The graph in Figure 9-11 shows how the suspended load of a stream increases as the discharge increases.

Silt and clay-sized particles are distributed fairly evenly through the depth of a stream but coarser particles in the sand-size range are carried in greater amounts lower down in the current, in the zone of greatest turbulence.

Bed Load. Materials in movement along a stream bottom constitute the **bed load,** in contrast to the suspended load and solution load. Since it is difficult to observe and measure the movement of the bed load, we have few data on the subject. Measurements on the Niobrara River near Cody, Nebraska, however, have shown that at discharges between 200 and 1,000 c.f.s., the bed load averaged about 50 per cent of the total load. But this is very high and in most streams the bed load probably does not represent more than ten per cent of the total load. Particles in the bed load move along in three ways: by saltation, rolling, or sliding.

The term **saltation** has nothing to do with salt; it is derived from the Latin *saltare,* "to jump." A particle moving by saltation jumps from one point on the stream bed to another. First it is picked up by a current of turbulent water and flung upward; then, if it is too heavy to remain in suspension, it drops to the stream floor again at some spot downstream.

Some materials are too large and too heavy to be picked up, even momentarily, by water currents. But they may be pushed and shoved along the stream bed, and depending

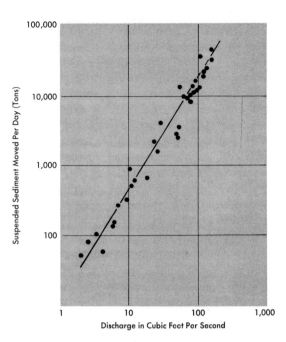

Figure 9-11 The suspended load of a stream increases very rapidly during floods, as illustrated by this graph based on measurements in the Rio Puerco near Cabezon, New Mexico. (*Redrawn from Luna B. Leopold and John P. Miller, Ephemeral Streams—Hydraulic Factors and Their Relation to the Drainage Net. Washington, D.C.: U.S. Geological Survey, Professional Paper 282-A, 1956, p. 11.*)

Figure 9-12 This diagram shows the velocities at which a stream erodes, transports, and deposits particles of different sizes. (*Redrawn from Filip Hjulström, Studies of the Morphological Activity of Rivers as Illustrated by the River Fyris. Upsala: Upsala Geol. Inst. Bull. 25, 1935, p. 298.*)

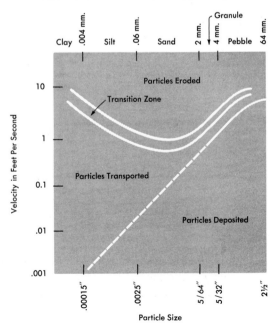

on their shape, they are moved forward either by **rolling** or by **sliding.**

EROSION　A stream does more than simply transport material that has been brought to it by other agencies of erosion, for it is an effective agent of erosion in itself. In various ways, an actively eroding stream may remove material from its channel or banks.

Direct Lifting. In turbulent flow, as we have seen, water travels along paths that are not parallel to the bed. The water eddies and whirls, and if an eddy is powerful enough, it dislodges particles from the stream channel and lifts them into the stream. If we assume that the bed of a stream is composed of particles of uniform size, then the graph in Figure 9-12 gives us the approximate stream velocities that are needed to erode particles of various sizes, such as clay, silt, sand, granules, and pebbles. A stream bed composed of medium sized sand grains, for example, can be eroded by a stream with a velocity of less than 1 foot per second. As the fragments become larger and larger, ranging from coarse sand to granules, to pebbles, increasingly higher velocities are required to move them.

But what we might *not* expect is that higher stream velocities are needed to erode smaller particles of clay and silt size. The reason is that smaller particles tend to pack together firmly; and the more firmly packed a deposit is, the more resistant it is to erosion. Moreover, the individual particles may be so small that they do not project high enough into the stream to be swept up by the turbulent water.

Notice, too, in Figure 9-12, that once a particle has been dislodged from the stream bed, it will continue to be carried along even though the stream's velocity decreases somewhat. In other words, it takes less velocity (hence, less energy) to keep a particle in movement than it does to erode the particle and start it moving.

Abrasion, Impact, and Solution. The solid particles carried by a stream may themselves act as erosive agents, for they are capable of abrading the bedrock itself or larger fragments in the bed of the stream. When the bedrock is worn by abrasion, it usually develops a series of smooth, curving surfaces, either convex or concave. Similarly, as individual cobbles or pebbles on a stream bottom are rubbed together while they are moved and rolled about by the force of the current, they become rounder and smoother.

Also erosive is the impact of large particles against the bedrock or against other particles, which knocks off fragments that are added to the load of the stream.

Some erosion also results from the solution of channel debris and bedrock in the water of the stream. Most of the dissolved matter carried by a stream, however, is probably contributed by the underground water that drains into it.

Slope Erosion by Running Water. So far, we have considered the erosion that takes place only along a stream channel—certainly the most conspicuous form of erosion by water —but the total area covered by stream channels is only a very small proportion of the total land surface drained by streams, perhaps about 1 per cent. Furthermore, most of the flood water carried by streams originates as runoff from the neighboring slopes. The runoff —flowing as a sheet of water called **slope wash,** or in closely spaced, shallow channels called **rills**—is sometimes powerful enough to overcome the soil's resistance to erosion, and it manages to transport a great deal of material downslope toward the stream channels.

The muddy water running off a plowed field or a newly graded slope during a heavy rain is a familiar example of the erosive power of runoff. In an area of 100 square miles with 100 miles of streams, it has been estimated that a sheet of water one-fourth of an inch thick will produce a runoff of 22,000 cubic feet per second. If this same sheet of water carried 10 per cent of solid matter by volume and flowed for 6 hours, it would remove between one-fourth and one-third of an inch of soil. Although the importance of slope erosion

by running water is often overlooked, it must play a significant role in the general process of erosion. We shall refer to it again later.

Time of Most Rapid Erosion. We have found that, other things being equal, the greater the stream's velocity the greater its erosive power. Obviously, then, the greatest erosive

Figure 9-14 Changes in the channel of the San Juan River near Bluff, Utah, during a flood in 1941. On September 9 and 15, periods of moderate discharge, the river flowed on a bed of gravel within the larger bedrock channel. On October 14, flood waters swelled to 59,600 c.f.s. and swept the gravel downstream, exposing the bedrock abrasion. With the subsidence of the flood, new gravel deposits brought from upstream began to build up the gravel bed of the river. Width of river on September 9 was approximately 150 feet. (*Redrawn from Leopold and Maddock, op. cit., p. 32.*)

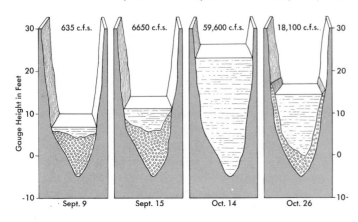

(and transporting) power of any stream is developed during flood time. When a stream is at flood stage, the water level rises and the channel is deepened. The fast-moving water picks up the layer of sand and gravel that usually lies on the bedrock of the stream channel during nonflood stages and sweeps it downstream. If the flood is great enough, the bedrock itself is exposed and eroded. A new layer of debris collects as the flood waters subside, but by that time great masses of material have been moved downstream toward the oceans, and the bedrock channel of the stream has been permanently lowered. Figure 9-14 illustrates this action. In general, then, we may say that erosion is most effective during flood periods.

DEPOSITION As soon as the velocity of a stream falls below the point necessary to hold material in suspension, the stream begins to deposit its suspended load. Deposition is a selective process. First, the coarsest material is dropped; then, as the velocity (and hence the energy) continues to slacken, finer and finer material settles out. We shall consider stream deposits in more detail elsewhere in this chapter, but another look at Figure 9-12 will show the size of particles that settle out at different

152

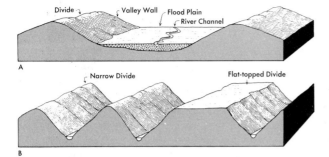

Figure 9-15 Cross-sectional sketches of typical stream valleys. The major features of valleys in cross section include divides, valley walls, river channel, and, in some instances, a flood plain. Divides may be either flat-topped or broadly rounded.

velocities. Thus, when the velocity of a stream falls below 1 foot per second, pebble-sized particles can no longer be carried, and they begin to fall to the bottom. At a velocity of about 0.1 foot per second, medium-sized sand grains are dropped; and below 0.01 foot per second, silt begins to settle out.

Features of Valleys

CROSS-VALLEY PROFILES Earlier in this chapter we mentioned the longitudinal profile of a stream (Figure 9-4). Now let us turn to a discussion of the cross-valley profile—that is, at right angles to the stream's line of flow. In Figure 9-15A, notice that the channel of the river runs across a broad, relatively flat **flood plain.** During flood time, when the channel can no longer accomodate the increased discharge, the stream overflows its banks and floods this area. On either side of the flood plain, **valley walls** rise to crests called **divides,** separations between the central valley and the other valleys on either side. In Figure 9-15B, no flood plain is present, for the valley walls descend directly to the banks of the river. This diagram also illustrates two different shapes of divides. One is broad and flat, the other is narrow, almost knife-edged. Both are in contrast to the broadly convex divides shown in A.

DRAINAGE BASINS A **drainage basin** is the entire area from which a stream and its tributaries receive their water. The Mississippi

and its tributaries drain a tremendous section of the central United States reaching from the Rockies to the Appalachians, and each tributary of the Mississippi has its own drainage area, which forms a part of the larger basin. Every stream, even the smallest brook, has its own drainage basin, shaped differently from stream to stream, but characteristically pear-shaped, with the main stream emerging from the narrow end (see Figure 9-16).

ENLARGEMENT OF VALLEYS We cannot say with assurance how running water first fashioned the great valleys and drainage basins of the continents, for the record has been lost in time. But we do know that certain processes are now at work in widening and deepening valleys, and it seems safe to assume that they also operated in the past.

If a stream were left to itself in its attempt to reach base level, it would erode its bed straight downward, forming a vertical-walled chasm in the process. But since the stream is not the only agent at work in valley formation, the walls of most valleys slope upward and outward from the valley floor. In time, the cliffs of even the steepest gorge will be angled away from the axis of its valley.

Figure 9-16 Each stream, no matter how small, has its own drainage basin, the area from which the stream and its tributaries receive water. This basin displays a pattern reminiscent of a tree leaf and its veins.

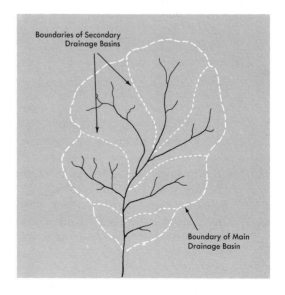

As a stream cuts downward and lowers its channel into the land surface, weathering, slope wash, and mass movement come into play, constantly wearing away the valley walls, pushing them further back. Under the influence of gravity, material is carried down from the valley walls and dumped into the stream, to be moved onward toward the seas. The result is a valley whose walls flare outward and upward from the stream in a typical cross-valley profile (Figure 9-17).

FEATURES OF NARROW VALLEYS

Waterfalls and Rapids. Waterfalls are among the most fascinating spectacles of the landscape. Thunderous and powerful as they are, however, they are actually short-lived features in the history of a stream. They owe their existence to some sudden drop in the river's longitudinal profile—a drop that may be eliminated with the passing of time.

Waterfalls are caused by many different conditions. Niagara Falls, for instance, is held up by a relatively resistant bed of dolomite underlain by beds of nonresistant shale (Figure 9-18). This shale is easily undermined by the swirling waters of the Niagara River as they plunge over the lip of the falls. When the undermining has progressed far enough, the dolomite collapses and tumbles to the base of the falls. The same process is repeated over and over again as time passes, and the falls slowly retreat upstream. Historical records suggest that the Horseshoe or Canadian Falls (by far the larger of the two falls at Niagara) have been retreating at a rate of 4 to 5 feet per year, while the smaller American Falls have been eroded away about 2 or 3 inches per year. The 7 miles of gorge between the foot of the falls and Lake Ontario are evidence of the headward retreat of the falls through time.

Yosemite Falls in Yosemite National Park, California, plunge 2,565 feet—over the Upper Falls, down an intermediate zone of cascades, and then over the Lower Falls. The falls leap from the mouth of a small valley high above

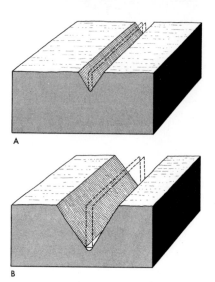

Figure 9-17 If a stream of water were the only agent in valley formation, we might expect a vertically walled valley no wider than the stream channel, as suggested by the dotted lines in A and B. Mass movement and slope wash, however, are constantly wearing away the valley walls, carving slopes that flare upward and away from the stream channel, as shown in the diagrams.

Figure 9-18 Niagara Falls tumbles over a bed of dolomite, underlain chiefly by shale. As the less resistant shale is eroded, the undermined ledge of dolomite breaks off, and the lip of the falls retreats. (*Redrawn from G. K. Gilbert, Niagara Falls and Their History. New York: American Book Company, 1896, p. 213.*)

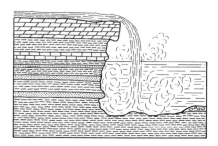

the main valley of the Yosemite. The Upper Falls alone measure 1,430 feet, 9 times the height of Niagara. During the Ice Age, glaciers scoured the main valley much deeper than they did the side valley. Then, when the glacier ice melted, the river in the main valley was left far below its tributary, which now joins it after a drop of nearly half a mile.

Rapids, like waterfalls, occur at a sudden drop in the stream channel. Although rapids do not plunge straight down as waterfalls do,

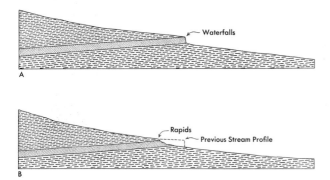

A

B

Figure 9-19 Rapids may represent a stage in the destruction of waterfalls, as suggested in this diagram.

the underlying cause of formation is often the same. In fact, many rapids have developed directly from pre-existing waterfalls (see Figure 9-19).

Potholes. As the bedrock channel of a stream is eroded away, **potholes** sometimes develop (see Figure 9-20). These are deep holes, circular to elliptical in outline, and a few inches to scores of feet in depth. They are most often observed in the stream channel during low water or along the bedrock walls, where they have been left stranded after the stream has cut its channel downward. Potholes are most common in narrow valleys, but they often occur in broad valleys as well.

A pothole begins as a shallow depression in the bedrock channel of a stream. Then, as the swirling, turbulent water drives sand, pebbles, and even cobbles around and around the depression, the continued abrasion wears the potholes ever deeper, as if the bedrock were being bored by a giant drill (see Figure 9-21). The initial depression may be caused by ordinary abrasion, or by some irregularity in the bedrock.

FEATURES OF BROAD VALLEYS If conditions permit, the various agents working toward valley enlargement ultimately produce a broad valley with a wide level floor. During periods of normal or low water, the river

running through the valley is confined to its channel. But during high water it overflows its banks and spreads out over the flood plain.

Meanders. The channel of the Menderes River in Asia Minor curves back on itself in a series of broad hairpin bends. In fact, the very name of the river is derived from the Greek *maiandros,* "a bend." Today, all such bends are called **meanders,** and the zone along

Figure 9-20 This nearly dry stream bed is marked by a series of potholes. Coarse sand and gravel, caught up in the eddies of turbulent water, served as the cutting materials that carved the holes. (*Photo by Paul MacClintock.*)

Figure 9-21 A cluster of pebbles in a pothole exposed at low water stage in the bed of the Blackstone River, Blackstone, Massachusetts. (*Photo by Alden, U.S. Geological Survey.*)

a valley floor that encloses a meandering river is called a **meander belt** (see Figures 9-22, 9-23).

Both erosion and deposition are involved in the formation of a meander. First, some obstruction swings the current of a stream against one of the banks, and then the current is deflected over to the opposite bank. Erosion takes place on the outside of each bend, where the turbulence is greatest. The material detached from the banks is moved downstream, there to be deposited in zones of decreased turbulence—either along the center of the channel or on the inside of the next bend. As the river swings from side to side, the meander continues to grow by erosion on the outside of the bends and by deposition on the inside. Growth ceases when the meander reaches a critical size, a size that increases with an increase in the size of the stream.

Because a meander is eroded more on its downstream side than on its upstream side, the entire bend tends to move slowly down-valley. This movement is not uniform, however, and under certain conditions the downstream sweep of a series of meanders is distorted into cutoffs, meander scars, and oxbow lakes.

In its down-valley migration, a meander sometimes runs into a stretch of land that is relatively more resistant to erosion. But the next meander upstream continues to move right along, and gradually the neck between them is narrowed. Finally, the river cuts a new, shorter channel, called a **neck cutoff,** across the neck. The abandoned meander is called an **oxbow,** because of its characteristic shape. Usually both ends of the oxbow are gradually silted in, and the old meander becomes completely isolated from the new channel. If the abandoned meander fills up with water, an **oxbow lake** results. Although a cutoff will eliminate a particular meander, the stream's tendency toward meandering still exists, and before long the entire process begins to repeat itself (Figures 9-24, 9-25).

As we found, a meander grows and migrates by erosion on the outside of the bend

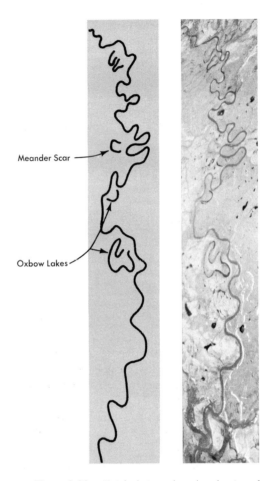

Figure 9-22 Aerial photograph and a drawing of meanders in an Alaskan stream. Note the oxbow lakes. (*Photo by U.S. Army Air Force.*)

Figure 9-23 The meander belt is the portion of the floodplain that encloses a meandering stream.

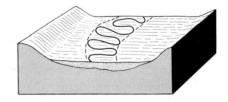

and by deposition on the inside. This deposition on the inside leaves behind a series of low ridges and troughs. Swamps often form in the troughs, and during flood time the river may develop an alternate channel through one of the troughs. Such a channel is called a **chute cutoff,** or simply a chute (see Figure 9-25).

Figure 9-24 This oxbow lake near Weslaco, Texas, was once a part of the meandering Rio Grande, which lies in the distance. An old bend in the river was cut through at the neck, became isolated from the river, and filled with water. (Photo by Standard Oil Co., N.J.)

The meandering river demonstrates a unity in ways other than the balance of erosion and deposition. The length of a meander, for example, is proportional to the width of the river, and this is true regardless of the size of the river. It holds for channels a few feet wide as well as those as large as that of the Mississippi. As shown in Figure 9-26A, this principle also is true of the Gulf Stream, even though this "river" is unconfined by solid banks. A similar relationship holds between the length of the meander and the radius of curvature of the meander (Figure 9-26B).

Braided Streams. On some flood plains, particularly where large amounts of debris are dropped rapidly, a stream may build up a complex tangle of converging and diverging channels separated by sand bars or islands. A stream of this sort is called a **braided stream.** When the velocity is checked either by a

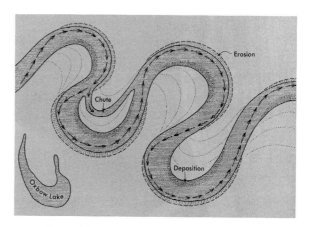

Figure 9-25 Erosion takes place on the outside of a meander bend, whereas deposition is most marked on the inside. If the neck of a meander is eroded through, an oxbow forms. A chute originates along the inside of a meander where irregular deposition creates ridges and troughs as the meander migrates.

Figure 9-26 A: Length of the meander increases with the widening meandering stream. B: A similar orderly relationship exists between length of the meander and the mean radius of curvature of the meander. (Redrawn from Luna B. Leopold and M. Gordon Wolman, "River Meanders," Geol. Soc. Am. Bull., LXXI (1960), p. 773.)

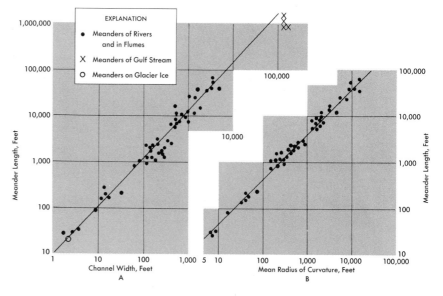

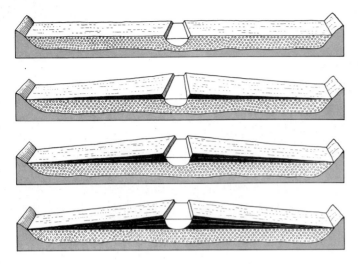

Figure 9-27 Natural levees, characteristic of many aggrading streams. These highly exaggerated diagrams show the building-up of wedge-shaped layers of silt that taper away from the stream banks toward valley walls. As the banks are built up, the floor of the stream channel also rises.

decrease in the stream's gradient or by a loss of water through infiltration into porous deposits, the energy of the stream also falls. Consequently, a large part of the stream's suspended load is suddenly dropped. The deposited material deflects the current into different channels, in search of an easier course. The braided pattern is commonly found on alluvial fans (see below), glacial outwash deposits, and along certain rapidly depositing rivers.

Natural Levees. In many flood plains, the water surface of the stream is held above the level of the valley floor by banks of sand and silt known as **natural levees,** a name derived from the French verb *lever,* "to raise." These banks slope gently, almost imperceptibly, away from their crest along the river toward the valley wall. The low-lying flood plain adjoining a natural levee may contain marshy areas known as **back swamps.** Levees are built up during flood time, when the water spills over the river banks onto the flood plain. Since the muddy water rising over the stream bank is no longer confined by the channel, its velocity and turbulence drop immediately, and much of the suspended load is deposited close to the river; but some is carried farther along, to be deposited across the flood plain. The

deposit of one flood is a thin wedge tapering away from the river; but over many years, the cumulative effect produces a natural levee that is considerably higher alongside the river banks than away from it (Figure 9-27). On the Mississippi delta, for instance, the levees stand 15 to 20 feet above the back swamps.

Although natural levees tend to confine a stream within its channel, each time the levees are raised slightly, the bed of the river is also raised. In time, the level of the bed is raised above the level of the surrounding flood plain. If the river manages to escape from its confining walls during a flood, it will assume a new channel across the lowest parts of the flood plain toward the back swamps.

Flood-Plain Deposits. The floors of most flood plains are covered by two and sometimes three different types of deposits. The coarsest material is deposited directly by the stream along its channel. During flood periods, finer sand, silt, and clay are spread across the flood plain, away from the river banks. In addition, relatively small amounts of debris of various types and sizes move down the valley walls under the influence of slope wash

Figure 9-28 Deposits underlying the flood plain of a slowly aggrading river or beneath a flood plain formed by erosion differ from those beneath a rapidly aggrading river's flood plain. A: Deposits are those to be expected beneath an erosional flood plain or one being slowly aggraded. Coarse river-channel deposits underlie the entire flood plain and are veneered with fine-grained sediments. B: The type of deposit beneath the flood plain of a rapidly aggrading river, the great bulk being fine-grained sediments deposited during flood periods. Coarse channel deposits may form a ribbon of gravel within the finer deposits.

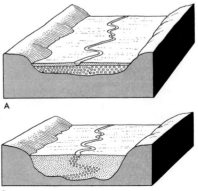

and mass movement and are spread along the sides of the valley floor. The distribution of the channel and flood deposits across a flood plain depends on the rate at which a stream builds up its valley floor.

A meandering stream is constantly shifting its channel, and over a period of time it may succeed in occupying every possible position across the plain. A cross section through the flood plain developed by such a stream reveals a cover of gravel capped by fine-grained sediments deposited during overbank flow (see Figure 9-28A). This pattern of sediments is typical of erosional flood plains and of very slowly aggraded flood plains.

But a meandering stream that builds up its flood plain at a rapid rate has less opportunity to occupy each spot across the valley floor. Consequently, its flood plain will be covered for the most part by fine sediments deposited during times of overflow. A cross section reveals an irregular band of coarse material, marking successive positions of the channel (see Figure 9-28B). Rapidly aggraded

flood plains show this pattern of deposition.

Deltas and Alluvial Fans. For centuries, the Nile River has been depositing sediments as it empties into the Mediterranean Sea, forming a great triangular plain with its apex upstream. This plain came to be called a **delta** because of the similarity of its shape to the Greek letter Δ (see Figure 9-29).

Whenever a stream flows into a body of standing water, such as a lake or an ocean, its velocity and transporting power are quickly stemmed. If it carries enough debris and if conditions in the body of standing water are favorable, a delta will gradually be built up. An ideal delta is triangular in plan, with the apex pointed upstream, and with the sediments arranged according to a definite pattern. The coarse material is dumped first, forming a series of dipping beds called **foreset beds**. But the finer material is swept farther along to settle across the sea or lake floor as **bottomset beds**. As the delta extends farther and farther out into the water body, the stream must extend its channel to the edge of the delta. As

159

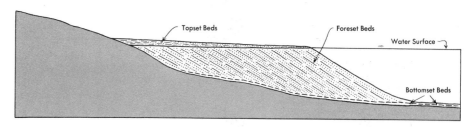

Figure 9-30 The ideal arrangement of sediments beneath a delta. Some of the material deposited in a water body is laid on the bottom of the lake or sea as bottomset beds. Other material is dumped in inclined foreset beds, built farther and farther into the body of water and partly covering the bottomset beds. Over the foreset beds the stream lays down topset beds.

it does so, it covers the delta with **topset beds,** which lie across the top of the foreset beds (see Figure 9-30).

Very few deltas, however, show either the perfect delta shape or this regular sequence of sediments. Many factors, including lake and shore currents, varying rates of deposition, the settling of delta deposits as a result of their compaction, and the down-warping of the earth's crust, all conspire to modify the typical form and sequence.

Across the top of the delta deposits, the stream spreads seaward in a complex of channels radiating from the apex. These **distributary channels** shift their position from time to time as they seek more favorable gradients.

An **alluvial fan** is the terrestrial counterpart of a delta. These fans are typical of arid and semiarid climates, but they may form in almost any climate if conditions are right. A fan marks a sudden decrease in the carrying power of a stream as it descends from a steep gradient to a flatter one—for example, when the stream flows down a steep mountain slope onto a plain. As the velocity is checked, the stream rapidly begins to dump its load. In the process, it builds up its channel, often with small natural levees along its banks. Eventually, as the levees continue to grow, the stream may flow above the general level. Then, during a time of flood, it seeks a lower level and shifts its channel to begin deposition elsewhere. As this process of shifting continues, an alluvial fan builds up (Figure 9-31).

Stream Terraces. A **stream terrace** is a relatively flat surface running along a valley,

Figure 9-31 An alluvial fan is the land counterpart of a delta. In this example in Death Valley, California, the streams flow only during the rare rains, carrying debris from the steep gulches along the cliff face. As the velocity of the streams is checked on the flat valley floor, material is deposited to form the alluvial fan. (*Photo by Sheldon Judson.*)

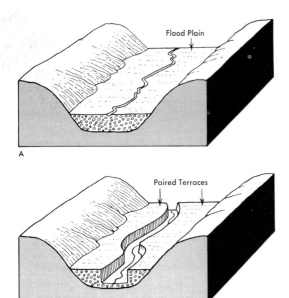

Figure 9-32 An example of the formation of paired terraces. In A, the stream has partially filled its valley and has created a broad flood plain. In B, some change in conditions has caused the stream to erode into its own deposits; the remnants of the old flood plain stand above the new river level as terraces of equal height. This particular example is referred to as a cut-and-fill terrace. (See also Figure 9-33.)

with a steep bank separating it either from the flood plain or from a lower terrace. It is a remnant of the former channel of a stream that now has cut its way down to a lower level.

The so-called **cut-and-fill terrace** is created when a stream first clogs a valley with sediments and then cuts its way down to a lower level (see Figures 9-32, 9-33). The initial aggradation may be caused by a change in climate that leads either to an increase in the stream's load or to a decrease in its discharge. Or the base level of the stream may rise, reducing the gradient and causing deposition. In any event, the stream chokes the valley with sediment and the flood plain gradually rises. Now, if the equilibrium is upset and the stream begins to erode, it will cut a channel down through the deposits it has already laid down. The level of flow will be lower than the old flood plain, and at this lower level the stream will begin to carve out a new flood plain. As time passes, remnants of the old flood plain

may be left standing on either side of the new one. Terraces that face each other across the stream at the same elevation are referred to as **paired terraces.**

Sometimes the downward erosion by streams creates **unpaired terraces** rather than paired ones. If the stream swings back and forth across the valley, slowly eroding as it moves, it may encounter resistant rock beneath the unconsolidated deposits. The exposed rock

Figure 9-33 A Roman mausoleum, partially buried in stream deposits, is exposed in this stream bank just north of Rome, Italy. In A.D. 50, when the mausoleum was built, the stream flowed at the same level as it does today, but the steep banks were not then present. Sometime after the third century A.D., this stream began to build up its flood plain until the valley floor stood at a level marked by the top of the modern bank. Thereafter the stream cut down to its present level, re-exposing the partially buried structure and leaving its old valley floor and flood plain standing as a low terrace. (See also Figure 9-32.) (*Photo by C. T. Stifter.*)

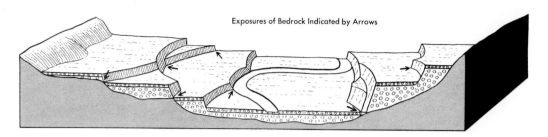

Figure 9-34 Unpaired terraces do not match across the stream that separates them. Here is one way in which they may form. The stream has cut through unconsolidated deposits within the valley. As it eroded downward, it also swept laterally across the valley and created a sloping surface. Lateral migration was stopped locally when the stream encountered resistant bedrock (see arrows) beneath the softer valley fill. This bedrock not only deflected the stream back across the valley but also protected remnants of the valley fill from further stream erosion and allowed them to be preserved as terraces. Because they are portions of a surface sloping across the valley, however, no single remnant matches any other on the opposite side of the river.

will then deflect the stream and prevent further erosion. A single terrace is left behind, with no corresponding terrace on the other side of the stream (see Figure 9-34).

Terraces, either paired or unpaired, may be cut into bedrock as well. A thin layer of sand and gravel usually rests on the beveled bedrock of these terraces.

Evidence That a Stream Cuts Its Own Valley

So far, we have been assuming that every stream has created its own valley. True, we have seen that other processes, such as slope wash and mass movement, have helped in val-

Figure 9-35 Terraces along the Madison River, Montana. The various levels have been formed by the river as it simultaneously swung laterally across, and cut downward into, deposits of sand and gravel laid down in front of a now-vanished glacier farther upstream. (*Photo by William C. Bradley.*)

ley enlargement; but we have taken it for granted that they rely on the streams to transport the material they produce and to create and maintain slopes on which they can operate. This assumption has not always been accepted, however. In fact, during the early 19th century, geologists devoted a great deal of time to demonstrating that valleys were not, as was then widely believed, great, original furrows in the earth's surface, along which the rivers flowed merely for want of a better place to go. Today, we are confident that most valleys have been created by the streams that flow through them and by the processes that these streams have encouraged. Let us review some of the evidence for this belief.

Most of us have observed at first hand the direct results of running water during a heavy rain. For instance, we can watch the actual headward erosion of small gullies in miniature drainage basins. What we are observing here is really a small stream in the process of forming and extending its valley. Merely by dipping up a cupful of water we can see evidence of the load carried by the stream, and we know that this debris must have come from the drainage basin of the stream. Erosion is going on as we watch, and the valley is growing larger as the stream moves the eroded material down-valley.

We know from observing modern streams that abrasion wears and polishes the beds and banks of bedrock and sometimes drills potholes deep into the rock floor. When we find these marks of stream activity high above the

162

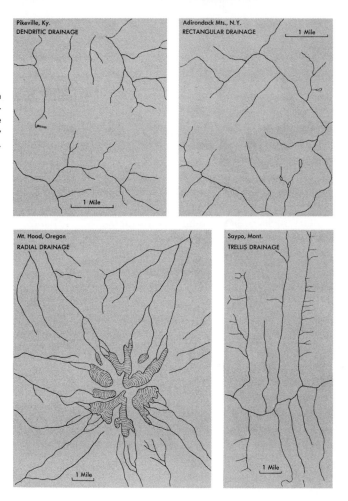

Figure 9-36 The over-all pattern developed by a stream system depends in part on the nature of the bedrock, and in part on the history of the area. See text for discussion.

Pikeville, Ky.
DENDRITIC DRAINAGE
1 Mile

Adirondack Mts., N.Y.
RECTANGULAR DRAINAGE
1 Mile

Mt. Hood, Oregon
RADIAL DRAINAGE
1 Mile

Saypo, Mont.
TRELLIS DRAINAGE
1 Mile

channel of a modern stream it is logical to assume that they were made by the stream when it was flowing at this higher level, and that the stream has since cut downward and deepened its valley.

As we have seen, a terrace records the fact that a stream once flowed at a higher level. And when we find terraces covered with sand and gravel high above a modern stream, again it is reasonable to assume that the stream has cut its way down to a lower level.

Along the walls of many streams, we can observe beds of rock formed from layers of sediments that were laid down in ancient seas, and we can match individual beds from one valley wall to the other. We know that these beds were laid down originally as continuous sheets and that some agency subsequently removed large sections of them. Barring evidence of crustal movement, we conclude that the stream flowing along the bottom of the valley has been responsible.

These and other arguments make it reasonably clear that a stream has created the valley through which it flows. No one argument or bit of evidence is final proof, of course. In fact, we know that some valleys were formed by earth movement and others were deepened by glaciers. Still, the weight of evidence points to the likelihood that most valleys have been formed by stream activity.

Stream Patterns and Stream Types

The over-all pattern developed by a system of streams and tributaries depends partly on the nature of the underlying rocks and partly on the history of the streams. Almost all streams follow a branching pattern in the sense that they receive tributaries; the tributaries, in turn, are joined by still smaller tributaries. But the manner of branching varies widely (see Figure 9-36).

A stream that resembles the branching habit of a maple, oak, or similar deciduous tree is called **dendritic,** "tree-like." A dendritic pattern develops when the underlying bedrock is uniform in its resistance to erosion and exercises no control over the direction of valley growth. This situation occurs when the bedrock is composed either of flat-lying sedimentary rocks or massive igneous or metamorphic rocks. The streams can cut as easily in one place as another; thus the dendritic pattern is, in a sense, the result of the random orientation of the streams (Figure 9-37).

Another type of stream pattern is **radial:** Streams radiate outward in all directions from a high central zone. Such a pattern is likely to develop on the flanks of a newly formed volcano, where the streams and their valleys radiate outward and downward from various points around the cone.

A **rectangular** pattern occurs when the underlying bedrock is criss-crossed by fractures that form zones of weakness particularly vulnerable to erosion. The master stream and its tributaries then follow courses marked by nearly right-angle bends.

Some streams, particularly in a belt of the Appalachian Mountains running from New York to Alabama, follow what is known as a **trellis** pattern. This pattern, like the rectangular one, is caused by zones in the bedrock that differ in their resistance to erosion. The trellis pattern usually, though not always, indicates that the region is underlain by alternate bands of resistant and nonresistant rock.

UNDERGROUND WATER

Earlier in this chapter we found that a portion of the water that falls on the surface of the earth seeps into the ground. In the following pages let us consider the movement and activity of this water.

Basic Distribution

Underground water, subsurface water, and **subterranean water** are all general terms used to refer to water in the pore spaces, cracks, tubes, and crevices of the consolidated and unconsolidated material beneath our feet.

Figure 9-37 Recent erosion has produced this dendritic stream pattern on a Wisconsin farm. (*Photo by Wisconsin Conservation Department.*)

Figure 9-38 A drop of water held between two fingers illustrates the molecular attraction that holds suspended water in the zone of aeration. Surface tension of the water is great enough to prevent its downward movement to the zone of saturation.

The study of underground water is largely an investigation of these openings and of what happens to the water that finds its way into them.

ZONES OF SATURATION AND AERATION Some of the water that moves down from the surface is caught by rock and earth materials and is checked in its downward progress. The zone in which this water is held is known as the **zone of aeration,** and the water itself is called **suspended water.** The spaces between particles in this zone are filled partly with water and partly with air. Two forces operate to prevent suspended water from moving deeper into the earth: (1) the molecular attraction exerted on the water by the rock and earth materials, and (2) the attraction exerted by the water particles on one another (see Figures 9-38, 9-39).

The zone of aeration can be subdivided into three belts: (1) **belt of soil moisture,** (2) **intermediate belt,** and (3) **capillary fringe.** Some of the water that enters the belt of soil moisture from the surface is used by plants, and some is evaporated back into the atmosphere. But some water also passes down to the intermediate belt, where it may be held by molecular attraction (as suspended water). Little movement occurs in the intermediate belt, except when rain or melting snow sends a new wave of moisture down from above.

Beneath the zone of aeration lies the **zone of saturation.** Here the openings in the rock and earth materials are completely filled with

ground water, and the surface between the zone of saturation and the zone of aeration is called the **ground-water table,** or simply the **water table.** The level of the water table fluctuates with variations in the supply of water coming down from the zone of aeration, with variations in the rate of discharge in the area, and with variations in the amount of ground water drawn off by plants and human beings.

It is the water below the water table, within the zone of saturation, that we shall focus on in the rest of this chapter.

Figure 9-39 Underground water's two major zones: zone of aeration and zone of saturation. The water table marks the upper surface of the zone of saturation. Within the zone of aeration is a belt of soil moisture, the source of moisture for many plants. From here, also, some moisture is evaporated back to the atmosphere. In many instances, this belt lies above an intermediate belt where water is held by molecular attraction and little movement occurs except during periods of rain or melting snow. In the capillary fringe, just above the water table, water rises a few inches to several feet from the zone of saturation, depending on the size of the interstices.

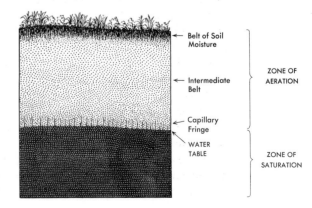

THE WATER TABLE   The water table is an irregular surface of contact between the zone of saturation and the zone of aeration. Below the water table lies the ground water; above it lies the suspended water. The thickness of the zone of aeration differs from one place to another, and the level of the water table fluctuates accordingly. In general, the water table tends to follow the irregularities of the ground surface, reaching its highest elevation beneath hills and its lowest elevation beneath valleys. Although the water table reflects variations in the ground surface, the irregularities in the water table are less pronounced.

In looking at the topography of the water table, let us consider an ideal situation. Figure 9-40 shows a hill underlain by completely homogeneous material. Assume that, initially, this material contains no water at all. Then a heavy rainfall comes along, and the water soaks slowly downward, filling the interstices at depth. In other words, a zone of saturation begins to develop. As more and more water seeps down, the upper limit of this zone continues to rise. The water table remains horizontal until it just reaches the level of the two valley bottoms on either side of the hill. Then, as additional water seeps down to the water table, some of it seeks an outlet into the valleys. But this added water is "supported" by the material through which it flows, and the water table is prevented from maintaining its flat surface. The water is slowed by the friction of its movement through the interstices and even, to some degree, by its own internal friction. Consequently, more and more water is piled up beneath the hill, and the water table begins to reflect the shape of the hill. The water flows away most rapidly along the steeper slope of the water table near the valleys, and most slowly on its gentler slope beneath the hill crest.

We can modify the shape of the ground-water surface by providing an artificial outlet for the water. For example, we can drill a well on the hill crest and extend it down into the saturated zone. Then, if we pumped out the ground water that flowed into the well, we would create a dimple in the water table. The more we pumped, the more pronounced the depression—called a **cone of depression**—would become.

Returning to our ideal situation, we find that if the supply of water from the surface were to be completely stopped, the water table under the hill would slowly flatten out as water discharged into the valleys. Eventu-

Figure 9-40   Ideally, the water table is a subdued reflection of the surface of the ground. In A and B, the water table rises as a horizontal plane until it reaches the level of the valley bottoms on either side of the hill. Thereafter, as more water soaks into the ground, it seeks an outlet toward the valleys. Were the movement of the water not slowed down by the material making up the hill, it would remain essentially horizontal. The friction caused by the water's passing through the material (and even to some extent the internal friction of the water itself) results in a piling up of water beneath the hill; the bulge is highest beneath the crest and lowest toward the valleys (C). The shape of the water table may be altered by pumping water from a well (D). The water flows to this new outlet and forms a cone of depression.

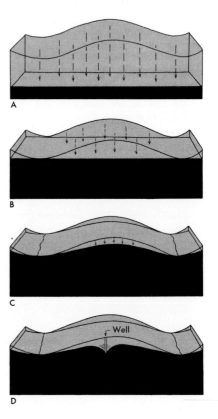

ally it would almost reach the level of the water table under the valley bottoms; then the flow would stop. This condition is common in desert areas where the rainfall is sparse.

Movement of Underground Water

Earlier in this chapter we considered the flow of water in stream channels at the earth's surface. In dealing with the underground we find that water seldom has such large channels in which to flow. Underground rivers do exist, but they are rare and generally occur only in areas of soluble rock such as limestone where water circulating through the rock can dissolve large caverns and tunnels.

When thinking of the flow of underground water we must generally change our scale of measurement from that to which we are accustomed to using for surface water. In the underground, although water does move, it usually moves very, very slowly. So we find that "feet per day" and, in some places, even "feet per year" provide a better scale of measurement. The main reason for this slow rate of flow is that the water must travel through small, confined passages if it is to move at all. It will be worthwhile, then, for us to consider the porosity and permeability of earth materials.

POROSITY The **porosity** of a rock is measured by the percentage of its total volume that is occupied by voids or interstices. The more porous a rock is, the greater the amount of open space it contains. Through these open spaces, underground water must find its way.

The range of porosity in earth materials is extremely great. Recently deposited muds (called **slurries**) may hold up to 90 per cent by volume of water, whereas unweathered igneous rocks such as granite, gabbro, or obsidian may hold only a fraction of 1 per cent. Unconsolidated deposits of clay, silt, sand, and gravel have porosities ranging from about 20 to as much as 50 per cent. But when these deposits have been consolidated into sedimentary rocks by cementation or compaction,

their porosity is sharply reduced. Average porosity values for individual rock types have little meaning because of the extreme variations within each type. In general, however, a porosity of less than 5 per cent is considered low; from 5 to 15 per cent represents medium porosity; and over 15 per cent is considered high.

PERMEABILITY Whether we find a supply of fresh ground water in a given area depends on the ability of the earth materials to transmit water, as well as on their ability to contain it. The ability to transmit underground water is termed **permeability.**

A permeable material that actually carries underground water is called an **aquifer,** from the Latin for "water" and "to bear." Perhaps the most effective aquifers are unconsolidated sand and gravel, sandstone, and some limestones. The permeability of limestone is usually due to solution that has enlarged the fractures and bedding planes into open passageways. The fractured zones of some of the denser rocks such as granite, basalt, and gabbro also act as aquifers, although the permeability of such zones decreases rapidly with depth (see discussion of joints in Chapter 4). Clay, shale, and most metamorphic and crystalline igneous rocks are generally poor aquifers.

Since the flow of underground water is usually very slow, it is largely laminar; in contrast, the flow of surface water is largely turbulent. There is one exception, however: the turbulent flow of water in large underground passageways formed in such rocks as cavernous limestone.

The energy that causes underground water to flow is derived from gravity. Gravity draws water downward to the water table; from there it flows through the ground to a point of discharge in a stream, lake, or spring. Just as surface water needs a slope to flow on, so must there be a slope for the flow of ground water. This is the slope of the water table, the **hydraulic gradient.** It is measured by dividing the length of flow (from the point of intake to the point of discharge) into the vertical distance between these two points, a distance called **head.** Therefore, hydraulic gradient is expressed as h/l, where h is head and l is length of flow from intake to discharge. Thus, if h is 10 feet and l is 100 feet, the hydraulic gradient is 0.1 or 10 per cent.

An equation to express the rate of water movement through a rock was proposed by the French engineer Henri Darcy in 1856. What is now known as Darcy's Law is essentially the same as his original equation. The law may be expressed as follows:

$$V = P\frac{h}{l}$$

where V is velocity, h is head, l the length of flow, and P a coefficient of permeability that depends on the nature of the rock in question. But since h/l is simply a way of expressing the hydraulic gradient, we may say that in a rock of constant permeability, the velocity of water will increase as the hydraulic gradient increases. Remembering that the hydraulic gradient and the slope of the ground-water table are the same thing, we may also say that the velocity of ground water varies with the slope of the water table. Other things being equal, the steeper the slope of the water table, the more rapid the flow. In ordinary aquifers, the rate of water flow has been estimated as not faster than 5 feet per day and not slower than 5 feet per year. It is true, however, that rates of over 400 feet a day and as low as a few inches a year have been recorded.

Figure 9-41 The flow of ground water through uniformly permeable material is suggested here. Movement is not primarily along the ground-water table; rather, particles of water define broadly looping paths that converge toward the outlet and may approach it from below. (*Redrawn from M. King Hubbert, "The Theory of Ground-water Motion," J. Geol., XLVIII, 1940, p. 930.*)

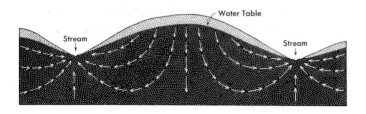

The movement of underground water down the slope of the water table is only a part of the picture, for the water is also in motion at depth. Water moves downward from the water table in broad looping curves toward some effective discharge agency, such as a stream, as suggested in Figure 9-41. The water feeds into the stream from all possible directions, including straight up through the bottom of the channel. We can explain this curving path as a compromise between the force of gravity and the tendency of water to flow laterally in the direction of the slope of the water table. This tendency toward lateral flow is actually the result of the movement of water toward an area of lower pressure, the stream channel in Figure 9-41. The resulting movement is neither directly downward nor directly toward the channel, but is rather along curving paths to the stream.

Ground Water in Nature

We have been assuming that ground water is free to move on indefinitely through a uniformly permeable material of unlimited extent. Actually subsurface conditions fall far short of this ideal situation. Some layers of rock material are more permeable than others, and the water tends to move rapidly through these beds in a direction more or less parallel to bedding planes. Even in a rock that is essentially homogeneous, the ground water tends to move in some preferred direction.

SIMPLE SPRINGS AND WELLS Underground water moves freely downward from the surface until it reaches an impermeable layer of rock or until it arrives at the water table. Then it begins to move laterally. Sooner or later it may flow out again at the surface of the ground in an opening called a **spring.**

Springs range from intermittent flows that disappear when the water table recedes during a dry season, through pint-sized trickles, to an effluence of 900 million gallons daily, the abundant discharge of springs along a 10-mile stretch of the Fall River in California.

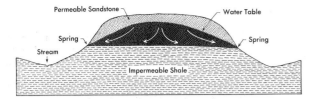

Figure 9-42 Nature seldom, if ever, provides uniformly permeable material. In this diagram, a hill is capped by permeable sandstone and overlies impermeable shale. Water soaking into the sandstone from the surface is diverted laterally by the impermeable beds. Springs result where the water table intersects the surface at the contact of the shale and sandstone.

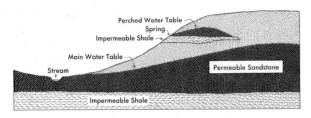

Figure 9-43 A perched water table results when ground water collects over an impermeable zone and is separated from the main water table.

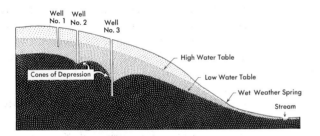

Figure 9-44 To provide a reliable source, a well must penetrate deep into the zone of saturation. In this diagram, Well No. 1 reaches only deep enough to tap the ground water during periods of high water table; a seasonal drop of this surface will dry up the well. Well No. 2 reaches to the low water table, but continued pumping may produce a cone of depression that will reduce effective flow. Well No. 3 is deep enough to produce reliable amounts of water, even with continued pumping during low water-table stages.

This wide variety of spring types is the result of underground conditions that vary greatly from one place to another. As a general rule, however, a spring results wherever the flow of ground water is diverted to a discharge zone at the surface (see Figure 9-42). For example, a hill made up largely of permeable

rock may contain a zone of impermeable material, as shown in Figure 9-43. Some of the water percolating downward will be blocked by this impermeable rock, and a small saturated zone will be built up. Since the local water level here is actually above the main water table, it is called a **perched water table.** The water that flows laterally along this impermeable rock may emerge at the surface as a spring. Springs are not confined to points where a perched water table flows from the surface, and it is clear that if the main water table intersects the surface along a slope, then a spring will form.

Even in impermeable rocks, permeable zones may develop as a result of fractures or solution channels. If these openings fill with water and are intersected by the ground surface, the water will issue forth as a spring.

A spring is the result of a natural intersection of the ground surface and the water table. But a well is an artificial opening cut down from the surface into the zone of saturation. A well is productive only if it is drilled into permeable rock and penetrates below the water table. The greater the demands that are made on a well, the deeper it must be drilled below the water table. Continuous pumping creates the cone of depression previously described, which distorts the water table and may reduce the flow of ground water into the well (see Figure 9-44). Wells drilled into fractured crystalline rock, such as granite, may produce a good supply of water at relatively shallow depths. But we cannot increase the yield of such wells appreciably by deepening them, since the number and size of the fractures commonly decrease the farther down we go (see Figure 9-45, p. 170).

Wells drilled into limestone that has been riddled by large solution passages may yield a heavy flow of water part of the time and no flow the rest of the time, simply because the water runs out rapidly through the large openings. Furthermore, water soaking down from the surface flows rapidly through limestone of this sort and may make its way to a well in a very short time. Consequently, water drawn from the

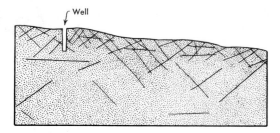

Figure 9-45 Wells may produce water from a fractured zone of impermeable rocks such as granite. The supply, however, is likely to be limited, not only because the size and number of fractures decrease with depth, but also because the fractures do not interconnect.

well may be contaminated, because there has not been enough time for impurities to be filtered out as the water passes from the surface to the well. In sandstone, on the other hand, the rate of flow is slow enough to permit the elimination of impurities even within a very short distance of underground flow. Harmful bacteria are destroyed in part by entrapment, in part by lack of food and by temperature changes, and in part by hostile substances or organisms met along the way, particularly in the soil.

ARTESIAN WATER Contrary to common opinion, artesian water does not necessarily come from great depths. But other definite conditions characterize an artesian water system: (1) The water is contained in a permeable layer, the aquifer, inclined so that one end is exposed to receive water at the surface; (2) the aquifer is capped by an impermeable layer; (3) the water in the aquifer is prevented from escaping either downward or off to the sides; and (4) there is enough head to force the water

above the aquifer wherever it is tapped. If the head is great enough, the water will flow out to the surface either as a well or a spring. The term **artesian** is derived from the name of a French town, Artois (originally called *Artesium* by the Romans), where this type of well was first studied.

THERMAL SPRINGS Springs that bring warm or hot water to the surface are called **thermal springs, hot springs,** or **warm springs.** A spring is usually regarded as a thermal spring if the temperature of its water is about 15°F higher than the mean temperature of the air. There are over 1,000 thermal springs in the western mountain regions of the United States, 46 in the Appalachian Highlands of the east, 6 in the Ouachita area in Arkansas, and 3 in the Black Hills of South Dakota.

Most of the western thermal springs derive their heat from masses of magma that have pushed their way into the crust almost to the surface and are now cooling. In the eastern group, however, the circulation of the ground water carries it to depths great enough for it to be warmed by the normal increase in earth heat (see "Thermal gradient" in Glossary).

GEYSERS A **geyser** is a special type of thermal spring that ejects water intermittently with considerable force. The word geyser comes from the name of a spring of this type in Iceland, *geysir*, probably based on the verb *geysa*, "to rush furiously."

Although the details of geyser action are still not understood, we do know that, in general, a geyser's behavior is caused by the arrangement of its plumbing and the proximity of a good supply of heat. Here is probably what happens. Ground water moving downward from the surface fills a natural pipe, or conduit, that opens upward to the surface. Hot igneous rocks, or the gases given off by such rocks, gradually heat the column of water in the pipe and raise its temperature toward the boiling point. Now, the higher the pressure on water, the higher its boiling point. And since water toward the bottom of the pipe is

Figure 9-46 The wells in the diagram meet the conditions that characterize an artesian system: (1) an inclined aquifer, (2) capped by an impermeable layer, (3) with water prevented from escaping either downward or laterally, and (4) sufficient head to force the water above the aquifer wherever it is tapped. In the well at the right, the head is great enough to force water out at the surface.

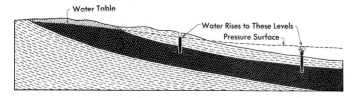

Figure 9-47 Old Faithful in Yellowstone National Park is America's most widely known geyser. The periodic eruption of a geyser is due to the particular pattern of its plumbing and its proximity to a liberal source of heat and ground water. (*Photo by Barton W. Knapp.*)

under the greatest pressure, it must be heated to a higher temperature than the water above before it will come to a boil. Eventually the column of water becomes so hot that either a slight increase in temperature or a slight decrease in pressure will cause it to boil. At this critical point, the water near the base of the pipe is heated to the boiling point. The water then passes to steam and, as it does so, expands, pushing the water above it toward the surface. But this raising of the heated col-

umn of water reduces the pressure acting upon it, and it, too, begins to boil. The energy thus developed throws the water and steam high into the air, producing the spectacular action characteristic of many geysers. After the eruption has spent itself, the pipe is again filled with water and the whole process begins anew.

We can compare this theoretical cycle with that of Old Faithful Geyser in Yellowstone National Park (see Figure 9-47). The first indication of a coming eruption at Old

Figure 9-48 Steam rises from a myriad of vents in Yellowstone's Geyser Basin. (*Photo by William C. Bradley.*)

Faithful is the quiet flow of water in a fountain some 4 to 8 feet high. This preliminary activity lasts for a few seconds and then subsides. It represents the first upward push of the column of water described in our theoretical case. This push reduces the pressure and thereby lowers the boiling point of the water in the pipe. Consequently, the water passes to steam; and less than a minute after the preliminary fountain, the first of the violent eruptions takes place. Steam and boiling water are thrown 120 to 170 feet into the air. The entire display lasts about 4 minutes. Emptied by the eruption, the tube then gradually refills with ground water, the water is heated, and in approximately 1 hour the same cycle is repeated. The actual time between eruptions of Old Faithful averages about 65 minutes but may be from 30 to 90 minutes.

Recharge of Ground Water

As we have seen, the ultimate source of most underground water is precipitation that finds its way below the surface through either natural means or through artificial means.

Some of the water from precipitation seeps into the ground, reaches the zone of saturation, and raises the water table. Continuous measurements over long periods of time at many places throughout the United States show an intimate connection between water level and rainfall (see Figure 9-49). Since water moves relatively slowly in the zone of aeration and the zone of saturation, fluctuations in the water table usually lag behind fluctuations in rainfall.

In many localities, the natural recharge of the underground supplies cannot keep pace with man's demands for ground water. Consequently, attempts are sometimes made to recharge these supplies artificially. On Long Island, New York, for example, water that has been pumped out for air-conditioning purposes is returned to the ground through special recharging wells or, in winter, through idle wells that are used in summer for air-conditioning. In the San Fernando Valley, California, surplus water from the Owens Valley aqueduct is fed into the underground in an attempt to keep the local water table at a high level.

Figure 9-49 Relationship between the water level in an observation well near Antigo, Wisconsin, and precipitation, as shown by records from 1945 to 1952. The water table reflects the changes in precipitation. The graphs represent 3-year running monthly averages. For example, 2.3 inches of precipitation for May means that precipitation averaged 2.3 inches per month from May 1947 to May 1950, inclusive. (*From A. H. Harder and William J. Drescher, Ground Water Conditions in Southwestern Langlade County, Wisconsin. Washington, D.C.: U.S. Geological Survey, Water Supply Paper, 1954.*)

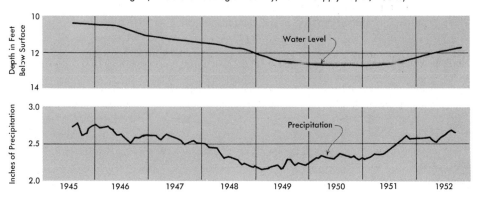

Caves and Related Features

Caves are probably the most spectacular examples of the handiwork of underground water. In dissolving great quantities of solid rock in its downward course, the water fashions large rooms, galleries, and underground stream systems as the years pass. In many caves, the water deposits calcium carbonate as it drips off the ceilings and walls, building up fantastic shapes of a material known as dripstone (see Figure 9-50).

Caves of all sizes tend to develop in highly soluble rocks such as limestone ($CaCO_3$), and small ones occur in the sedimentary rock dolomite [$CaMg(CO_3)_2$]. Rock salt ($NaCl$), gypsum ($CaSO_4 2H_2O$), and similar rock types are the victims of such rapid solution that underground caverns usually collapse under the weight of overlying rocks before erosion can open them at the surface.

Calcite, the main component of limestone, is highly insoluble in pure water. But when the mineral is attacked by water containing small amounts of carbonic acid, it undergoes rapid chemical weathering; and most natural water does contain carbonic acid (H_2CO_3), the combination of water with carbon dioxide. The carbonic acid reacts with the calcite to form calcium bicarbonate, $Ca(HCO_3)_2$, a soluble substance that is then removed in solution. If not redeposited, it eventually reaches the ocean.

The first signs of solution in limestone usually appear along original lines of weakness, such as bedding surfaces or fractures. As water seeps into these areas, it dissolves some of the rock and enlarges the openings. The dissolved material is moved onward by the underground water and is either redeposited or discharged into streams. As time passes, the openings grow larger and larger, until finally they form large passageways. Whether this cave-forming activity goes on above the water table, at the water table, or at some distance beneath it is a question that is still being argued. Most investigators, however, believe that caves are usually formed below the water table and are exposed later on, when the water table in the area is lowered by downward-cutting surface streams.

Regardless of where caves are originally formed, we know that the weird stone formations so characteristic of most of them must have developed above the water table, when the caves were filled with air. These bizarre shapes are composed of calcite deposited by underground water that has seeped down

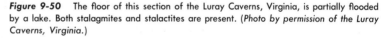

Figure 9-50   The floor of this section of the Luray Caverns, Virginia, is partially flooded by a lake. Both stalagmites and stalactites are present. (*Photo by permission of the Luray Caverns, Virginia.*)

through the zone of aeration. They develop either as **stalactites,** looking like stony icicles hanging from the cave roof (Greek, *stalactos,* "oozing out in drops") or as **stalagmites,** heavy posts growing up from the floor (Greek, *stalagmos,* "a dropping or dripping"). When a stalactite and a stalagmite meet, a **column** is formed.

A stalactite forms as water charged with calcium bicarbonate in solution seeps through the cave roof. Drop after drop forms on the ceiling and then falls to the floor. But during the few moments that each drop clings to the ceiling, a small amount of evaporation takes place; some carbon dioxide is lost, and a small amount of calcium carbonate is deposited. Over the centuries, a large stalactite may gradually develop. Part of the water that falls to the cave floor runs off, and part is evaporated. This evaporation again causes the deposition of calcite, and a stalagmite begins to grow upward to meet the stalactite hanging down.

On the ground surface above soluble rock material, depressions sometimes develop that reflect areas where the underlying rock has been carried away in solution. These depressions, called **sinkholes** or merely **sinks,** usually form when the surface collapses into a large cavity beneath. Surface water may then drain through the sinkholes to the underground, or if their subterranean outlets become clogged, they may fill with water to form lakes. An area with numerous sinkholes is said to display **karst topography,** from the name of a plateau in Yugoslavia and northeastern Italy where this type of landscape is extensively developed.

SUMMARY

Water near and at the earth's surface moves from oceans to atmosphere to land and back to the oceans in the hydrologic cycle.

The flow of most water is turbulent, but sometimes, particularly beneath the surface, the flow is laminar. Water in a stream flows down a gradient, has a velocity, and is measured in terms of discharge per unit time. As discharge increases, so also does width, depth, and velocity of a stream.

The base level of a stream is the point below which it cannot erode. Material carried by a stream may be in solution, or in suspension, or moved along the channel floor as bed load. Erosion, most rapid in periods of flood is accomplished by direct lifting, by abrasion, impact, and solution. Deposition takes place when a stream's velocity (and hence its energy) decreases.

In general, stream valleys are characterized by divides, valley walls, stream channels, and usually by flood plains. A valley widens as a stream erodes in its channel and as mass movement and slope erosion push back the valley walls. Narrow valleys include waterfalls and rapids. Broad valleys have flood plains, meanders, braided streams, natural levees, and stream terraces.

Most valleys are cut by the streams that flow through them. The patterns of stream channels reflect the nature of the underlying rock and the stream history.

Water beneath the ground is distributed largely in a zone of saturation separated from the surface by a zone of aeration. The top of the zone of saturation is the ground water table and is very often a subdued reflection of the topography.

The porosity of earth materials is a function of the total void space it contains. Permeability is the ability of material to transmit water.

Most ground water flow is laminar and is driven by gravity. Velocity equals $P\frac{h}{l}$, where P is the coefficient of permeability, h is the head and l is the length of flow.

Wells draw water from the zone of saturation. Artesian wells are those in which water rises above the top of the aquifer. Springs occur when the ground surface intersects the water table. Thermal springs are heated by still-warm igneous rocks and by the normal increase of earth's temperature with depth. Geysers are thermal springs marked by periodic, violent eruptions.

Most caves result from the solution of limestone by underground water. After the caves have been formed they may be decorated by the deposition of new limestone in the form of stalactites and stalagmites. Karst topography is characterized by sink holes which mark the collapse of rock into underlying caves.

ADDITIONAL READING

Bretz, J Harlan, "Vadose and Phreatic Features of Limestone Caverns," *J. Geol.*, L (1942), 675–811.

De Wiest, Roger J., *Geohydrology*. New York: John Wiley & Sons, 1965.

Hjulstrem, Filip. "Transportation of Detritus by Running Water," in *Recent Marine Sedients, A Symposium*, ed. Parker D. Trask. Tulsa: Am. Assoc. Petroleum Geol. (1939), 3–31.

Holland, H. D., and others, "On Some Aspects of the Chemical Evolution of Cave Waters," *J. Geol.*, LXXII (1964), 36–67.

Hoyt, William G., and Walter B. Langbein, *Floods*. Princeton: Princeton University Press, 1955.

Hubbert, M. King, "The Theory of Ground Water Motion," *J. Geol.*, XLVIII (1940), 785–944.

Kuenen, P. H., *Realms of Water*. New York: John Wiley & Sons, 1955.

Leopold, Luna B., "Rivers," *American Scientist*, L (1962), 511–37.

———, Gordon Wolman, and John P. Miller, *Fluvial Processes in Geomorphology*. San Francisco: W. H. Freeman and Co., 1964.

Meinzer, O. E., *The Occurrence of Ground Water in the United States*. Washington, D.C.: U.S. Geological Survey Water-Supply Paper 489, 1923.

———, *Ground Water in the United States, A Summary*. Washington, D.C.: U.S. Geological Survey Water-Supply Paper 836–D, 1939.

———, ed., *Hydrology (Physics of the Earth, IX)*. New York: McGraw-Hill Book Co., 1942.

Todd, D. K., *Ground Water Hydrology*. New York: John Wiley & Sons, 1959.

10

Glaciers, Mass Movement, and Wind

Having considered the activity and effect of water both at the surface and underground, here we look at water in another form, the ice of glaciers. We will then examine landslides and related phenomena (generally referred to as the mass movement of surface material), and finally study the movement of the atmosphere as a geologic agent.

176

GLACIERS

The seas and rivers of moving ice known as glaciers have attracted inquisitive men deep into the Arctic, Antarctic, and mountainous regions of the world. There they have discovered that glaciers are active agents of erosion, transportation, and deposition, and that these impressive masses of ice were far more widespread in the past than they are now. Geologists have learned, too, that the ice of the last great glacial period has modified and molded great stretches of landscape in what are now the temperate zones.

Formation of Glacier Ice

A **glacier** is a mass of ice that has been formed by the recrystallization of snow, and that flows forward, or has flowed at some time in the past, under the influence of gravity. This definition eliminates the pack ice formed from sea water in polar latitudes and—by convention—icebergs, even though they are large fragments broken from the seaward end of glaciers.

Like surface streams and underground reservoirs, glaciers depend on the oceans for their nourishment. Some of the water drawn up from the oceans by evaporation falls on the land in the form of snow. If the climate is right, part of the snow may last through the summer without melting. Gradually, as the years pass, the accumulation may grow deeper and deeper, until at last a glacier is born.

In areas where the winter snowfall exceeds the amount of snow that melts away during the summer, stretches of perennial snow known as snowfields cover the landscape. At the lower limit of a snowfield lies the **snow line.** Above the snow line, glacier ice may collect in the more sheltered areas of the snowfields. The exact position of the snow line varies from one climatic region to another. In polar regions, for example, it reaches down to sea level, but near the equator it recedes to the mountain tops. In the high mountains of East Africa, for instance, it ranges from elevations of 15,000 to 18,000 feet. The highest snow lines in the world are in the dry regions known as the "horse latitudes," which lie between the parallels 20° to 30° north and south of the equator. Here the snow line reaches higher than 20,000 feet.

Fresh snow falls as a feathery aggregate of complex and beautiful crystals with a great variety of patterns. All the crystals are basically hexagonal, however, and all reflect their internal arrangement of hydrogen and oxygen atoms (see Figure 10-1). Snow is not frozen rain; rather, it forms from the condensation of water vapor at temperatures below freezing.

After snow has been lying on the ground for some time, it changes from a light, fluffy mass to a heavier, granular material called **firn,** or névé (nay-vay). "Firn" derives from a Greek adjective meaning "of last year," and "névé" is a French word from the Latin for "snow." Solid remnants of large snow banks, those tiresome vestiges of winter, are largely firn.

Several processes are at work in the transformation of snow into firn. The first is **sublimation,** a general term for the process of a

Figure 10-1 Snowflakes exhibit a wide variety of patterns, all hexagonal and all reflecting the internal arrangement of hydrogen and oxygen. It is from snowflakes that glacier ice eventually forms.

solid material passing into the gaseous state without first becoming a liquid. In sublimation, molecules of water vapor escape from the snow, particularly from the edges of the flakes. Some of the molecules attach themselves to the center of the flakes, where they adapt themselves to the structure of the snow crystals. Then, as time passes, one snowfall follows another, and the granules that have already begun to grow as a result of sublimation are packed tighter and tighter together under the pressure of the overlying snow.

Water has the unique property of increasing in volume when it freezes; conversely it decreases in volume as the ice melts. But the cause and effect may be interchanged: If added pressure on the ice squeezes the molecules closer together and reduces its volume, the ice may melt. In fact, if the individual granules are in contact, they begin to melt with only a slight increase in pressure. The resulting meltwater trickles down and refreezes on still lower granules at points where they are not yet in contact. All through this process, however, the basic hexagonal structure of the original snow crystals is maintained.

Gradually, then, a layer of firn granules, ranging from a fraction of a millimeter to approximately 3 or 4 millimeters in diameter,

is built up. The thickness of this layer varies, but 100 feet seems to be average on many mountain glaciers.

The firn itself undergoes further change as continued pressure forces out most of the air between the granules, reduces the space between them, and finally transforms it into **glacier ice,** a true solid composed of interlocking crystals. It takes on a blue-gray color from the air and the fine dirt that it contains.

The ice crystals that make up glacier ice are minerals; the mass of glacier ice, made up of many interlocking crystals, is a metamorphic rock, for it has been transformed from snow into firn and eventually into glacier ice. Later, we will see that glacier ice itself undergoes further metamorphism.

CLASSIFICATION OF GLACIERS   The glaciers of the world fall into three principal classifications: (1) valley glaciers, (2) piedmont glaciers, and (3) ice sheets.

Valley glaciers are streams of ice that flow down the valleys of mountainous areas (see Figure 10-2). Like streams of running water, they vary in width, depth, and length. A branch of the Hubbard Glacier in Alaska is 75 miles long, whereas some of the valley glaciers that dot the higher reaches of the western moun-

Figure 10-2 Mountain glaciers in the St. Elias Range, Alaska. (*Photo by Austin Post.*)

tains of the United States are only a few hundred yards in length. Valley glaciers that are nourished on the flanks of high mountains and that flow down the mountain sides are sometimes called **mountain glaciers** or **Alpine glaciers.** Very small mountain glaciers are referred to as **cliff glaciers, hanging glaciers,** or **glacierets.** A particular type of valley glacier sometimes grows up in areas where large masses of ice are dammed by a mountain barrier along the coast; some of the ice escapes through valleys in the mountain barrier to form an **outlet glacier,** as it has done along the coasts of Greenland and Antarctica.

Piedmont glaciers form when glaciers emerge from their valleys and spread out to form an apron of moving ice on the plains below.

Ice sheets are broad, moundlike masses of glacier ice that tend to spread radially under their own weight. The Vatna Glacier of Iceland is a small ice sheet, 750 feet thick, measuring about 75 miles by 100 miles. A localized sheet of this sort is sometimes called an **icecap.** The term **continental glacier** is usually reserved for great ice sheets that obscure the mountains and plains of large sections of a continent, such as those of Greenland and Antarctica. On Greenland, ice exceeds 10,000 feet in thickness near the center of the icecap. The greatest known thickness of ice in Antarctica is more than 14,000 feet, in Marie Byrd Land.

Distribution of Modern Glaciers. Modern glaciers cover approximately 10 per cent of the land area of the world, about 5,780,000

Figure 10-3 Isolated peaks protrude through the Antarctic icecap. (*Photo by F. J. Rootes.*)

square miles; of this, the Greenland and Antarctica ice sheets account for about 96 per cent. The Antarctica ice sheet covers approximately 4,860,000 square miles, and the Greenland sheet covers about 670,000 square miles. Small icecaps and numerous mountain glaciers scattered around the world account for the remaining 4 per cent.

NOURISHMENT AND WASTAGE OF GLACIERS When the weight of a mass of snow, firn, and ice above the snow line becomes great enough, movement begins and a glacier is created. The moving stream flows downward across the snow line until it reaches an area where the loss through evaporation and melting is so great that the forward edge of the glacier can push no farther. A glacier, then, can be divided into two zones: (1) **a zone of accumulation** and (2) **a zone of wastage** (Figure 10-4).

The position of the front of a glacier depends on the relationship between the glacier's rate of nourishment and its rate of wastage. When nourishment just balances wastage, the

Figure 10-4 A glacier is marked by a zone of accumulation and a zone of wastage. Within a glacier, ice may lie either in the zone of fracture or deeper in the zone of flow. A valley glacier originates in a basin, the cirque, and is separated from the headwall of the cirque by a large crevasse, the bergschrund.

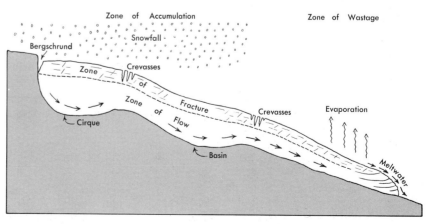

front becomes stationary and the glacier is said to be in equilibrium. This balance seldom lasts for long, however, for a slight change in either nourishment or wastage will cause the front to advance or melt back.

Below the snow line, wastage takes place through a double process of evaporation and melting known as **ablation.** If a glacier terminates in a body of water, great blocks of ice break off and float away in a process called **calving.** This is the action that produces the icebergs of the polar seas.

GLACIER MOVEMENT Except in rare cases, glaciers move only a few inches or at most a few feet a day. That they actually do move, however, can be demonstrated in several ways. The most conclusive test is to measure the movement directly, by emplacing a row of stakes across a valley glacier. As time passes, the stakes move downvalley with the advancing ice, the center stakes more rapidly than those near the valley walls. A second source of evidence is provided by the distribution of rock

material on the surface of a glacier. When we examine the boulders and cobbles lying along a valley glacier, we find that many of them could not have come from the walls immediately above, and that the only possible source lies upvalley. We can infer, then, that the boulders must have been carried to their present position on the back of the glacier. Another indication of glacier movement is that when a glacier melts, it often exposes a rock floor that has been polished, scratched, and grooved. It is simplest to explain this surface by assuming that the glacier actually moved across the rock floor, producing the observed effects with embedded debris.

Clearly, then, a glacier does move. In fact, different parts of it move at different rates. But though we know a good bit about how a glacier flows forward, certain phases are not yet clearly understood. In any event, we can distinguish two zones of movement: (1) an upper zone between 100 and 200 feet thick, which reacts like a brittle substance—that is, it breaks sharply rather than undergoing grad-

Figure 10-5 Small glaciers on Ellesmere Island, Northwest Territory, Canada, flow from a larger glacier through narrow valleys and down into a broader valley. (*Photo by Austin Post.*)

Figure 10-6 Patterns of ice flow on the Seward lobe of the Malaspina Glacier, Alaska. (*Photo by Austin Post.*)

ual, permanent distortion, and (2) a lower zone, which, because of the pressure of the overlying ice, behaves like a plastic substance (see the section on behavior of material in Chapter 8). The first is the **zone of fracture;** the second is the **zone of flow.**

As plastic deformation takes place in the zone of flow, the brittle ice above is carried along. But the zone of flow moves forward at different rates—faster in some parts, more slowly in others—and the rigid ice in the zone of fracture is unable to adjust itself to this irregular advance. Consequently, the upper part of the glacier cracks and shatters, giving rise to a series of deep, treacherous **crevasses.**

A glacier attains its greatest velocity somewhere near the valley floor, in midstream, for the sides and bottom are retarded by friction against the valley walls and beds. In this respect the movement of an ice stream resembles that of a stream of water.

The mechanics of ice flow are still a matter of study—a study made difficult by the fact that we cannot actually observe the zone of flow, since it lies concealed within the glacier. Yet the ice from the zone of flow eventually emerges at the snout of the glacier, and there it can be studied. We find that by the

time it has emerged it is brittle; but it retains the imprint of movement by flow. The individual ice crystals are now several inches in size; in contrast, crystals in ice newly formed from firn measure but a fraction of an inch. We can conclude that the ice crystals have grown by recrystallization as they passed through the zone of flow. The ice at the snout is also marked by bands that represent shearing and differential movement within the glacier. Recrystallization has taken place along many of the old shear planes, and along others the debris carried forward by the ice has been concentrated. These observations suggest that some movement in the zone of flow has taken place as a result of shearing.

Results of Glaciation

MOVEMENT OF MATERIAL Glaciers have special ways of eroding, transporting, and depositing earth materials. A valley glacier, for example, acquires debris by means of frost action, landsliding, and avalanching. Fragments pried loose by frost action clatter down from neighboring peaks and come to rest on the back of the glacier. And great snowbanks, unable to maintain themselves on the steep slopes of the mountain-sides, avalanche downward to the glacier, carrying along quantities of rock debris and rubble. This material is buried beneath fresh snow or avalanches, or else tumbles into gaping crevasses in the zone of fracture and is carried along by the glacier.

When a glacier flows across a fractured or jointed stretch of bedrock, it may lift up large blocks of stone and move them off. This process is known as **plucking,** or **quarrying.** The force of the ice flow itself may be strong enough to pick up the blocks, and the action may be helped along by the great pressures that operate at the bottom of a glacier. Suppose the moving ice encounters a projection of rock jutting up from the valley floor. As the glacier ice forces itself over and around the projection, the pressure on the ice is increased and some of the ice around the rock may melt. This meltwater trickles toward a place of lower pressure, perhaps into a crack in the rock itself. There it refreezes, forming a strong bond between the glacier and the rock. Continued movement by the glacier may then tear the block out of the valley floor.

At the heads of valley glaciers, plucking and frost action sometimes work together to pry rock material loose. Along the back walls of the collection basins of mountain glaciers, great hollows called **cirques** (pronounced sirks), or **amphitheaters,** develop in the mountain-side. As the glacier begins its movement downslope, it pulls slightly away from the back wall, forming a crevasse known as a **bergschrund.** One wall of the bergschrund is formed by the glacier ice; the other is formed by the nearly vertical cliff of bedrock. During the day, meltwater pours into the bergschrund and fills the openings in the rock. At night, the water freezes, producing pressures great enough to loosen blocks of rock from the cliff. Eventually, these blocks are incorporated into the glacier and are moved away from the headwall of the cirque.

The streams that drain from the front of a melting glacier are charged with **rock flour,** very fine particles of pulverized rock. So great is the volume of this material that it gives

Figure 10-7 Rock fragments embedded in glacier ice often gouge scratches or striations in bedrock as the ice moves across it. This exposure in northeastern Wisconsin reveals that ice movement was parallel to the orientation of the striations. (*Photo by Raymond C. Murray.*)

the water a characteristically grayish-blue color similar to that of skim milk. Here, then, is further evidence of the grinding power of the glacier mill.

Glaciers also pick up rock material by means of abrasion. As the moving ice drags rocks, boulders, pebbles, sand, and silt across the glacier floor, the bedrock is cut away as though by a great rasp or file. And the cutting tools themselves are abraded. It is this mutual abrasion that produces rock flour and gives a high **polish** to many of the rock surfaces across which a glacier has ridden. But abrasion sometimes produces scratches, or **striations,** on both the bedrock floor and on the grinding tools carried by the ice. More extensive abrasion creates deep gouges, or **grooves,** in the bedrock. The striations and grooves along a bedrock surface show the direction of the glacier's movement.

EROSIONAL EFFECTS   The erosional effects of glaciers are not limited to the fine polish and striations mentioned above, however. For glaciers also operate on a much grander scale, producing spectacularly sculptured peaks and valleys in the mountainous areas of the world.

Cirques. As we have seen, a cirque is the basin from which a mountain glacier flows, the focal point for the glacier's nourishment. After a glacier has disappeared and all its ice has melted away, the cirque is revealed as a great amphitheater or bowl, with one side partially cut away. The back wall rises a few hundred feet to over 3,000 feet above the floor, often as an almost vertical cliff. The floor of a cirque lies below the level of the low ridge separating it from the valley of the glacier's descent. A lake that forms in the bedrock basin of the cirque floor is called a **tarn** (Figure 10-8).

Horns, Arêtes, and Cols. A **horn** is a spire of rock formed by the headward erosion of a ring of cirques around a single high mountain. When the glaciers originating in these cirques finally disappear, they leave a steep, pyramidal mountain outlined by the headwalls of the cirques. The classic examples of a horn is the famous Matterhorn of Switzerland.

An **arête** (pronounced a-ret′, from the French for "fishbone," "ridge," or "sharp edge") is formed when a number of cirques gnaw into a ridge from opposite sides. The ridge becomes knife-edged, jagged, and serrated.

Figure 10-8 A tarn occupies the basin in this cirque in the Rocky Mountains. (*Photo by Austin Post.*)

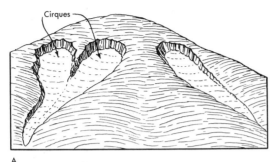

Cirques

A

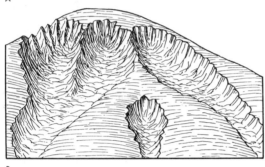

B

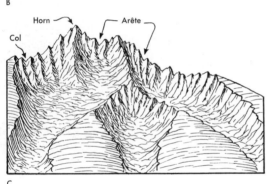

Horn — Arête —

Col

C

Figure 10-9 The progressive development of cirques, horns, arêtes, and cols. In the first diagram, valley glaciers have produced cirques; but since erosion has been moderate, much of the original mountain surface has been unaffected by the ice. The result of more extensive glacial erosion is shown in the second diagram. In the final drawing, glacial erosion has affected the entire mass and has produced not only cirques but also a matterhorn, cols, and jagged, knife-edged arêtes. (*Redrawn from William Morris Davis, "The Colorado Front Range," Annals Assoc. Am. Geo., I, 1911, p. 57.*)

A **col** (from the Latin *collum*, "neck"), or pass, is fashioned when two cirques erode headward into a ridge from opposite sides. When their headwalls meet, they cut a sharp-edged gap in the ridge.

Glaciated Valley. Rather than fashion their own valley, glaciers probably follow the course of pre-existing valleys, modifying them in a variety of ways; but usually the valleys have a broad **U-shaped** cross-profile, whereas mountain valleys created exclusively by streams have narrow, V-shaped cross-profiles. Since the tongue of an advancing glacier is relatively broad, it tends to broaden and deepen the V-shaped stream valleys, transforming them into broad, U-shaped troughs. And since the moving body of ice had difficulty manipulating the curves of a stream valley, it tends to straighten and simplify the course of the original valley. In this process of straightening, the ice snubs off any spurs of land that extend into it from either side. The cliffs thus formed are shaped like large triangles or flatirons with their apex upward, and are called **truncated spurs** (see Figures 10-10, 10-11, 10-12).

Glaciers also give a mountain valley a characteristic longitudinal profile from the cirque downward. The course of a glaciated valley is marked by a series of **rock basins,** probably formed by plucking in areas where the bedrock was shattered or closely jointed. Between the basins are relatively flat stretches underlain by rock more resistant to plucking. As time passes, the rock basins may fill up with water, producing a series of lakes that are sometimes referred to as **pater noster lakes** because they resemble a string of beads.

Hanging valleys are another characteristic of mountainous areas that have undergone glaciation. The mouth of a hanging valley is left stranded high above the main valley through which a glacier has passed. As a result, streams from hanging valleys plummet into the main valley in a series of falls and plunges. Hanging valleys may be formed by processes other than glaciation, but they are almost always present in mountainous areas that formerly supported glaciers and are thus very characteristic of past valley glaciation.

What has happened to leave these valleys stranded high above the main valley floor? During the time when glaciers still moved down the mountains, the greatest accumulation of ice would tend to travel along the central valley. Consequently, the erosive action there would be greater than in the tributary valleys, with their relatively small glaciers, and the main valley floor would be cut correspondingly deeper. This action would be even more pronounced where the main valley was underlain by rock that was more susceptible to erosion than the rock under the tributary valleys. Fi-

Figure 10-10 A mountainous area (A) before, (B) during, and (C) after glaciation. (Redrawn from William Morris Davis, "The Sculpture of Mountains by Glaciers," Scottish Geographical Magazine, XXII, 1906, pp. 80, 81, and 83.)

Figure 10-11 A long valley glacier with many tributaries, in Alaska. (Photo by U.S. Army Air Force.)

Figure 10-12 This valley in the Beartooth Mountains, Montana, shows the typical U-shaped profile of a glaciated valley. (Photo by George McGill.)

A

B

C

nally, some hanging valleys were probably created by the straightening and widening action of a glacier on the main valley. In any event, the difference in level between the tributary valleys and the main valley does not become apparent until the glacier has melted away.

Cutting deep into the coasts of Alaska, Norway, Greenland, Labrador, Chile, and New Zealand are deep, narrow arms of the sea—**fiords.** Actually, these inlets are stream valleys that were modified by glacier erosion and then partially filled by the sea (see Figure 10-13, p. 186). The deepest known fiord, in Chile, has a maximum depth of about 4,250 feet.

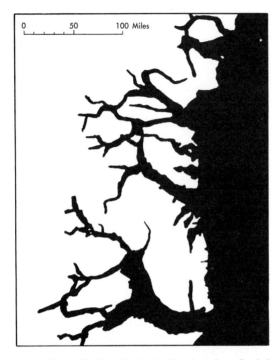

Figure 10-13 Glaciated valleys have been flooded by the sea (*black*) to produce these fiords along the coast of Greenland. (*Redrawn from Louise A. Boyd and others, "The Fiord Region of East Greenland," Am. Geog. Society, Special Publication No. 18, 1935, p. xii.*)

Figure 10-14 The range in the size of the particles composing till is very large. In this photograph of an exposure of till near Guilford, Connecticut, note the boulders and cobbles mixed with smaller particles ranging all the way down to colloid size. Spade gives scale. (*Photo by Sheldon Judson.*)

Some valleys have been modified by continental glaciers rather than by the valley glaciers that we have been discussing so far. The valleys occupied by the Finger Lakes of central New York State are good examples. These long, narrow lakes lie in the basins that were carved out by the ice of a continental glacier. As the great sheet of ice moved down from the north, its progress seems to have been checked by the northern scarp of the Appalachian Plateau. But some of the ice moved on up the valleys that had previously drained the plateau. The energy concentrated in the valleys was so great that the ice was able to scoop out the basins that are now filled by the Finger Lakes.

Asymmetric Rock Knobs and Hills. Glacier erosion of bedrock in many places produces small, rounded, asymmetric hills with gentle, striated, and polished slopes on one side and steeper slopes lacking polish and striations on the opposite side. An assemblage of these undulating knobs is referred to as **rôches moutonnées** (from the French for "rocks" plus "curved"). The now-gentle slope faced the advancing glacier and was eroded by abrasion. The opposite slope has been steepened by the plucking action of the ice as it rode over the knob. Large individual hills have the same asymmetric profiles as the smaller hills. Here, too, the gentle slope faced the moving ice.

TYPES OF GLACIAL DEPOSITS The debris carried along by a glacier is eventually deposited, either because the ice that holds it melts or, less commonly, because the ice smears the debris across the land surface.

The general term **drift** is applied to all deposits that are laid down directly by glaciers or that, as a result of a glacial activity, are laid down in lakes, oceans, or streams. The term dates from the days when geologists thought that the unconsolidated cover of sand and gravel blanketing much of Europe and America had been made to drift into its present position either by the sea or by icebergs. Drift can be divided into two general categories: **stratified** and **unstratified.**

Deposits of Unstratified Drift. Unstratified drift laid down directly by glacier ice is called **till.** It is composed of rock fragments of all sizes mixed together in random fashion, ranging all the way from boulders weighing several tons to tiny clay and colloid particles (see Figure 10-14). Many of the large pieces are striated, polished, and faceted as a result of the wear they underwent while being transported by the glaciers (Figure 10-15). Some of the material picked up along the way was smeared across the landscape during the glacier's progress, but most of it was dumped when the rate of wastage began to exceed the rate of nourishment and the glacier gradually melted away.

Till is deposited by receding glaciers in a great variety of topographic forms such as moraines and drumlins.

Moraines. Moraine is a general term used to describe many of the landforms that are composed largely of till. A **terminal moraine,** or **end moraine,** is a ridge of till that marks the utmost limit of a glacier's advance. These ridges range in size from ramparts hundreds of feet high to very low, interrupted heaps of debris. A terminal moraine forms when a glacier reaches the critical point of equilibrium—the point at which it wastes away at exactly the same rate as it is nourished. Although the front of the glacier is now stable, ice continues to push down from above, delivering a continuous supply of rock debris. As the ice melts in the zone of wastage, the debris is dumped and the terminal moraine grows. At the same time, water from the melting ice pours down over the till and sweeps part of it out in a broad flat fan

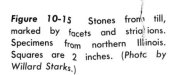
Figure 10-15 Stones from till, marked by facets and striations. Specimens from northern Illinois. Squares are 2 inches. (*Photo by Willard Starks.*)

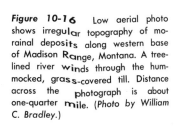
Figure 10-16 Low aerial photo shows irregular topography of morainal deposits along western base of Madison Range, Montana. A tree-lined river winds through the hummocked, grass-covered till. Distance across the photograph is about one-quarter mile. (*Photo by William C. Bradley.*)

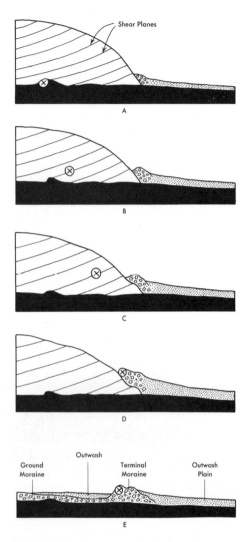

Figure 10-17 A sequence of diagrams to suggest the growth of a terminal moraine at the edge of a stable ice front. The progressive movement of a single particle (X) is shown. In *A*, it is moved by the ice from the bedrock floor. Forward motion of ice along a shear plane carries it ever closer to the stabilized ice margin, where finally it is deposited as a part of the moraine in diagram *D*. *E* represents the relation of the terminal moraine, ground moraine, and outwash after the final melting of the glacier.

that butts against the forward edge of the moraine like a giant ramp (Figure 10-17).

The terminal moraine of a mountain glacier is crescent-shaped, with the convex side extending downvalley. The terminal moraine of a continental ice sheet is a broad loop or series of loops t̶ raceable for many miles across the countryside.

Behind the terminal moraine, and at varying distances from it, a series of smaller ridges known as **recessional moraines** may build up. These ridges ma̶ rk the position where the glacier front was st̶ abilized temporarily during the retreat of the g̶ lacier.

Not all the rock debris carried by a glacier finds its way to the terminal and recessional moraines, however. A great deal of till is laid down as the m̶ ain body of the glacier melts to form gently roll̶ ing plains across the valley floor. Till in this form̶ , called a **ground moraine**, may be a thin vene̶ er lying on the bedrock, or it may form a dep̶ osit scores or even hundreds of feet thick, par̶ tially or completely clogging preglacial valle̶ ys.

Finally, va̶ lley glaciers produce two special types of morai̶ nes. While a valley glacier is still active, larg̶ e amounts of rubble keep tumbling down fro̶ m the valley walls, collecting along the side̶ of the glacier. When the ice melts, all this de̶ bris is stranded as a ridge along each side of th̶ e valley, forming a **lateral moraine.** At its d̶ ownvalley end, the lateral moraine grades in̶ to the terminal moraine.

The other s̶ pecial type of deposit produced by valley glaci̶ ers is a **medial moraine**, created when two vall̶ ey glaciers join to form a single ice stream; m̶ aterial formerly carried along on the edges of t̶ he separate glaciers is combined in a single moraine near the center of the enlarged glacier. A streak of this kind builds up whenever a tributary glacier joins a larger glacier in the main valley. Although medial moraines are very characteristic of living glaciers, they are seldom preserved as topographic features after the disappearance of the ice.

Drumlins. Drumlins are smooth, elongated hills composed largely of till. The ideal drumlin shape has an asymmetric profile with a blunt nose pointing in the direction from which the vanished glacier advanced, and with a gentler, longer slope pointing in the opposite direction. Drumlins range from 25 to 200 feet in height, the average somewhat less than 100 feet. Most drumlins are between a quarter-mile and a half-

Figure 10-18 This aerial photograph shows the drumloidal patterns of hills and intervening grooves formed parallel to the flow of glacier ice on the Nechako Plateau, British Columbia. Weedon Lake is $5\frac{1}{2}$ miles long. View is northeast in the direction of ice movement. (*Photo by U.S. Army Air Force.*)

Figure 10-19 Outwash forms at the snout of the Brady Glacier, Fairweather Range, Alaska. (*Photo by Austin Post.*)

mile in length, usually several times longer than they are wide.

In most areas, drumlins occur in clusters, or **drumlin fields.** In the United States, these are most spectacularly developed in New England, particularly around Boston; in eastern Wisconsin; in west-central New York State, particularly around Syracuse; in Michigan; and in certain sections of Minnesota. In Canada, extensive drumlin fields are located in western Nova Scotia and in northern Manitoba and Saskatchewan; Figure 10-18 shows a drumlin field in British Columbia.

Just how drumlins were formed is still not clear. Since their shape is a nearly perfect example of streamlining, it seems probable that they were formed deep within active glaciers in the zone of plastic flow.

Deposits of Stratified Drift. Stratified drift is ice-transported material that has been washed and sorted by glacial meltwaters according to particle size. Since water is a much more selective sorting agent than ice, deposits of stratified drift are laid down in recognizable layers, unlike the random arrangements of particles typical of till. Stratified drift occurs in outwash and kettle plains, eskers, kames, and varves—all discussed below.

Outwash Sand and Gravel. The sand and gravel that are carried outward by meltwater from the front of a glacier are referred to as **outwash.** As a glacier melts, streams of water heavily loaded with reworked till, or with material *washed* directly from the ice, weave a complex, braided pattern of channels across the land in front of the glacier (Figure 10-19).

These streams, choked with clay, silt, sand, and gravel, rapidly lose their velocity and dump their load of debris as they flow away from the ice sheet. In time, a vast apron of bedded sand and gravel is built up that may extend for miles beyond the ice front. If the zone of wastage happens to be located in a valley, the outwash deposits are confined to the lower valley and compose a **valley train.** But along the front of a continental ice sheet the outwash deposits stretch out for miles, forming what is called an **outwash plain.**

Kettles. Sometimes a block of stagnant ice becomes isolated from the receding glacier during wastage and is partially or completely buried in till or outwash before it finally melts. When it disappears, it leaves a **kettle,** a pit or depression in the drift. These depressions range from a few feet to several miles in diameter, and from a few feet to over 100 feet in depth. Many outwash plains are pockmarked with kettles and are referred to as **pitted outwash plains.** As time passes, water sometimes fills the kettles to form lakes or swamps, features found through much of Canada and northern United States.

Eskers and Crevasse Fillings. Winding, steep-sided ridges of stratified gravel and sand, sometimes branching and often discontinuous, are called **eskers.** They usually range in height from about 10 to 50 feet, although a few are over 100 feet high. Eskers range from a fraction of a mile to over 100 miles in length, but they are only a few feet wide. Most investigators (but not all) believe that eskers were formed by the deposits of streams running through tunnels beneath stagnant ice. Then, when the body

Figure 10-20 This outwash plain in North Dakota was produced by a now-vanished glacier. It is underlain by stratified sand and gravel. The crop is flax. (*Photo by Saul Aronow, U.S. Geological Survey.*)

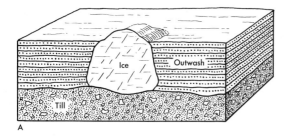

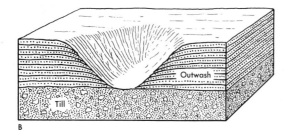

Figure 10-21 Sequence in the formation of a kettle. A block of stagnant ice is almost buried by outwash in A. The eventual melting of the ice produces a depression, as shown in B. In some instances, outwash may completely bury the ice block. Some kettles are formed in till.

of the glacier finally disappeared, the old stream deposits were left standing as a ridge.

Crevasse fillings are similar to eskers in height, width, and cross profile; but unlike the sinuous and branching pattern of eskers, they run in straight ridges. As their name suggests, they were probably formed by the filling of a crevasse in stagnant ice.

Kames and Kame Terraces. In many areas, stratified drift has built up low, relatively steep-sided hills called **kames,** either as isolated mounds or in clusters. Unlike drumlins, kames are of random shape and the deposits that make them up are stratified. They were formed by the material that collected in openings in stagnant ice. In this sense they are similar to crevasse fillings, but without the linear pattern.

A **kame terrace** is a deposit of stratified sand and gravel that has been laid down between a wasting glacier and an adjacent valley wall. When the glacier disappears, the deposit stands as a terrace along the side of the valley.

Varves. A **glacial varve** is a pair of thin sedimentary beds, one coarse, one fine. This

Figure 10-22 Esker near Tweed, Ontario, Canada. (*Photo by Geological Survey of Canada.*)

Figure 10-23 This isolated kame in eastern Wisconsin was formed by the partial filling of an opening in stagnant glacier ice. The melting of the ice has left this steep-sided hill of stratified material. (*Photo by Raymond C. Murray.*)

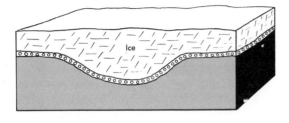

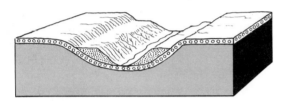

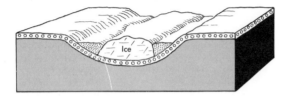

Figure 10-24 The sequence in the development of a kame terrace. Ice wasting from an irregular topography lingers longest in the valleys. While the ice still partially fills one of these valleys, outwash may be deposited between it and the valley walls. The final disappearance of the ice leaves the outwash in the form of terraces along the sides of the valley.

pair of beds is usually interpreted as being the deposits of a single year and is thought to form in the following way. During the period of summer thaw, waters from a melting glacier carry large amounts of clay, fine sand, and silt out into lakes along the ice margin. The coarser particles sink fairly rapidly and blanket the lake floor with a thin layer of silt and silty sand. But as long as the lake is unfrozen, the wind creates currents strong enough to keep the finer clay particles in suspension. When the lake freezes over in the winter, these wind-generated currents cease, and the fine particles sink through the quiet water to the bottom, covering the somewhat coarser summer layer. A varve is usually a fraction of an inch thick, though thicknesses of two or three inches and, in rare instances, of a foot or more are known.

Comparison of Valley and Continental Glaciation Features. Some of the glacial features that we have been discussing are more common in areas that have undergone valley glaciation; others usually occur only in regions that have been overridden by ice sheets; many other features, however, are found in both types of area. Table 10-1 lists the features and compares the incidence of them that is characteristic of the two types.

Figure 10-25 Varves deposited in a now-extinct glacial lake near Hanover, New Hampshire. (*Photo by R. W. Sayles.*)

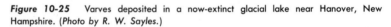

Table 10-1 Features of Valley and Continental Glaciations

Features	Valley	Continental
Striations, polish, etc.	Common	Common
Cirques	Common	Absent
Horns, arêtes, cols	Common	Absent
U-shaped valleys, truncated spurs, hanging valleys	Common	Rare
Fiords	Common	Absent
Till and stratified drift	Common	Common
Terminal moraines	Common	Common
Recessional moraines	Common	Common
Ground moraines	Common	Common
Lateral moraines	Common	Absent
Medial moraines	Common, easily destroyed	Absent
Drumlins	Rare or absent	Locally common
Kettles	Common	Common
Eskers, crevasse fillings	Rare	Common
Kames	Common	Common
Kame terraces	Common	Present in hilly country

Development of the Glacial Theory

Geologists have made extensive studies of the behavior of modern glaciers and have carefully interpreted the traces left by glaciers that disappeared thousands of years ago. On the basis of their studies, they have developed **the glacial theory.** This holds that *in the past, great ice sheets covered large sections of the earth where no ice now exists, and that existing glaciers once extended far beyond their present limits.*

THE BEGINNINGS The glacial theory took many years of trying to explain the occurrence of the vast expanses of drift strewn across northern Europe, the British Isles, Switzerland, and adjoining areas. The exact time when inquisitive minds first began to seek an explanation of these deposits is shrouded in the past. But by the beginning of the 18th century, explanations of what we now know to be glacial deposits and features were finding their way into print. According to the most popular early hypothesis, a great inundation had swept these deposits across the face of the land with cataclysmic suddenness, or else had drifted them in by means of floating icebergs. Then, when the flood receded, the material was left stranded in its present location.

By the turn of the 19th century, a new theory was in the air—the theory of ice transport. We do not know who first stated the idea or when it was first proposed, but it seems quite clear that it was not hailed immediately as a great truth. As the years passed, however, more and more observers became intrigued with the idea. The greatest impetus came from Switzerland, where the activity of living glaciers could be studied on every hand.

In 1821, J. Venetz, a Swiss engineer delivering a paper before the Helvetic Society, presented the argument that Swiss glaciers had once expanded on a great scale. It has since been established that from about 1600 to the middle of the 18th century there actually was a time of moderate but persistent glacier expansion in many localities. Abundant evidence in the Alps, Scandinavia, and Iceland indicates that the climate was milder during the Middle Ages than it is at the present, that communities existed and farming was carried on in places later invaded by advancing glaciers or devastated by glacier-fed streams. We know, for example, that a silver mine in the valley of Chamonix was being worked during the Middle Ages and that it was subsequently buried by an advancing glacier, where it lies to this day. And the village of St. Jean de Perthuis has been buried under the Brenva Glacier since about 1600.

Although Venetz' idea did not take hold immediately, by 1834 Jean de Charpentier was arguing in its support before the same Helvetic Society. Yet the theory continued to have more opponents than defenders. It was one of the skeptics, Jean Louis Rodolphe Agassiz, who did more than anyone else to develop the glacial theory and bring about its general acceptance.

LOUIS AGASSIZ Agassiz (1807–1873), a young zoologist, had listened to Charpentier's explanation; afterwards, he undertook to demonstrate to his friend and colleague the error of his ways. During the summer of 1836, the two men made a trip together into the upper Rhône Valley to the Getrotz Glacier. Before the summer was over, it was Agassiz who was convinced of his error. In 1837, he spoke before the Helvetic Society championing the glacial theory and suggesting that during a "great ice age" not only the Alps but much of northern Europe and the British Isles were overrun by a sea of ice.

Agassiz' statement of the glacial theory was not accepted immediately, but in 1840 he visited England and won the support of leading British geologists. In 1846 he arrived in America, where in the following year he be-

came professor of zoology at Harvard College and later founded the Museum of Comparative Zoology. In this country, he convinced geologists of the validity of the glacial theory; by the third quarter of the 19th century the theory was firmly entrenched. The last opposition died with the turn of the century.

PROOF OF THE GLACIAL THEORY What proof is there that the glacial theory is valid? The most important evidence is that certain features produced by glacier ice are produced by no other known process. Thus, Agassiz and his colleagues found isolated stones and boulders quite alien to their present surroundings. They noticed, too, that boulders were actually being transported from their original location by modern ice. Some of the boulders they observed were so large that rivers could not possibly have

Figure 10-26   The extent of Pleistocene glaciation (*white areas*) in the Northern Hemisphere. (*Redrawn from Ernst Antevs, "Maps of the Pleistocene Glaciations," Geol. Soc. Am. Bull., XL, 1929, p. 636.*)

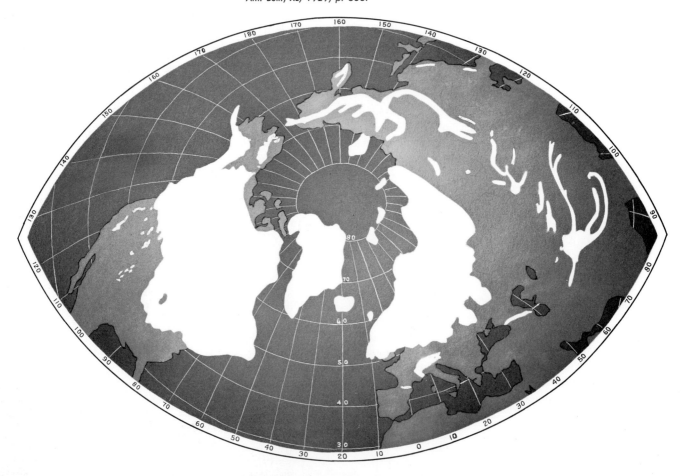

moved them, and others were perched on high places that a river could have reached only by flowing uphill. They also noticed that when modern ice melted it revealed a polished and striated pavement unlike the surface fashioned by any other known process. To explain the occurrence of these features in areas where no modern glaciers exist, they postulated that the ice once extended far beyond its present limits.

Notice that the proof of glaciation lies not in the authority of the textbook or the lecture. It lies in observing modern glacial activity directly and in comparing the results of this activity with features and deposits found beyond the present extent of the ice.

GRAVITY AND THE MASS MOVEMENT OF SURFACE MATERIAL

We have seen that water and ice erode and move material and model the earth's surface. These two agents are driven by gravity. But gravity also operates without any obvious association of water and ice, and it is to this process that we now turn.

Gravity acts to move the products of weathering, and even unweathered bedrock, to lower and lower levels. This movement of surface material caused by gravity is known as **mass movement.** Sometimes it takes place suddenly in the form of great landslides and rock falls from precipitous cliffs, but often it occurs almost imperceptibly, as in the slow creep of soil across gently sloping fields. Mass movement, then, is one type of adjustment that earth materials make to their physical environment; it is one of the many ways in which erosion acts to wear down the land masses of the earth.

Factors of Mass Movement

Gravity provides the energy for the downslope movement of surface debris and bedrock. But several other factors, particularly water, augment gravity and ease its work.

Immediately after a heavy rainstorm, you may have witnessed a landslide on a steep hillside or on the bank of a river. Movement of this sort is often mistakenly attributed to the "lubricating action" of water. But water does not "grease the skids" in the strict sense of the phrase. With many minerals water actually acts not as a lubricant but as an *anti*lubricant. We must conclude that heavy rains do not promote movement by "lubrication."

Water does aid in downslope movements, however. In many unconsolidated deposits, the pore spaces between individual grains are filled partly with moisture and partly with air. And so long as this condition persists, the surface

Figure 10-27 A large slab of massive Wingate sandstone has fallen and shattered at the foot of this precipitous cliff, where the San Juan River now begins to move away the fragments. (*Photo by William C. Bradley.*)

tension of the moisture gives a certain cohesion to the soil. But when a heavy rain comes along and forces all the air out of the pore spaces, this surface tension is completely destroyed. The cohesion of the soil is reduced, and the whole mass becomes more susceptible to down-slope movement. The presence of water also adds weight to the soil on a slope, although this added weight is probably not a very important factor in promoting mass movement.

Water that soaks into the ground and completely fills the pore spaces in the slope material contributes to instability in another way. The water in the pores is under pressure, which tends to push apart individual grains or even whole rock units and to decrease the internal friction or resistance of the material to movement. Here again, water assists in mass movement.

Gravity can move material only when it is able to overcome the material's internal resistance against being set into motion. Clearly, then, any factor that reduces this resistance to the point where gravity can take over contributes to mass movement. The erosive action of a stream, an ocean, or a glacier may so steepen a slope that the earth material no longer can resist the pull of gravity and is forced to give in to mass movement. In regions of cold climate, alternate freezing and thawing of earth materials may be enough to set them in motion. The impetus needed to initiate movement may also be furnished by earthquakes, excavations, or blasting operations, or even by the gentle activities of burrowing animals and growing plants.

Behavior of Material

In Chapter 8 we found that earth material under stress within the earth could behave as elastic, plastic, or fluid substances. Materials in motion down a slope can also behave in the same ways.

We could actually study any type of mass movement and classify it on the basis of these three types of movement. But we would have

Figure 10-28 The beginning of slump or slope failure along the sea cliffs at Gay Head, Massachusetts. Note that the slump block is tilted back slightly, away from the ocean. This slump block eventually moved downward and outward toward the shore along a curving surface, a portion of which is represented by the face of the low scarp in the foreground. (*Photo from Gardner Collection, Harvard University.*)

to assemble an excessive amount of technical data, and we would find the picture complicated by the fact that material often behaves in different ways during any one movement. So we shall simply classify mass movement as either *rapid* or *slow.*

Rapid Movements

Catastrophic and destructive movements of rock and soil, the most spectacular and easily recognized examples of mass movement, are popularly known as "landslides." But the geologist subdivides this general term into slump, rock slides, debris slides, mudflows, and earthflows.

LANDSLIDES Landslides include a wide range of movements, from the slipping of a stream bank to the sudden, devastating release of a whole mountainside. Some landslides involve only the unconsolidated debris lying on bedrock; others involve movement of the bedrock itself.

Slump. Sometimes called **slope failure, slump** is the downward and outward movement of rock or unconsolidated material traveling as a unit or as a series of units. Slump usually occurs where the original slope has been sharply steepened, either artificially or naturally. The material reacts to the pull of gravity as if it were an elastic solid, and large blocks of the slope move downward and outward along curved planes. The upper surface of each block is tilted backward as it moves.

Figure 10-28 shows a slump beginning at Gay Head, Massachusetts. The action of the sea has cut away the unconsolidated material at the base of the slope, steepening it to a point where the earth mass can no longer support itself. Now the large block has begun to move along a single curving surface, as suggested in Figure 10-29.

Once a slump has been started, it is often helped along by rainwater collecting in basins between the tilted blocks and the original slope. The water drains down along the surface on which the block is sliding and promotes further movement.

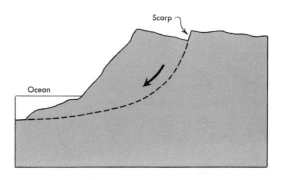

Figure 10-29 This diagrammatic cross section shows the type of movement found in a slump similar to that pictured in Figure 10-28. A block of earth material along the steepened cliffs has begun to move downward along a surface that curves toward the ocean.

Rock slides. The most catastrophic of all mass movements are **rock slides**—sudden, rapid slides of bedrock along planes of weakness. A great rock slide occurred in 1925 on the flanks of Sheep Mountain, along the Gros Ventre River in northwestern Wyoming, not far from Yellowstone Park (see Figure 10-30, p. 198). An estimated 50 million cubic yards of rock and debris plunged down the valley wall and swept across the valley floor. The nose of the slide rushed some 350 feet up the opposite wall and then settled back, like liquid being sloshed in a great basin. The debris formed a dam between 225 and 250 feet high across the valley, the dammed-up river creating a lake almost 5 miles long. The spring floods of 1926 raised the water level to the lip of the dam, and in mid-May the water flooded over the top. So rapid was the downcutting of the dam that the lake level was lowered about 50 feet in 5 hours. During the flood that followed, several lives were lost in the town of Kelly, in the valley below.

The Gros Ventre slide was a long time in the making, and there was probably nothing that could have been done to prevent it. Conditions immediately before the slide are shown in the top diagram in Figure 10-31 (p. 199). In this part of Wyoming, the Gros Ventre valley cuts through sedimentary beds inclined between 15° and 21° to the north. The slide occurred on the south side of the valley. Notice that the sandstone bed is separated from the limestone strata by a thin layer of clay. Before

Figure 10-30 Aerial photograph of the Gros Ventre rockslide in northwestern Wyoming. The lake in the lower left of the picture has been dammed by a landslide that moved down into the valley of the Gros Ventre River. The area from which the material slid is about a mile-and-a-half long and is well marked by the white scar down the center of the photograph. The adjoining slopes appear dark because of a vegetative cover of trees and bushes, a cover that has not yet re-established itself in the slide area. (*Photo by U.S. Army Air Force.*)

the rock slide occurred, the sandstone bed near the bottom of the valley had been worn thin by erosion. The melting of winter snows and the heavy rains that fell during the spring of 1925 furnished an abundant supply of water that seeped down to the thin layer of clay, soaking it and reducing the adhesion between it and the overlying sandstone. When the sandstone was no longer able to hold its position on the clay bed, the rock slide roared down the slope. The lower diagram of Figure 10-31 suggests the amount of material that was moved from the spur of Sheep Mountain to its resting place on the valley floor.

A more recent rock slide occurred in southwestern Montana a few minutes before midnight on August 17, 1959. An earthquake whose focus was located just north of West Yellowstone, Montana, triggered a rock slide in the mouth of the Madison Canyon, about 20 miles to the west. An estimated 80 million tons of rock slid from the south wall of the canyon down to the valley bottom, where it dammed up a lake 5 miles long and 100 feet deep. At least a score of people lost their lives in the Madison River Campground area below the slide (see Figures 10-32 and 10-33).

Debris Slides. A **debris slide** is a small, rapid movement of largely unconsolidated material that slides or rolls downward and produces a surface of low hummocks with small, intervening depressions. Movements of this sort are common on grassy slopes, particularly after heavy rains, and in unconsolidated material along the steep slopes of stream banks and shorelines.

Warnings of Landslides. We usually think of a landslide as breaking loose without warning, but it is more accurate to say that people in the area simply fail to detect the warnings.

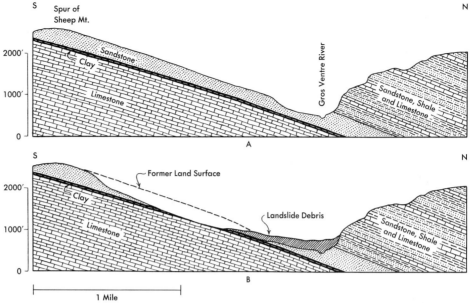

S — Spur of Sheep Mt. — N

2000'
Sandstone
Clay
1000'
Limestone
0
A
Gros Ventre River
Sandstone, Shale and Limestone

S — N

2000'
Former Land Surface
Clay
1000'
Limestone
Landslide Debris
0
B
Sandstone, Shale and Limestone

1 Mile

Figure 10-31 Diagrams to show the nature of the Gros Ventre slide. *A* shows the conditions existing before the slide took place. *B* represents the area of the slide and the location of the debris in the valley bottom. Note that the sedimentary beds dip into the valley from the south. The large section of sandstone slid downward along the clay bed. (*Redrawn from William C. Alden, "Landslide and Flood at Gros Ventre, Wyoming," Transactions, Am. Inst. of Mining and Metallurgical Engineers, LXXVI, 1928, p. 348.*)

Figure 10-32 The Madison River Canyon before the landslide of August, 1959. The slide began on the forested valley wall on the far side of the river. The debris clogged the river channel to form a lake. The spot where this fisherman once stood is now under 100 feet of water. Compare with Figure 10-33. (*Photo by Montana Power Co.*)

Figure 10-33 An aerial view of the Madison Canyon after the landslide. An outlet channel for the newly formed lake has been cut across the landslide dam. (*Photo by William C. Bradley.*)

For example, a disastrous rock slide at Goldau, Switzerland, in 1806, wiped out a whole village, killing 457 people. The few who lived to tell the tale reported that they themselves had no warning of the coming slide, but that animals and insects in the region may have been more observant or more sensitive. For several hours before the slide, horses and cattle seemed to be extremely nervous, and even the bees abandoned their hives. Some slight preliminary movement probably took place before the rock mass actually broke loose.

During the spring of 1935, slides took place in clay deposits along a German superhighway that was being built between Munich and Salzburg. The slides came as a complete surprise to the engineers, but for a full week the workmen had been murmuring, "Der Abhang wird Lebendig" (the slope becomes alive). Landslides are often preceded by slowly widening fissures in the rock near the upward limit of the future movement.

There is some evidence that landslides may recur periodically in certain areas. In southeastern England, not far from Dover, extensive landslides have been occurring once every 19 to 20 years. Some observers feel that there may be some correlation between such periodical mass movement and periods of excessive rainfall. On steep slopes in very moist tropical or semitropical climates, for instance, landslides do seem to follow a cyclic pattern. First, a landslide strips the soil and vegetation from a hill slope. In time, new soil and vegetation develop, the old scar heals, and when the cover reaches a certain stage, the landsliding begins again. Although landslides may occur in cycles, our data are as yet far too scanty to support firm conclusions.

MUDFLOWS   A **mudflow** is a well-mixed mass of rock, earth, and water that flows down valley slopes with the consistency of newly mixed concrete. In mountainous, desert, and semiarid areas, mudflows manage to transport great masses of material.

The typical mudflow originates in a small, steep-sided gulch or canyon where the slopes and floor are covered by unconsolidated or un-

stable material. A sudden flood of water, from cloudbursts in semiarid country or from spring thaws in mountainous regions, flushes the earth and rocks from the slopes and carries them to the stream channel. Here the debris blocks the channel until the growing pressure of the water becomes great enough to break through. Then the water and debris begin their course down-valley, mixing together with a rolling motion along the forward edge of the flow. The advance of the flow is intermittent, for sometimes it is slowed or halted by a narrowing of the stream channel; at other times it surges forward, pushing obstacles aside or carrying them along with it.

Eventually, the mudflow spills out of the canyon mouth and spreads across the gentle slopes below. No longer confined by the valley walls or the stream channel, it splays out in a great tongue, spreading a layer of mud and boulders that ranges from a few inches to several feet in thickness. Mudflows can move even large boulders weighing 85 tons or more for hundreds of feet, across slopes as gentle as 5°.

EARTHFLOWS   **Earthflows** are a combination of slump and the plastic movement of unconsolidated material. They move slowly but

Figure 10-34 An earthflow in a roadcut near Dallas, Texas, shows the sharp scar high on the slope and, farther down, the area of soil movement by flow. Compare with Figure 10-35. *(Photo by C. W. Brown.)*

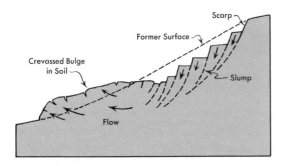

Figure 10-35 In this diagram of an earthflow, note the scarp and slump blocks that have pulled from the flow in the upper section. In the downslope section, the flowing has expressed itself at the surface by bulging and cracking the sod.

perceptibly and may involve from a few to several million cubic yards of earth material. Some of the material behaves like an elastic solid, and some like a plastic substance, depending on its position in the moving mass.

The line at which a slump pulls away from the slope is marked by an abrupt **scarp,** or cliff, as shown in Figure 10-34. Notice that the slump zone is made up of a series of blocks that move downward and outward, tilting the original surface back toward the slope. Farther down, the material tends to flow like a liquid, often beneath the vegetative cover. At the downslope limit of an earthflow, the sod often bulges out and fractures (see Figure 10-35). Earthflows occur in unconsolidated material lying on solid bedrock and are usually helped along by the presence of excessive moisture.

TALUS   Strictly speaking, a **talus** is a slope built up by an accumulation of rock fragments at the foot of a cliff or a ridge. The rock fragments are sometimes referred to as **rock waste** or **slide-rock.** In practice, however, talus is widely used as a synonym for the rock debris itself.

In the development of a talus, rock fragments are loosened from the cliff and clatter downward in a series of free falls, bounces, and slides. As time passes, the rock waste finally builds up a heap or sheet of rock rubble. An individual talus resembles a half-cone with its apex resting against the cliff face in a small gulch. A series of these half-cones often forms

a girdle around high mountains, completely obscuring their lower portions. Eventually, if the rock waste accumulates more rapidly than it can be destroyed or removed, even the upper cliffs become buried, and the growth of the talus stops. The slope angle of the talus varies with the size and shape of the rock fragments. Although angular material can maintain slopes up to 50°, rarely does a talus ever exceed angles of 40°.

A talus is subject to the normal process of chemical weathering, particularly in a moist climate. The rock waste is decomposed, especially toward its lower limit, or toe, and the material there may grade imperceptibly into a soil.

Slow Movements

Slow mass movements of unconsolidated material are harder to recognize and less fully understood than rapid movements; yet they are extremely important in the sculpturing of the land surface. Since they operate over long periods of time, they are probably responsible for the transportation of more material than are rapid and violent movements of rock and soil.

Before the end of the 19th century, William Morris Davis aptly described the nature of slow movements.

> The movement of land waste is generally so slow that it is not noticed. But when one has learned that many land forms result from the removal of more or less rock waste, the reality and the importance of the movement are better understood. It is then possible to picture in the imagination a slow washing and creeping of the waste down the land slopes; not bodily or hastily, but grain by grain, inch by inch; yet so patiently that in the course of ages even mountains may be laid low.[1]

CREEP   In temperate and tropical climates, a slow downward movement of surface material known as **creep** operates even on gentle slopes with a protective cover of grass and

[1] William Mooris Davis, *Physical Geography* (Boston: Ginn & Company, 1898), p. 261.

trees. It is hard to realize that this movement is actually taking place. Since the observer sees no break in the vegetative mat, no large scars or hummocks, he has no reason to suspect that the soil is in motion beneath his feet.

Yet this movement can be demonstrated by exposures in rock soil profiles (Figure 10-36), and by the behavior of tree roots, of large blocks of resistant rock, and of man-built objects such as fences and railroads (Figure 10-37). Figure 10-38 shows a section through a hillside underlain by flatlying beds of shale, limestone, clay, sandstone, and coal. The slope is covered with rock debris and soil. But notice that the beds near the base of the soil bend downslope and thin out rapidly. These beds are being pulled downslope by gravity and are strung out in ever-thinning bands that may extend for hundreds of feet. Eventually, they approach the surface and lose their identity in the zone of active chemical weathering.

The same diagram shows other evidence that the soil is moving. Although when viewed

from the surface the tree appears to be growing in a normal way, it is actually creeping slowly down the slope. Since the surface of the soil is moving more rapidly than the soil beneath it, the roots of the tree are unable to keep up with the trunk. Consequently, they are spread out like great streamers along the slope.

We can discover evidence of the slow movement of soil in displaced fences and tilted telephone poles and gravestones. On slopes where resistant rock layers crop up through the soil, fragments are sometimes broken off and distributed down the slope by the slowly moving soil.

Many other factors cooperate with gravity to produce creep. Probably the most important is moisture in the soil, which works to weaken the soil's resistance to movement. In fact, any process that causes a dislocation in the soil brings about an adjustment of the soil downslope under the pull of gravity. Thus, the burrows of animals tend to fill downslope, and

Figure 10-36 Near-vertical beds are bent downslope in their upper portion by gravity. (*Photo by U.S. Geological Survey.*)

Figure 10-37 Railroad along a tributary valley to the Yukon River has been distorted out of line by downslope movement. (*Photo by Atwood, U.S. Geological Survey.*)

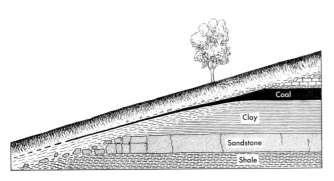

Figure 10-38 The partially weathered edges of horizontal sedimentary rocks are dragged downslope by soil creep. The tree is also moving slowly downslope, as is evidenced by the root system spread out behind the more rapidly moving trunk. (*Redrawn from C. F. S. Sharpe and E. F. Dosch, "Relation of Soil-Creep to Earthflow in the Appalachian Plateaus," J. Geomorphology, V, December, 1942, p. 316, by permission of Columbia Univ. Press.*)

the same is true of cavities left by the decay of organic material, such as the root system of a dead tree. The prying action of swaying trees, the tread of animals, and even of men, may also aid in the motion. The end result of all these processes, aided by the influence of gravity, is to produce a slow and inevitable downslope creep of the surface cover of debris and soil.

SOLIFLUCTION   The term **solifluction** (from the Latin *solum*, "soil," and *fluere*, "to flow") refers to the downslope movement of debris under saturated conditions in high latitudes where the soil is strongly affected by alternate freezing and thawing. Solifluction is most pronounced in areas where the ground freezes to great depths. But even moderately deep seasonal freezing promotes solifluction.

Solifluction takes place during periods of thaw. Since the ground thaws from the surface downward, the water that is released cannot percolate into the subsoil and adjacent bedrock, which are still frozen and therefore impermeable to water. As a result, the surface soil becomes sodden and waterladen and tends to flow down even the gentlest slopes. Solifluction is an important process in the reduction of land masses in arctic climates, where it transports great sheets of debris from higher to lower elevations.

During the glacier advances of the Pleistocene (see Chapter 20), a zone of intense frost action and solifluction bordered the southward moving ice. In some places we can still find the evidence of these more rigorous climates preserved in distorted layers of earth material just below the modern soil (Figure 10-39).

Frost action plays queer tricks in the soils of the higher elevations and latitudes. Strange polygonal patterns made up of rings of boul-

Figure 10-39 Beds of silt, sand, and clayey gravel have been contorted by differential freezing and thawing during the more rigorous climates of glacial times. The gravel at the base of the exposure is clayey, gravelly till deposited directly by glacier ice. Above this are the highly contorted beds of water-laid sand (*dark*) and silt (*light*), which were originally flat-lying. The modern soil has developed across the contortions. The white of the silt bands is due to precipitation of calcium carbonate from soil water. The brush hook is about 18 inches long. Exposure north of city of Devils Lake, east-central North Dakota. (*Photo by Saul Aronow, U.S. Geological Survey.*)

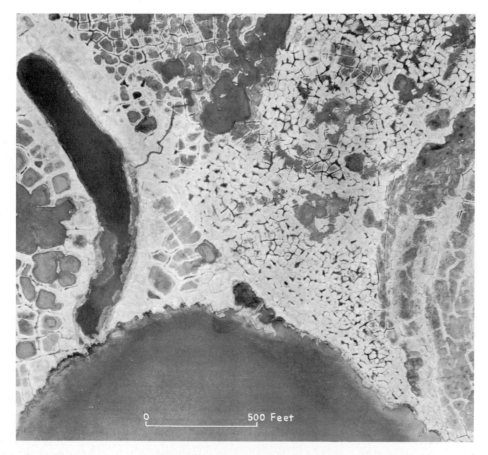

Figure 10-40 Aerial photograph of polygonal patterns developed by ice wedges in the coastal plain of northern Alaska. (*Photo by U.S. Coast and Geodetic Survey.*)

ders surrounding finer material, stripes of stones strewn down the face of hillsides, great tabular masses of ice within the soil, and deep ice wedges that taper downward from the surface —all are found in areas where the ground is deeply frozen (see Figure 10-40). The behavior of frozen ground is one of the greatest barriers to the settlement of Arctic regions. The importance of these regions has increased in recent years, and studies begun by Scandinavian and Russian investigators are now being intensively pursued by American scientists.

ROCK GLACIERS **Rock glaciers** are long tongues of rock waste that form in the valleys of certain mountainous regions. Though they consist almost entirely of rock, they bear a striking resemblance to ice glaciers. A typical rock glacier is marked by a series of rounded ridges, suggesting that the material has behaved as a viscous mass.

Observations on active rock glaciers in Alaska indicate that movement takes place because of interstitial ice within the mass. Favorable conditions for the development of glaciers include a climate cold enough to keep the ground continuously frozen, steep cliffs to supply debris, and coarse blocks that allow for large interstitial spaces. Measurements on modern rock glaciers over an 8-year period showed that the front moved 1.6 feet per year and that on the surface the average maximum movement was 2.6 feet per year.

WORK OF THE WIND

Wind is another effective agent in transporting earth materials, particularly in arid and semi-arid regions, but in more humid areas as well. Moreover, even in parts of the world where the action of the wind is negligible today, we find evidence that it has been more effective at certain times in the past.

Movement of Material

Wind velocities increase rapidly with height above the ground surface. The general movement of wind is forward, across the sur-

Figure 10-41 This rock glacier is in the Wrangell Mountains, Alaska. (*Photo by Austin Post.*)

face of the land. But within this general movement, the air is moving upward, downward, and from side to side. In the zone a few feet above ground surface, the average velocity of upward motion in an air eddy is approximately one-fifth the average forward velocity of the wind. This upward movement greatly affects the wind's ability to transport small particles of earth material, as we shall see.

Right along the surface of the ground there is a thin but definite zone where the air moves very little or not at all. Field and laboratory studies have shown that the depth of this zone depends on the size of the particles that cover the surface. On the average, the depth of this "zone of no movement" is about one-thirtieth the average diameter of the surface grains (see Figure 10-42). Thus, over a surface of evenly distributed pebbles with an average diameter of 30 mm, the zone of no movement would be about 1 mm deep. This fact, too, has a bearing on the wind's ability to transport material.

DUST STORMS AND SANDSTORMS   Material blown along by the wind usually falls into two size groups. The diameter of wind-driven sand grains averages between 0.15 mm and 0.30 mm, with a few grains as fine as 0.06 mm. All particles smaller than 0.06 mm are classified as dust.

In a true **dust storm,** the wind picks up fine particles and sweeps them upward hundreds or even thousands of feet into the air, forming a great cloud that may blot out the sun and darken the sky. In contrast, a **sandstorm** is a low, moving blanket of wind-driven sand with an upper surface 3 feet or less above the ground. Actually, the greatest concentration of moving sand is usually just a few inches above the ground surface, and individual grains seldom raise even as high as 6 feet. Above the blanket of moving sand, the air is quite clear, and a man on the ground appears to be partially submerged, as though he were standing in a shallow pond. Often, of course, the dust and sand are mixed together in a wind-driven

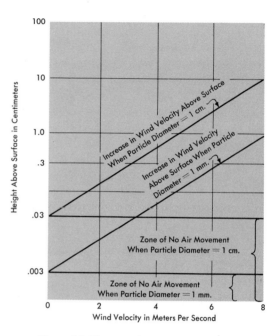

Figure 10-42   In a thin zone close to the ground there is little or no air movement, regardless of the wind velocity immediately above. This zone is approximately one-thirtieth the average diameter of surface particles. Two zones are shown in the graph: one for surfaces on which the particles average 1 millimeter in diameter, and one for surfaces with 1-centimeter particles. Diagonal lines represent the increase in velocity of a wind of given intensity blowing over surfaces covered with particles of 1 millimeter and 1 centimeter average diameter, respectively. (*Reproduced by permission from R. A. Bagnold, The Physics of Blown Sand and Desert Dunes. London: Methuen & Co., Ltd., 1941, p. 54.*)

storm. But the wind soon sweeps the finer particles off, and eventually the air above the blanket of moving sand becomes clear.

Apparently, then, the wind handles particles of different size in different ways. A dust-sized grain is swept high into the air, and a sand-sized grain is driven along closer to the ground. The difference arises from the strength of the wind and the terminal velocity of the grain.

The terminal velocity of a grain is the constant rate of fall attained by the grain when the acceleration due to gravity is balanced by the resistance of the fluid—in this case, the air—through which the grain falls. Terminal velocity varies only with the size of a particle when shape and density are constant. As the particle size increases, both the pull of gravity and the air resistance increase too. But the pull of gravity increases at a faster rate than the air resistance: A particle with a diameter of 0.01 mm has a terminal velocity in air of about 0.01 meter per second; a particle with a 0.2 mm diameter has a terminal velocity of about 1 meter per second; and a particle with a diameter of 1 mm has a terminal velocity of about 8 meters per second.

To be carried upward by an eddy of turbulent air, a particle must have a terminal velocity that is less than the upward velocity of the eddy. Close to the ground surface, where the upward currents are particularly strong, dust particles are swept up into the air and carried in suspension. Sand grains, however, have terminal velocities greater than the velocity of the upward moving air; they are lifted for a moment and then fall back to the ground. But how does a sand grain get lifted into the air at all if the eddies of turbulent air are unable to support it?

MOVEMENT OF SAND GRAINS   Careful observations, both in the laboratory and on open deserts, show sand grains moving forward in a series of jumps, in a process known as **saltation.** We used the same term to describe the motion of particles along a stream bed. But there is a difference: An eddy of water can actually lift individual particles into the main current whereas wind by itself cannot pick up sand particles from the ground.

Sand particles are thrown into the air only under the impact of other particles. When the wind reaches a critical velocity, grains of sand begin to roll forward along the surface. Suddenly, one rolling grain collides with another; the impact may either lift the second particle into the air or cause the first to fly up.

Once in the air, the sand grain is subjected to two forces. First, gravity tends to pull it down to earth again, and eventually it succeeds. But even as the grain falls, the horizon-

tal velocity of the wind drives it forward. The resulting course of the sand grain is parabolic from the point where it was first thrown into the air to the point where it finally hits the ground. The angle of impact varies between 10° and 16° (see Figure 10-43).

When the grain strikes the surface, it may either bounce off a large particle and be driven forward once again by the wind, or it may bury itself in the loose sand, perhaps throwing other grains into the air by its impact.

In any event, it is through the general process of saltation that a sand cloud is kept in motion. Countless grains are thrown into the air by impact and are driven along by the wind until they fall back to the ground. Then they either bounce back into the air again or else pop other grains upward by impact. The initial energy that lifts each grain into the air comes from the impact of another grain, and the wind contributes additional energy to keep it moving. When the wind dies, all the individual particles that compose the sand cloud settle back down to earth.

Figure 10-43   A sand grain is too heavy to be picked up by the wind, but may be put into the air by saltation. Here a single grain is rolled forward by the wind until it bounces off a second grain. Once in the air, it is driven forward by the wind, then pulled to the ground by gravity. It follows a parabolic path, hitting the ground at an angle between 10° and 16°.

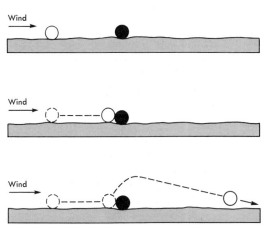

Some sand grains, particularly the large ones, never rise into the air at all, even under the impact of other grains. They simply roll forward along the ground, very much like the rolling and sliding of particles along the bed of a stream of water. It has been estimated that between one-fifth and one-quarter of the material carried along in a sandstorm travels by rolling, the rest by means of saltation.

Notice that once the wind has started the sand grains moving along the surface, initiating saltation, the wind no longer acts to keep them rolling. The cloud of saltating grains obstructs the wind and shields the ground surface from its force; thus, as soon as saltation begins, the velocity of near-surface winds drops rapidly. Saltation continues only because the impact of the grains continues. The stronger the winds blow during saltation, the heavier will be the blanket of sand, and the less the possibility that surface grains will be rolled by the wind.

MOVEMENT OF DUST PARTICLES   As we have seen, dust particles are small enough and have low enough terminal velocities to be lifted aloft by currents of turbulent air and to be carried along in suspension. But just how does the wind lift these tiny particles in the first place?

Laboratory experiments show that under ordinary conditions particles smaller than 0.03 mm in diameter cannot be swept up by the wind once they have settled to the ground. In dry country, for example, dust may lie undisturbed on the ground even though a brisk wind is blowing. But if a flock of sheep passes by and kicks loose some of the dust, a dust plume will rise into the air and move along with the wind.

The explanation for this seeming reluctance of dust particles to be disturbed lies in the nature of air movement. The small dust grains lie within the thin zone of negligible air-movement at the surface. They are so small that they do not create local eddies and disturbances in the air, and the wind passes them by. Alternatively, the dust particles may be shielded by larger particles against the action of the wind.

Some agent other than the wind must set dust particles in motion and lift them into a zone of turbulent air—perhaps the impact of larger particles, or sudden downdrafts in the air movement. Irregularities in a plowed field or in a recently exposed stream bed may help the wind to begin its work by creating local turbulence at the surface. Also, vertical downdrafts of chilled air during a thunderstorm sometimes strike the ground with velocities of 25 to 50 miles an hour and churn up great swaths of dust.

Erosion

Erosion by the wind is accomplished through two processes: **abrasion** and **deflation.**

ABRASION   Like the particles carried by a stream of running water, saltating grains of sand driven by the wind are highly effective abrasive agents in eroding rock surfaces. As we have seen, wind-driven sand seldom rises more than 3 feet above the surface of the earth, and measurements show that most of the grains are concentrated in the 18 inches closest to the ground. In this 18-inch layer the abrasive power of the moving grains is concentrated.

Although evidence of abrasion by sand grains is rather meager, there is enough to indicate that this erosive process does take place. For example, we sometimes find fence posts and telephone poles abraded at ground level and bedrock cliffs with a small notch along their base. In desert areas the evidence is more impressive, for here the wind-driven sand has in some places cut troughs or furrows in the softer rocks. The knife-edge ridges between these troughs are called **yardangs,** a term used in the deserts of Chinese Turkestan, where they were first described; the furrows themselves are called **yardang troughs.** The cross profile of one of these troughs is not unlike that of a glaciated mountain valley in miniature, the troughs ranging from a few inches to perhaps 25 feet in depth. They run in the usual direction of the wind, and their deepening by sand abrasion has actually been observed to occur during sandstorms.

Figure 10-44 Ventifacts exhibit a variety of facets, pits, ridges, and grooves, as well as surface sheen. Scale is indicated by 2-inch squares. (*Photo by Walter R. Fleischer.*)

The most common products of abrasion are certain pebbles, cobbles, and even boulders that have been eroded in a particular way. These pieces of rock are called **ventifacts** (from the Latin for "wind" and "made"). They are found not only on deserts, but also along modern beaches—in fact, wherever the wind blows sand grains against rock surfaces (Figures 10-44, 10-45, 10-46).

The surface of ventifacts is characterized by a relatively high gloss or sheen and by a variety of facets, pits, gouges, and ridges.

The face of an individual ventifact may display only 1 facet or 20 facets—or more—sometimes flat, but more commonly they are curved. Where two facets meet, they often form a well-defined ridge, and the intersection of 3 or more facets gives the ventifact the appearance of a small pyramid. Apparently, the surface becomes pitted when it lies across the direction of wind movement at an angle of 55° or more; it becomes grooved when it lies at angles of less than 55°.

DEFLATION **Deflation** (from the Latin "to blow away") is the erosive process of the wind carrying off unconsolidated material. The process creates several recognizable features in the landscape. For example, it often scoops out ba-

Figure 10-45 A ventifact with 3 well-developed facets, on the floor of the Mojave Desert, California. Pocket knife to right of ventifact gives scale. (*Photo by Sheldon Judson.*)

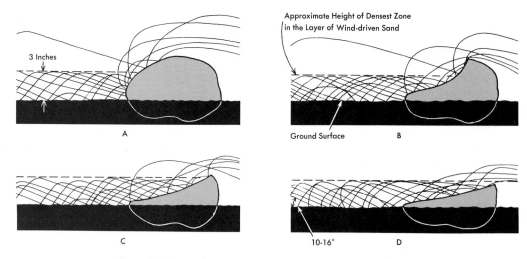

Figure 10-46 A facet on a ventifact is cut by the impact of grains of wind-driven sand. (*Redrawn from Robert P. Sharp, ''Pleistocene Ventifacts East of the Big Horn Mountains, Wyoming,'' J. Geol., LVII, 1949, p. 182.*)

sins in soft, unconsolidated deposits ranging from a few feet to several miles in diameter. These basins are known as **blowouts,** for obvious reasons.

In arid and semiarid country we sometimes see finely honeycombed rocks, and others called **pedestal rocks,** that have been fashioned into weird pillars resembling toadstools. Although wind has often been cited as the cause of these

formations, differential weathering is primarily responsible. The wind has merely removed the loose products of weathering.

Deflation removes only the sand and dust particles from a deposit and leaves behind the larger particles of pebble or cobble size. As time passes, these stones form a surface cover, known as a **desert pavement,** that cuts off further deflation.

Figure 10-47 Wind has excavated this blowout in unconsolidated sand deposits of Terry Andrae State Park, near Lake Michigan in eastern Wisconsin. (*Photo by Wisconsin Conservation Department.*)

Deposition

Whenever the wind loses its velocity, and hence its ability to transport the sand and dust particles it has picked up from the surface, it drops them back to the ground. The landscape features formed by wind-deposited materials are of various types, depending on the size of particles, the presence or absence of vegetation, the constancy of wind direction, and the amount of material available for movement by the wind. We still have a great deal to learn about this sort of deposit, but there are certain observations and generalizations that seem quite valid.

LOESS   Loess is a buff-colored, unstratified deposit composed of small, angular mineral fragments. Loess deposits range in thickness from a few inches to 30 or more feet in the central United States, to several hundred feet in parts of China. A large part of the surface deposits across some 200,000 square miles of the Mississippi River basin is made up of loess, and this material has produced the modern fertile soils of several Midwestern states, particularly Iowa, Illinois, and Missouri (see Figure 10-48).

Most geologists, though not all, believe loess to be material originally deposited by the wind. They base their conclusion on several facts. The individual particles in a loess deposit are very small, strikingly like the particles of dust carried about by the wind today. Moreover, loess deposits stretch over hill slopes, valleys, and plains alike, an indication that the material has settled from the air. And the shells of air-breathing snails present in loess strongly impugn the possibility that the deposits were laid down by water.

Many exposures in the north-central United States reveal that loess deposits there are intimately associated with glacial deposits built

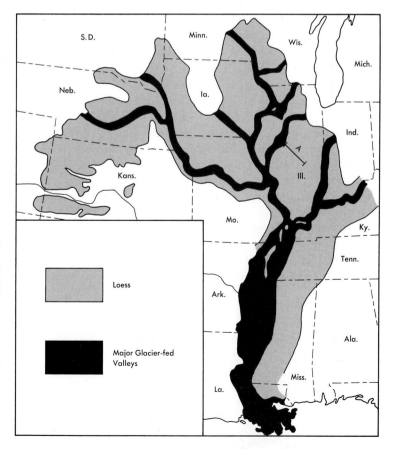

Figure 10-48 The great bulk of the loess in the central United States is intimately related to the major glacier-fed valleys of the area and was probably derived from the flood plains of these valleys. In Kansas and parts of Nebraska, however, the loess is probably nonglacial in origin and has presumably been derived from local sources and the more arid regions to the west. The line of section marked A in Illinois refers to Figure 10-50.

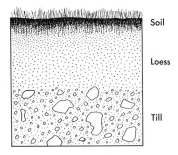

Figure 10-49 In many places, unweathered till is overlain by loess on which a soil zone has developed. The lack of a weathering zone on the till beneath loess often indicates rapid deposition of the loess immediately after the disappearance of the glacier ice and before weathering processes could affect the till. Not until loess deposition has slowed or halted is there time available to allow weathering and organic activity capable of producing a soil.

up during the Great Ice Age. Since the loess lies directly on top of the glacial deposits in many areas, it seems likely that it was deposited by the wind during periods when glaciation was at its height, rather than during interglacial intervals. Also, since there is no visible zone of weathering on deposits, the loess probably was laid down on the newly formed glacial deposits before any soil could develop on them (Figure 10-49).

Certain relationships between the loess deposits in the Midwest and the streams that drain the ancient glacial areas serve to strengthen the conclusion that there is a close connection between glaciation and the deposit of wind-borne materials. Figure 10-50, for example, shows that the major glacial streams cut across the loess belt and that the thickness of the loess decreases toward the east and away from the banks of the streams. Moreover, the mean size of the particles decreases away from the glacial streams. These facts can best be explained as follows. We know that loess is not forming in this area at the present, so we must look for more favorable conditions in the past. During the Great Ice Age of the Pleistocene, the rivers of the Midwest carried large amounts of debris-laden meltwater from the glaciers. Consequently, the flood plains of these rivers built up at a rapid rate and were broader than they are today. During periods of low water, the flood plains were wide expanses of gravel, sand,

silt, and clay exposed to strong westerly winds. These winds whipped the dust-sized material from the flood plains, moved it eastward, and laid down the thickest and coarsest of it closest to the rivers.

All loess, however, is not derived from glacial deposits. In one of the earliest studies of loess, it was shown that the Gobi Desert has provided the source material for the vast stretches of yellow loess that blanket much of northern China, and that gives the characteristic color to the Yellow River and the Yellow Sea. Similarly, much of the land used for cotton-growing in the eastern Sudan of Africa is thought to be made up of particles blown from the Sahara Desert to the west. Finely divided mineral fragments are swept up in suspension during desert sandstorms and are carried along by the wind far beyond the confines of the des-

Figure 10-50 Loess related to the major glacier-fed rivers in the Midwest shows a decrease in thickness away from the rivers and a decrease in the size of individual particles. An example is shown in this diagram, based on data gathered along the line *A* in Figure 10-48. (Redrawn from G. D. Smith, "Illinois Loess—Variations in Its Properties and Distributions," U. of Ill. Agricultural Experiment Station, Bull. 490, 1942, Figures 5 and 6.)

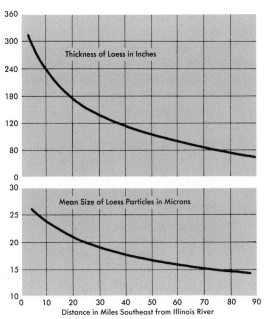

ert. Clearly, then, the large amounts of very fine material present in most deserts would make an excellent source of loess.

SAND DEPOSITS Unlike deposits of loess, which blanket whole areas, sand deposits assume certain characteristic and recognizable shapes. Wind often heaps the sand particles into mounds and ridges called **dunes,** which sometimes move slowly along in the direction of the wind. Some dunes are only a few feet in height, but others reach tremendous sizes. In southern Iran, dunes have grown to 700 feet in height, with bases over 3,000 feet wide.

As the velocity of the wind falls, so does the energy available for the transportation of material; consequently, deposition of material takes place. We need to examine this relationship more closely and to explain why sand is deposited in the form of dunes rather than as a regular, continuous blanket.

The Wind Shadow. Any obstacle—large or small—across the path of the wind will divert moving air and create a "wind shadow" to the leeward, as well as a smaller shadow to the windward immediately in front of the obstacle. Within each wind shadow the air moves in eddies, with an average motion less than that of the wind sweeping by outside. The boundary between the two zones of air moving at different velocities is called the **surface of discontinuity** (see Figure 10-51).

When sand particles driven along by the wind strike an obstacle, they settle in the wind shadow immediately in front of it. Because the wind velocity (hence energy) is low in this wind shadow, deposition takes place and gradually a small mound of sand builds up. Other particles move past the obstacle and cross through the surface of discontinuity into the leeward wind shadow behind the barrier. Here again the velocities are low, deposition takes place, and a mound of sand (a dune) builds up—a process aided by eddying air that tends to sweep the sand in toward the center of the wind shadow (see Figures 10-52, 10-53).

Wind Shadow of a Dune. Actually, a sand dune itself acts as a barrier to the wind, and by

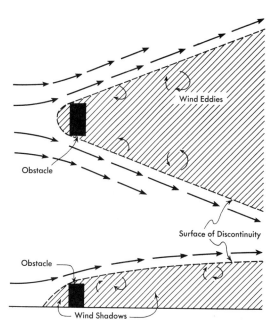

Figure 10-51 The shaded area indicates the wind shadow created by an obstacle. The wind is diverted over and around the obstacle. Within the wind shadow, wind velocity is low and air movement is marked by eddies. A surface of discontinuity separates the air within the wind shadow from the air outside. (*Reproduced by permission from R. A. Bagnold, op. cit., p. 190.*)

Figure 10-52 Because of its momentum, the sand in the more rapidly moving air outside the wind shadow either passes through the surface of discontinuity to settle in the wind shadow behind the obstacle or strikes the obstacle and falls in the wind shadow in front of the obstacle. (*Reproduced by permission from R. A. Bagnold, op. cit., p. 190.*)

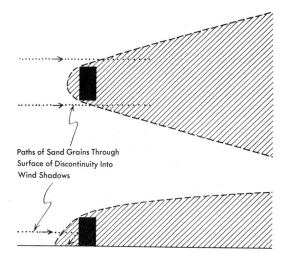

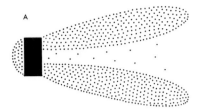
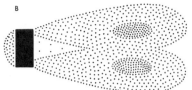
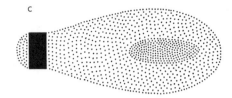

Figure 10-53   Sand falling in the wind shadow tends to be gathered by wind eddies within the shadow to form a shadow dune, as shown in this sequence of diagrams. (Reproduced by permission from R. A. Bagnold, op. cit., p. 190.)

disrupting the flow of air, it may cause the continued deposition of sand. A profile through a dune in the direction toward which the wind blows shows a gentle slope facing the wind and a steep slope to the leeward. A wind shadow exists in front of the steep leeward slope, and it is here that deposition is active. The wind drives the sand grains up the gentle windward slope to the dune crest and then drops them into the wind shadow. The steep leeward slope is called the **slip face** of the dune because of the small sand slides that take place there.

The slip face is necessary for the existence of a true wind shadow. Here is how the slip face is formed. A mound of sand affects the flow of air across it, as shown in the topmost diagram of Figure 10-54. Notice that the wind flows over the mound in streamlined patterns. These lines of flow tend to converge toward the top of the mound and diverge to the leeward. In the zone of diverging air flow, velocities are less than in the zone of converging flow. Consequently, sand tends to be deposited on the leeward slope just over the top of the mound where the velocity begins to slacken. This slope steepens because of deposition, and eventually the sand slumps under the influence of gravity. The slump usually takes place at an angle of about 34° from the horizontal. A slip face is thus produced, steep enough to create a wind shadow in its lee. Within this shadow, sand grains fall like snow through quiet air. Continued deposition and periodic slumping along the slip face account for the slow growth or movement of the dune in the direction toward which the wind blows.

Shoreline Dunes. Not all dunes are found in the deserts. Along the shores of the ocean and of large lakes, ridges of windblown sand called **fore dunes** are built up even in humid climates. They are well developed along the southern and eastern shores of Lake Michigan, along the Atlantic coast from Massachusetts southward, along the southern coast of California, and at various points along the coasts of Oregon and Washington (see Figure 10-55).

These fore dunes are fashioned by the influence of strong onshore winds acting on the sand particles of the beach. On most coasts, the vegetation is dense enough to check the inland movement of the dunes, and they are concentrated in a narrow belt that parallels the shoreline. These dunes usually have an irregular surface, sometimes pock-marked by blowouts (see "deflation," above).

Sometimes, however, in areas where vegetation is scanty, the sand moves inland in a series of ridges at right angles to the wind. These **transverse dunes** exhibit the gentle wind-

Figure 10-54   The development of a slip face on a dune. Wind converges on the windward side of the dune and over its crest, and diverges to the lee of the dune. The eventual result is the creation of a wind shadow in the lee of the dune. In this wind shadow, sand falls until a critical angle of slope (about 34°) is reached. Then a small landslide occurs, and the slip face is formed. (*Reproduced by permission from R. A. Bagnold, op. cit., p. 202.*)

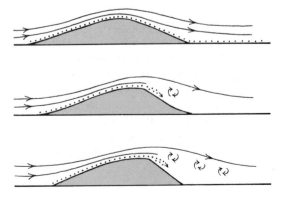

Figure 10-55   These shoreline dunes form complex patterns behind the beach at Coos Bay, Oregon. The beach serves as a source of sand and this source is continuously renewed by longshore currents of ocean water. Onshore winds (from the left) drive the beach sand inland. (Photo shows about 1,500 feet across.)

common in coastal areas and in various places throughout the southwestern states. Ancient parabolic dunes, no longer active, exist in the upper Mississippi Valley and in Central Europe.

Longitudinal Dunes. Longitudinal dunes are long ridges of sand running in the general direction of wind movement. The smaller types are less than 10 feet high and about 200 feet long. In the Libyan Desert, however, they commonly reach a height of 300 feet and may extend for 60 miles across the country. There they are known as **seif dunes** (rhymes with "strife"), from the Arabic word for "sword."

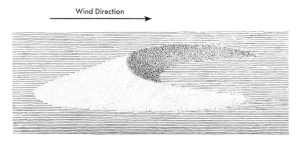

Wind Direction

Figure 10-56   A barchan is a crescent-shaped dune with its horns pointed downwind and its slip face on the inside of the crescent.

Figure 10-57   These barchans are moving across the Pampa de Islay, Peru, in the direction in which their horns point. (*Photo by Aerial Explorations, Inc.*)

ward slope and the steep leeward slope characteristic of other dunes. Transverse dunes are also common in arid and semiarid country where sand is abundant and vegetation sparse.

Barchans. **Barchans** (pronounced bar-kans) are sand dunes shaped like a crescent, with their horns pointing downwind. They move slowly with the wind, the smaller ones at a rate of about 50 feet a year, the larger ones about 25 feet a year. The maximum height obtained by a barchans is about 100 feet, and their maximum spread from horn to horn is about 1,000 feet (see Figures 10-56, 10-57).

Just what leads to the formation of a barchan is still a matter of dispute. Certain conditions do seem essential, however: a wind that blows from a fixed direction, a relatively flat surface of hard ground, a limited supply of sand, and a lack of vegetation.

Parabolic Dunes. Long, scoop-shaped, parabolic dunes look rather like barchans in reverse—that is, their horns point upwind rather than downwind. They are usually covered with sparse vegetation that permits limited movement of the sand. Parabolic dunes are quite

SUMMARY

Snow metamorphoses to ice and if enough ice accumulates it will flow under the influence of gravity. Glacier ice occurs in valley glaciers, piedmont glaciers, and ice sheets. They advance when the accumulation of snow exceeds wastage, and shrink when wastage exceeds accumulation. A thin brittle zone overlies a plastic zone.

Erosion by ice takes place by plucking and abrasion. It produces striations, polish, and grooves on rock surfaces, and cuts cirques, horns, arêtes, cols, U-shaped valleys, fiords, and asymmetric rock knobs and hills. Glacial deposits include till in the form of moraines and drumlins, and outwash plains, eskers, crevasse fillings, kames, and kame terraces.

Gravity works directly on earth materials to carry them to lower and lower levels. The material may respond as an elastic solid, a plastic substance, or a fluid. Rapid movements include landslides, mudflows, earthflows, and talus falls. Slow movements are those of creep, solifluction, and rock glaciers.

Wind moves two different sizes of material—sand and dust. Sand grains are moved by saltation and rolling. Dust grains move in suspension. Erosion by wind produces ventifacts and blow-outs. Deposition of dust produces loess, a deposit derived both from the deserts and from glacial outwash. Sand collects into dunes, including barchans, parabolic dunes, and longitudinal dunes.

ADDITIONAL READING

Andersson, J. G., "Solifluction, a Component of Subaerial Denudation," *J. Geol.,* XIV (1906), 91–112.

Bagnold, R. A., *The Physics of Blown Sand and Desert Dunes.* London: Methuen & Co., 1941.

Charlesworth, J. K., *The Quaternary Era* (2 vols.). London: Edward Arnold, 1957.

Flint, Richard Foster, *Glacial and Pleistocene Geology.* New York: John Wiley & Sons, 1957.

Gautier, E. F., *Sahara, The Great Desert,* trans. D. F. Mayhew. New York: Columbia University Press, 1935.

Muller, S. W., *Permafrost or Permanently Frozen Ground and Related Engineering Problems.* Ann Arbor, Mich.: J. W. Edwards, 1947.

Sharp, R. P., "Pleistocene Ventifacts East of the Big Horn Mountains, Wyoming," *J. Geol.,* LVII (1949), 175–95.

Sharpe, C. F. S., *Landslides and Related Phenomena.* New York: Columbia University Press, 1938.

Tabor, Stephen, "Perennially Frozen Ground in Alaska: Its Origin and History," *Geol. Soc. Am. Bull.,* LIV (1943), 1433–1548.

Terzaghi, Karl, "Mechanism of Landslides," *Geol. Soc. Am. Bull.,* Berkey Volume (1950), 83–123.

Thwaites, F. T., *Outline of Glacial Geology.* Madison, Wis.: Published by the author, 1956.

Wahrhaftig, Clyde, and Allan Cox, "Rock Glaciers in the Alaska Range," *Geol. Soc. Am. Bull.,* LXX (1959), 383–436.

Zeuner, F. E., *The Pleistocene Period, Its Climate, Chronology, and Faunal Successions.* London: Hutchinson and Co., 1959.

11

Oceans and Shorelines

More than 70 per cent of the surface of the earth lies deep in mystery beneath the oceans, essentially unknown and unexplored. Yet these regions are of the utmost importance to the geologist, for it was in the oceans and seas of the past that most sedimentary rocks formed —rocks that today cover three-quarters of the continental land masses—and the great ocean basins seem clearly linked to the origin of the continents.

We are only beginning to piece together the complex picture of the ocean floors—their topography, composition, and history, and the nature of the chemical and physical processes that operate across them. In this chapter we shall trace in briefest outline some of the facts that have been assembled and some of the problems that have arisen concerning the oceans and ocean basins.

Figure 11-1 On the land hemisphere map, centered on western Europe, land and sea are about evenly divided. But an indisputable predominance of the seas is revealed on the water hemisphere map, centered on New Zealand.

Land Hemisphere

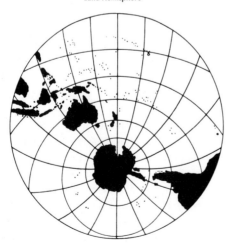

Water Hemisphere

OCEAN WATER

The Distribution of Sea Water

The Northern Hemisphere is sometimes referred to as the "land hemisphere," because north of the equator the oceans and seas cover only about 60 per cent of the earth's surface, whereas in the Southern Hemisphere over 80 per cent is flooded by marine waters. Between 45°N and 70°N, the ocean occupies only 38 per cent of the surface; in contrast, 98 per cent of the surface is covered by the ocean between 35°S and 65°S.

The greatest ocean depth so far recorded, at a spot in the Pacific Ocean near the island of Guam is 36,198 feet—almost 7 miles—which is considerably greater than the height of Mt. Everest, the world's highest mountain, which is slightly more than 29,000 feet above sea level. The average ocean depth is about 12,400 feet; the mean elevation of the continents is approximately 2,700 feet (see Figure 11-2).

It has been estimated that the globe would be covered with a layer of water about 1½ to 2 miles thick if all the irregularities of the sur-

Figure 11-2 The relative distribution of land and sea. Note that the mean ocean depth is 12,460 feet, whereas the mean elevation of the land is only 2,757 feet.

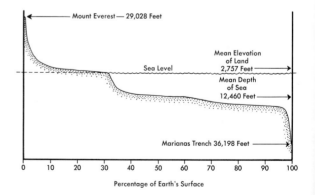

face were eliminated. Such a situation has probably never existed in the past, nor need we worry about its occurring in the future. Modern oceans are confined to great basins and, presumably, so were the oceans of the past. We shall discuss the characteristics of these basins in some detail later in the chapter.

The Nature of Sea Water

About half of the known elements have been identified in sea water, and many others undoubtedly await discovery. Included among the materials known to be dissolved in the sea are the chlorides that give sea water its familiar saltiness, all the gases found in the atmosphere, and a large number of less abundant materials, including such rare elements as uranium, gold, and silver.

SALTS DISSOLVED IN SEA WATER Through millions of years of geologic time, the rivers of the world have been slowly transporting tremendous quantities of dissolved material to the oceans. Some of this material, such as iron, silicon, and calcium, is used by plants and animals in their life processes and is in effect removed from the water. As a result, the amount of these elements present in solution is less than we would expect to find, judging from the rate at which rivers are currently supplying them to the oceans. On the other hand, we find a relatively high percentage of the "salt" ions, notably Cl^-, even though rivers are presently supplying these materials at a relatively low rate. Salt ions have continued to collect in the sea water because plants and animals do not concentrate them and because they are extremely soluble.

Since the proportions of the various salt ions are relatively constant throughout the oceans, in a given place a measurement of any one of them enables us to compute the abundance of the others. The total concentration of salt ions—that is, the salinity of the sea water—varies from place to place, however. At the equator, heavy precipitation dilutes the sea water, reducing its salinity. In the Arctic and Antarctic areas, the melting of glacier ice also serves to reduce the saltiness of the seas. But in the subtropical belts to the north and south, low rainfall and high evaporation tend to increase the salinity, as is indicated below in Figure 11-3.

Table 11-1   The Major Constituents Dissolved in Sea Water

Ion		Percentage of All Dissolved Material
Chlorine	Cl^-	55.04
Sodium	Na^+	30.61
Sulfate	SO_4^{2-}	7.68
Magnesium	Mg^{2+}	3.69
Calcium	Ca^{2+}	1.16
Potassium	K^+	1.10
Bicarbonate	HCO_3^-	.41
		99.69

From H. U. Sverdrup, Martin W. Johnson, and Richard H. Fleming. *The Oceans* (Englewood Cliffs, N.J.: Prentice-Hall, Inc., 1942), p. 166.

Figure 11-3 Total salinity varies in the oceans from south to north across the equator. The low salinity of surface waters in the vicinity of the equator is attributed to the freshening effect of heavy tropical rains. North and south of this zone the rainfall decreases, and evaporation increases; as a result, the total salinity of the surface waters increases. (*Redrawn from R. H. Fleming and Roger Revelle, "Physical Processes in the Oceans," in Trask, Recent Marine Sediments—A Symposium. Tulsa: Am. Assoc. Petroleum Geol., 1939, p. 88.*)

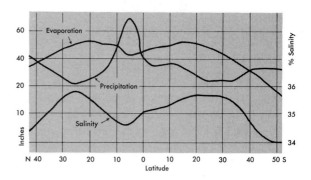

GASES DISSOLVED IN SEA WATER   Although all the gases found in the atmosphere are also present in water, probably the most important are oxygen and carbon dioxide. Near the surface of the oceans the water is saturated with both gases, but their concentration and relative proportions vary with depth. As the surface water circulates downward through the first few scores of feet, intense plant activity depletes the supply of carbon dioxide. At the same time, oxygen is given off by the plants. Consequently, this near-surface zone is deficient in carbon dioxide and tends to be oversaturated with oxygen.

Below the depth to which light can penetrate effectively, however, plant activity falls off and the amount of oxygen in solution decreases. Of the oxygen present, some is used by animals and some becomes involved in the oxidation of organic matter settling toward the bottom. At the same time, the relative amount of carbon dioxide increases, because there is no plant activity to deplete it. Thus, with increasing depth, oxygen becomes relatively less abundant and carbon dioxide relatively more abundant.

Were it not for the slow circulation of sea water through the ocean basins, water at the greatest depths would be devoid of oxygen. Actually, at the bottom of some ocean basins, the circulation of water is so slow that almost no oxygen is present, and the water has become stagnant. Here, there are high concentrations of hydrogen sulfide. This is true, for example, in the Black Sea below a depth of 450–500 feet, and in many of the Norwegian fiords whose glacially-deepened basins lie below the general level of the adjacent floor of the North Atlantic. Because of the almost complete absence of oxygen at the bottom of these basins, sediments lying there oxidize very slowly, if at all. Consequently, a high content of organic matter and the hydrogen sulfide compounds that are produced give these deposits characteristic black color. It is probable that petroleum was formed in some environment such as this in the ancient seas.

THE MOVEMENT OF SEA WATER

The movement of sea water is of two general types: (1) the movement of the average level of the surface either up or down relative to the land—called **changes of sea level,** and (2) the transfer of water from one place to another in ocean basins by movements generally referred to as **currents.**

Changes of Sea Level

The level of the sea in relation to dry land is constantly changing. The daily changes caused by tides are familiar enough; but much slower fluctuations are no less real or important; in fact, in the geologic past such changes have been very extensive and significant.

EUSTATIC AND TECTONIC CHANGES OF SEA LEVEL   It is easy enough to measure the daily changes in sea level caused by the rise and fall of tides along the coastline. But there are other movements so slow that they are revealed only by long-continued records of sea level, or so local and rare that they are not generally recognized.

A change in sea level relative to land can be caused by the upward or downward movement of either the ocean or the land, or by their combined movement. If the movement is confined to the ocean, change of level is **eustatic,** a term that refers to the static condition or continuing stability of the landmass. When the relative sea level changes because of land movement, the change is **tectonic** (from the Greek for "builder" or "architect"), in reference to the movements that shape the earth's surface (see Chapter 8).

Often it is difficult, if not impossible, to distinguish between eustatic and tectonic movements of sea level by observing only a small section of the shore. Eustatic changes of level, however, are worldwide; and when recording stations over an extensive area report a long-

Figure 11-4 In the recent geologic past, ocean waves beveled this platform across tilted rocks on the California coast south of San Francisco. Today the platform stands slightly above sea level as evidence of a change in level between land and sea. In this instance, geologists believe that the motion has been tectonic and that the land has moved upward relative to the sea. (*Photo by William C. Bradley.*)

continued movement of the sea, the movement can safely be termed eustatic. In contrast, tectonic movements tend to be local and spasmodic, controlled as they are by the forces that crumple and distort solid earth materials.

Eustatic movements may be caused in various ways. If the amount of water locked up in glaciers and lakes increases, the sea level falls; then, if the glaciers melt or if the lakes are drained, the sea level rises. Or sea level may rise or fall as a result of changes in the size of ocean basins, either because of continuing deposition of sediments on their floors or because of actual deformation by earth forces. Still an-

other cause of eustatic change lies in the addition or removal of water from the earth's surface. Volcanoes are constantly adding to our atmosphere new water that eventually finds its way to the sea. And water is constantly being trapped in sedimentary deposits and incorporated in such minerals as clay, causing at least a temporary loss to the oceans.

Tectonic and eustatic changes are continuously taking place around the globe; mean sea level is endlessly rising and falling. Although recent changes in sea level are slight, we have ample evidence that they are in fact actually occurring at present.

Figure 11-5 Torghatten Island off the coast of Norway testifies to a 400-foot drop in sea level, the distance from the dotted line to the surface of the present-day ocean. Note the benches that were cut at the time of higher sea level. A tunnel was cut by wave action when the sea stood at the higher level. Here the earth's crust has moved upward after being warped down by the weight of the now vanished Scandinavian ice sheet. (*Photo by C. A. Ericksen.*)

RECENT CHANGES IN SEA LEVEL   On the basis of tidal measurements made at various points around the world, observers have concluded that a eustatic rise in sea level is taking place at the present time. The flooding of many river mouths from New England southward indicates that the rise has a long history, substantiated by the discovery of submerged stumps of ancient trees and primitive artifacts. The invasion of the sea is attributed to the melting of mountain glaciers and to the depletion of the Greenland and Antarctic icecaps. But there is still enough water stored in modern glaciers to raise the sea another 70 to 200 feet if it were all to melt, as it probably will in time.

Modern changes in sea level caused by tectonic movements have been observed in localities where the crust of the earth is known to be undergoing deformation at the present day.

Currents

Sea water is in constant movement, in some places horizontal, in others downward, and in still others upward. Its rate of movement varies from spot to spot, but it has been estimated that there is a complete mixing of all the water of the oceans about once every 1,800 years. If we assume that movements similar to those of the present have been going on throughout the long history of the earth, by studying modern seas, we can gain an insight into the history recorded in sedimentary rocks that were once muds and sands on the floor of ancient seas.

Although we still cannot explain completely the movements of the modern oceans, we do know that they are caused chiefly by tides, by the changing density of sea water, by wind, and by the rotation of the earth.

TIDAL CURRENTS   The attractive forces that operate among the sun, the moon, and the earth set the waters of the ocean in horizontal motion to produce tidal currents. The speed of these currents may reach several miles per hour if local conditions are favorable. Velocities in excess of 12 miles per hour develop during the

spring tides in Seymour Narrows, between Vancouver Island and British Columbia, and tidal currents of half this velocity are not uncommon. The swiftest currents usually build up where a body of sea water has access to the open ocean only through a narrow and restricted passage. Such currents are capable of moving particles up to, and including, those of sand size, and they may be strong enough to scour the sea floor.

DENSITY CURRENTS   The density of sea water varies from place to place with changes in temperature, salinity, and the amount of material held in suspension. Thus cold, heavy water sinks below warmer and lighter water;

Figure 11-6   Twice a day the tides rise and fall along this section of the Connecticut coast at Buffalo Bay near Madison. (*Photos by Sheldon Judson.*)

water of high salinity is heavier than water of low salinity and sinks beneath it; and heavy muddy water sinks beneath light, clear water.

In the Straits of Gibraltar, the water passage between the Atlantic and the Mediterranean, differences in density are partially responsible for a pair of currents flowing one above the other. The Mediterranean, lying in a warm, dry climatic belt, loses about 5 feet of water every year through evaporation. Consequently, the saltier, heavier water of the Mediterranean moves outward along the bottom of the Straits and sinks downward into the less salty, lighter water of the Atlantic. At the same time, the lighter surface water of the Atlantic moves into the Mediterranean basin. The water flowing from the Mediterranean settles to a depth of a little over 3,000 feet in the Atlantic and then spreads slowly outward beyond the equator on the south, the Azores on the west, and Ireland on the north. It has been estimated that as a result of this activity the water of the Mediterranean basin is changed once every 75 years (see Figure 11-7).

The density of water is also affected by variations in temperature. As a result of such variations, water from the cold Arctic and Antarctic regions creeps slowly toward the warmer environment near the equator. The cold, relatively dense water from the Arctic sinks near Greenland in the North Atlantic and can be traced to the equator and beyond as far as 60°S. Denser and colder water moves downward to the sea floor off Antarctica and creeps northward, pushing beneath the North Atlantic water. In fact, the Antarctic water reaches well north of the equator before it loses its identity. The speed of these currents has yet to be measured accurately, but estimates put the rate of movement of Antarctic water along the sea floor at a mile or more per day.

A third type of density current, known as a **turbidity current,** results because turbid or muddy water has a greater density than clear water and therefore sinks beneath it. Evidence that marine turbidity currents exist in the ocean is largely indirect. We can demonstrate how these currents operate on a small scale in the laboratory, and they have actually been observed in fresh-water lakes and reservoirs, so it seems safe enough to assume that they also exist in the oceans.

Moreover, turbidity currents seem to offer the most plausible explanation of certain de-

Figure 11-7 A density current flows from the Mediterranean Sea through the Straits of Gibraltar and spreads out into the Atlantic Ocean. High evaporation and low rainfall in the Mediterranean area produce a more saline and hence heavier water than the water of the neighboring Atlantic Ocean. As a result, Mediterranean water flows out through the lower portion of the Straits, and lighter Atlantic water moves above it and in the opposite direction to replace it. The higher temperature of the Mediterranean water is more than counteracted by its greater salinity, and the water sinks to a level in the Atlantic somewhat lower than 3,000 feet below the surface.

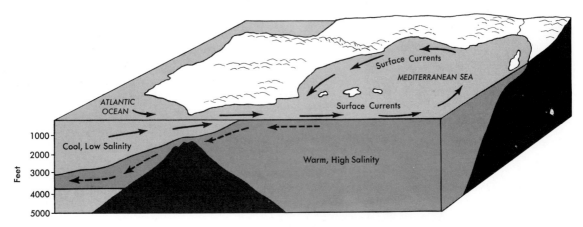

posits that have been studied from the deep ocean basins. Samples of sediments from these basins contain thin layers of sand that could not have been carried so far from shore by the slow drift of water along the ocean floor. But rapidly moving turbidity currents would be quite capable of moving the sand down the slopes of the ocean basins to the deep floors.

Analysis of other samples from the ocean floor reveals that particles become progressively finer from bottom to top of the deposit. The best explanation of this graded bedding is that the deposit was laid down by a turbidity current carrying particles of many different sizes, and that the larger particles were the first to be dropped on the ocean floor. Such deposits are called **turbidites.**

Turbidity currents may be set in motion by the slumping and sliding of material along the slopes of the ocean basin under the influence of gravity, either by itself or aided by the jarring of an earthquake. Or the currents may be created by the churning up of bottom sediments under the influence of violent storms.

Figure 11-8   This photograph shows a muddy Alaskan stream entering the clearer waters of the Gulf of Alaska. Although turbid, the stream water does not sink, because it is still lighter than the salt water of the ocean.

MAJOR SURFACE CURRENTS   The major movements of water near the ocean's surface occur in such currents as the Gulf Stream, the Japanese Current, and the Equatorial Currents. These great currents are caused by a variety of factors, including the prevailing winds, the rotation of the earth, variations in the density of sea water, and the shape of ocean basins. Let us examine, by way of illustration, the surface currents of the Atlantic Ocean in both the Northern and Southern Hemispheres, as shown in Figure 11 9.

The **Equatorial Currents** lie on each side of the equator, and they move almost due west. They derive their energy largely from the trade winds that blow constantly toward the equator, from the northeast in the Northern Hemisphere and from the southeast in the Southern Hemisphere. The westerly direction of the currents is explained by the **Coriolis effect.** This effect is produced by the rotation of the earth, which causes moving objects to veer to the right in the Northern Hemisphere and to the left in the Southern Hemisphere. As the water driven by the trade winds moves toward the equator, it is deflected west in both hemispheres.

As a result, the North and South Equatorial Currents are formed. As these currents approach South America, one is deflected north and the other mainly south. This deflection is caused largely by the shape of the ocean basins, but it is aided by the Coriolis effect and by the slightly higher level of the oceans along the equator where rainfall is heavier than elsewhere.

The North Equatorial Current moves into the Caribbean waters and then northeastward, first as the Florida Current and then as the Gulf Stream. The Gulf Stream, in turn, is deflected to the east (to the right) by the Coriolis effect. This easterly movement is strengthened by prevailing westerly winds between 35°N and 45°N, where it becomes the North Atlantic Current. As it approaches Europe, the North Atlantic Current splits. Part of it moves northward as a warm current past the British Isles and parallel to the Norwegian coast. The other part is deflected southward as the cool Canaries Current,

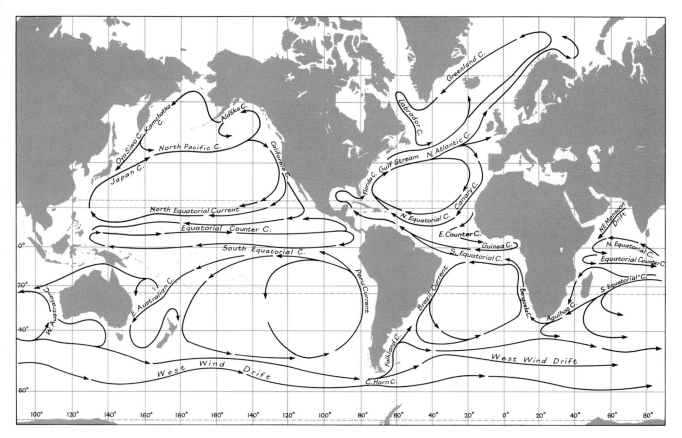

Figure 11-9 Major surface currents of the oceans of the world.

and eventually is caught up against the Northeast Trade Winds, which drive it into the North Equatorial Current.

In the South Atlantic, the picture is very much the same—a kind of mirror image of the currents in the North Atlantic. After the South Equatorial Current is deflected mainly southward, it travels parallel to the eastern coast of South America as the Brazil Current. Then it is bent back to the east (toward the left) by the Coriolis effect and is driven by prevailing westerly winds toward Africa. This easterly moving current veers more and more to the left until finally, off Africa, where it is known as the Benguela Current, it is moving northward. This stream in turn is caught up by the trade winds and is turned back into the South Equatorial Current.

The cold surface water from the Antarctic regions moves along a fairly simple course, uncomplicated by large landmasses. It is driven in an easterly direction by the prevailing winds from the west. In the Northern Hemisphere, however, the picture is complicated by conti-

nental masses. Arctic water emerges from the polar seas through the straits on either side of Greenland, to form the Labrador Current on the west and the Greenland Current on the east. Both currents subsequently join the North Atlantic Current and are deflected easterly and northeasterly.

We need not examine in detail the surface currents of the Pacific and Indian oceans. We can note, however, that the surface currents of the Pacific follow the same general patterns as those of the Atlantic. Furthermore, the surface currents of the Indian Ocean differ only in detail from those of the South Atlantic.

THE OCEAN BASINS

Most geologists now agree that the continents of the world are composed largely of sialic rock overlying a layer of heavier, crystalline simatic rock. (For a discussion of the terms sial and sima, see "Types of Igneous Rocks" in Chapter 3). The sialic layers seem to be missing from the deep ocean basins, however, for the ocean floor is apparently made up of simatic rock along with a covering of sediments that reaches a thickness of 5,000 to 6,000 feet in places but that probably averages about 3,000 feet. We may think of the continents, then, as great blocks of relatively light material buoyed up on masses of denser material.

Most of the sea water surrounding the continents is held in one great basin that girdles the Southern Hemisphere and branches northward under the Atlantic, Pacific, and Indian oceans. The Atlantic and Pacific oceans in turn are connected with the Arctic Ocean through narrow straits. But the oceans still flood over the margins of the continents, for even this great, fingered basin cannot contain all the water of the earth.

Topography of the Sea Floor: Continental Shelves, Slopes, and Ocean Deeps

The margins of the continents that lie flooded beneath the seas are referred to as **continental shelves.** The average width of these shelves is a little over 40 miles, but there are many local variations. Along the western coast of South America, for example, the shelf is altogether missing, or at best, but a few miles in width. In contrast, the shelf reaches out 150 miles off Florida, about 350 miles off the coast of South America south of the Rio de la Plata, and from 750 to 800 miles off the Arctic coasts of Europe and Russia.

The seaward edge of the continental shelves has an average depth of about 430 feet, but it is commonly as deep as 600 feet (100 fathoms) or as shallow as 300 feet. Soundings indicate that the topography of the shelves changes somewhat from one place to another, but there seems to be a general lack of spectacular features. Some shelves, such as those off Labrador, Nova Scotia, and New England, show the marks of vanished continental glaciers, the material they deposited in some places and eroded away in others. The surface of almost all the shelves is irregularly marked by hills, valleys, and de-

pressions of low to moderate relief. Furthermore, soundings along the shelf bordering the eastern coast of North America show the presence of submarine terraces that record former lower levels of the ocean, just as higher levels are recorded by terraces stranded above sea level.

Generally, the shelves incline gently toward the ocean basins until they are abruptly terminated by the steeper **continental slopes** that descend thousands of feet into the ocean deeps. Continental slopes are steepest in their upper portion, and commonly extend more than 12,000 feet downward. In certain places where earth movements have created deep trenches in the ocean floor, the continental slopes reach to much greater depths. Off the island of Mindanao, in the Philippines, the slope drops down for some 30,000 feet. Scarring the face of the continental slopes at various places around the world are deep submarine canyons; but the floor of the great world-encircling basin that contains the oceans is far more irregular than the surface of the continental shelves and slopes. The more soundings that are made, the more complex and spectacular the topography appears (see Figure 11-10). The ocean floor is divided into innumerable smaller basins and is marked by plains, plateaus, valleys, towering peaks, and mountain ranges.

SUBMARINE VALLEYS   The surfaces of the continental shelves, slopes, and ocean deeps are all furrowed by **submarine valleys** of varying width, depth, and length, rather like the valleys of the continents. The origin of the deep, spectacular valleys, the submarine canyons that crease the continental slopes, is still in dispute, but the origin of the lesser valleys along the shallow continental shelves is fairly well understood.

Some of the valleys that cut across the continental shelves seem to be seaward extensions of large valleys on the adjoining land. One of the best-known submarine valleys is the submerged extension of the Hudson Valley off the eastern coast of the United States. This valley extension is relatively straight, cuts down about

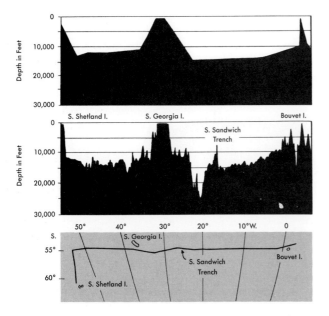

Figure 11-10 The more depth determinations we have, the more complex our picture of the ocean floor becomes. The location of a line of profile is shown in the lowest of the three diagrams. The upper diagram is a section along this line of profile and is based on very few depth determinations. The middle diagram, a section along the same line of profile, is based on more extensive soundings of the ocean floor than the first profile. (*Redrawn from H. U. Sverdrup and others, op. cit., p. 18.*)

200 feet into the continental shelf, and widens from about 3 miles at the coastline to approximately 15 miles at its seaward end. It is speculated that this and similar valleys, such as those in the China Sea, were cut during periods of Pleistocene glaciation (see Chapter 20), when sea level was perhaps 300 feet lower than it is at present, and when large portions of the continental shelves were exposed to erosion by land streams.

In addition to these larger stream valleys, there are smaller troughs in the continental shelves that are presumed to have been cut by tidal scouring. Several troughs of this sort occur off the northeastern coast of the United States. Other valleys were apparently cut on the continental shelves by glacier ice that may simply have deepened already existing valleys.

More difficult to explain are the deep submarine canyons along the continental slopes and along the floor of the deep ocean basins.

The canyons on the continental slopes have been known since the latter part of the 19th century. Today, even though soundings are scattered and incomplete, it seems certain that submarine canyons are characteristic of the continental slopes all around the world. Some canyons, such as those on the slopes off the Hudson and Congo rivers, appear to be extensions of valleys on the land or on the continental shelves. Others seem to have no association with such valleys. In any event, these canyons have V-shaped cross profiles and gradients that decrease along the lower sections of the continental slopes. Their slightly winding courses may extend out to sea as far as 145 miles, as does the Congo canyon. Some canyons cut down more than a mile beneath the surface of the continental slope.

Sonic depth measurements have revealed that other submarine valleys, some as deep as 12,000 feet or more, run for great distances across the floors of the ocean out beyond the continental slopes. Valleys of this sort are known in both the Atlantic and the Pacific, but data on them are too meager to permit exact descriptions, much less explanations of their origin.

Running generally from north to south along the center of the Atlantic Ocean is a broad zone, known as the **Mid-Atlantic Ridge**, that rises above the general elevation of the deep ocean basin. A submarine valley 25 to 50 miles wide and hundreds of feet deep follows along the crest of this ridge in the North Atlantic and probably also in the South Atlantic.

Oceanographers have suggested that this submarine valley is similar to the Valley of the Dead Sea in the Near East and to the so-called Rift Valley of Africa, which contains such lakes as Tanganyika and Nyassa. These land valleys have been caused by the down-dropping of sections of the earth's crust. The submarine valley on the crest of the Mid-Atlantic Ridge may have been formed in the same way.

SEAMOUNTS Dotting the ocean floors are drowned, isolated steep-sloped peaks called **seamounts.** They stand at least 3,000 feet above

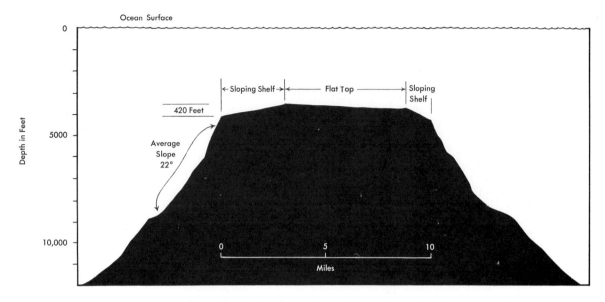

Figure 11-11 Soundings in the Pacific Ocean during World War II revealed the presence of many flat-topped submarine mountains called guyots. The guyot in this profile is located at 8.8° N., 163.1° E. (*Redrawn from H. H. Hess, "Drowned Ancient Islands of the Pacific Basin," Am. J. Sci., CCXLIV, 1946, p. 777.*)

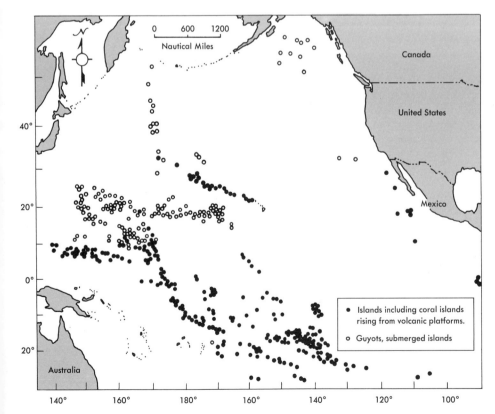

Figure 11-12 Guyots of the Pacific Ocean basin occur in groups, as do the chains of present-day volcanic-based islands. (*Redrawn from H. W. Menard, "Geology of the Pacific Floor," Experientia, XV, No. 6, 1959, pp. 210, 212.*)

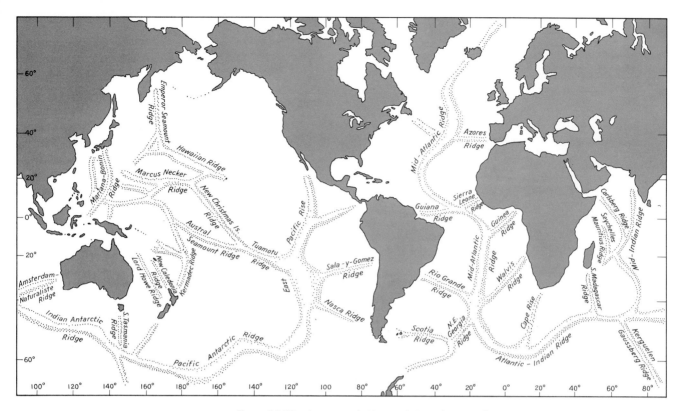

Figure 11-13 A system of ridges and rises of topography segment the ocean basins into smaller units.

the surrounding ocean floor, their crests covered by depths of water measured in thousands of feet. Seamounts have been identified in all the oceans, but the greatest number by far are reported from the Pacific Ocean. There, by the mid-1960's, some 1,500 such peaks had been mapped; it is estimated that 10 times this number remain to be discovered.

Most seamounts have sharp peaks, and, insofar as we can tell, they are all of volcanic origin. Some of the peaks have flat tops, called **tablemounts,** or **guyots** (pronounced gee-yoz— hard "g" as in geese) in honor of Arnold Guyot, a Swiss-American geologist of the mid-19th century. Guyots are thought to be volcanic cones whose tops have been cut off by the action of surface waves. Most evidence suggests that the guyots then sank beneath the sea, but it is also possible that they were drowned by a rise in sea level (see Figures 11-11, 11-12).

SUBMARINE RIDGES, RISES, AND FRACTURES Among the major features of the deep ocean basins are long, submerged ridges and rises.

In general, ridges have steep sides and irregular topography. The rises differ in being broader and gentler in form. They rise thousands of feet above the deep ocean floor and in some places actually appear above the surface to form islands. These ridges and rises form a more or less integrated system of high topography that segments the deep oceans into smaller basins (see Figure 11-13).

In addition to these two forms, long towering escarpments caused by earth movements scar some sections of the ocean floor. Thus, the Mendocino, Murray, Clipperton, and Clarion fracture zones stretch westward into the Pacific from the coasts of the United States and Central America (see Figure 11-14). The vast Mendocino Escarpment reaches heights of 8,000 feet and extends 2,000 miles into the central Pacific.

Less well-known but similar fractures and related escarpments lie to the south of this system. And fracture systems of similar magnitude may offset the Mid-Atlantic Ridge just north of the equator.

229

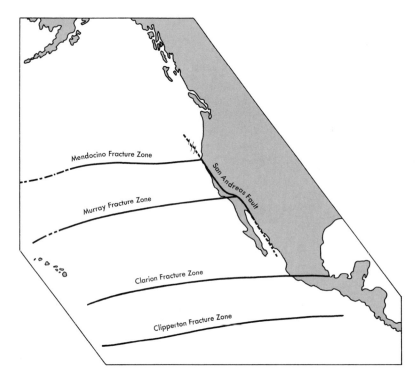

Figure 11-14 Long fracture zones in the sea floor reach westward into the Pacific from western North America and Central America. See text for discussion. (*Redrawn from H. W. Menard, "Deformation of the North-eastern Pacific Basin and the West Coast of North America," Geol. Soc. Am. Bull., LXVI, 1955.*)

DEEP-SEA TRENCHES The greatest ocean depths occur in great arcuate, or bow-shaped, trenches on the sea floor bordering some of the continents. Several of these trenches dip to more than 30,000 feet below the ocean surface, and they may reach 125 miles in breadth and 1,500 miles in length. Since arcuate chains of islands are often located near these deep trenches, they are sometimes known as **island arc deeps.** So far as we know, most of them occur in the Pacific Ocean, particularly the western part and in Indonesian waters (see Figure 11-15).

These deep-sea trenches were formed by tectonic movements of the earth's crust, but the exact mechanism involved has not yet been satisfactorily explained.

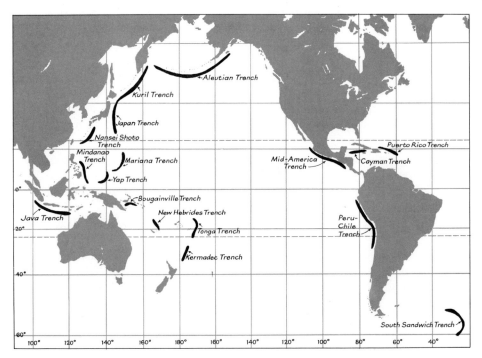

Figure 11-15 Deep-sea trenches outline the Pacific Ocean.

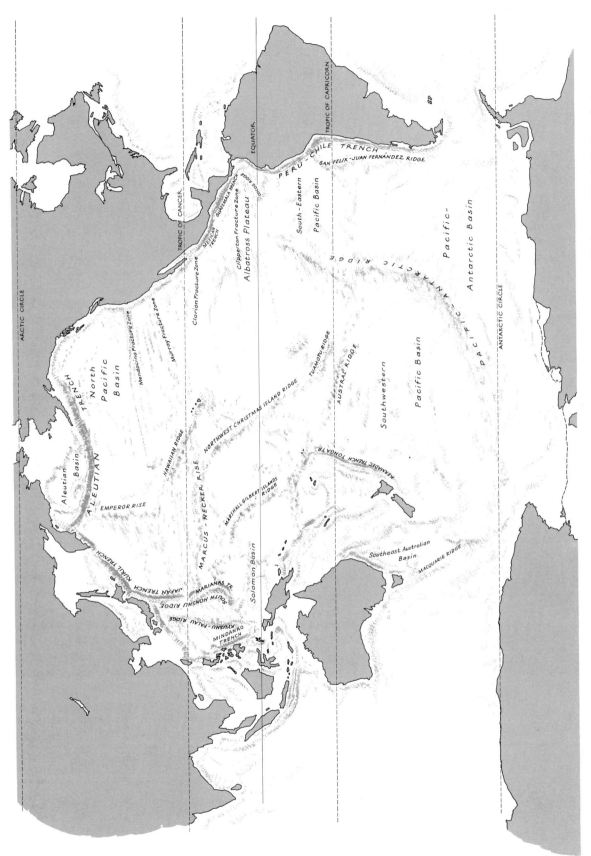

Figure 11-16 Major topographic features of the Pacific Ocean basin.

Sediments of the Ocean

In earlier chapters, we have spoken from time to time of the processes by which earth materials are weathered, eroded, transported, and finally deposited to be transformed into sedimentary rocks. The great ocean basins of the world constitute the ultimate collection area for the sediments and dissolved material that are carried from the land. And the great bulk of the sedimentary rocks found on our modern landmasses were once deposits on the sea floors of the past. In this section we shall speak briefly of sediments being laid down in modern oceans and seas—the sediments destined to become the sedimentary rocks of the future.

DEPOSITS ON THE CONTINENTAL SHELVES Theoretically, when particles of solid material are carried out and deposited in a body of water, the largest particles should fall out nearest the shore and the finest particles farthest away from the shore, in a neatly graduated pattern. But there are a great many exceptions to this generalization. Many deposits on the continental shelves show little tendency to grade from coarse to fine away from the shoreline. We would expect to find sand close to shore only—actually it shows up from place to place all along the typical continental shelf right up to the lip of the continental slope. It is particularly common in areas of low relief on the shelf. In fact, on glaciated continental shelves, sand mixed with gravel and cobbles constitutes a large part of the total amount of deposited material.

Also common on the continental shelves are deposits of mud, especially off the mouths of large rivers and along the course of ocean currents that sweep across the river-laid deposits. Mud also tends to collect in shallow depressions across the surface of the shelves, in lagoons, sheltered bays, and gulfs.

Where neither sand nor mud collects on the shelves, the surface is often covered with fragments of rock and gravel. This is commonly the case on open stretches of a shelf, where strong ocean currents can winnow out the finer material, and off rocky points and exposed stretches of rocky shoreline. In narrow straits running between islands or giving access to bays, the energy of tidal and current movements is often so effectively concentrated that the bottom is scoured clean and the underlying solid rock is exposed.

Strangely, although the geologic record indicates many calcareous deposits laid down in the ancient seas, eventually to give rise to the rock we call limestone, only a few calcareous deposits are being built up on the continental shelves of modern seas. And most of these limy mud deposits are being built up in warmer waters, particularly near coral reefs. No satisfactory explanation accounts for the apparent deficiency.

DEPOSITS ON THE CONTINENTAL SLOPES Although we have less information about the deposits being laid down on the continental slopes than we have about the shelf deposits, evidence indicates that here, too, gravel, sand, mud, and bedrock are all found on the bottom. And deposition, it seems, is taking place even more rapidly on the slopes than on the shelves.

DEPOSITS ON THE DEEP-SEA FLOOR The deposits that spread across the floors of the deep sea are generally much finer than those on the slopes and shelves lying off the continents, although occasional beds of sand have been found even in the deeps. Deep-sea deposits of material derived from the continents are referred to as **terrigenous** ("produced on the earth") deposits. Those formed of material derived from the ocean itself are **pelagic** ("pertaining to the ocean") deposits.

Among the terrigenous deposits are beds of wind-borne volcanic ash that has fallen over the ocean and has settled through thousands of feet of water to the sea bottom. In the polar regions, silts and sands from glacier ice make up much of the bottom deposit, and around the margins of the continents we often find deep-sea mud deposits of silt and clay washed down from the landmasses. Much of the ocean bottom, especially in the Pacific, is covered by an extremely fine-grained deposit known as **brown clay,** which may have originated on the continents and then drifted out into the open ocean.

In the Antarctic and Arctic oceans some of the deep ocean sediments are believed to have been ice-rafted from the land to the oceans by icebergs. These glacial marine deposits are chiefly silt containing coarse fragments. Near the landmasses are extensive layers of sand and coarse silt deposited by turbidity currents—the turbidites discussed previously.

Most of the pelagic deep-sea deposits consist of **oozes,** sediments of which at least 30 per cent by volume is made up of the hard parts of very small, sometimes microscopic, organisms. These hard parts are constructed of mineral matter extracted from the sea water by

Figure 11-17 Major topographic features of the Atlantic Ocean basin.

tiny plants and animals. With the death of the organisms, the remains sink slowly to the sea floor. In composition, the oozes are either calcareous or siliceous.

Two calcareous oozes are common in the deep seas. In one—**globigerina ooze**—the limy shells of minute one-celled animals called **Globigerina** abound; in the other—**pteropod ooze** —the shells of tiny marine molluscs predomi-

nate. Globigerina oozes cover large portions of the floors of the Atlantic, Pacific, and Indian oceans, while the greatest known concentration of pteropod ooze is in a long belt running from north to south in the Atlantic Ocean midway between South America and Africa.

Siliceous oozes included **radiolarian ooze,** made up largely of the delicate and complex hard parts of minute marine protozoa called

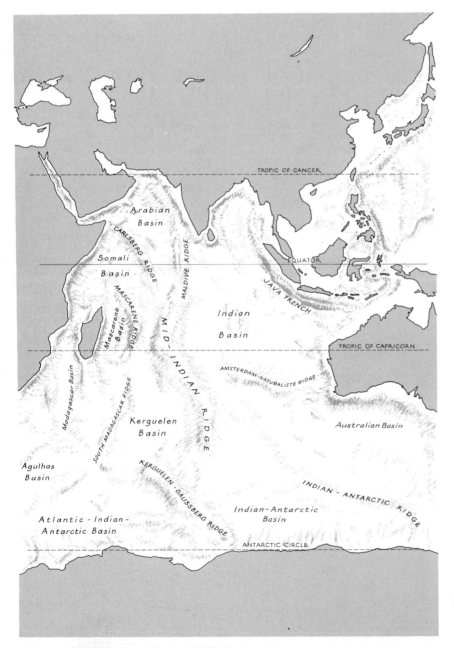

Figure 11-18 Major topographic features of the Indian Ocean basin.

Radiolaria, and by **diatomaceous ooze**, made up of the siliceous cell walls of one-celled marine algae known as **diatoms.** Radiolarian ooze predominates in a long east-west belt in the Pacific Ocean just north of the equator; while the greatest concentration of diatomaceous ooze occurs in the North Pacific and in the Antarctic Ocean.

Some of the pelagic deposits of the sea floor have apparently crystallized directly from sea water, and these we refer to as **authigenic** (from the Greek, "born on the spot"). In large areas of the southern Pacific Ocean, the silicate mineral **phillipsite** constitutes the great bulk of the sediments, but the mineral grains are too large to have been transported by the currents in the area of their present location; thus, they are thought to have crystallized directly from sea water.

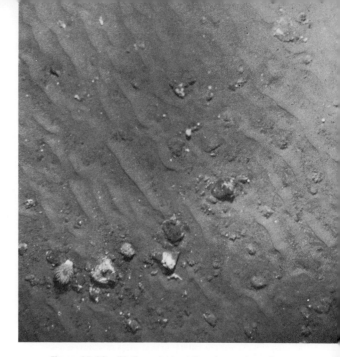

Figure 11-19 Ripple-marked sand on the continental shelf between George's and Brown's Banks, off the New England coast. The ripple marks indicate currents moving diagonally from the upper right toward the lower left. The "sand dollar" in the lower left is 2 to 3 inches in diameter. (*Photo by D. M. Owen, Woods Hole Oceanographic Institution.*)

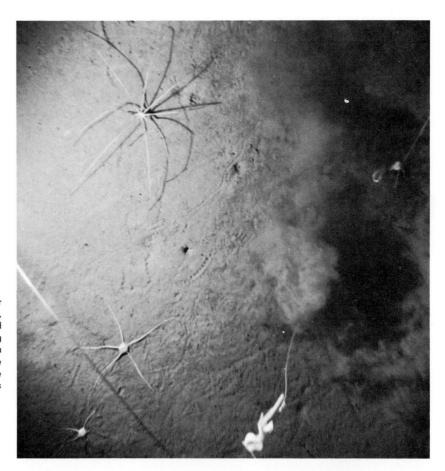

Figure 11-20 This muddy sea floor is south of Cape Cod, Massachusetts, at a depth of 6,000 feet. The cloud of sediment was raised by a fishing line and sinker. The larger animal is a sea spider measuring 28 inches. The smaller, five-armed animals are brittle stars. (*Photo by D. M. Owen, Woods Hole Oceanographic Institution.*)

More spectacular authigenic deposits are the **manganese nodules** (see Figure 11-21). These average 10 inches in diameter and when cut open exhibit the patterns of concentric growth. Composed largely of oxides of manganese and iron, they contain in addition the oxides of many of the rarer elements. It is estimated that they cover some 20 per cent of the floor of the Pacific. Their composition and abundance have suggested a potential commercial use as an ore not only of manganese but also of such rarer elements as cobalt, titanium, and zirconium.

Most sediments are deposited in the shallow waters of the continental shelves or on the slopes leading down to the deep sea. Very few sediments get to the deep sea floor, where the rate of sedimentation on average seems to be 0.5 inches per 1,000 years or less. In contrast, on shelves and slopes the rate appears to be 10 to 20 times this rate.

Figure 11-21 This photograph of the deep sea floor was taken in the Atlantic Ocean at a depth of nearly 18,000 feet. The objects are manganese nodules. The largest is about 6 inches in maximum dimension. (*Photo by Lamont Geological Observatory.*)

Figure 11-22 Map showing type and distribution of deep-sea sediments. (*Redrawn from F. P. Shepard, Submarine Geology, 2nd ed. New York: Harper & Row, Publishers, 1963, Fig. 198.*)

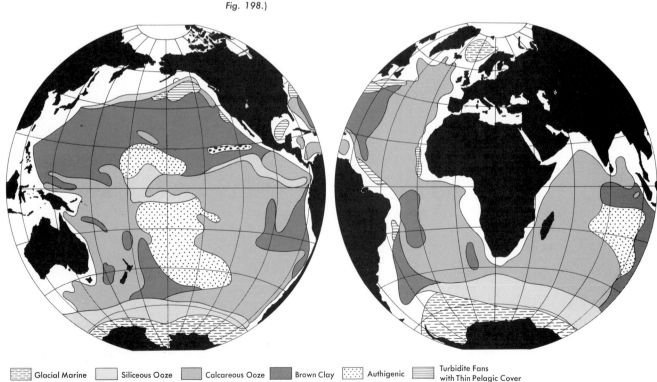

Glacial Marine   Siliceous Ooze   Calcareous Ooze   Brown Clay   Authigenic   Turbidite Fans with Thin Pelagic Cover

Few people have occasion to make a detailed study of the ocean currents or of the topography of the ocean floor; but most of us have many opportunities to observe the activity of water along the shorelines of oceans or lakes. The nature and results of wave action along such shorelines can be a drama of power and persistence.

The Processes

The energy that works upon and modifies a shoreline comes largely from the movement of water produced by tides, by wind-formed waves, and, to a lesser extent, by tsunami (see Chapter 7). Since we have already discussed tidal currents, we may now turn to the nature and behavior of wind-formed waves as they advance against a shoreline.

WIND-FORMED WAVES Most water waves are produced by the friction of air as it moves across a water surface. The harder the wind blows, the higher the water is piled up into long **wave crests** with intervening troughs, both crests and troughs at right angles to the wind. The distance between two successive wave crests is the **wave length,** and the vertical distance between the wave crest and the bottom of an adjacent trough is the **wave height** (Figure 11-23). When the wind is blowing, the waves it generates are called a **sea.** But wind-formed waves persist even after the wind that formed them dies. These waves, or **swells,** may travel for hundreds or even thousands of miles from their zone of origin.

We are concerned with both the movement of the wave form and motion of water particles in the path of the wave. Obviously the wave form itself moves forward at a measurable rate. But in deep water, the water particles in the path of the wave describe a circular orbit: Any given particle moves forward on the crest of the wave, sinks as the following trough approaches,

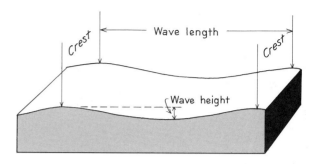

Figure 11-23 Diagrammatic explanation of terms used in describing waves of water.

Figure 11-24 The motion of water particles relative to wave motion in deep water. Water particles move forward under the crest and backward under the trough, in orbits that decrease in diameter with depth. Such motion extends downward to a distance of about one-half the wave length. (*Redrawn from U.S. Hydrographic Office Publication 604, 1951, Fig. 1-2.*)

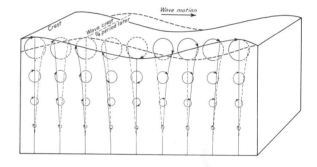

moves backward under the trough, and rises as the next crest advances. Such a motion can best be visualized by imagining a cork bobbing up and down on the water surface as successive wave crests and troughs pass by. The cork itself makes only very slight forward progress under the influence of the wind. Wave motion extends downward, until at a depth equal to about one-half the wave length it is virtually negligible. But between this level and the surface, water particles move forward under the crest and backward under the trough of each wave, in orbits that decrease in diameter with depth (Figure 11-24).

As the wave approaches a shoreline and the water becomes more shallow, definite changes take place in the motion of the particles and in the form of the wave itself. When the depth of water is about half the wave length, the bottom begins to interfere with the motion of water particles in the path of the wave and their orbits become increasingly elliptical. As a result, the length and velocity of the wave decrease and its front becomes steeper. When the water becomes shallow enough and the front of the wave steep enough, the wave crest falls forward as a breaker, producing what we call **surf**. At this moment, the water particles within the wave are thrown forward against the shoreline. The energy thus developed is then available to erode the shoreline or to set up currents along the shore that can transport the sediments produced by erosion.

WAVE REFRACTION AND COASTAL CURRENTS
Although most waves advance obliquely toward a shoreline, the influence of the sea floor tends to bend or refract them until they approach the shore nearly head-on.

Let us assume that we have a relatively straight stretch of shoreline with waves approaching it obliquely over an even bottom that grows shallow at a constant rate. As a wave crest nears the shore, the section closest to land feels the effect of the shelving bottom first and is retarded, while the seaward part continues along at its original speed. The effect is to swing the wave around and to change the direction of its approach to the shore, as shown in Figure 11-25.

As a wave breaks, not all its energy is expended on the erosion of the shoreline. Some of the water thrown forward is deflected and moves laterally, parallel to the shore. The energy of this water movement is partly used up by friction along the bottom, and partly by the transportation of material.

Refraction also helps explain why, on an irregular shoreline, the greatest energy is usually concentrated on the headland and the least along the bays. Figure 11-26 shows a bay separating two promontories, and a series of wave crests sweeping in to the shore across a bottom that is shallow off the headland and deep off the mouth of the bay.

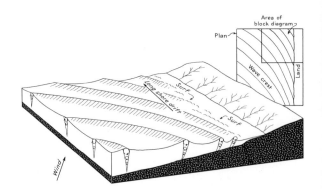

Figure 11-25 Wave crests that advance at an angle on a straight shoreline and across a bottom that shallows at a uniform rate are bent shoreward, as suggested in this diagram. Refraction is caused by the increasing interference of the bottom with the orbits of water-particle motion within the wave.

Figure 11-26 Refraction of waves on an irregular shoreline. It is assumed that the water is deeper off the bay than off the headlands. Consider that the original wave is divided into three equal segments, A-B, B-C, and C-D. Each segment has the same potential energy. But observe that by the time the wave reaches the shore, the energy of A-B and C-D has been concentrated along the short shoreline of headlands A'-B' and C'-D', whereas the energy of B-C has been dispersed over a greater front (B'-C') around the bay. Energy for erosion per unit of shoreline is therefore greater on the headlands than along the bay.

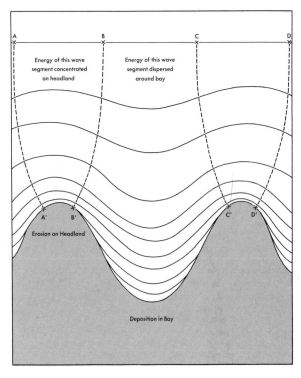

Where the depth of the water is greater than one-half the wave length, the crest of the advancing wave is relatively straight. Closer to shore, off the headlands, however, the depth becomes less than half the wave length, and the wave begins to slow down. In the deeper water of the bay it continues to move rapidly shoreward until there, too, the water grows shallow and the wave crest slows. This differential bending of the wave tends to make it conform in a general way to the shoreline. In so doing, the wave energy is concentrated on the headland and dispersed around the bay, as suggested in Figure 11-26.

A composite profile of a shoreline from a point above high tide seaward to some point below low tide reveals features that change constantly as they are influenced by the nature of waves and currents along the shore. All features are not present on all shorelines, but several are present in most shore profiles. The **offshore** section extends seaward from low tide. The **shore**, or **beach**, section reaches from low tide to the foot of the **sea cliff** and is divided into two segments. In front of the sea cliff is the **backshore**, characterized by one or more **berms**, which resemble small terraces with low ridges on their seaward edges built up by storm waves. Seaward from the berms to low tide is the **foreshore**. Inland from the shore lies the **coast**. Deposits of the shore may veneer a surface that is cut by the waves on bedrock and is known as the **wave-cut terrace**. In the offshore section, too, there may be an accumulation of unconsolidated deposits composing a **wave-built terrace** (Figure 11-27).

The shoreline profile is ever-changing. During great storms the surf may pound in directly against the sea cliff, eroding it back and at the same time scouring down through the beach deposits to abrade the wave-cut terrace. As the storm (and hence the available energy) subsides, new beach deposits build up out in front of the sea cliff. The profile of a shoreline at any one time, then, is an expression of the available energy: It changes as the energy varies. This relation between profile and available energy is similar to the changing of a stream's gradient and channel as the discharge (and therefore the energy) of the stream varies (see Chapter 9).

Shoreline Features

Not even shorelines have escaped man's constant desire for classification into neat pigeonholes. But to date no completely acceptable system of classification has been devised. For many years it was common practice to group shorelines as **emergent** or **submergent**, depending upon whether the sea had gone down or had come up in relation to the landmass. Thus, large sections of the California coast, having

Figure 11-27 Some of the features along a shoreline, and the nomenclature used in referring to them. (*In part, after Shepard, op. cit., p. 168.*)

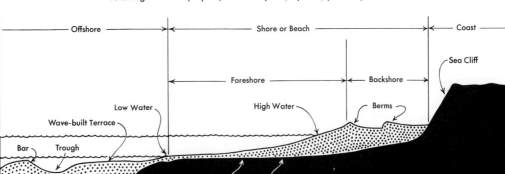

emerged from the sea during geologically recent times, would be termed emergent. Across the continent, the shoreline of New England indicates that it has been drowned by a slowly rising sea and would be referred to as submergent. The system has been criticized because some of the features that were thought to represent emergence of land actually form where the land is being submerged. Conversely, along shorelines of submergence, features thought to characterize emergence may also develop.

Another attempt at a classification is based on the processes that form shorelines. Some have major features traceable to glacial erosion, others to glacial deposition. The system divided along these lines has much to recommend it. Nevertheless, we shall examine some of the individual shoreline features without attempting to fit them into an all-inclusive system.

Erosion and deposition work hand in hand to produce most of the features of the shoreline. An exception to this generalization is an off-

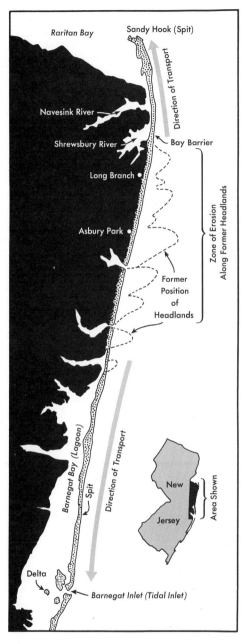

Figure 11-30 Erosion by the sea has pushed back the New Jersey coastline as indicated on this map. Some of the material eroded from the headlands has been moved northward along the coast to form Sandy Hook, a spit. To the south, a similar but longer feature encloses Barnegat Bay, a lagoon with access to the open ocean through a tidal inlet. (*After an unpublished map by Paul MacClintock.*)

shore island that is merely the top of a hill or a ridge that was completely surrounded by water as the sea rose in relation to the land. But even islands formed in this way are modified by erosion and deposition.

FEATURES CAUSED BY EROSION **Wave-cut cliffs** are common erosional features along a shore, particularly where it slopes steeply down beneath the sea (see Figure 11-28). Here waves can break directly on the shoreline, and thus expend the greatest part of their energy in eroding the land. Wave erosion pushes the wave-cut cliff steadily back, producing a wave-cut terrace or platform at its foot. Since the surging water of the breaking waves must cross this terrace before reaching the cliff, it loses a certain amount of energy through turbulence and friction. So the farther the cliff retreats, and the wider the terrace becomes, the less effective are the waves in eroding the cliff. If sea level remains constant, the retreat of the cliffs becomes slower and slower.

Waves pounding against a wave-cut cliff produce various features, as a result of the differential erosion of the weaker sections of the rock. Wave action may hollow out cavities, or **sea caves,** in the cliff, and if this erosion should cut through a headland, a **sea arch** is formed. The collapse of the roof of a sea arch leaves a mass of rock, a **stack,** isolated in front of the cliff (see Figure 11-29).

FEATURES CAUSED BY DEPOSITION Features of deposition along a shore are built of material eroded by the waves from the headlands, and of material brought down by the rivers that carry the products of weathering and erosion from the land masses. For example, part of the material eroded from a headland may be drifted by currents into the protection of a neighboring bay, where it is deposited to form a sandy beach.

The coastline of northeastern New Jersey (Figure 11-30) illustrates some of the features caused by deposition. Notice that the Asbury Park-Long Branch section of the coastline is a zone of erosion that has formed by the destruction of a broad headland area. Erosion still goes on along this part of the coast, where the soft sedimentary rocks are easily cut by the waves of the Atlantic. The material eroded from this section is moved both north and south along the coastline. Sand swept northward is deposited in Raritan Bay and forms a long, sandy beach projecting northward, a **spit** known as Sandy Hook.

Just south of Sandy Hook, the flooded valleys of the Navesink River and of the Shrewsbury River are bays that have been almost completely cut off from the open ocean by sandy beaches built up across their mouths. These beaches are called **bay barriers.**

Sand moved southward from the zone of erosion has built up another sand spit. Behind it lies a shallow lagoon, Barnegat Bay, that receives water from the sea through a **tidal inlet,** Barnegat Inlet. This passage through the spit was probably first opened by a violent storm, presumably of hurricane force. Just inside the inlet a delta has been formed of material partly deposited by the original breakthrough of the bar and partly by continued tidal currents entering the lagoon.

Long stretches of the shoreline from Long Island to Florida, and from Florida westward around the Gulf Coast, are marked by shallow, often marshy lagoons separated from the open sea by narrow sandy beaches. Many of these beaches are similar to those that enclose Barnegat Bay, apparently elongated spits attached to broad headlands. Others, such as those that enclose Pamlico Sound at Cape Hatteras, North Carolina, have no connection with the mainland. These sandy beaches are best termed **barrier islands.** It has been suggested that these islands originated from spits that were detached from the mainland as large storms breached them at various points. Some geologists think that they may represent spits isolated from the mainland by a slowly rising sea level. Still a third possibility is that over a long period of time wave action has eroded sand from the shallow sea floor and has heaped it up in ridges that lie just above sea level.

Another depositional feature, **a tombolo,** is a beach of sand or gravel that connects two is-

lands, or connects an island with the mainland. Numerous examples exist along the New England coastline, fewer off the West Coast, although Morro Rock, a small, steep-sided island, is tied to the California mainland by a tombolo.

CORAL REEF SHORELINES   In tropical and semitropical waters lying within a belt between about 30° N and 25° S, many shorelines are characterized by coral reefs of varying sizes and types. These reefs are built up by individual corals with calcareous skeletons, as well as by other lime-secreting animals and plants. The coral-reef shorelines are of three types: the **fringing reef,** the **barrier reef,** and the **atoll.** A fringing reef grows out directly from a landmass, whereas a barrier reef is separated from the main body of land by a lagoon of varying width and depth opening to the sea through passes in the reef. An atoll is a ring of low, coral islands arranged around a central lagoon.

The origin of atolls has been debated for well over a century, ever since Charles Darwin first advanced his explanation in 1842. Darwin postulated that an atoll begins as a fringing reef around a volcanic island. Since the island rests as a dead load on the supporting material, it begins to subside, but at a rate slow enough for the coral to maintain a reef. With continued subsidence, the island becomes smaller and smaller, and the actively growing section of the reef becomes a barrier reef. Then, with the final disappearance of the island below the sea, the upward-growing reef encloses only a lagoon and becomes a true atoll. In support of this theory are many volcanic islands in the Pacific now surrounded by barrier reefs. Furthermore, investigations on Bikini Island (an atoll) indicate that the volcanic rock core is surmounted by several thousand feet of coral rock. Finally, geophysical evidence suggests that there actually has been a subsidence of some of the volcanic islands of the Pacific.

The subsidence theory originally advanced by Darwin, however, does not explain the nearly constant depth of countless modern lagoons within the atolls. In part to overcome this difficulty, the so-called **glacial-control theory** has been advanced. Proponents of this explanation of atoll formation have postulated that volcanic islands were truncated at a lower sea level during one or more of the Pleistocene ice advances. Around the edges of such wave-planed platforms the coral reefs began to grow as the continental glaciers melted and sea level rose. The coral islands around the edge of the platforms would then ring lagoons of more or less constant depth. In summary, there is evidence in support of each theory. When the final answer is known, both may be applicable.

SUMMARY

Oceans cover more than 70 per cent of the earth's surface. The level of the sea rises and falls not only with the tides but also because of eustatic and tectonic processes.

Ocean water is circulated by tidal currents, by wind-driven surface currents, and by density currents which move to the deep ocean bottoms and are caused by variations in temperature, salinity, and turbidity of the water.

Ocean basins are divided into areas of shelves, slopes, and deep ocean basins. Among the major topographic features are submarine canyons and valleys, deep sea trenches, rises and ridges, and seamounts.

Shorelines are modified by energy derived from wind-driven waves. Erosional features include cliffs, stacks, caves and arches. Depositional features include spits, beaches, bay barriers, barrier islands, and tombolos.

ADDITIONAL READING

Carson, Rachel, *The Sea Around Us* (rev. ed.). New York: Oxford University Press, 1961.

Cotter, Charles H., *The Physical Geography of the Oceans*. New York: American Elsevier Pub. Co., 1965.

King, Cuchlaine A. M., *An Introduction to Oceanography*. New York: McGraw-Hill Book Co., 1963.

Menard, H. W., *Marine Geology of the Pacific*. New York: McGraw-Hill Book Co., 1964.

Pickard, George L., *Descriptive Physical Oceanography*. New York: Macmillan, 1964.

Shepard, F. P., *Submarine Geology* (2nd ed.). New York: Harper & Row, 1963.

Sverdrup, H. U., Martin W. Johnson, and Richard H. Fleming, *The Oceans*. Englewood Cliffs, N.J.: Prentice-Hall, 1942.

12

Time in Geology

The importance of time in geologic processes has been touched upon in connection with almost every topic discussed in previous chapters. It has been suggested and inferred repeatedly that lengthy spans of time seem to have been necessary to bring the earth to its present condition. We should now devote our attention specifically to the subject of time and its measurement as applied to geology.

ABSOLUTE AND RELATIVE TIME

We may think of geologic time in two ways: relative and absolute. **Relative time** relates to whether one event in earth history came *before or after* another event, but disregards years. **Absolute time** measures whether a geologic event took place a *few thousand years* ago, a *billion years* ago, or at some date even further back in earth history.

Relative and absolute time in earth history have their counterparts in human history. In tracing the history of the earth, we may want to know whether some occurrence, such as a volcanic eruption, preceded or followed another, such as a rise in sea level, and how these two events are related in time to a third event, perhaps a mountain-building episode. In human history, too, we try to establish relative positions in time. Thus, in studying American history it is important to know that the Revolution preceded the War Between the States, and that the Canadian-American boundary was fixed some time between these two events.

Sometimes, of course, events in both earth history and human history can be established only in relative terms. But our record becomes increasingly precise as we fit more and more events into an actual chronological calendar. If we did not know the date of the U.S.-Canadian boundary treaty—only that it was signed between the two wars—we could place it between 1783 and 1861, but we could be no more precise than that. Recorded history, of course, provides us with the actual date, 1846.

Naturally, we would like to be able to date geologic events with precision. But so far this has been impossible, and the accuracy achieved in determining the dates of human history, at least written human history, will probably never be achieved in geology. Still, we can determine approximate dates for many geologic events. Even though they may lack the precision possible in recent human history, they are probably of the correct order of magnitude. For instance, we can say that the dinosaurs became extinct

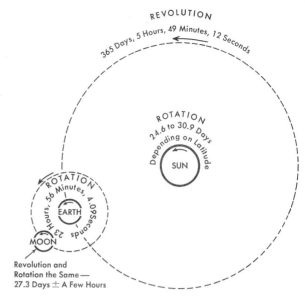

Figure 12-1 Astronomical "clocks," some more reliable than others. Notice the times of revolution and rotation. The diagram is not intended to portray true relative sizes and shapes of orbits.

about 63 million years ago, and that about 11,000 years ago the last continental glacier began to recede from New England and the area bordering the Great Lakes.

YEARS AND SEASONS

The rotation and revolution of the earth provide us with our most important and useful measures of time—the year and the day. Commencing with crude observations of the changing seasons and positions of the heavenly bodies, man has become quite accurate in fixing the length of the year as 365 days, 5 hours, 49 minutes, and 12 seconds. Although such measures as the week, hour, minute, or second (defined as 1/31,556,-925.9 of the year) are accepted standards of time measurement, they are purely artificial fractional measures invented by man. Obviously, if the length of the year should change or vary, so would the second and all of its multiples. It is now proposed to adopt a new standard for defining the second—9,192,631,770 cycles of vibration of the cesium atom. This atomic standard is being checked against the astronomic standard with the hope of discovering whether there are actual variations in either. The lengths of the year and the day are accepted as basic to time measurement, but the geologist is interested to know how long these familiar cycles have been in effect.

Evidence for our regular yearly journey around the sun exists in the form of seasonal effects. Because the axis of the earth is inclined to the plane along which it travels, characteristic changes of light, temperature, and precipitation are repeated with the seasons. These effects exercise a profound influence on the food supply and growth patterns of plants and animals and, locally at least, on the erosion, transportation, and deposition of sediments. Seasonal effects are recorded in living and nonliving materials in many ways and have thereby become permanently recorded in the earth's crust.

GROWTH RINGS IN PLANTS AND ANIMALS

The best-known seasonal records preserved in living organisms are **tree rings.** The width and spacing of the rings depend on temperature, light, and moisture variations that are largely of a seasonal nature. Each ring consists of 2 parts: the so-called "summer wood," which has small cells with thick walls, and the "spring wood," which has larger cells with thinner walls. The study of tree rings, called **dendrochronology,** has made significant contributions to the dating of individual archaeological sites, especially in the arid portions of the American

Figure 12-2 Growth rings in a highly magnified section of Douglas fir wood. The cells of the summer wood are small with thick walls. Spring wood has large cells with thinner walls. (*Courtesy General Biological Supply House, Inc., Chicago.*)

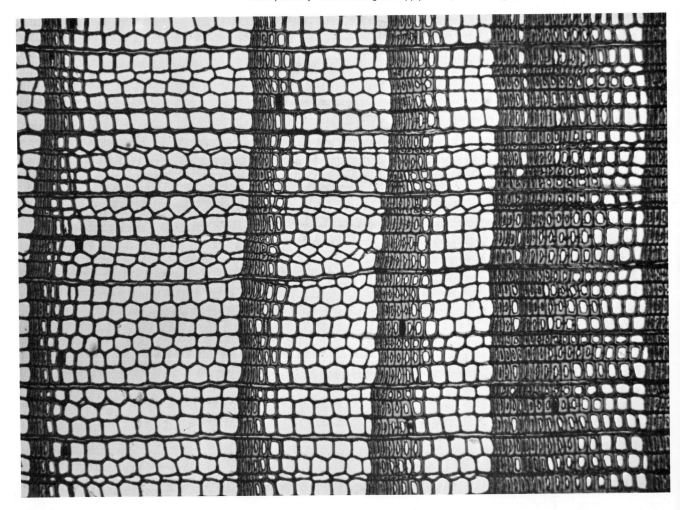

Figure 12-3 Oldest known living thing, the Methuselah tree, a bristlecone pine over 4,800 years old. The specimen is still growing in the White Mountains, east of Bishop, California. (*Courtesy Laboratory of Tree-Ring Research, University of Arizona.*)

Southwest where wood is easily preserved. A continuous chronology going back to 1550 B.C. has been pieced together for that region, and many important ruins have been dated by pieces of structural wood.

Figure 12-4 Fresh-water clam (*Legumia recta*) from Lake Michigan, showing well-marked annual growth rings. Length is 3½ inches.

An even longer sequence of rings exists in the individual trunks of the sequoia trees of California. Studies of the annual rings prove that some of them are over 3,000 years old. The sequoia trees have long been regarded as the oldest living things on earth, but this claim has been challenged by a less spectacular tree, the bristlecone pine, which is found in various drier parts of California, Nevada, and Utah. The oldest tree of this species so far dated is at least 4,800 years old (Figure 12-3).

Animals also respond to seasonal changes, usually by variations in growth rates corresponding with variations in the favorability of growth conditions. Shells of clams (Figure 12-4) and other aquatic organisms show growth "rings" much like those of trees. Fish scales reveal their age by similar marks. Less well-known examples are layering in the spines and otoliths (ear bones) of fish, in coral growths, in the horns of mammals, and in the limb bones of certain reptiles.

VARVES—SEDIMENTARY RECORDS OF SEASONAL CHANGE

The effects of seasonal change are not confined to living things. A great deal of the earth is exposed to recurrent variations in precipitation during wet and dry seasons. Under favorable conditions these variations are reflected in the erosion and deposition of sediment. Ideally, for the leaving of records, there should be an interval of little or no deposition followed by one of rapid sedimentation, corresponding to seasons of low and high stream-flow.

Figure 12-5 . Varves formed of alternating silt and clay, near mouth of Sherman Creek, Ferry County, Washington. (*Courtesy U.S. Geological Survey.*)

Any deposit reflecting a yearly cycle is a **varve** (see Chapter 10). The clearest and most easily interpreted varves are associated with glaciers. In and near most ice fields, the seasons of melting and freezing are sharply marked, and there are abundant lakes and ponds in which deposits may be preserved. During the warm season, when snow and ice are melting, a large quantity of sediment is deposited in adjacent bodies of water, and a relatively thick layer of coarser sediment is laid down. With the onset of winter, when water ceases to flow and the ponds and lakes are covered by ice, no sedimentation occurs. During this quiet period, however, very fine clay particles and some dead organic matter slowly settle to the pond and lake bottoms, forming a thinner layer of finer and usually darker material. As a result of these conditions, each varve consists of two gradational parts. Actual observations of varves in the process of formation, and examination of ancient deposits, reveal that glacial varves usually range from a fraction of an inch to several inches in thickness. Thus, the record of hundreds of years may easily accumulate in one lake or pond.

Varves, like tree rings, may be thick or thin, depending on the length and relative warmth of the seasons. As a matter of fact, the variation in the spacing of thick and thin varves permits geologists to correlate one set of varves with another, just as one tree may be correlated with another. The most complete sequences of varves are created in lakes that are formed as large continental glaciers melt away. The oldest varve accumulation lies near the point of maximum extent of the glacier, and the latest may still be forming at the glacier's edge. Between the two points lie a series of sediment-filled lakes with overlapping varve histories.

Through great effort, geologists have traced the record of retreat of the last ice sheets in Europe and America. Unfortunately, there are gaps in the records that can be filled in only by estimates. In Scandinavia a connection with the present has been established, and the record, with certain portions estimated, reaches backward for about 10,000 to 15,000 years. In North America the varve chronology, again with some estimated periods, reaches back some 20,000 years. In view of the uncertainties and imperfections of the method, it is impossible to say exactly how far back varve records go. Evidence seems adequate, however, to carry the count at least 15,000 years back in time.

Glacial varves have been found associated with evidences of ice action in very old deposits laid down during earlier ice ages. The antiquity of these older records is indicated by the fact that the rocks containing them have been deeply buried and hardened by heat or pressure. Undoubtedly, these older varves were formed under conditions that were not significantly different from conditions that prevail today in glacial areas.

Many banded deposits that are thought to record yearly events are also found in nonglacial sediments. Lake deposits, shale formations of marine origin, and salt beds often contain varves or varve-like beddings that probably have resulted from seasonal changes in the sediment supply. Several dozen such deposits or formations, each containing hundreds or even thousands of varves, have been discovered.

The evidence of more or less regular rings in fossil wood and shells, taken in connection with varved sediments from all geologic ages, seems to indicate that seasonal changes have been affecting the surface of the earth for a very long time.

Figure 12-6   Varves in the Green River Formation, Garfield County, Colorado. The darker bands contain relatively more organic matter. On the basis of varve counts, this formation is calculated to have taken 11,500,000 years to accumulate. Magnification about 4x. (*Courtesy U.S. Geological Survey.*)

HOW OLD IS THE EARTH?

Granting that the earth has been making a yearly circuit of the sun for many, many years, we are led to ask just how many such journeys it may have made—or, in other words, how old it is. Until fairly recent times, the origin and age of the earth were not considered to be subjects for serious inquiry. Interpretations of Hebrew scripture, basis of the Christian faith of the Western world, were considered to be the final and sufficient word on the subject. In 1654, Archbishop James Usher concluded from scriptural analysis that the earth had been created in 4004 B.C. This was printed as a marginal date in several editions of the Bible and was quite generally believed by most Christians. A few years later, a learned Biblical scholar, Dr. John Lightfoot of Cambridge, felt that he could be even more specific, and wrote that "Heaven and earth, center and circumference, were made in the same instance of time, and clouds full of water, and man was created by the Trinity on the 26th of October 4004 B.C. at 9 o'clock in the morning." The idea of a 6,000-year-old earth was entirely satisfactory as long as there were no reasons for believing otherwise. It is interesting to note, however, that ancient Hindu thinkers had placed the age of the earth at almost 2 billion years.

As the spirit of scientific inquiry began to assert itself, the age of the earth became a subject for serious consideration. Facts were few and meaningful observations were just beginning to be undertaken. Yet to some thinkers every natural feature of the landscape gave evidence of great antiquity. The cutting of valleys, the advance and retreat of glaciers, the destruction of coasts by erosion and their restoration by deposition, all seemed to demand long time periods. But quantitative data were needed, and in the 18th and 19th centuries a few preliminary attempts were made to actually measure and evaluate certain properties of the earth in order to establish its age.

Among the natural phenomena that seemed to offer clues in the search were (1) the saltiness

Figure 12-7 A radioactive specimen takes its own photograph. The piece of ore on the left contains dark-colored uranium minerals in a matrix of nonradioactive material. Placed against a photographic film, the radioactive areas affect the silver compounds in the same manner as light. (*Courtesy Wards Natural Science Institution.*)

of the ocean, (2) the internal heat of the earth, and (3) the rate of deposition of sediments.

It was assumed in the first case that the original ocean was fresh and that salt had been added at approximately the current rate ever since rivers commenced to run. Therefore, if we divide the amount of sodium now in the ocean by the amount brought in annually, we have the age of the ocean. The method gives answers of 90 to 100 million years.

It was assumed in the second method that the earth must have cooled from an originally molten condition. Since the approximate rate of cooling and the present temperature can be measured, the entire period of cooling may be calculated. This gives a span of 20 to 40 million years. As an incidental argument, it was contended that no known source of heat could have supported the sun's output for much longer than a 20-million-year period, and that the earth could not be older than the sun.

Finally, with regard to deposition of sediments, it was reasoned that if we determine how many feet of sediment have been laid down and how long it takes a foot to accumulate under average conditions, we may by simple division arrive at an estimate of how long erosion and deposition have been going on. Latest figures show that the cumulative maximum thickness of rock laid down since abundant fossils appeared is at least 450,000 feet or about 80 miles. Although rates of deposition vary from time to time and place to place, an average of one foot in 1,000 years may not be far wrong. At this rate, the fossil-bearing sedimentary rocks would have taken 450 million years to accumulate.

Although these earlier hypotheses were well conceived and the supporting calculations were mathematically correct, they involved so many unknowns and gave such varied results that no one now has much confidence in any of them. It is likely that the seas have always been about as salty as they now are, and we know from the presence of thick salt beds that much salt has been returned to the lands from the seas. It is also known that the earth contains its own heat-producing radioactive elements, which would totally confuse any calculations based on gradual cooling from an original molten state. The heat of the sun is now known to be provided by nuclear reactions and not by ordinary combustion as once was supposed. Finally, the rates of formation of a foot of sediment range from thousands of years for limy ooze to a few hours for river-laid sand, so that it seems impossible to arrive at reliable rates of deposition. Aside from indicating that periods longer than 6,000 years are needed, these methods still failed to provide a reliable estimate of the age of the earth.

RADIOACTIVITY

An unexpected method of determining the age of the earth and of specific formations came with the discovery of radioactivity late in the 19th century. **Radioactivity** is the spontaneous transmutation of one element into another by the emission of particles from the atomic nuclei. Three types of products are emitted: **alpha** (α)

rays, **beta** (β) **rays**, and **gamma** (γ) **rays.** These rays can be detected, counted, and measured by suitable instruments, such as the Geiger counter.

The Theoretical Basis for Age Determination

All radioactive elements are subject to disintegration from the moment they come into existence. But a specific atom may disintegrate immediately or it may remain intact for millions of years. The spontaneous behavior of the individual atom is unpredictable and not governed by any known law. Nevertheless, aggregations of atoms, like aggregations of people, are subject to mathematical rules. There is no way we can predict the death of a specific person, but we can forecast quite accurately what proportion of a given group will die yearly and how many will be alive at any given time. Since the potential life of a radioactive atom may be infinitely long, the total period of activity of a large group of atoms is impossible to predict. It is easier and more meaningful to measure the time interval in which half of the atoms of a large group or specimen have disintegrated. This interval is called the **half-life**, a term widely used in nuclear studies. If half of a certain population has disintegrated in a million years, then half of those remaining will

Figure 12-8 Radioactivity, hourglass, and human survival compared. In each curve there is a decrease with time, but the rates are different. Half the radioactive material has disintegrated quite early in the total existence of the specimen; the remainder disintegrates at the same rate, diminishing by half each half-life period until it approaches the zero point. In the hourglass the sand runs steadily; half is gone when the time is half gone, and at the end of the specified time all the sand is gone. In a given human population half the persons are dead when the mean lifetime has been reached; the decline is slow at first, rapid later.

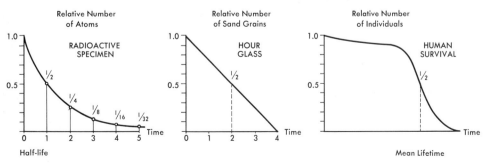

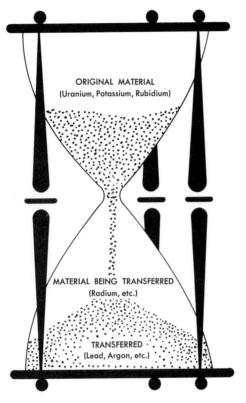

Figure 12-9 Radioactive disintegration operates like an hourglass. In both cases a given amount of original, or "parent," material is transferred or changed so that it can be measured separately. The difference lies in the rate of transfer. (*After Howell, 1959.*)

Two fundamental characteristics of radioactivity are of interest to geologists. In the first place, the rate of radioactive disintegration is not significantly influenced by external terrestrial conditions. Specimens subjected to extremes of temperature and pressure show no variation in activity, and we can assume that disintegration has always proceeded at the present rate no matter what conditions within the earth's crust may have been. The second important property is the production within the earth of heat energy that apparently can cause earth movements, volcanic eruptions, and other evidence of internal change (see Chapter 8).

The dating of radioactive materials depends on the correct determination of the ratios of original, or parent, materials to derived, or daughter, products. We can make a rather crude comparison between this principle and the operation of the old-fashioned hourglass, which "told time" by the passage of sand from one compartment to another (Figure 12-9).

disintegrate in the next million years, and so on. At first, the decline in abundance of a radioactive material is rapid, but later on, as it approaches its end stages, the decline is progressively slower.

The half-life existence of radioactive elements ranges from a fraction of a second to billions of years. Many kinds of atoms with short half-life periods were probably once common in the universe but have declined to the vanishing point. Others with longer periods have traveled but a fraction of the way to extinction. Although there appears to have been only one large-scale creation of radioactive elements, scientists have created artificially many types of radioactive substances that in general have relatively short half-lives. Also not to be overlooked are short-lived radioactive substances that are currently being produced in the atmosphere and on the earth by powerful cosmic rays issuing from space.

Figure 12-10 Diagram showing half-life system of measuring radioactive decay of rubidium 87.

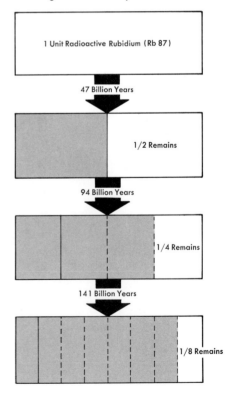

If the rate of transfer (decay or disintegration) of the material is known, the ratio between the amount of material already transferred and that remaining will tell how long the "clock" has been operating. Obviously, the sample must have remained in a closed system with nothing added or subtracted since it began to operate. A cracked hourglass which allows sand grains to escape is not a reliable time teller. In nature it is the escape from, or addition to, the chemical systems that pose the most serious problem: For example some radioactive products are gaseous and may be driven off by heat and pressure through minute cracks or pores in rock. Geologists take all precautions to see that their specimens are as unweathered and free of fractures as possible.

At present four radiometric systems have proven to be widely applicable. They are based on the decay of radioactive isotopes of uranium, potassium, rubidium (Figure 12-10), and carbon. The first three are useful in dating of minerals and rocks, the last is applicable to organic materials that have been alive within the past 50,000 years. Table 12-1 gives the pertinent data on each of these systems.

For recent geologic events involving organic material, only one radioactive element has been used with any real success, and that is carbon-14.

The carbon-14 method, first developed at the University of Chicago by Willard F. Libby, works as follows: When neutrons from outer space, sometimes called cosmic rays, bombard nitrogen in the outer atmosphere, they convert a proton of the nitrogen nucleus to a neutron, thereby forming carbon-14.

The carbon-14 combines with oxygen to form a special carbon dioxide, $C^{14}O_2$, which circulates in the atmosphere and eventually

Table 12-1 **Major Methods in Geochronometry**

Nuclides	Half-Life (Years)	Effective Range (Years)°	Materials
U^{238}-Pb^{206}	4.50×10^9	10^7-T_0	Zircon, uraninite, pitchblende
U^{235}-Pb^{207}	0.71×10^9	10^7-T_0	Zircon, uraninite, pitchblende
Rb^{87}-Sr^{87}	4.7×10^{10}	10^7-T_0	Muscovite, biotite, lepidolite, microcline, glauconite, whole metamorphic rock
K^{40}-Ar^{40}	1.30×10^9 (total)	10^5-T_0†	Muscovite, biotite, hornblende, phlogopite, glauconite, sanidine, whole volcanic rock, sylvite (arkose, sandstone, siltstone)°°
C^{14}	$5,710 \pm 30$	0–50,000	Wood, charcoal, peat, grain, tissue, charred bone, cloth, shells, tufa, ground water, ocean water

° T_0 = age of the earth, i.e., 4.6×10^9 yrs.
°° For paleogeographic studies.
† Under certain favorable conditions the lower limit of this method can be extended to approximately 10^4 yrs.

Table courtesy Isotopes, Inc.

C-14

N

reaches the earth's surface, where it is absorbed by living matter. It has been found that the distribution of carbon-14 around the world is almost constant. Its abundance is independent of longitude, latitude, altitude, and the type of habitat of living matter.

There is, then, a certain small amount of carbon-14 in all living matter. And when an organism—whether plant or animal—dies, its supply of carbon-14 is, of course, no longer replenished by life processes. Instead, the carbon-14, with a half-life of about 5,700 years, begins spontaneously to change back to $_7N^{14}$. The longer the time that has elapsed since the death of the organism, the less the amount of carbon-14 that remains. So when we find carbon-14 in a buried piece of wood or in a charred bone, by comparing the amount present with the universal modern abundance, we can work out the amount of time that has elapsed since the material ceased to take in $C^{14}O_2$—that is, since the organism died.

Radiocarbon dating has been applied to a great variety of materials, including wood, peat, seeds, shells, charcoal, leaves, bone, manuscripts, rope, and cloth. The method has been checked by applying it to human artifacts and tree rings whose ages are known by other methods. The agreement is close and lends confidence to the dating of older materials. Literally thousands of dates have been obtained that are of interest not only to geologists but also to anthropologists, archaeologists, and historians.

Figure 12-11   Carbon-14 is formed from nitrogen in the atmosphere and is incorporated in all living things. The rate of addition and disintegration is constant and in equilibrium. Carbon-14 disappears from dead organic matter by reverting to nitrogen; the amount remaining in a dead specimen is a measure of age.

1/2 C-14
Remains 5,700 Years

1/8 C-14
Remains 17,100 Years

1/32 C-14
Remains 28,500 Years

Insignificant
After 45,000 Years

BURIED CHARCOAL TELLS ITS OWN AGE

"Fossil" Fission Tracks as Age Indicators

As early as 1900 it was observed that mica will show discolored areas around radioactive particles embedded in it. These pleochroic halos are caused by the bombardment of the mica by high-energy fragments set free by the spontaneous fission of scattered uranium atoms. Workers at the General Electric Research Laboratory at Schenectady, New York, studied pleochroic halos under high magnification and found numbers of small tubes, like minute bullet holes, that had been ploughed out by the outward-moving fission fragments. These holes can be enlarged by etching with acid and then counted and studied in detail.

Figure 12-12 Fossil fission tracks in biotite mica. The crystal was etched in hydrofluoric acid to enlarge the tracks which radiate from a microscopic impurity containing a larger number of uranium atoms. Magnification about 3000x. (*Courtesy P. Buford Price.*)

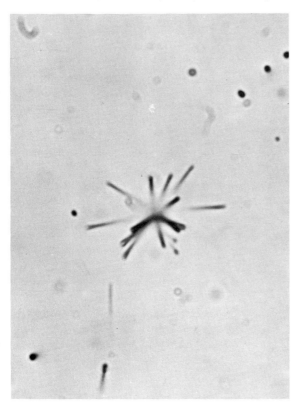

In order to obtain an age estimate, it is necessary to know how many uranium atoms have already disintegrated in a given volume of mineral and how many have not yet disintegrated. The first figure can be determined by counting the naturally occurring tracks; to get the second figure the sample is artificially bombarded in a reactor with neutrons that cause the remaining uranium atoms to disintegrate, leaving another set of tracks which can in turn be counted.

About 10 minerals and natural glasses have been found to contain fission tracks suitable for dating. The method is not without pitfalls. It has been discovered, for instance, that the tracks are "erased," or healed, when the containing material is heated above a few hundred degrees. Samples that have been near enough to the surface of the earth to have been subject to cosmic rays also give unreliable dates. The best results are expected to come in the study of materials less than about 100 million years old. Already the method has been successfully applied to the study of many rocks and minerals and to the meteoritic fragments called **tektites.** It is frequently possible to date the same specimen both by fission tracks and by some other methods, thus providing a test of the accuracy of both procedures.

MISCELLANEOUS AGE-DATING METHODS

The earth is apparently full of chemical and physical "clocks" running with various speeds and degrees of accuracy. The search for additional time measures is continuing and the process of testing them is proceeding at an accelerated rate throughout the world. We can briefly mention some of the newer or less well-known methods. For example, a number of techniques based on the various isotopes in the two series from uranium to lead (see Table 12-1) have been suggested. The idea is that some daughter products might be enriched or depleted in relation to their parents by certain processes associated with sedimentation or differential solution. Another method employs **beryllium-10** which is produced by cosmic rays in the atmosphere, as is carbon-14. Beryllium-10 has a half-life of 2.5 million years, and although it is not taken into organisms, it is buried in sediments whose age of last exposure to the atmosphere can theoretically be calculated. A third system, the **chlorine method,** is based on the fact that, when certain rocks are exposed at the surface, Cl^{36} (half-life 300,000 years) is produced through the interaction of cosmic rays and stable chlorine. The ratio of Cl^{36} to stable chlorine gives the length of exposure time.

The **thermoluminescence method** is based on the fact that many natural minerals emit light when they are heated to temperatures below red heat. This light, which is emitted only once, records the amount of previous disruptions caused by disintegrating radioactive elements. In general, the older the sample, the more the damage and the greater the thermoluminescence.

A chemical method is based on the rate of breakdown of amino acids produced and left in rocks by organisms. The rate of disintegration is different for different acids, if temperatures are the same. Thus, older rocks have the more stable types of amino acids, younger ones have all types. This method gives only rough approximations, or relative dates, however.

THE GEOLOGIC COLUMN AND THE TIME SCALE

The essential facts of any historical subject are often more comprehensible if presented in tabular chronological form. Geologists have found it useful to relate their information about the past history of the earth to a fairly simple arbitrary outline called the **geologic column.** The beginnings of this arrangement go back to the 18th century when observers first saw the need for naming the various related groups of rocks they found in nature. It soon became clear that the best method would have to be based on the relative ages of the rocks involved; in other words, the column should portray the chronological order of origin from oldest to youngest.

The most difficult problem was, and still is, the matter of subdividing the record. The units that were recognized and named are based on what the early observers considered to be natural interruptions in the rock record. These interruptions are made evident, at least locally, by actual physical discontinuities (unconformities) and by discontinuities in the orderly evolution of fossil forms. Progress was slow, since there was no general plan, no central authority, and no clear idea about how much or what might ultimately be classified.

The divisions that gradually emerged and are currently used were proposed chiefly in Europe, where geology had its beginning. Although early workers believed these units to be firmly based on world-wide "natural" interruptions in deposition, it is now clear that they are quite arbitrary. The difficulty of adapting a local classification to a complex world-wide situation has become all too apparent. Adjustments have been made, however, and the present geologic column is, with few exceptions, a product of investigations carried on in Europe during the 19th century.

Derivation of Names

The derivation of the **period** names presented in Table 12-2 will illustrate the unsystematic way in which the geologic column grew or accumulated. The Cambrian, Ordovician, and Silurian are named for ancient native tribes of Wales and England. The Devonian comes from Devonshire, England. The Mississippian and Pennsylvanian are American names taken from the Mississippi Valley and the State of Pennsylvania respectively. Europeans do not use these names, favoring instead the Carboniferous, so named from the coal content of the rocks. The Permian is derived from the Perm Province on the flanks of the Ural Range in Russia. The term Triassic comes from a typical 3-fold association of distinctive formations in Germany, but no particular place is implied. The Jurassic gets its name from the Jura Alps. The Cretaceous is not named for a particular locality, but for the characteristic high content of chalk (*creta* being the Latin for chalk). The Tertiary and Quaternary derive from still another naming procedure: In one of the earlier schemes, the terms Primary, Secondary, Tertiary, and Quaternary were used for successively older deposits. Of these, only the last two have survived in general usage. The subdivisions of the Tertiary and Quaternary (the **epochs**) get their names from the so-called presence-absence method based on fossil content. For example, of the fossil species found in the Eocene (Gr. *eos*, dawn + *kainos*, recent, meaning "dawn of the recent") from 1% to 5% are still alive in the eastern Atlantic. Fossils of the Pliocene (Gr. *pleion*, more + *kainos*, "more of the recent") include from 50% to 90% of still-living species.

Table 12-2 The Geologic Time Scale

Era	Period	Epoch	*Millions of Years Ago (Approx.)*	*Duration in Millions of Years (Approx.)*	*Relative Durations of Major Geological Intervals*
Cenozoic	Quaternary	Recent	0–1	1	Cenozoic
		Pleistocene			Mesozoic
	Tertiary	Pliocene	1–13	13	Paleozoic
		Miocene	13–25	12	
		Oligocene	25–36	11	
		Eocene	36–58	22	
		Paleocene	58–63	5	
Mesozoic	Cretaceous		63–135	72	
	Jurassic		135–181	46	
	Triassic		181–230	49	
Paleozoic	Permian		230–280	50	
	Pennsylvanian		280–310	30	
	Mississippian		310–345	35	Precambrian
	Devonian		345–405	60	
	Silurian		405–425	20	
	Ordovician		425–500	75	
	Cambrian		500–600	100	
Precambrian	Upper	Although many local subdivisions are recognized, no world-wide system has been evolved. The Precambrian lasted for at least 2½ billion years. Oldest dated rocks are about 3,300 million years old.			
	Middle				
	Lower				

Reference to the time scale shows that the periods have been combined in lengthy intervals called **eras.** These are based on the stage of evolution of characteristic life forms. Paleozoic means "ancient life"; Mesozoic, "middle life," and Cenozoic, "recent life." Like the naming of the months of the year or the days of the week, the development of the geologic time scale was neither well-planned nor consistent; nevertheless, we seem to have no alternative now but to use these schemes in spite of imperfections.

What has been said to this point applies to the divisions of actual rock masses into groups ranging from oldest to youngest as they occur around the globe. When we add actual ages in years to these units, we have a geologic time scale. In effect, the terms we apply to time units are the terms that were originally used to distinguish rock units. Thus, we speak either of Cambrian *time* or of Cambrian *rocks.* When we speak of time units, we are referring to the geologic time scale. When we speak of rock units, we are referring to the geologic column.

The geologic time scale is given in Table 12-2. Notice the terms **eras, periods,** and **epochs** across the top of the table. These are general time terms. Thus, we speak of the Paleozoic Era, or the Permian Period, or the Pleistocene Epoch. The rock terms **system** and **series** correspond with the time terms **period** and **epoch,** respectively. There is no generally accepted rock term equivalent to **era,** but the term **erathem** has been suggested.

SUMMARY

A major contribution of geology is the concept that the earth is very old. From evidence of seasonal changes, such as tree rings and from annual sedimentary deposits called varves, it is thought that the earth has been revolving and rotating in a relatively steady manner for at least 2 billion years.

Attempts to answer the question, "How old is the earth?" on a scientific basis began in the late 18th century. Crude estimates based on the amount of salt in the ocean, the rate of deposition of sediments, and the rate of cooling of the earth, did little more than indicate that the traditional idea of a 6,000-year-old creation was almost certainly in error.

The discovery of the spontaneous breakup of certain elements—known as radioactivity—opened up a new and more certain method of finding not only the age of the earth but also many rocks and minerals of its crust. Since the rate of breakup of radioactive atoms is not influenced by ordinary terrestrial conditions, a number of natural dating methods are provided by measuring the amount of material already disintegrated (as known from the daughter products) as compared with that yet to disintegrate. The chief radioactive transformations that are useful in age determination are uranium to lead, thorium to lead, potassium to argon, rubidium to strontium, and carbon-14 to nitrogen.

Analysis of thousands of specimens has given the following "time table of creation": earth solidified about 4.5 billion years ago; first extensive permanent rock masses formed about 3.5 billion years ago; fossil record begins about 3 billion years ago; abundant fossil record commences with the beginning of the Cambrian Period about .6 billion years ago.

The geologic time table is an arbitrary arrangement of divisions and subdivisions of geologic time. When the names of the time divisions are applied to actual rocks the standard geologic column results.

ADDITIONAL READING

Albritton, Claude C., ed., *The Fabric of Geology*. San Francisco: Freeman, Cooper and Co., 1964.

Dunbar, C. O., and John Rodgers, *Principles of Stratigraphy*. New York: John Wiley & Sons, 1957.

Faul, H., ed., *Nuclear Geology*. New York: John Wiley & Sons, 1954.

Hurley, Patrick M., *How Old is the Earth?* Garden City: Doubleday Anchor Books, 1958.

Knopf, Adolph, "The Geologic Records of Time," in *Time and Its Mysteries*, Series III. New York: New York University Press, 1949, pp. 33–59.

Kulp, J. L., "Geologic Time Scale." *Science*, Vol. 133, 1961, pp. 1105–1114.

——— and others, "Geochronology of Rock Systems." *Annals*, New York Academy of Sciences, Vol. 91, 1961, pp. 159–594.

Libby, Willard F., "Radiocarbon Dating," *Science*, Vol. 133, 1961, pp. 621–629.

Wilmarth, M. G., *The Geologic Time Classification of the United States Geological Survey Compared with Other Classifications*. Washington: The U.S. Geological Survey, Bulletin 769, 1925.

Zeuner, F. E., *Dating the Past; an Introduction to Geochronology*. London: Methuen and Co., 1952.

13

Early History of the Earth

Among the earliest triumphs of science was the demonstration that the earth is not flat and is not the center of the universe. Following these discoveries came an increasing flood of knowledge about the structure and composition of the planet. Its surface has been explored and mapped, it has been weighed and measured, its motions have been determined with accuracy, and its constituents have been chemically analyzed so far as they are accessible.

All factual and statistical information about the earth is vital to humanity, and through it we are led naturally to the question of its origin —how did the earth come into being and what has been its history?

Since these questions are within the scope of historical geology, we should now briefly discuss them.

THE COSMIC BEGINNINGS

At one time in the remote past, the constituents of the earth were part of a larger mass which was to become the solar system. The history of the planet as such began when its constituents were gathered into a region of space separate and apart from the materials which became the other members of the solar system. Since that time, it is generally believed, only relatively minor amounts of matter have been added to or subtracted from the earth. The earliest "proto-earth" has been compared to a cloud of smoke or dust, to a mass of cinders, or to the head of a comet. There is considerable reason to believe that the chief constituents were small pellets of stony material called **chondrules.** These bodies, which have been found in a large number of meteorites and are dated about $4\frac{1}{2}$ to 5 billion years old, contain the necessary solid or nonvolatile molecules from which the earth could be formed. In the beginning, they must have been mixed, frozen, or "glued" together by additional liquid and gaseous matter of unknown composition. Such a heterogeneous mass of loosely packed material would have had a strong resemblance to a comet but would, of course, have been much larger than any now existing in this system.

What happened between the formation of the original cloud of small solid particles and the present time is a subject of extensive study and speculation. In reconstructing this interval, we must take into account the known composition and structure of the earth, and also the physical and chemical laws which govern the properties and behavior of large aggregations of matter.

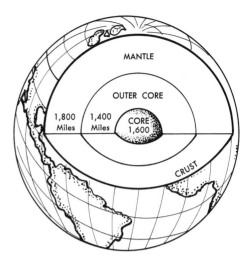

Figure 13-1 Interior of the earth showing the core and major shells. Figures in miles.

PRESENT STRUCTURE OF THE EARTH

Many essential physical facts about the earth have already been reviewed in Chapters 1 and 7. You will recall that the solid part of the globe is composed of 3 concentric parts: the core, the mantle, and the crust. The arrangement in shells or spheres continues outward through the watery layer, or hydrosphere, and the various levels of the gaseous atmosphere. This layered, or stratified, structure from heavier within to lightest without is perhaps the most salient characteristic of the earth, and the most important clue to its manner of development.

Density increases downward within the earth and, as far as is known, so does heat. The rate of increase may not be uniform, however, for the outer part of the core appears to be molten whereas the inner core is solid. This condition could be explained by differences in composition; for the present it is sufficient to note that the interior is hot and that part of it is in a molten condition.

HEAT AND THE EARTH'S THERMAL HISTORY

It has been said that if we understood the thermal history of the earth the rest would be easy. Most thinking on the early formative period of the earth is concerned with the origin of heat and its reactions with materials already present.

At one time, when it was believed that the earth had been torn directly from the sun, the internal heat was regarded as having been derived from that body. Another idea is that the impact of infalling meteorites and the consequent compaction by gravity could account for the heat. At present, however, it is generally believed that most of the past and present inner heat of the earth is generated by self-contained, radioactive materials.

It is argued that relatively large quantities of long-lived radioactive elements such as uranium, thorium, and potassium-40 were originally distributed uniformly among the materials that aggregated to form the earth. The heat generated by spontaneous disintegration of these widely distributed and deeply buried elements could not escape; it slowly accumulated and at length melted the entire earth. Since the earth is no longer molten it is obvious that radioactive heating must have diminished. This is a natural consequence of the known decline of radioactive effects with time. It is calculated that the initial rate of heat production, from the once more abundant radioactive material, was at least 8 times the present rate. It is also supposed that convection currents brought much of the radioactive material near the surface of the earth where the heat could be dissipated into space without affecting the interior.

The concept that the earth was once entirely molten is accepted by most geologists. No other hypothesis seems adequate to explain the almost perfect arrangement of material in shells according to density. The following brief summary of the probable early history of the earth will treat the development of the individual shells in terms of the molten-earth theory. Incidentally, it seems very significant that the earth may be the only one of the inner members of the solar system that has a shell-like structure. The moon, Mars, and Venus appear to be far more homogeneous, may never have been molten, and may have had, therefore, a different history from that of the earth.

THE CORE OF THE EARTH

The formation of a heavy iron core within the earth could have resulted through the melting of the original homogeneous material and the downward displacement of the heavier fraction toward the center. The melting phase is calculated to have taken place about 4.5 billion years ago. The sinking of the iron, which is equal to one-third of the earth's total mass, may have occurred rather suddenly. The event would have profoundly influenced the whole earth and its subsequent history. We do know that the metallic core is responsible for magnetic and electrical effects that extend far into space. Indeed, it is the weakness of such effects in the vicinity of the moon, Venus, and Mars that leads to the conclusion that the earth may have had a different history from that of those neighboring bodies.

THE MANTLE

The **mantle**, which makes up about two-thirds of the total mass of the earth, may be regarded as the source of the other parts; its lighter constituents moved upward to become the crust, hydrosphere, and atmosphere while the heavier fractions sank to form the core. It is intermediate in density and is presumably made up of elements such as iron and magnesium combined with silicon in minerals such as eclogite, dunite, and peridotite. There are distinct concentric zones within the mantle along with transition zones between it and the core below and the crust above.

Perhaps the most interesting problem relating to the history of the mantle is whether it has been or could be moved by heat-driven convection currents (Figure 13-2). Most investigators believe that, at some stage in its evolution, a molten planet would be affected by systematic large-scale currents rising in certain areas and falling in others. Gases, vapors, and light material would appear in the upwelling areas to be

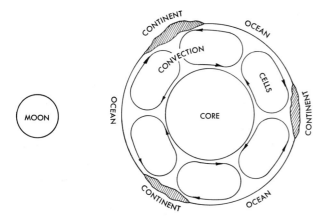

Figure 13-2 Diagrammatic arrangement of convection currents, showing how the continental material accumulates over the descending zones and the ocean basins lie over the ascending zones. Moon for comparative size. (*After R. S. Dietz, from "Studies on Oceanography," 1964, pp. 465–478.*)

left behind as a sort of "scum" when the cooled heavier currents descended. By this method the light continental rocks could have been segregated. It seems possible too, that the continental nuclei could in general have been centered over the descending currents whereas the ocean basins formed over the rising currents. The present distribution of land and oceans does not clearly indicate this arrangement, however.

Other possible influences of convection currents might include the actual splitting apart of land masses and their transport from one relative position to another. Many investigators believe the evidence indicates that the ocean bottoms too have been split and moved by currents in the mantle. These highly speculative matters will be discussed in Chapter 21.

THE CRUST

The outermost solid shell of the solid earth is called the **crust,** a term that originated when it was generally believed that the entire interior of the earth was molten. Although ideas about the interior have changed, the term "crust" is still useful in designating the outer shell, which has different properties from those of the mantle below it. As we saw in Chapter 7, the crust contains 2 distinct sublayers: an upper one, the **sial,** composed chiefly of minerals containing silicon and aluminum, and a lower one, the **sima,** composed chiefly of minerals containing silicon and magnesium. The upper layer is similar to the common light-colored igneous rocks, granite and granodiorite, while the lower layer resembles gabbro and basalt. The density of the sial is about 2.65, that of the sima 2.9. Thus, the crust also shows a stratification by density.

Figure 13-3 Generalized structure of the earth as shown by a section from the outer crust to the center (below) and the structure of the crust with some comparative information or depths of mining and drilling.

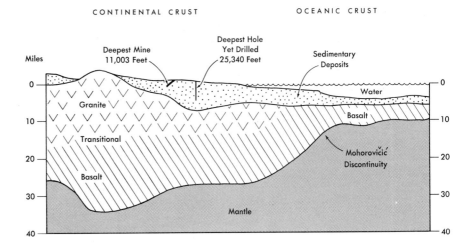

Reserving discussion of the continents as such until later, we will deal here in a general way only with the origin and composition of their constituents. We have mentioned reasons for believing that the lighter silicic material has been derived from the mantle by gravitational displacement, chiefly during a molten stage. According to this concept, the continental material is a scum, or residue, brought to the surface by convection. How the lighter rocks actually formed is essentially a chemical problem of extracting silica-rich products from the basaltic layer or from the even heavier materials of the upper mantle. There are many ways in which this could occur; suffice it to say that melting and mixing of the heavier rocks would release lighter silica-rich fractions that would be forced upward toward the surface. During their upward journey they would combine with or dissolve a variety of relatively scarce elements such as uranium, which would also be incorporated in the crust as mineral deposits or trace elements.

Most of the material released from below would be in the form of basalt, which makes up the lower level of the crust. The lighter and even more silicic material of the continents would be formed by the addition of water. If the upwelling materials solidified, melted, recrystallized, and remelted a number of times, then we might expect a light, thoroughly mixed surface scum to accumulate.

The major features of the earth's surface are reflections of the physical nature of the two types of crustal rocks. The continents, because they are lighter, rise higher and float in the heavier underlying material much as icebergs float in water. Icebergs float about five-sixths submerged; continents float about nine-tenths submerged.

If the water could be removed from the ocean basins, we would see the continental masses rising abruptly from the ocean floors, and instead of an even gradation in elevation from ocean depths to mountain heights, two very distinct levels of the earth's surface (Figure 11-2). One of these levels, lying between sea level and 3,000 feet, encompasses about 20 per cent of the earth's surface; the other level, which constitutes the ocean floor and has a mean depth of about 12,000 feet, makes up 25 per cent of the earth's surface. Only a small percentage of the dry land rises above 10,000 feet to form the highest mountains, and a correspondingly small part of the ocean floor descends to the abyssal depths.

THE OCEANS AND ATMOSPHERE

Resting on the surface of the earth are sheets of water and layers of gas that make up the hydrosphere and atmosphere. These levels, which are arranged according to density, complete the shell-like structure of the earth. Water is essentially incompressible and homogeneous, but the atmospheric constituents are compressible and exhibit distinct "spheres" or layers. The origin of these liquid and gaseous constituents must also be examined in any over-all view of the origin of the present earth.

Earth may have been misnamed, for it appears to be characterized more by its extensive waters than by its dry land. Oceans and seas roll over 71 per cent of its surface to occupy a total of 139,400,000 square miles. Lakes, streams, glaciers, and snow fields are other manifestations of water that modify the so-called "dry land." The total volume of water in the oceans is estimated at 330 million cubic miles, and if the lands were leveled out, water would cover the entire globe to a depth of 8,000 feet.

How can we explain the origin of the oceans, especially when water is so rare in the universe and solar system? Water cannot exist as a liquid except within rather narrow limits of temperature, and the compound H_2O in any form decomposes above a few thousand degrees. No other visible planet appears to cradle seas or broad sheets of water, although water vapor exists on Venus and Mars and ice probably constitutes large parts of the major planets. Water cannot persist for long on small bodies such as the moon or Mercury, for the molecules gradually escape the pull of gravity and pass into outer space.

The presence of oceans, therefore, raises 2 important questions: (1) How was water produced in large quantities in the first place? (2) How could conditions remain favorable for liquid water for such long periods of time?

The traditional picture of creation that prevailed in prescientific times assumed that the lands and oceans appeared in ready-made working order. Later on, when the idea of a molten, sun-derived earth held sway, the origin of the ocean was generally attributed to precipitation from a primitive atmosphere which contained all the earth's water in the form of dense clouds of steam and vapor. When the earth cooled sufficiently, torrential rains fell to form boiling pools and eventually oceans and seas. This fascinating picture has been modified by more recent observations and experiments. The modern geologist looks to the most ancient rocks for clues to the origin of the atmosphere and oceans, for sedimentary rocks can originate only through the reaction of air and water on particles of solid material.

The disintegration and decomposition of ordinary igneous rocks can supply the rock-forming elements that are dissolved in sea water and tied up in the sedimentary rocks. Other constituents, however, including water, carbon dioxide, chlorine, nitrogen, and sulfur, are much too plentiful in the sea and atmosphere, and in sedimentary rocks, to be attributed to weathering alone. It is the problem of these so-called **excess volatiles** that leads us directly back to a consideration of the origin of the earth's air and water. Two possibilities have been proposed. Either the earth has inherited its water and other excess volatiles from an original ocean and atmosphere, or they have arisen gradually from the earth's interior during geologic time.

The simplified picture of a molten earth with a heavy, saturated atmosphere implies that the oceans were formed quite suddenly when the earth cooled sufficiently to retain bodies of water. Such an origin, however, cannot be easily reconciled with present conditions. For example, the original atmosphere would have had to consist largely of carbon dioxide to yield all the carbonate (CO_3) that is now tied up in

Figure 13-4 Grand Geyser, Yellowstone National Park, a manifestation of the internal heat of the earth. Geysers occur mainly in areas of waning volcanic action. (*Courtesy Union Pacific Railroad.*)

limestone ($CaCO_3$) and dolomite ($MgCO_3$). Since there is relatively little carbonate rock in the Precambrian, it seems unlikely that carbon dioxide could have been an abundant constituent of the early atmosphere. Similarly, the oceans would have been made strongly acid by the chlorine they contained, until enough sodium had been eroded from the rocks to neutralize the chlorine by forming ordinary salt. In view of these and many other difficulties that arise when we start with an assumption of all constituents in a primitive ocean and atmosphere, geologists have turned to the possibility of gradual accumulation from the earth's depths. If the "excess volatiles" were derived slowly from the earth's interior, there would have been no large initial store of carbon dioxide in the early atmosphere, and limestone would have been deposited through time at a more or less constant rate as the necessary constituents arose from the earth. The oceans would never have been excessively acid, and conditions favorable for marine life would have been established rather early. It has been calculated that the present rate of production of new water (water that has not before risen to the surface) could fill the existing basins in 30 million years.

As to the atmosphere, we might expect many compounds of hydrogen, since this element is the major constituent of the universe and also is common in space. Hydrogen and oxygen yield water vapor, H_2O; hydrogen and carbon form methane, CH_4; and hydrogen and nitrogen form ammonia, NH_3. The abundant presence of these gases in the atmospheres of the major planets, such as Jupiter and Saturn, suggests that they may have been common in the early atmosphere of the earth. This idea is particularly favored by those who believe that life originated in such an environment. This early hydrogen-rich atmosphere is assumed to have gradually changed, leaving only indirect clues to its presence.

The change to a second atmosphere involves the origin of relatively large quantities of free oxygen. This element is essential for life processes and for the many oxidation reactions that occur on our present earth. Oxygen is now being liberated continuously from CO_2 and H_2O by photosynthesis in green plants; of course, this process cannot have been important at first when few plants existed. Free oxygen is also being formed in the upper atmosphere from the decomposition of water vapor by solar energy, but hardly in sufficient quantity to provide all the oxygen in the atmosphere and the sedimentary rocks. The two processes together, however, probably could have brought about the present condition.

Insofar as the geologic record goes, there seems to have been a significant increase in atmospheric oxygen between the early Precambrian and the late Precambrian. A good deal of unoxidized iron occurs in the earlier rocks, whereas most of the iron in the later rocks is oxidized. This difference means that oxygen probably first accumulated in amounts sufficient to combine with or satisfy all the

elements that were available to it and then began to build up in free form in the present atmosphere. It may have reached a state of approximate equilibrium in middle Precambrian time. The increased oxygen would have gradually destroyed methane by burning it to carbon dioxide, and ammonia would have been oxidized to free nitrogen, giving the present high proportion of that gas. The relation of oxygen to the problem of the origin and evolution of life will be discussed in Chapter 14.

CONTINENTS AND OCEAN BASINS

We have emphasized that the earth is composed of shells or layers, arranged from heavier inward to lighter outward. This nice scheme eventually encounters difficulties, however, for it does not seem to hold when we come to the outer level of the crust, that most important surface on which we live. This discrepancy raises most perplexing questions: Why isn't the granitic scum spread uniformly over the surface? Why do continents exist at all? In thinking about these things, most investigators accept as proven the idea that the stuff from which the continents are made had been derived from within the earth, presumably from the upper part of the mantle, by normal, or noncatastrophic, chemical segregation followed by intrusive and extrusive action. It is also held by many that the continents have grown by a process of **accretion,** or addition of successively younger belts around primitive nuclei. Beyond these assumptions there is wide disagreement, and a multitude of hypotheses are in the process of evaluation. Before we can consider the problem further, a brief look at the major features of the ocean basins and continents may be helpful.

SOME FUNDAMENTAL CONTRASTS   The continents may be contrasted with the ocean basins by saying that (1) they are topographically higher (explained by their lower density); (2) they are chemically more siliceous with more light-colored, fewer heavy minerals and rocks

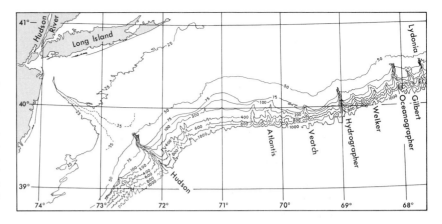

Figure 13-5 Topography of the shelf and slope off part of the eastern coast of the United States showing different types of submarine canyons. The Hudson Canyon can be traced far across the shelf; others, such as the Lydonia, Oceanographer, and Hydrographer Canyons, cut into the outer margin of the shelf, while others are restricted to the slope itself. Depth contours in fathoms.

(also explained by gravitational derivation); (3) they are peculiarly shaped and arranged; and (4) they are geologically complex.

The ocean basins, by way of contrast, are topographically lower; their rocks are heavier, darker, and less siliceous; and their structure is less complex.

Looking at topographic and geologic details, we find that continents are marked by elongated curving mountain chains in which **folds, faults,** and **granitic intrusions** are associated. Continental volcanoes, which emit **andesite** and other acidic lavas, occur mainly along these ranges. Other continental features are deep, elongated subsiding troughs, or **geosynclines;** shallow basins; and broad, gently sloping plains covered by alluvial deposits.

The ocean basins are not merely submerged continental landscapes. They consist of irregular lower parts (**basins, deeps,** and **depressions**) and irregular higher parts (**plateaus** and **terraces**). There are also very long, deep, and narrow depressions called **trenches** and broader ones called **troughs.** Scattered about are hundreds of conical, steep-sided eminences (flat-topped ones are called **guyots** or **tablemounts,** pointed ones are **seamounts** or **seaknolls**), which appear to be extinct or dormant volcanoes. Those that reach the surface may support coral growth and become coral islands. Oceanic volcanoes emit chiefly basalt. Some volcanoes are distributed along definite lines, others are entirely haphazard.

Most amazing of all oceanic features are the steep-sided, rough **ridges;** these form a branching, world-circling system totaling over 400,000 miles in length. The ridges lie chiefly midway between the continents, and in the Atlantic Basin especially, they closely parallel the adjacent shores. The Atlantic segment of the system and parts of others have a rift, or trench, along the summit, obviously opened up by tensional forces. The mid-ocean ridges are marked not only by faulting and attendant earthquakes, but also by active volcanoes, not all of which reach the surface of the water.

Transitional from the ocean basins to the continents are the **continental slopes,** which rise rather steeply from the depths, and the **continental shelves,** which are really submerged portions of the continents. That water happens to occupy the ocean basins creates a somewhat deceptive situation in that the fundamental distinguishing characteristic of ocean basins is not the presence or absence of water. At present, the oceans are overflowing their basins and have encroached on the borders of the continents, in places as much as several hundred miles.

The continental slopes and shelves may be marked by deep submarine canyons; by occasional islands, such as Great Britain, with geologic features like the nearby continents; or by curving island arcs, like the Aleutians or Japanese islands, with rocks and structures intermediate between those of the oceans and continents. Island arcs are highly active geologically, with strong volcanism and numerous earthquakes.

THE BEGINNING OF THE ROCK RECORD

What has been said about the early history of the earth up to this point has been very general and in many ways highly speculative. We have dealt with the origin of the various solid,

267

liquid, and gaseous "spheres" without much reference to specific times or places. We have done so because we have no actual rocks or specimens which preserve a record of the earlier part of the earth's history. Although the constituents of all the rocks were here from the beginning, they were not in the forms in which we now find them. Constant melting and metamorphism destroyed many generations of rocks before those which make up the present continents came into being.

A new era of earth history literally began when permanent rock masses were formed. The remainder of this chapter deals with that portion of time between the formation of the oldest known continental rocks and the appearance of the first abundant fossils in the Cambrian Period. The term Precambrian might be applied to *all* time before the Cambrian, but it is usually understood to mean only that part represented by actual rocks.

ROCKS OF THE PRECAMBRIAN

Rocks of practically all types are found in the Precambrian, and as a general rule they are harder and more highly metamorphosed with increasing age. The most common type, **gneiss**, discussed in Chapter 6, is a banded crystalline rock that originates by heat and pressure from sedimentary or igneous or even other metamorphic rocks.

Along with the various types of gneiss are intrusive masses of **granite** and other related light-colored igneous rocks. Vast thicknesses of volcanic or extrusive material such as basalt are also common. Greatly altered volcanic material of uncertain origin, designated by the inclusive term **greenstone** also occurs. **Graywacke**, a coarse, sandy, sedimentary rock accumulated rapidly and with little weathering, is common in the older terrains. **Conglomerates** of all types abound, and **quartzite, slate, phyllite,** and **schist** are plentiful. Ordinary unaltered sandstone, dolomite, limestone, and shale are more common in the later Precambrian, reflecting less metamorphic action.

Figure 13-6 Precambrian metamorphic rocks deep in the Grand Canyon, Arizona. The vertical gneisses and schists were eroded and covered by horizontal deposits of Cambrian age. The break between the two rock types represents at least 1 billion years. (*Courtesy A. S. Gallenson.*)

Minerals from which radiometric dates can be obtained may be found in many of the rock types mentioned above, but the most reliable dates come from minerals that formed at the same time as the enclosing rock. The oldest continental rocks, as dated by radiometric methods, were formed somewhat over 3,000 million years ago. The earliest dates from Africa are 3,000 to 3,300 million years; from North America 3,100 to 3,400 million years; from Europe 3,500 million years; and from Australia 3,000 million years. These dates are not scattered widely in the respective continents but come in compact, more or less centrally located tracts that are referred to as the **nuclei** or **cores** of the continents. They are also called **shields** because of their gently convex profiles. The rock types of these ancient areas are not being formed on the continents at present—the closest comparison is the volcanic island arcs such as the Japanese, Aleutian, East Indies, and West Indies areas. In other words, the earliest land masses were like present-day volcanic archipelagoes.

When closely studied, the oldest rocks seem to constitute the deeply eroded and deformed "roots" of vanished mountains or mountain islands. Here great bodies of granitic material, mostly intruded from depth, alternate in complex fashion with bodies of sediment downfolded from above into pockets and troughs where they have escaped erosion but have been greatly affected by heat and pressure.

In order to understand these ancient terrains, it is necessary to recall what has been mentioned about the formation of granite (p. 103) and about geosynclines (p. 134–135).

Granite and similar crystalline rocks are associated with almost all continental mountain ranges, not only those that have topographic prominence today but also those which have been eroded and buried in past geologic periods. Another important point is that granite is extremely rare in oceanic basins and islands; its origin must be in some way closely related to continental growth. There is good evidence for believing that granite must form from material that has already been subjected to surface processes; in other words, it does not appear to come directly from deep-seated mantle or lower crust material, rather its origin is from sedimentary or metamorphic rocks. Given sufficient heat almost any type of continental rock may melt to form potential granite, merely reversing the more obvious process whereby granite gives rise to potential sedimentary rocks by weathering. The so-called "granite problem" is complex, but it is obvious that granite has increased in volume through time to contribute a large fraction of the continental rocks, especially the older Precambrian portions.

As mentioned above the ancient continental nuclei have, in addition to granite, remnants of downfolded basins with rocks showing various degrees of metamorphism and with gneiss as a common constituent. That these contorted and truncated downfolds are the roots of former geosynclines seems a logical conclusion. Geosynclines and mountain-building are related, just as granite and mountain-building are associated, a fact which strengthens the conclusion that the ancient foundations of the con-

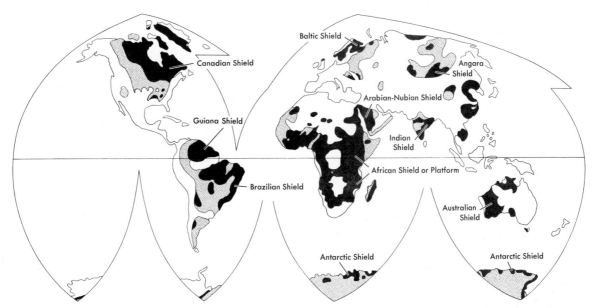

Figure 13-7 The chief Precambrian shield areas of the world. Black indicates Precambrian rocks at the surface; stipple, Precambrian under shallow sedimentary cover.

tinents, at least so far as we can study them, are the roots of successive mountain ranges welded together to constitute a "basement" for younger materials.

NORTH AMERICA
AS AN IDEAL CONTINENT

We speak of North America as an ideal continent in the geological sense because its structure and history illustrate a process of development imperfectly or incompletely illustrated in other continents. North America began as a relatively small land mass and grew outward by successive **orogenies** that added material to the margins. Figure 13-8 shows the inferred location of the old nucleus and the successive tracts added through geologic time. Thus, the continent has a central shield area of very old rocks that is partly exposed and partly covered by younger sediments. Beyond the edges of the stable shield, successively younger elon-

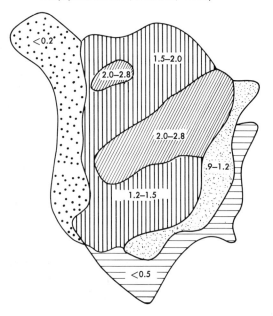

Figure 13-8 Generalized outline of North America showing ages and inferred dates of origin of the major orogenic provinces. Age limits are given in billions of years. (*Modified from Hurley, et al.,* Journal of Geophysical Research, *December, 1962.*)

gate mountain chains are arranged more or less concentrically about the nucleus. Some are mostly worn away (Appalachians), some are almost buried (Ouachita), and some are young and newly formed (Rockies). At the outermost margins are great thicknesses of young sediment, some areas of which are true geosynclines yet to be folded into mountains.

The primitive "heartland" of North America is a roughly oval area stretching from Labrador to Wyoming and called the Superior-Wyoming province. The formation of this ancient land came through the intrusion of vast masses of granite into pre-existing lavas and sediments about 2.5 billion years ago. The pre-existing rocks are obviously even older. They are rich in silica and low in carbonates and could have originated from previous granitic rocks that have not survived. The island-like Superior-Wyoming area did not founder, however, but began to shed sediments outward to create additional lowlands and shallow seas. This new generation of rocks includes silicic volcanic flows, arkoses, and graywackes, and a few beds of dolomite.

Eventually, a second generation of granitic masses intruded the sediments surrounding the Superior-Wyoming province to create the even more extensive Churchill and Central provinces. These are dated from 1.8 to 2.5 billion years. The Churchill province makes up much of the exposed Canadian Shield area, but the Central province that occupies a big portion of the United States is mostly covered by sediments. It does appear, however, in uplifts of the southern and central Rocky Mountains, the Black Hills, the Ozark Mountains, and the Grand Canyon.

A third great episode of rock- and mountain-making, which created the Grenville province, came about 1.0 billion years ago. Rocks of this age make up about 20 per cent of North America, chiefly the eastern and southern parts from Labrador to Mexico. Greenland, too, is chiefly composed of rocks of this age. The sediments that were invaded by granite include quartzite and carbonates with fossils of calcareous algae.

Figure 13-9 Air view of rocks and structures in the Precambrian shield near Great Slave Lake, Canada. The great fault separates Precambrian granite on the left from Precambrian sediments on the right. The body of water is McDonald Lake. (*Courtesy Department of Mines and Technical Surveys, Canada.*)

A predominantly sedimentary and volcanic sequence, little deformed and almost devoid of intrusions, came after the Grenville in the Great Lakes area. Included are conglomerates and the poorly sorted heterogeneous *Gowganda conglomerate*, which proves the Precambrian glaciation of several thousand square miles of the shield. Tillite is also found in the late Precambrian of Greenland. The quiet period is represented also by the Belt Series of Montana and the Grand Canyon Series of Arizona. These latest Precambrian beds are so like the succeeding Cambrian that where the two are together it is difficult to make a distinction between them.

MINERAL RESOURCES OF THE CANADIAN SHIELD The shield area of North America is rich in mineral wealth; in fact, the presence of great ore deposits has been the chief reason for geologic study of this vast region. Gold appears to have been deposited abundantly in connection with the earlier intrusions; most of the gold mines are in Ontario and Quebec. The largest gold mine in the United States, the Homestake Mine, is in the Precambrian rock of the Black Hills, which represent an isolated upfolded part of the rock types that continue under the younger rocks over much of the United States. In addition to gold, the Canadian portion of the shield has the richest nickel mines in the world, and tremendous deposits of copper and uranium.

Important also, in both the United States and Canada, are the abundant iron ores. These ores were formed by sedimentary processes in the later part of the Precambrian and were enriched or concentrated by weathering during later times. The famous "iron ranges" of Minnesota, Wisconsin, and Michigan belong to this

271

series. The most productive of the ranges is Mesabi, counted as the greatest metal deposit in the United States. With the depletion of the ores in the vicinity of Lake Superior, intensified development of other large deposits in Ontario and Quebec has taken place.

CLASSIFICATION OF NORTH AMERICAN PRE-CAMBRIAN   Many schemes of classification, and scores of local names, have been applied to rock formations in the Canadian Shield. There is now a general tendency to divide the Precambrian into four subdivisions as follows: at the base, the *Archean* (including rocks from 3.2 billion to about 2.5 billion years old), closed by the strong Kenoran disturbance. This is followed by the *Lower Proterozoic* (with rocks from 2.5 to 1.7 billion years old), closed by the Hudsonian disturbance. The *Middle Proterozoic* covers the period from 1.7 to 1.0 billion years ago and was closed by the Grenville disturbance. The last part of the Precambrian includes rocks formed between 1.0 and .6 billion years ago; it grades into the Paleozoic without notable breaks. Over 400 radiometric dates have been obtained to support this classification, making the Canadian Shield the best-dated Precambrian area on earth.

OTHER CONTINENTS

SOUTH AMERICA   About half of South America has Precambrian rocks at or relatively near the surface. Three large areas are recognized: the Guiana Shield bounded by the Orinoco River, the Atlantic Ocean, and the Amazon Valley; the Central Brazilian Shield, including most of the southern drainage of the Amazon; and the Coastal Brazilian Shield, along the eastward bulge of the continent.

The South American shields have been mostly emergent since Precambrian time, but the Amazon Valley which cuts between two of them has been repeatedly submerged by shallow seas since the early Paleozoic. Important deposits of iron are found in the younger Precambrian.

BALTIC SHIELD AND EUROPE   Most of Europe is underlain by Precambrian rocks. They are found in many mountain ranges and make up the surface of the Baltic Shield, which is chiefly in Sweden and Finland. The Precambrian is under a thin blanket of sediments throughout northern Russia. The Precambrian is

Figure 13-10 "The sugarloaf," an imposing monolith eroded from hard Precambrian rock, rises well above the massive formation that juts into the harbor area at Rio de Janeiro, Brazil. (*Courtesy Pan American Airways.*)

Figure 13-11 Remnants of thick sedimentary formation considered to be a glacial deposit of Precambrian age. South Angola. (*Courtesy R. T. Novotny.*)

also found in northern Scotland and neighboring islands, and in various areas of the continent, such as the Alps, Vosges, Brittany, the Massif Central of France, northwest Spain, Sardinia, and the Carpathians.

THE ANGARA SHIELD AND OTHER ASIATIC PRECAMBRIAN AREAS   A good deal of northern Asia, especially Siberia, is underlain by Precambrian rocks. These are at the surface in the Angara Shield and under shallow cover over the much larger area of the Siberian Platform. The Precambrian is usually divided into the Archaeozoic and Proterozoic, the latter with a major final division called the **Sinian,** which passes without break into the Cambrian.

Many other Precambrian outcrops are found in Asia, but they are not in close surface proximity so as to constitute shield areas. The Urals, Himalayas, Pamirs, and many other mountains have Precambrian cores. Many isolated Precambrian areas are found in China, including thick sections of the Sinian series with beds of tillite. The Precambrian of Asia yields iron ore in China; gold, copper, and semi-precious stones in Siberia; and gold in Korea.

AFRICA   Africa has the most extensive record of Precambrian rocks of any of the continents. It is more properly called a platform than a shield; in fact, it appears to have been welded together from a number of nuclear areas, or shields. The Arabian-Nubian Shield is partly in the Arabian Peninsula and partly in Egypt, having been split by the relatively recent Red Sea rift. This is a very complex area of old rocks with some important mineral deposits. The continent of Africa has been remarkably free of deformation since the Precambrian. Practically all of the metallic mineral deposits of the continent are of Precambrian origin. Gold seems to have been produced in abundance somewhat over 2 billion years ago, and lead, zinc, copper, and uranium came later, at about 1 billion years.

Radiometric dating of African rocks has lagged, but it is certain that the immensely long Precambrian record will be unraveled and classified as modern methods are applied.

AUSTRALIA   Precambrian rocks are near or at the surface of most of western and central Australia, which is one of the major shield

Figure 13-12 Ayers Rock, an eroded remnant of Precambrian rock in the central desert region of Australia. Said to be the world's largest monolith, it is 1,100 feet high and 5½ miles in diameter at the base. (*Courtesy Qantas Empire Airways Ltd.*)

areas of the earth. Of special interest in the Middle Late Proterozoic are extensive beds of coarse, unsorted debris, supposedly of glacial origin, which would indicate continental glaciers over most of Australia at this time.

In Australia the boundary between the Precambrian and Cambrian is transitional and difficult to place, indicating no significant structural unrest as the Paleozoic commenced. Many fossil remains are found in the transitional beds. No trilobites are known, however, and opinion is divided about whether or not these ancient fossils are of Cambrian age.

ANTARCTICA Although Antarctica is mostly covered by ice, it is known from exposures along the margins that the larger part of the continent, East Antarctica, is a shield area of complex older rocks. The oldest dates determined so far (1966) are about 1.8 billion years, but some of the rocks are less than 400 million years old and would thus be Paleozoic and not Precambrian. Rocks are chiefly highly metamorphosed or *plutonic* (intruded from depth). No significant ores are known.

INDIA About two-thirds of the surface of India consists of Precambrian rocks. The oldest series is chiefly gneiss intruded by granite of unknown thickness and age. Lying upon this is the Cuddapah System, a little deformed and slightly metamorphosed sequence of shale, conglomerate, limestone, and other ordinary sediments, which reaches a thickness of 20,000 feet. Yet higher, in the central part of the peninsula, is the Vindhyan System, consisting of well-stratified, almost horizontal beds of sandstone, shale and limestone. These can be identified as marine, fluvial, and estuarine in origin. Traces of primitive organisms have been found, and the rocks are considered to be very late Precambrian, with perhaps even some Cambrian at the top.

BROAD FEATURES OF THE PRECAMBRIAN

From what has been said, it is obvious that the Precambrian rock record is vast and complex. This is understandable when we consider that it is a record of at least 2.5 billion years of

274

time, or about four-fifths of the interval for which a record actually exists. In spite of the unsatisfactory state of knowledge of this record, it is still possible to make significant general statements about the sequence of events and the processes in operation.

In the first place, the evidence is clear that the continents have grown outward, or accreted, at the expense of bordering islands and ocean basins. The older rocks are almost always in the central parts of the shields and the younger, currently forming ones are at the margins. It is also clear that what remains of the ancient primitive continents are the roots of mountain ranges or orogenic belts where granitic bodies are intermixed in complex fashion with down-folded, elongate, sediment-filled geosynclines.

There has also been an increase in the relative mass of thickened, stable, continental material, as compared with eroded sediments. This is so because the sediment produced through time has been largely converted to metamorphic material and welded to the continents. There has also been an increase in the amount of carbonate rocks, especially those resulting from biologic processes. Thus, dolomite and limestone are rare in the earlier periods, but become more and more important with the passage of time, until a high point is reached in the early Paleozoic. This change undoubtedly resulted from the increased prevalence of lime-secreting organisms. Insofar as igneous rocks are concerned, those produced on the continents have become generally less basic and more acidic.

SUMMARY

The constituents of the earth had a lengthy history before they actually became a planet. The earth as such is thought to have formed from a cloud of dust and gas surrounding the primitive sun. Subsequent to the accretion of its constituents the entire earth apparently was completely melted by heat originating from self-contained and widely dispersed radioactive elements. As a direct consequence of melting, the planet took on a density stratification with a heavier central core, followed outward by the successively lighter mantle, crust, oceans, and atmosphere. The segregation of these shells was facilitated by deep convection currents in the mantle. The origin of water and atmosphere was from within the earth.

The continents present a special problem because the constituents are not in a uniform layer but rather in separate patches. It is thought that the land masses began to form over areas of upwelling currents and have expanded by addition of successive belts of rock about their margins. The earliest known continental rocks are of sedimentary origin but they were obviously derived from pre-existing but unpreserved sources. Gneiss, a banded, crystalline metamorphic rock of diverse origin is the most abundant Precambrian rock. Granite is also common and appears to form by heat acting on previously segregated near-surface rocks.

All the major continents have a nucleus or "shield" area of ancient Precambrian rocks made up of granitic intrusions and downfolded masses of sedimentary origin which seem to represent the troughs of geosynclines. In North America, for example, the oldest portion has a central position extending from Labrador to Wyoming. Following outward are successively younger belts with young mountains and geosynclines at the border. Important Precambrian areas are the Baltic in Europe, the Angara in Siberia, most of Africa, east Antarctica, much of Australia and the Guiana-Brazil area of South America. Most of these have rich mineral deposits with gold being notably abundant in older areas and iron in younger ones. Widespread evidence of possible glaciation is found on most continents near the close of the Precambrian.

ADDITIONAL READING

Bates, D. R., *The Earth and Its Atmosphere.* New York: Basic Books, Inc., 1957.

Brancazio, Peter J., ed., *The Origin and Evolution of Atmospheres and Oceans.* New York: John Wiley & Sons, 1964.

Clark, T. H., and C. W. Stearn, *The Geologic Evolution of North America.* New York: The Ronald Press Co., 1960.

Engel, A. E. J., "Geologic Evolution of North America." *Science,* Vol. 140, no. 3563, pp. 143–152.

Gill, James E., *The Proterozoic in Canada.* Royal Society of Canada, Special Publication No. 2. Toronto: University of Toronto Press, 1957.

Gutenberg, B., ed., *The Internal Constitution of the Earth.* New York: Dover Publications, 1954.

Poldervaart, Arie, ed., *Crust of the Earth.* New York: Geological Society of America, Special Paper 62, 1955.

Rankama, Kalervo, *The Geologic Systems: The Precambrian 1.* New York: Interscience Publishers, 1963.

Smart, W. M., *The Origin of the Earth.* Cambridge, England: Cambridge University Press, 1951.

The Planet Earth (a *Scientific American* book). New York: Simon and Schuster, 1957.

Vening Meinesz, F. A., *The Earth's Crust and Mantle.* New York: American Elsevier Pub. Co., 1964.

Walton, Matt, "Granite Problems." *Science,* Vol. 131, 1959, pp. 635–645.

14

The Origin of Life
and the Meaning of Fossils

The problem of how life originated on the earth is currently the object of keen attention from scientists in such diverse fields as chemistry, geology, and astronomy. They are interested not only in solving the problem of earth life but also in learning whether life exists anywhere else besides the earth. The answer to the question of extraterrestrial life is being sought at tremendous cost through explorations of space, the moon, and other planets. Statistically, it appears probable that conditions favorable for life do exist on many bodies throughout the universe and that organic creatures comparable to human beings have evolved on some of them. At present, however, the possibility of advanced life on other planets of our own local solar system seems very remote.

THEORIES OF LIFE

One theory of life is that it has spread to all favorable planets by spores or simple key molecules capable of enduring journeys through space. This is the theory of **"panspermia"**; if it is true, the history of life began at some remote time and place beyond the reach of scientific investigation. At present, however, it seems more likely that life has appeared spontaneously at many times and places, including at least once on this planet. Investigators are bringing much thought and experimentation to bear on the possibility of an independent origin of earth life. Here the geologist is able to make a distinct contribution by reconstructing the physical environment in which the event would have taken place.

It seems safe to assume that life could come into existence only after the earth had passed through the molten phase, between 3 and 4 billion years ago. In that period, water began to accumulate on a large scale, an indication of a prevailing temperature between 0 and 100 degrees C—the relatively narrow range in which life as we know it can exist. Also, it is reasonable to suppose that all the chemical elements essential to life were here from the time of water production and that they were being dissolved and dispersed according to their various properties so as to be available to life almost everywhere. We do not know the composition of the atmosphere, but the evidence is that it was oxygen-poor rather than oxygen-rich as it now is.

Sources of energy—such as solar radiation, electrical discharges in the form of lightning, heat from volcanic fields and hot springs, and radiation products from naturally occurring radioactive minerals—were certainly present on the earth from its solidification and were available at the time life emerged.

There seems to be no question that the environment was favorable for life: Water, proper temperature, raw chemicals, and energy

Figure 14-1 A hot spring in Yellowstone National Park. Some authorities believe life may have originated in natural springs of heated water. *(Courtesy Union Pacific Railroad.)*

sources were all in simultaneous existence. The crucial question to answer, if indeed it can be answered at all, is whether life could have appeared spontaneously; that is, without supernatural intervention. The answer to this question is being sought by active experimentation in laboratories throughout the world. These investigations naturally go hand in hand with current research in other aspects of molecular biology and genetics.

THE VITAL SYNTHESIS

Many important and surprising facts have been discovered when the proper constituents have been brought together under conditions like those which probably prevailed on the primitive earth. As an example, 14 of the common amino acids have been synthesized by passing a mixture of methane, ammonia, and water through a heated silica tube at a temperature of 900 to 1,000 degrees C. Similar effects have been obtained by passing electric discharges through a mixture of methane, ammonia, hydrogen, and water. In yet another experiment, methane gas was bubbled through a water solution of ammonia. The resulting mixture of methane and gaseous ammonia was then passed through pulverized volcanic rock that had been heated to about 1,000 degrees C—a sequence of events similar to what could have happened in a volcanic field in earlier stages of the earth. From these experiments not only were amino acids produced, but they were strung together in chains.

We can summarize these experiments by stating that when methane, ammonia, and water are acted upon by energy sources presumably available in primitive times, the purines (adenine and guanine), sugars such as ribose and deoxyribose, the nucleoside adenosine, and the nucleotides AMP, ADP, and ATP can be synthesized step by step. These compounds, if properly combined, constitute living matter. It is the process of getting them "properly combined" which is the central problem of the origin of life. So great is the gap in complexity between the amino acids and the simplest known living things that a justifiable doubt still exists about whether life could arise spontaneously. Some say that the gap has already been crossed and that "life" has been created in the test tube. Others claim on statistical grounds that the proper combination of units could not come about in nature in the time available. The deep-seated belief that a supernatural force (God) is required and an aversion to the idea that life appeared by chance have naturally entered into the argument. Those who place weight on probability statistics need to be reminded that the simplest living things now known are not necessarily the simplest possible forms of life. Molecules that are relatively less complex than the lowest existing form of life may possess the essential power of growth and replication and the capability of further evolutionary development. What is required is not a fully formed cell or even a lengthy strand of DNA; merely a self-replicating molecule of the simplest kind will suffice to meet these requirements.

A further pitfall in thinking about the origin of life lies in assuming that it originated under conditions like those which now prevail. Life, once it began, could have affected its own environment in ways unfavorable to a second origin. For instance, oxygen, which began to be liberated by photosynthesis, is capable of breaking up not only methane and ammonia but also the delicate molecules that could exist in an oxygen-poor environment. A second more obvious barrier that arose from the presence of life was the spread of energy-seeking organisms that were ready and able to prey upon any living matter that might be formed. This is the simple answer to the question of why evolution does not repeat itself. The offspring of any particular stage are inimical to the existence of weaker competitors, including their own ancestors. Man, for instance, would not look with benevolence on another animal about to challenge his position as man.

The general tone of thought about the appearance of life on earth is that it came when conditions were right. Certainly, as long

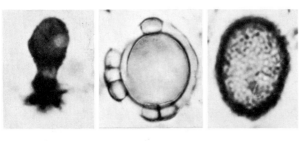

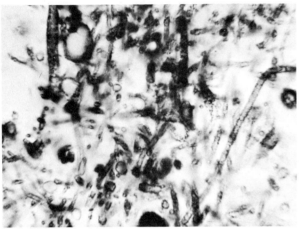

Figure 14-2 Primitive algae and other microorganisms from the Gunflint chert near Schreiber, Ontario, Canada. All are highly magnified. The age is between 1.7 and 2.1 billion years. (*Courtesy Elso S. Barghoorn.*)

Figure 14-3 A colony of calcareous algae in the Precambrian rocks of Glacier National Park, Montana. The concentric layers of limestone were built up by algae in shallow water, and the whole mass was later buried by sediment.

as science is making such notable strides in understanding the basis of life, it would be unwise to say that life is or must be an incomprehensible mystery.

THE FOSSIL RECORD

No paleontologist seriously expects to find actual remains of the earth's first living inhabitants; they were surely much too fragile and delicate to leave coherent remains. Genes, chromosomes, and viruses, however, may illustrate what the first living things were like. When the cellular level of existence was reached, the chances for preservation were greatly improved.

Many significant discoveries of very ancient fossils have been made within the last few years. Among these are remains of minute rod-shaped organisms, probably bacteria, in sedimentary rocks of South Africa said to be 3,000,000,000 years old. Better and more abundantly preserved microorganisms, positively identified as bacteria and blue-green algae, have been found in the Precambrian Gunflint Formation of the Lake Superior region, dated as approximately 2 billion years old (Figure 14-2). Flint, in which these fossils occur, is a dense, homogeneous siliceous rock that is thought to precipitate rapidly in sea water. A detailed report dated 1965 lists 12 species from the Gunflint Formation ranging from single-celled spherical forms to branched and unbranched filamentous ones. Similar fossils have also been described from Precambrian rocks of central Australia; their suggested age is from 700,000,000 to 900,000,000 years.

Associated with most of these microscopic fossils, and also occurring by themselves in many other deposits, are the so-called stromatolites, which are regarded as traces of primitive algae. These layered, cabbage-like mounds are found in limestone or dolomite. The thin, stony layers composing these rounded forms were apparently precipitated by mat-like growths of algae that are not in themselves preserved.

280

Stromatolites are found in calcareous rocks of all the continents (Figure 14-3). Similar if not identical structures are forming in shallow waters at the present time.

METAZOANS APPEAR

As would be expected, the earliest known fossils are of one-celled plants. We have as yet found no fossils of one-celled Precambrian animals. The evolutionary steps from plants to animals remain in the realm of speculation. Another significant advance, that from single-celled to many-celled (metazoan) animals, is also obscure. But the search for Precambrian metazoans has not been entirely fruitless—recent discoveries in widely separated areas prove the existence of several of the major phyla in Precambrian time.

Elongate, sediment-filled burrows and borings that wind through sedimentary rock are attributed to worms, even though the worms themselves have not been preserved. Such burrows or tracks are known in a number of Precambrian formations and indicate that rather advanced animals representing at least one of the worm-like phyla existed. Another metazoan phylum of ancient derivation is the **coelenterata**, represented by jellyfish and related animals. A single impression of a jellyfish-like organism was discovered in the Nankoweap Formation, deep in the Grand Canyon; the age is definitely Precambrian and may be as great as 1 billion years. Coelenterates of various types also make up most of the forms found in rocks of southeastern Australia, which are probably but not positively of Precambrian age.

Continued search will undoubtedly reveal additional fossils but what has been discovered indicates that even though water was present and sedimentary rocks could form, life was scarce and of a primitive nature for at least four-fifths of the earth's history. The late appearance of higher organisms is probably due to the small supply of oxygen in the atmosphere.

Figure 14-4 Impressions of jellyfish-like organisms from the Precambrian Bass formation of the Grand Canyon. (*Courtesy Raymond M. Alf.*)

Before such creatures could thrive, oxygen had to be built up slowly through the photosynthetic activity of algae, which could live only in shallow water into which sunlight could penetrate.

Before continuing the story of living things, we must digress briefly to discuss fossils as such and the means of their preservation.

WHAT IS A FOSSIL?

A **fossil** is the remains or evidences of an ancient organism preserved by natural means in materials of the earth's crust. Fossils exist because dead organisms are not always entirely decomposed or disintegrated. The processes of destruction which begin with death may be halted at any stage so that the resulting remains may be entire and perfect or fragmentary and imperfect. Naturally, hard parts such as bones, teeth, shells, and wood will resist destruction longer than will soft tissues; correspondingly they are the more common in the fossil record. The chief methods of preservation are described briefly below.

ENTIRE ORGANISM PRESERVED Complete fossil organisms are spectacular. Most notable are the frozen carcasses of ice age mammals,

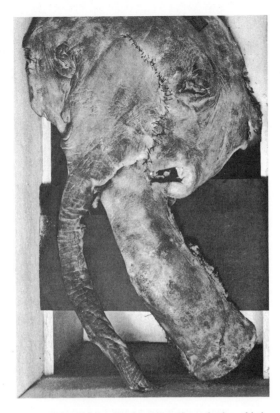

Figure 14-5 Head, trunk, and one foreleg of baby woolly mammoth taken from frozen ground in Alaska. Dredging and excavating have exposed vast amounts of fossil material, including bones, skin, and hair, in various parts of Alaska.

Figure 14-6 Fossil shells from the vicinity of Paris, France. These illustrate the preservation of unaltered hard parts. Although the shells are at least 40 million years old, the original material is only slightly bleached and softened.

particularly mammoths, which occasionally come to light in frozen ground of the Arctic regions. Hair, skin, internal organs, and stomach contents are included. Complete specimens of large animals are also occasionally taken from bogs; a woolly rhinoceros from the district of Sarunia, Poland, came from an oil seep. In the category of entire organisms we may also list the dessicated or mummified remains that occur in caves or dry sand.

UNALTERED HARD PARTS PRESERVED Bone, wood, teeth, and shells are in themselves fairly resistant and durable. They may lie unchanged in dry sediment or in caves for thousands of years and even in moist sediment they may exist indefinitely. It is common for the organic matter to be removed from bone, leaving only the mineral constituents. These "dry" bones may then remain unchanged or they may be petrified or replaced by mineral matter.

Calcite, a common mineral, is secreted by many organisms in building their shells; once formed it may remain unaltered. A few organisms are composed of silica, which is also a very stable mineral.

CARBON RESIDUES PRESERVED When an organism or part of an organism is buried in moist sediment or in quiet water, the volatile constituents—nitrogen, hydrogen, and oxygen —are lost, and a carbon-rich residue remains. This process is called **carbonization** or **distillation.** Leaves (Figure 14-7), crustaceans, fish, and soft-bodied aquatic organisms are commonly preserved by this method.

PETRIFACTION OR REPLACEMENT Under favorable conditions, hard, porous substances (such as bone, wood, and shell) may be replaced by mineral matter so that more or less perfect stony reproductions result. The original material may be partly or entirely replaced. Commonly, only the minute internal cavities and canals are filled with mineral matter; such specimens are said to be **permineralized.** If the process goes to completion until cell walls and

Figure 14-7 Fossil leaf (*Aralia*) preserved as carbonaceous residue in fine-grained shale. Scale represents 1 inch. (*Courtesy University of Utah Geology Museum.*)

Figure 14-8 A petrified tree trunk standing vertically in volcanic breccia from which it has been freed by erosion. This specimen is one of many petrified trees exposed on Specimen Ridge, south side of Lamar River, Yellowstone Park, Wyoming. Age is middle Eocene. (*Courtesy Erling Dorf.*)

solid matter are also replaced, the object is completely petrified (see Figure 14-8). Even the microscopic structure may be retained.

Circulating mineral-bearing solutions are essential for petrifaction. The most common materials carried by ground water are calcite ($CaCO_3$) and silica (SiO_2); fossils replaced by these compounds are accordingly said to be **calcified** or **silicified**. A great variety of other minerals—including pyrite, marcasite, dolomite, barite, fluorite, gypsum, hematite, galena, sulfur, and talc—act as petrifying agents.

CASTS AND MOLDS Shells of invertebrate animals which are commonly preserved as casts and molds, provide the best-known fossils. Slowly moving underground water may dissolve a shell entirely, leaving only a hollow space or mold. This may faithfully preserve the shape and surface markings but give no internal structure. If later on such a hollow mold is filled with mineral matter, a cast is created (Figure 14-9). Again, no internal structures are preserved.

Figure 14-9 Casts of brachiopod shells in limestone. Traces of the original shell material adhere to these impressions, but the fossils and matrix are otherwise the same. This type of preservation is typical of most marine fossils. Scale represents 1 inch.

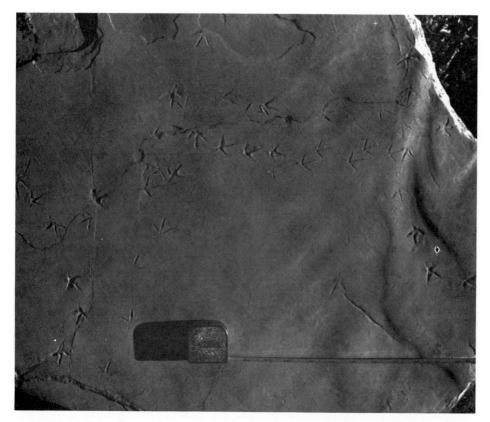

Figure 14-10 Bird tracks from the Green River Formation near Thistle, Utah. (*Courtesy H. D. Curry.*)

Other interesting examples of molds are natural footprints of animals (Figure 14-10), the hollow spaces left by tree trunks buried in lava, and the insects in amber which have been known for centuries from the Baltic region of Europe. Of course, if these molds could be filled naturally by solid material we could get casts of footprints, trees, or insects, as the case may be. Shallow molds, such as those made by leaves or thin shells, are commonly referred to as impressions.

THE EVOLUTIONARY SIGNIFICANCE OF FOSSILS

Fossils have been referred to as the *corpus delecti* of evolution. They are, in other words, the actual dead remains which prove that life on earth has changed or evolved. Without fossils the past history of life might have been vaguely imagined, but the forms that actually existed would never be known. To the average person fossils may be mere curiosities; to the expert they are not only clues to past conditions

and events but also essential links in the great evolutionary chain of organic beings. No study of fossils is complete unless they are both related to the environment in which they lived and assigned to a place in their particular ancestral line or lines.

The study of organic evolution is shared by biology and geology, more specifically by molecular biology and paleontology. We can not here delve into the many important contributions of biology, but a brief mention of the areas in which geology has contributed will be worthwhile before we commence a review of the actual fossil record.

Proof of Change

Fossils for the most part belong to species no longer alive. This fact by itself proves that life on the earth has changed with time. The realization of this probably stirred theological opposition to the study of fossils, because the recognition of myriads of extinct and inferior beings appears to reflect adversely on the power and intelligence of God. Even more disturbing

Figure 14-11 *Homo diluvi testis*—He who witnessed the Flood. This fossil of a giant salamander was declared by Johann Scheuchzer in 1726 to be the remains of a miserable sinner who had perished in the Deluge.

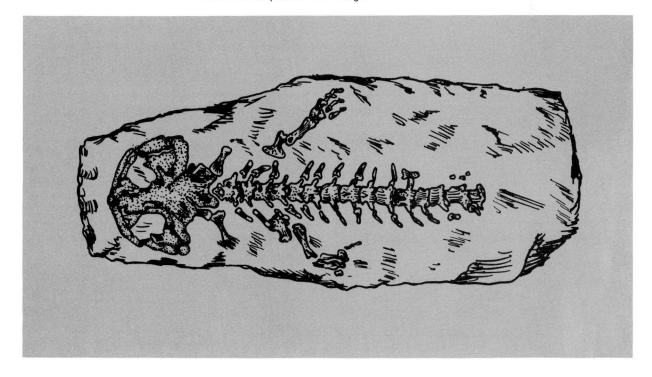

Figure 14-12 Energy cycles of the earth are powered ultimately by the sun. Land plants obtain and store energy that is taken in turn by herbivore, carnivore, and scavenger; residues are decomposed by bacteria. Energy fixed by marine plants likewise passes along a similar food chain from lower to higher forms. Water, too, passes in a cyclical manner from the ocean into the atmosphere, onto the land, and back to the ocean. (*Courtesy* Scientific American.)

was the theory of evolution conceived by Charles Darwin. To Darwin, the evidence seemed to require that the ancestors of still-living forms were to be found as fossils and that all organisms came from one or a few simple beginnings. Evolution in this sense is now almost universally accepted by informed people. Fossils constitute the prime evidence of evolution and evolution is one of the most far-reaching discoveries of modern time. Here we shall make only a brief mention of the many significant generalizations that can be drawn from the study of fossils. You should note the following topics and seek for examples as we continue the story of life.

Energy Sources and Food Chains

It is obvious that any creature which cannot make its own food from available raw materials must take it from other living things. Nothing can exist unless it is preceded by a suitable food (energy) source. All present-day food chains or pyramids depend on plants, whose energy is derived by photosynthesis from solar radiation. There are other manifestations of solar energy that are of interest to geologists.

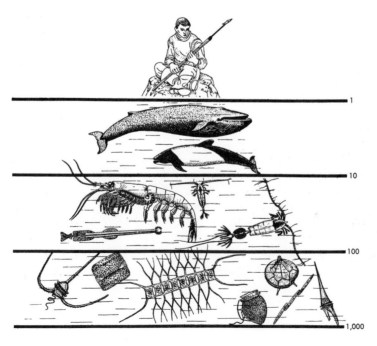

Figure 14-13 A simplified food pyramid of Arctic life. The basic food supply is floating plant plankton. This is eaten by animal plankton, which is in turn consumed by whales and other marine vertebrates. Man occupies the summit of the pyramid when he captures whales or fish. (*Courtesy* Scientific American.)

Thermal differences give rise to wind and water currents so that they flow continuously over the earth as major factors of weather and climate. Water and wind erode and spread rock particles to create sedimentary rocks. Sedimentary rocks require air or water for their formation. Other evidences such as ripple-marks, mud-cracks, and raindrop impressions reveal water in action. The point of these remarks is that sedimentary rocks give evidence that at the time of their formation solar energy was falling on the earth, that water existed, and that life had a suitable energy source with which to operate.

Once plants were in existence, animals could follow. Herbivores harvest plants, and one or several types of carnivores feed, in turn, on the herbivores. Man, of course, sits more or less comfortably on top of nearly all food pyramids (Figure 14-13). Paleontology verifies the existence of food chains from the very beginning of life. Before the successive types of dependent animals have appeared, there is always evidence of a preceding adequate food supply. It is no coincidence, then, that the first fossils were plants, that the earliest abundant plants were algae, that the earliest animals were passive, nonaggressive types, and that with the passage of time more efficient carnivores equipped with alert senses, claws, and teeth dominated the scene.

Physical Change and Biological Opportunity

What is behind the evolutionary changes which have produced abundant and diversified organic beings from a few simple ancestors? The answer as seen by the paleontologist is that biologic change has been forced on organisms by physical changes in the earth. Both the physical and the biological world have changed and are still changing, but physical change is dominant and has dictated the general direction of biological change. One of the chief problems of paleontology is to detect how organisms have come to "fit" their respective niches.

It is easier to understand this correlation if it can be demonstrated that both the organism and its environment have co-existed for periods sufficiently long for natural selection to have taken place.

Geological study shows that all major types of environments have characterized the earth in the prehistoric past. Evidence of glaciers, tropical forests, deserts, lakes, caves, and other habitats can be read from the rocks, proving that life has always had a variety of opportunities or challenges to meet. Even more important, no habitat has remained static; life could not rest or stagnate, it had to react or perish.

React or Perish

When any organism, including man, is confronted by a critical change in its surroundings, it must, in theory at least, change, move, or perish. By changing, it may adapt to the new conditions; by moving, it may leave an unfavorable situation so as to remain with its customary environment; by remaining without change, it may be driven to extinction.

If we read the record correctly, the most common reaction of life forms has been to move or emigrate as conditions change. This action is not, of course, the result of conscious analysis; adaptations exist whereby plants and animals will be dispersed so as to escape local areas into new environments, whether or not such dispersal is necessary or beneficial at all times.

Migration and Dispersal of Organisms

So far as is known, each species of plant or animal came into being once and only once and at one place only. Thus, any organism, living or extinct, that is found in more than one locality has had to migrate from its place of origin. The problem of how organisms have managed to cross wide bodies of water so as to reach islands or even distant continents is diffi-

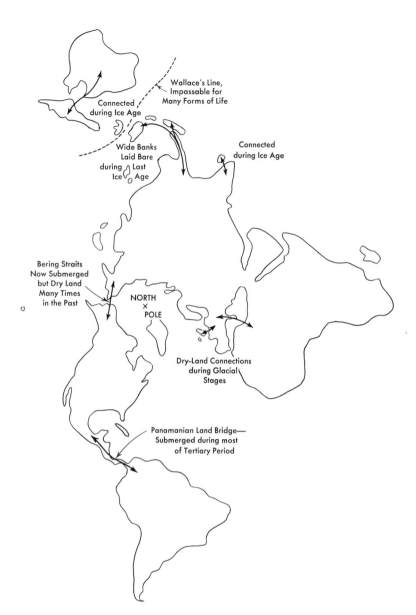

Wallace's Line,
Impassable for
Many Forms of Life

Connected
during Ice Age

Wide Banks
Laid Bare
during Last
Ice Age

Connected
during Ice Age

Bering Straits
Now Submerged
but Dry Land
Many Times
in the Past

NORTH
× POLE

Dry-Land Connections
during Glacial
Stages

Panamanian Land Bridge—
Submerged during most
of Tertiary Period

Figure 14-14 Migration routes make it possible for most forms of life to disperse widely. Land bridges and shallow shelves connect all the great land masses, and plants and animals can spread widely if climatic conditions are favorable.

cult to answer without the assistance of geology. The fact that North America and Asia have been joined on a number of occasions by way of the Bering Straits explains how elephants and men passed from the Old World to the New and how camels and beavers could spread in the opposite direction. Another important land bridge is the Isthmus of Panama. Geological information shows that this tract was submerged during much of the Tertiary Period, thereby allowing the uninhibited evolution of many peculiar forms of life such as ground sloths; these creatures existed nowhere except in South America until the land bridge appeared and allowed them to escape.

The distribution of present-day vegetation would be impossible to explain except on the basis of the great ice sheets whose history is known from geological evidence. Examples could be multiplied, but the field of **biogeography,** or study of the distribution of organisms, is a good example of a borderline field that depends heavily on what can be learned about the past to explain the present.

Emigration does not always prove successful, however. The world has always been full of dead end streets and blind alleys into which organisms may drift or be driven, and thus be separated for good or bad from the mainstreams of existence.

Isolation

The formation of new species is favored by the isolation of relatively small breeding populations that are cut off from other contemporary populations by one means or another. Darwin perceived this when he studied the separate races or species of plants, birds, and reptiles that were isolated on the various islands of the Galapagos Archipelago (see Figure 14-15).

Islands, mountain peaks, valleys, bays, and many other geographic features have their peculiar inhabitants, formed, it is evident, by their having been cut off or separated from former continuous populations.

A very important contribution of geology is the demonstration of how populations may be separated by natural means. Thus, the Galapagos Islands arose by volcanic action that formed new territory; Ceylon was cut off from India, and Sicily from Italy, and England from

Figure 14-15 Darwin's finches. All 14 species are believed to have evolved from a single ancestral type. Two broad groups are represented: the tree finches, *above,* and the ground finches, *below.* Number 1 is a woodpecker-like finch; 2 inhabits mangrove swamps; 3, 4, and 5 are large, medium, and small insect-eaters; 6 is a vegetarian; 7 is a single species of warbler-finch; and 8 is an isolated species from Cocos Island. Of the ground finches, 9, 10, and 11 are large, medium, and small; 12 is sharp-beaked; and 13 and 14 are cactus-eaters. Each species has become adapted to certain islands or certain types of food. (*Courtesy* Scientific American.)

the continent of Europe by rising seas of the glacial period. Mountain peaks were surrounded by ice and were refuges for life when the lowlands were devastated by continental glaciers. Mountain glaciers, on the other hand, force organisms to lower levels, perhaps into isolated valleys. Always the scene is an ever-shifting landscape in which life can exist only by constant change. The changes may be minor or they may be so great that new species are created. No other explanation seems to account for what is seen at present or reconstructed from the fossil record.

PATTERNS OF SURVIVAL

Among the repeating reactions that have affected many types of organisms are convergence, divergence, and radial adaptation. **Convergence** applies to organisms that were originally unlike but came to resemble each other by slow evolutionary changes. Thus, the extinct ichthyosaur, a reptile, resembles the living swordfish and porpoise. All have achieved a form which succeeds in the open ocean where they live or have lived.

Divergence is the opposite of convergence; its effect is to create unlike organisms from the same or similar ancestors. Thus, from an ancient, primitive flesh-eating ancestor we derive dogs, bears, and seals, each adapted to different food and way of life.

Radial adaptation is a term that may be applied to the whole grand process of evolution or to significant segments of it. It may be visualized in a crude way by an imaginary view looking downward into a large spreading tree in such a way that the major branches are seen to radiate outward from the central trunk. In actuality, radial adaptation is the spreading of any group into all possible environments. Every

290

phylum of plants or animals has followed this pattern—some with great success, some in a limited way only. You will note that the essential story of any group can be shown by a branching diagram, its "family tree" or, more technically, its **phylogenetic chart.** Some groups show only a few simple branches, others are best illustrated by many spreading and sub-dividing lines. It is the constructing of family trees and the relating of these trees to changing environments which is the heart of paleontological research.

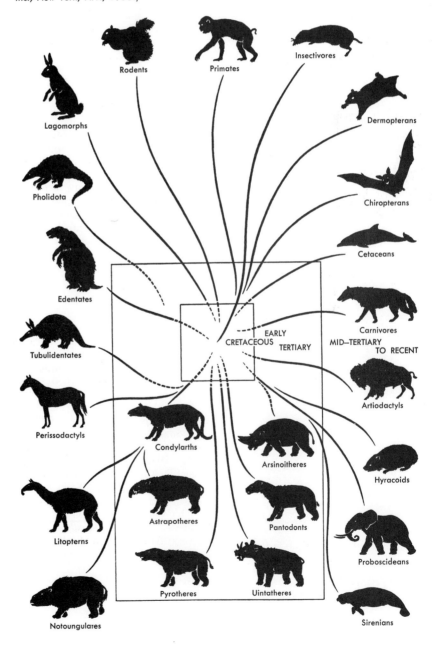

Figure 14-17 Radial adaptations and relationships of the various orders of placental mammals. The forms within the square were extinct by the close of the early Tertiary. (*Reprinted with permission from Colbert,* Evolution of Vertebrates, *John Wiley & Sons, Inc., New York, N.Y., 1955.*)

SUMMARY

An important event of the Precambrian was the appearance of life on earth. The synthesis of the first simple organisms may have been a spontaneous event made possible by the simultaneous occurrence of water solutions of essential elements with a suitable temperature range, an oxygen-poor atmosphere, abundant hydrocarbons, and effective energy sources. Remains of bacteria-like organisms have been reported in rocks estimated at 3 billion years old. Limy structures and organic residues also indicate very ancient life, but multicellular animals do not appear until the Late Precambrian (1 billion to .6 billion years ago) when worms, brachiopods, and coelenterates are found.

Fossils are the remains or evidences of ancient organisms. They may be preserved as impressions, casts, and molds, as petrifactions, as carbonaceous residues, or rarely, in unaltered form. The study of fossils is called paleontology; chief subdivisions are invertebrate paleontology, vertebrate paleontology, paleobotany, and micropaleontology.

The study of fossils lends strong support to the idea of organic evolution; it proves that past life, like present life, was based on energy and that food pyramids always existed. Other important generalities are that alterations in the physical environment have forced organisms to adapt, to migrate, or to face extinction. The most common reaction appears to have been migration, and organisms have been dispersed throughout the globe to find new living space or in many instances to become isolated in small groups where accelerated evolution has taken place. The many examples of convergence, divergence, and radial adaptation that have been discovered, go far in explaining what is seen in the present world. Many thousands of species have been exterminated in the past, but the major phyla have persisted with few exceptions since the early Paleozoic.

ADDITIONAL READING

Ager, D. B., *Principles of Paleoecology*. New York: McGraw-Hill Book Co., 1963.

Augusta, J., and Z. Burian (translated by G. Horn), *Prehistoric Animals*. London: Spring Books, 1956.

Beerbower, J. R., *Search for the Past*. Englewood Cliffs, N.J.: Prentice-Hall, 1960.

Colbert, Edwin H., *Evolution of the Vertebrates*. New York: John Wiley & Sons, 1955.

Fenton, C. L., and M. A. Fenton, *The Fossil Book*. Garden City: Doubleday, 1958.

Hecker, R. F. (translated by M. K. Elias and R. C. Moore), *Introduction to Paleoecology*. New York: American Elsevier Pub. Co., 1965.

Kay, M., and E. H. Colbert, *Stratigraphy and Life History*. New York: John Wiley & Sons, 1965.

Matthews, W. H., III, *Fossils—An Introduction to Prehistoric Life*. New York: Barnes and Noble, 1962.

Moody, P. A., *Introduction to Evolution*. New York: Harper & Row, 1962.

Oparin, A. J., *The Origin of Life on Earth*. New York: Academic Press, 1957.

Rutten, M. G., *Geologic Aspects of the Origin of Life on Earth*. New York: American Elsevier Pub. Co., 1962.

Shimer, H. W., and R. R. Shrock, *Index Fossils of North America*. New York: John Wiley & Sons, 1944.

Simpson, G. G., *This View of Life: The World of an Evolutionist*. New York: Harcourt, Brace & World, 1964.

———, *The Geography of Evolution*. Philadelphia: Chilton Books, 1965.

Stirton, R. A., *Time, Life and Man—The Fossil Record*. New York: John Wiley & Sons, 1959.

15

Keys to the Past

Geology is usually regarded as a derived science, meaning that it is based on the more fundamental sciences of physics and chemistry. Even so, it is marked by certain principles and techniques not widely used in other basic sciences. Geologists may employ exact physical, chemical, and mathematical terms in describing the elements and aggregations of elements which make up the earth, but there remain the aspects of time and change that require

294

Figure 15-1 A scene after the Deluge, from a famous painting by Filippo Palizzi. Animals are pictured leaving the Ark to repopulate the devastated world.

different treatment. Geology is, in fact, largely historical and is deeply concerned with happenings in the distant past. But the past is not observable and is never repeatable; much of it is too complex for satisfactory mathematical treatment and even more of it cannot be reproduced by experiment. These difficulties apply especially to historical geology, which deals almost exclusively with change through time.

Faced with the difficulties of reconstructing and interpreting the past, the geologist may have to be satisfied with inconclusive or uncertain explanations. The student of human history faces the same problems. But in both cases the lack of absolute certainty is no excuse for ignoring vital questions that obviously exist. About all that the historian can do is to "keep digging" and make sure that his explanations take into account what can now be observed and that they do not violate established laws and principles. The most important general concepts that have guided our thinking about the past may be reviewed at this point.

UNIFORMITARIANISM

History shows that there have been a number of ways of thinking about the origin and past history of the earth. To some thinkers the past has been controlled by all-powerful gods who created all things to suit their particular ends. To others the earth has appeared as a product of natural processes without plan or purpose. The time element has also been viewed in various ways. Some regard the past as being of infinite duration, and point to the possibility that the earth has passed through an infinite variety of past conditions. In contrast, others believe in a specific beginning and hence a limited duration of the earth. The idea of an extremely limited past derives chiefly from literal interpretations of Judeo-Christian scriptures which compress all origins into six 24-hour days. Even the substitution of thousand-year "days" for shorter ones doesn't really help much. The choice is between extremely long periods or extremely short ones.

Belief in a "quick creation" was widespread in the prescientific era. An essential corollary of this belief is the idea that the earth was shaped by vast cataclysmic events unlike anything witnessed in modern time. Noah's flood was held to be one of the last of the universal catastrophies. The belief in universal world-shaking events is called **catastrophism.** In its original form this view is now held by very few people.

An opposite viewpoint began with such original thinkers as Leonardo da Vinci, who interpreted what he could see in the rocks and soils in terms of everyday processes. The idea that the best way to understand the past is to study the present gradually gained ground. A now famous maxim, "The present is the key to the past," expresses the concept in simplest form.

The term **uniformitarianism,** which came to be applied to the school of thought opposed to catastrophism, comes from the word "uniform." Uniform is defined as: "always the same, regular, even and not varying." Some of these synonyms give a more correct idea of uniformitarianism than do others. Geologists do not believe, for example, that conditions of the past have always been the same as they now are, for traces of change are plainly in evidence. It is not the earth or any part of it that is changeless, it is the laws of nature that are assumed to be unvariable in their operations. Uniformitarianism rejects supernatural (miraculous or incomprehensible) effects as long as known natural ones will suffice. It appeals to known laws or principles rather than to unproven or un-

Figure 15-2 Baron Georges Cuvier (1769–1832), versatile French genius whose studies of fossil remains from the environs of Paris proved that life has varied and changed in the past. He favored the idea of catastrophic change and argued against the theory of organic evolution. (*Brown Brothers.*)

provable suppositions. It seeks explanations based on processes that can be observed in action at the present and not those based on pure imagination. It would also favor having these everyday, natural processes acting at approximately the same rates and scales as they now do, provided that these rates and scales could accomplish the observed results in the time available.

Few students care to argue against uniformitarianism insofar as it pertains to the well-established "law of nature," but there are differences of opinion about the rates or intensity of action of these laws in the past. A catastrophist might contend that the twisting and breaking of strata, the transportation of huge blocks of rock, the violent cutting of canyons, and the wholesale destruction of life is within the power of a great universal flood—and he would be right. The uniformitarianist, however, believes that these same effects can be explained by less violent operations spread over a longer time span; he thinks he is probably more nearly correct for he has the evidence of actual observation of the present on his side.

There have obviously been more violent and extensive volcanic eruptions in the past than any recorded in human history. The evidence of a great ice age shows that modern glaciers are feeble compared with those of the past. Craters on the moon and on Mars signify impacts unlike any recorded by man. Yet the principles governing water action, volcanic eruption, ice movement, and falling bodies have remained the same—only the intensity of action has varied.

In the sense that uniformitarianism implies the operation of timeless, changeless laws or principles, we can say that nothing in our incomplete but extensive knowledge disagrees with it. It has been by application of this concept (we hesitate to call it a "law") that we have had our greatest success in unraveling the past. By uniformitarianism we achieve the most reasonable and rational explanations requiring not only the least expenditure of energy but also a minimum of hypotheses. Until we have good reason to do otherwise, we will continue to explain evidences of past events by comparing them with what can be seen at present. Our case is well stated by the pioneer geologist, Lyell (1797–1875) who assembled the first comprehensive textbook of geology:

> In attempting to explain geological phenomena, the bias has always been on the wrong side; there has been a disposition to reason *a priori* on the extraordinary violence and suddenness of changes, both in the inorganic crust of the earth, and in organic types, instead of attempting strenuously to frame theories in accordance with the ordinary operations of nature.

SUPERPOSITION

The ways in which sedimentary rocks are deposited and preserved has been described in Chapter 5. Sedimentary formations are the documents of geologic history. If properly interpreted, each bed of rock or geologic formation

Figure 15-3 Sir Charles Lyell (1797–1875). His writings established historical geology on a firm basis and greatly influenced later workers, including Charles Darwin. (Crown Copyright Geological Survey photograph. Reproduced by permission of the Controller of H. M. Stationery Office.)

Figure 15-4 Formations in the walls of the Grand Canyon. Because of the scanty soil and vegetation, the formations and contacts between the formations are well exposed. Differences in resistance to erosion leave the harder formations standing as cliffs, the softer ones forming slopes. The Kaibab Limestone is especially resistant, and its top forms the level plain above the canyon rim. (Courtesy Union Pacific Railroad.)

reveals a specific event or environmental condition that existed in the past. Thus, one formation may be a product of a shallow sea, another of a dry desert, another of a flood plain. Obviously, one formation tells only a small part of the total story and is as relatively incomplete as one page of a book. To get as much of the story as possible we must consider all the pages or formations, **and we must consider them in their proper order.** Books are bound with the pages in sequence and are provided with numbers to aid in keeping them properly arranged. The "book of the earth" is neither neatly arranged nor clearly numbered; it is more like an ancient manuscript ravaged and fragmented by the effects of time. Patient study is needed to arrange the pieces and read the story.

From observations and reasoning about the relations among sedimentary rock layers comes one of the fundamental tenets of historical geology, the **principle of superposition,** which is that: **In any undeformed sequence of sedimentary rocks (or other surface-deposited material such as lava), each bed is younger than the one below it and older than the one above it.** This statement expresses such a simple and self-evident fact that it seems scarcely worth emphasizing. Nevertheless, it is the most important generalization in the realm of earth history. Figure 15-5 may clarify the concept of superposition. The arrangement of the playing cards in the diagram corresponds very closely to a typical geologic map of a section of the earth with flatlying sediments. The analogy is good because we are dealing in both cases with relatively thin, but wide, sheet-like bodies that

Figure 15-5 A stack of playing cards illustrates the principle of superposition. The arrangement from bottom to top shows the order in which the cards were laid down. The boxes on the right give the order of superposition for all the cards except the one that does not touch the others. The "age" of this card cannot be determined by superposition alone. Compare the simplified map (Figure 15-6) for superposition in the arrangement of stratified rocks.

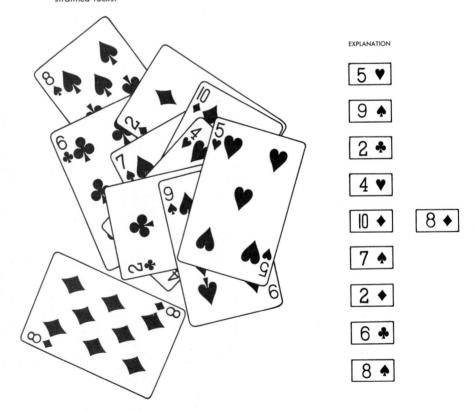

Figure 15-6 A geologic map of part of north-central Texas. Here the rocks are all of sedimentary origin and are almost flat-lying. The correct order of deposition can be determined by superposition of the various formations. Problem: How do we know that the rocks on the left side are older than those on the right side, and which way do the rocks of the older and younger sets of formations dip, or incline? Hint: If you were standing on the banks of one of the rivers where it passes from one formation to another, would you see younger or older beds in the hills on either side? Study the explanation for the correct order of superposition and see if you can determine how it was arrived at.

are piled upon one another in an overlapping manner. Note the following features:

1. No one spot on the "map" has all the cards (or formations) present in the area. By applying the principle of superposition, however, we can determine the correct sequence of all cards except the one isolated by itself. The correct order of cards is given by the key, or legend.
2. Once we understand the arrangement of the cards, we can predict with fair accuracy which ones will be found under any given spot. This procedure is comparable to the methods a geologist uses in predicting what formations will be penetrated by an oil well.
3. A card (or formation) that does not touch or interfinger with other units cannot be placed in its correct position by superposition alone. Such areas must be "dated" by other means, mainly by the use of fossils, as we shall see in the next chapter.

Variations and Extensions
of the Principle of Superposition

Strictly speaking, superposition refers to the placing of one thing over or upon something else. The accumulation of sedimentary layers is a perfect geologic example of superposition and provides indisputable proof of the order in which the layers were formed. But the geologist does not depend entirely on strict superposition in working out geologic history. Any relationship that indicates which of two events occurred first is useful and significant. Thus, we not only look for masses of rock lying one upon another but we also observe the relationships of any earth material or structures that may lie within, against, around, or upon other materials.

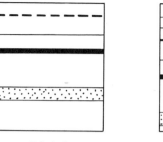 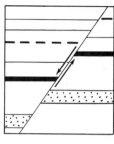 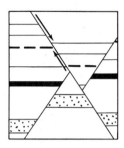

| Unfaulted
Sedimentary Beds | Normal Fault
Lowers Left Side | Second Normal Fault
Lowers Right Side |

Figure 15-7 Diagrammatic cross sections showing the effect of two faults on a section of horizontal beds. Notice how the second fault cuts and offsets the first one so that their relative ages can be determined.

Figure 15-8 Cross-cutting relationships reveal the order of formation of veins, dikes, and intrusions. Here older, dark-colored, banded rock has been cut by younger, light-colored veins. (*Photo by Dr. F. J. Pettijohn.*)

CROSS-CUTTING RELATIONSHIPS Although sedimentary beds do not intersect or cut across each other, faults and intrusive igneous bodies commonly show **cross-cutting relationships.** Faults may cross faults, igneous bodies may cross igneous bodies, and of course, both may also transect sedimentary layers. Conditions can be very complex, but careful observation and mapping usually leave little doubt about the correct order of events (see Figure 15-7).

When two igneous bodies intersect or cross, it is obvious that the older one must have been opened up to provide space for the younger one to intrude. In other words, at the place of juncture the younger one is continuous, the older one discontinuous, regardless of the size of the bodies involved.

Faults are merely planes of movement and have no mass. When one fault crosses another, their relative ages must be determined by considering offsetting relationships. The effects of earlier faults are disrupted by later ones. Fault relationships are determined by using key beds, which in sedimentary rocks are usually thin, distinctive units that can be traced and recognized over wide areas. In general, the youngest fault follows a straight course; others are offset or disrupted.

ORDER OF GROWTH OF CRYSTALS AND ORGANISMS Order of formation is an important consideration in the study of mineral deposits.

300

Geologists are interested in finding out the proper succession of events in the formation of a particular deposit, for such information may yield clues to the location of other deposits. Many minerals grow or crystallize in open spaces that provide ample opportunity for later generations of crystals to grow upon or over preceding ones. Crusts and bands are produced as recently deposited material surrounds earlier deposits. Many different periods of deposition may be recorded in veins and crevices. The study of ore deposits is complicated by the fact that minerals may grow within other minerals as well as upon them and that heat and pressure may completely obliterate a great deal of the evidence. The order of events eventually may have to be decided from microscopic study of minute specimens.

Organisms, like crystals, also grow over and upon each other in various ways. The great coral reefs are impressive examples of superimposed growth. The shells of dead animals become overgrown by living organisms and lime-secreting plants, and layers of many generations may accumulate on even a small object. And,

Figure 15-9 Succession of mineral deposits within an open fracture to produce a vein. 1 indicates original wall rock, 2 and 3 are successive coatings deposited in the fracture, 4 is a growth of crystalline material, 5 is unfilled space.

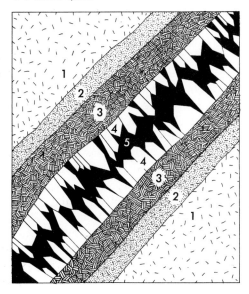

of course, superposition clearly indicates the order of growth.

INTRUSIVE RELATIONSHIPS   Igneous material arises from the depths of the earth and may solidify either below or on the surface. Lava flows and beds of volcanic ash are commonly deposited on the surface in distinct layers, and their correct order of formation can readily be determined by superposition. But superposition does not apply to subterranean igneous bodies that have been forcibly injected between or among pre-existing sedimentary beds. The igneous bodies known as **sills** (see p. 48) originate from molten material that has been forced along bedding planes so as to be parallel with the enclosing layers. After a sill has solidified, it may be folded and faulted in the same manner as the enclosing sediments. Although the rock types composing sills are easily distinguished from sediments, it is difficult to distinguish a lava flow deposited on the surface and then buried from a sill intruded between older sediments. In making this distinction, we note that the heat of a sill will affect adjacent rock both below and above, whereas the heat of a flow affects only the rock below. Then, too, the surface of a lava flow may show bubble-like cavities and cracks, indicating exposure to the air; these effects are absent in sills.

INCLUDED, OR DERIVED, FRAGMENTS   Relatively large rock fragments are frequently found embedded in other rocks in a manner which indicates that they must have come from some pre-existing source and are therefore older than the matrix in which they are embedded. **Conglomerate,** which is a consolidated gravel, is composed mostly of these so-called derived fragments. A typical conglomerate has pieces of all the harder rocks in its source area which were picked up and brought together by stream action. These fragments are usually large enough to contain diagnostic minerals, rocks, or even fossils that can be related specifically to older deposits.

A geologist may have to examine certain fossils very closely before he can say whether

or not they came from an earlier deposit or originated with the formation in which they now occur. Derived or reworked fossils are usually broken and waterworn. Of course, entire skeletons or large plants could not be exhumed, transported, and reburied intact.

Another type of derived material is dislodged and engulfed by igneous material as it moves upward through the earth. Obviously, such pieces must be older than the surrounding matrix. Unmelted pieces of sedimentary rock in a large granite mass, for instance, prove the sediment to be older. If, on the other hand, we find rounded pebbles of granite in a sedimentary bed, we know the granite is older.

SUCCESSION IN LANDSCAPE DEVELOPMENT
What we have already said about methods of determining the order of geologic events applies chiefly to solid rocks. Our discussion would be incomplete without some mention of the methods used in unraveling the history of the surface features of the earth's crust. Even the most monotonous landscapes show the effects of successive events and changing climates, and we know that the features were not all produced at the same time. The geologist has the interesting problem of reconstructing the history of landscapes from the various forms that compose them. For example, the peaks of many high mountain ranges were sharpened and furrowed by glaciers that have melted away, and the areas once occupied by ice are now being reshaped by running water. In many areas there are step-like terraces or beaches that were cut by the waves of lakes that have since dried up. These old lake beds may be invaded by sand dunes or cut by streams, depending on subsequent climatic changes.

A study of the changes in rivers, lakes, deserts, and glaciers involves the fundamental idea of superposition, but there is the added complication of explaining the surface forms. River terraces, especially, are highly instructive but difficult to interpret, for streams are very sensitive to climatic changes, and the same river may run slowly or swiftly, swell in volume or dwindle away, and remove or deposit sedi-

Figure 15-10 Gravel—the debris of vanished formations. A typical beach or stream bed contains rock fragments derived from many older formations. A study of the pebbles in gravel or conglomerate frequently yields valuable clues concerning the order of geologic events. (*Courtesy U.S. Geological Survey.*)

Figure 15-11 Age relationships of intrusive and sedimentary rocks. In the sketch on the left, pebbles of the granite rock are found in the overlying sandstone, proving that the igneous rock is older. In the situation on the right, unmelted pieces of sandstone are shown within the granite, indicating that the sandstone is older.

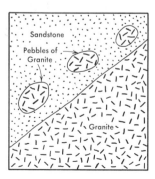
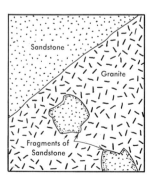

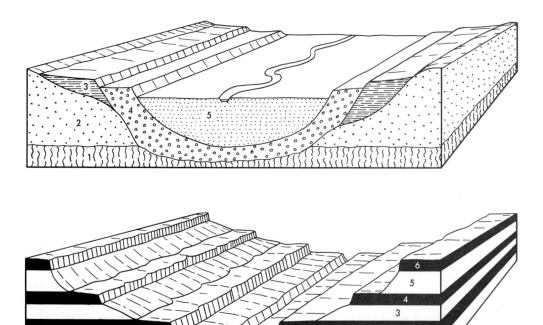

Figure 15-12 Terrace formation. In the lower figure the valley profile is step-like, as in the Grand Canyon. The different ledges and slopes are arranged according to superposition: oldest at the bottom, youngest on top. In the upper diagram the effects of cut and fill show that the successive benches are older above and younger below. The true order of age is determined by superposition in all cases. Thus, in the upper figure the valley was once filled with material 3, which was cut into and mostly removed. Then, number 4 was laid down on and against 3, and the process was repeated. Terrace formations and cut and fill can be very complex processes.

ment, all within the same valley, or **flood plain.** Thus, a terrace may have been cut on bedrock or on previous river deposits; it may have been made by a small river meandering from side to side or by a large river occupying the entire valley. The river valley may have been filled and partly emptied of sediment several times, leaving a variety of deposits to record its changes.

Lakes in arid regions expand and shrink as climates change. The rise and fall of water levels are recorded by terraces and beaches, but it is surprisingly difficult to determine just what the true order of events has been. Likewise, glaciers in expanding and retreating leave surface evidences and thin layers of debris to record their fluctuations.

In dealing with the history of landscapes, we look chiefly for evidence indicating which of two events has effaced or disturbed the other. The sequence of cutting and filling of river

valleys can be determined by noticing which deposits cut into or lie against or on other deposits. Contrary to the situation in canyons where bedrock is exposed, we may find that older deposits make up higher terraces and younger ones lower terraces. For examples of cut-and-fill relationships, see Figure 15-12.

Problems of Applying the Principle of Superposition

We have already inferred that the principle of superposition does not apply to rock layers that have been greatly disturbed after their deposition. Beds that were originally perfectly level may be broken, tilted, and even turned completely over during mountain-building movements. It is common in mountainous areas to see beds that have been tipped up at steeper and steeper angles until they are standing on end. If they go beyond this angle, they are

303

said to be **overturned,** and the bedding planes that originally faced upward now face downward. Superposition cannot apply to rocks in this disturbed position, and they must be restored, in theory at least, to their original position before they can be correctly interpreted. The problem of determining which side of a

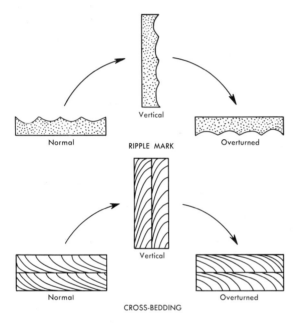

Figure 15-13 The overturning of sedimentary layers illustrated by ripple marks and cross-bedding. The distinctive appearance of certain original features enables us to know whether they are still in their original position or if they have been tipped up and overturned.

Figure 15-14 Chief Mountain, Glacier National Park, Montana. A great overthrust fault has carried the older mountain rocks forward over the younger rocks of the foothills. Chief Mountain is but a small erosional remnant of a much larger sheet of rocks. The movement on the fault has been estimated at 15 miles.

bed of rock was originally up and which down presents interesting possibilities for geologic detective work. Thus, the sharp crests of ripple-marks point upward, and their rounded troughs curve downward. The reverse appearance indicates overturning. Small channels that were cut and filled before burial are convex downward if undisturbed. If turned over, they are convex upward and appear unnatural (see Figure 15-13).

Folding is not the only action by which order of rock layers is reversed. Actual breaking or fracturing of strata may also force older rocks upon younger ones. If vast sections of the earth are powerfully compressed, faults will appear along which great masses are pushed upward and forward. These faults are known as **thrust faults** or **reverse faults.** They are areas in which dislocated masses have moved forward many miles to occupy positions on top of rocks of entirely different age and origin. If, during these movements, rocks that were originally older come to rest on younger ones, the principle of superposition obviously cannot apply. All such instances must be carefully examined; and if the rocks are well exposed, fault planes will be discovered with evidences of intense mechanical disruption, such as crushed and broken rock material and gouged or grooved surfaces that indicate movement.

Closely allied to the blocks moved by thrust faults are large landslide masses. The force of gravity acting on elevated rock masses, especially those that are saturated with water or those in submarine environments, may cause them to slip downward over lower beds. The process of sliding may be slow or rapid, and the masses involved may cover many square miles. If older rocks slide over or fall on younger rocks, we have another instance of deceptive superposition. Landslides and similar materials usually show many indications of breakage and contortion and may even occur in the form of broken fragments called **breccias.** Careful study may reveal the source of the disrupted rocks and provide a logical reason why they have moved from their original positions.

RECONSTRUCTING PAST EVENTS

Even though a long series of events may have disturbed the sedimentary rocks of a region, it is still possible to reconstruct the major features of the past and to apply the principle of superposition. The reconstruction must be done diagrammatically or with models, and it always commences in the present and proceeds backward in time. In effect, the geologist mentally removes the evidences of each significant event to reveal the condition of things before the event took place. Thus, if the last event in a particular area was a lava flow, the geologist "removes" the igneous rock and reconstructs a picture of conditions as they were before the eruption occurred. If faulting had preceded the lava flow, he moves the faulted strata to their original unbroken position. If there is evidence of folding, he graphically straightens out the beds to a horizontal position. Eroded material he "replaces" as far as possible to re-create mountains or larger land areas. Unconformities and losses in the record will leave many gaps, but substitute evidence may be recovered in nearby areas. Thus, through painstaking mapping and study, the broad features of the history of any area of sedimentary rocks may be reconstructed.

Figure 15-15 Determining the sequence of past events. A shows the present landscape and subsurface conditions. Removing the evidence of successively older events reveals the past history of the area. In B, the effects of erosion (as shown by the canyon) are removed, showing that the lava flow was continuous across the area. In C, the volcano and its subterranean conduit and surface flows are removed, exposing what was once a gravel-covered plain. In D the original height of the fault is restored together with some of the debris that has weathered from the scarp. In E the fault is removed by sliding the beds back to their original positions so that corresponding beds match. This reveals the folded condition of the beds that preceded the faulting. Finally, in section F, the beds are unfolded and the original condition of the area is revealed.

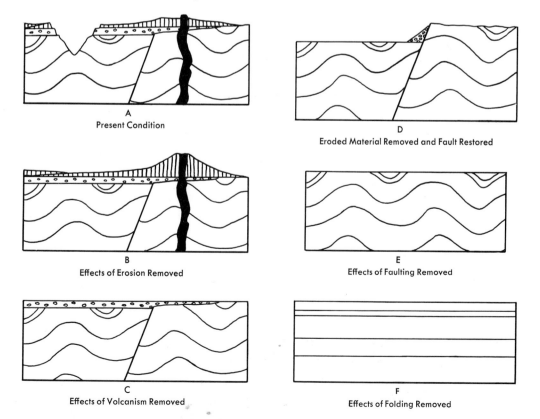

A
Present Condition

B
Effects of Erosion Removed

C
Effects of Volcanism Removed

D
Eroded Material Removed and Fault Restored

E
Effects of Faulting Removed

F
Effects of Folding Removed

FAUNAL SUCCESSION

A third generalization of great importance in thinking about the past history of the earth is the **principle of faunal succession,** which is that: **Groups of fossil plants and animals succeed one another in a definite and determinable order and each period of time can be recognized by its respective fossils.** Note that this statement does not specify the manner of origin of the different groups of fossils; it is true regardless of whether or not organic evolution is true.

The principle of faunal succession was not conceived as an unsupported theory; it was discovered through the accumulation and study of thousands of fossil collections from all parts of the earth. Anyone who is interested can repeat the process of collection and comparison if he wishes, as long as he is careful to apply the principle of superposition to his work. When superposition is taken into account it is always found that the oldest abundant fossils are the trilobites. An Age of Trilobites can be recognized on all continents. Later, in successively higher and younger rocks we recognize an Age of Fishes, an Age of Coal Forests, an Age of Reptiles, an Age of Mammals, and an Age of Man. These terms, of course, pertain to the groups of organisms that were especially plentiful and characteristic during certain periods. Within each of the great "ages" there are numerous minor subdivisions marked, for example, by certain species of trilobites, certain kinds of fish, and so on. That the same succession of ages is found on each major land mass, never out of order and never repeated in the same area, proves uniform world-wide similarity and correlation.

It should be understood that not all fossil-bearing periods are present everywhere. The Grand Canyon, for example, is a magnificent display of rock layers, but it shows only 3 of the 12 major fossil-bearing periods of the earth's history. Records of 3 of the missing periods were never deposited in this area, but they were laid down in southern Nevada a short distance away. Here they are found in proper order "sandwiched" between formations that are also present in the Grand Canyon. The other 5 periods are too young to be represented in the Canyon; they are found in the high cliffs and plateaus of southern Utah above and some distance back from the Canyon rim.

Sedimentary layers do not go entirely around the earth like the rings of an onion; they resemble more the leaves of a cabbage which overlap and interfinger. Even in a cabbage the relation and relative age of any leaf can be determined by applying the idea of

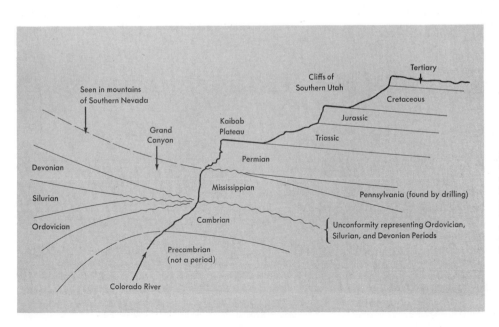

Figure 15-16 Diagrammatic cross section through the Grand Canyon and cliffs of southern Utah. Note that only 3 of the standard geologic periods are represented in the canyon. Unconformities record the positions of 4 other periods and 4 additional ones are represented in the cliffs that are not a part of the canyon.

superposition. Superposition and faunal succession go hand in hand and the geologist in the field uses both simultaneously. Nevertheless, superposition is basic and proves faunal succession.

BIOTIC ASSOCIATION

The principle of faunal succession can be proven in a second way, by **biotic association,** or the fact that specific fossils or groups of fossils do or do not occur consistently together. Proof comes again from study and comparison of thousands of collections of fossils. For example, trilobites are commonly found with cup corals but never with oysters; dinosaurs occur with cycads but never with horses. We must understand that there is not a complete replacement of one group of life forms by an entirely new group as once supposed, rather there are overlapping histories throughout the entire record. Thus, the earliest crocodiles lived with the dinosaurs while later crocodiles live with man, but man and dinosaurs did not live together.

The principle of biotic association may be clarified by the following discussion and diagrams. In the illustrations (Figures 15-17 to 15-20) a number of large inclusive life groups are represented by diagrammatic figures placed in the geologic intervals where they have been found. Thus, the generalized dinosaur skull represents all dinosaurs, both primitive and advanced. Of course, any fossil form may be found by itself, but it is more common to find several or many kinds of fossil associated in one deposit, as indicated by the diagram. Assume for purposes of illustration that the forms indicated in the Jurassic collection have been collected from a single formation. This collection (Figure 15-17), by itself, would merely prove that dinosaurs, cycads, linguloid brachiopods, *Pectens*, oysters, and *Inoceramus* pelecypods lived simultaneously, but as yet we could deduce nothing about the proper position of the Jurassic collection in time or of the meaning of its fossils in terms of evolution.

Figure 15-17 Jurassic collection: oyster, linguloid brachiopod, dinosaur, *Pecten*, cycad, and *Inoceramus*.

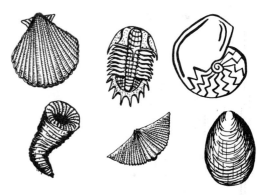

Figure 15-18 Devonian collection: *Pecten*, trilobite, goniatite cephalopod, cup coral, spirifer, and linguloid brachiopod.

Now let us turn to a second collection, gathered from rocks beneath the Jurassic (we will see in time that these are classified as Devonian) (Figure 15-18). As we compare the two collections, we notice many obvious differences in the specimens, but find that pectens and linguloid brachiopods are present in both. We could assume that trilobites, cup corals, and goniatite cephalopods preceded the dinosaurs, cycads, and oysters, but details about times of first appearance or extinction would still be missing and the chart would be incomplete.

Now assume that a third collection, representing the Triassic, has been found at some distant locality and we wish to relate it to the

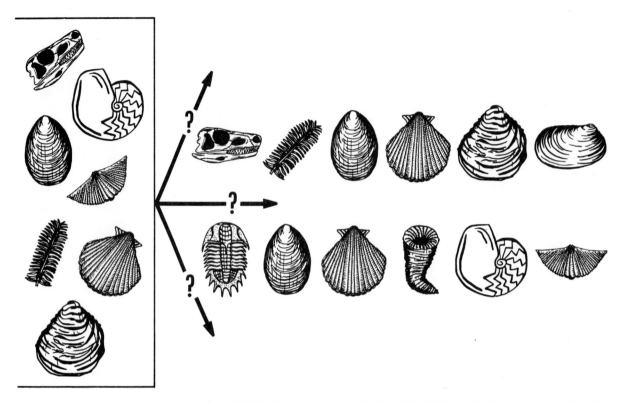

Figure 15-19 How a new collection (the Triassic) is correlated with Jurassic and Devonian collections. Why is one position more logical than either of the others?

other collections. If the Triassic collection was found in its proper sequence, we could place it without further study. For the sake of a more realistic picture, we will assume we do not know where it was found and that we must determine its relative position in time by studying the fossils it contains. In other words, we must decide whether to place it before the Devonian, between the Devonian and Jurassic, or after the Jurassic (Figure 15-19). If we place it before the Devonian, we are assuming that dinosaurs, oysters, and cycads have either been overlooked in Devonian collections or have appeared more than once in geologic time. If we choose to place the new collection after the Jurassic, we assume that cup corals and goniatite cephalopods were overlooked in the Jurassic or that they originated more than once.

Our assumptions of an incomplete record or the recurrence of identical forms may conceivably be correct, but they are obviously unnecessary. By placing the Triassic collection between the Jurassic and Devonian, we are able to maintain a continuous existence for all the fossil forms and can safely add another step to the chart. Also, since the Triassic resembles the Jurassic more than it does the Devonian, we may tentatively place it closer to the Jurassic in time. As subsequent collections come to light, they will fill in the remainder of the chart and will show eventually the times of arrival, periods of abundance, and final extinction of the various life forms.

This discussion illustrates the type of information on which the idea of the succession of life was established. No one thought it up on a theoretical basis; it came to light only after patient, systematic searching by many diligent collectors all over the world.

The progressive evolutionary changes of life on earth can thus be demonstrated by two methods: the study of superposition and the study of associations of organisms.

Understand clearly that the principle of life succession does not mean that simple or unspecialized animals are not found in young

308

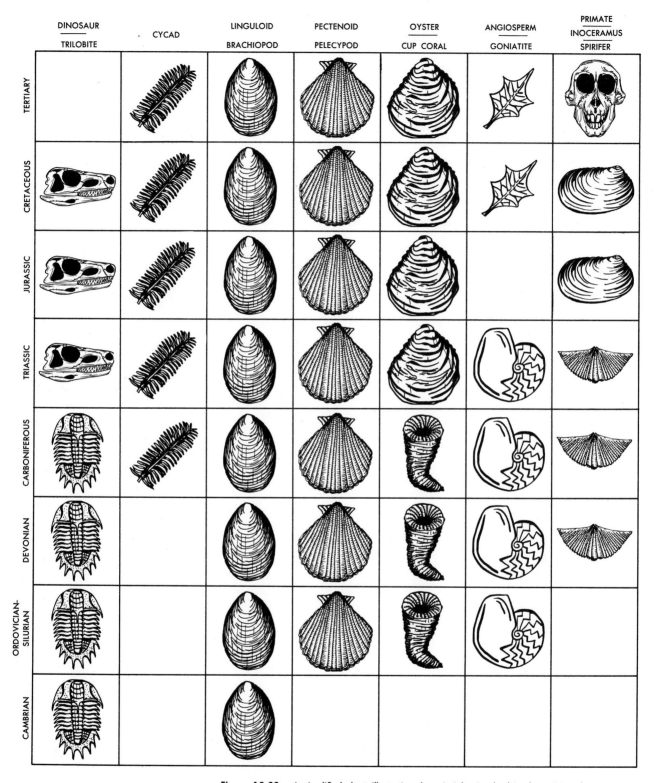

	DINOSAUR / TRILOBITE	CYCAD	LINGULOID BRACHIOPOD	PECTENOID PELECYPOD	OYSTER CUP CORAL	ANGIOSPERM GONIATITE	PRIMATE INOCERAMUS SPIRIFER

Figure 15-20 A simplified chart illustrating the principles involved in determining the correct succession of life forms on earth and how fossils are used to date rocks or periods of time. Notice that this diagram is a continuation of the 3 preceding illustrations. Although the drawing is diagrammatic, the individual fossil groups represented are correctly placed according to their existence in time. Example: dinosaurs are known only from the Triassic, Jurassic, and Cretaceous, and have never been found in association with primates.

rocks or that complex and highly specialized organisms are not present in old rocks. The principle applies only to comparisons made between the total life of successive geologic intervals and between members of the same general group. Thus, a simple sponge from a later period of time cannot be compared with a complex crustacean from an early period. Sponges must be compared with sponges and crustaceans with crustaceans. When we trace successive members of the same group through time or compare the total life of a later period with that of an earlier one, we see that significant changes have occurred. Whether or not the changes are always progressive might be debated as a philosophical point, but it seems safe to say that there is an ever-increasing tendency toward a more complete utilization of all energy sources, better adaptation to the environment, and greater complexity of organization with the passage of time.

Faunal succession as revealed by the study of fossils does not constitute positive proof of organic evolution, in spite of the fact that most students regard it as such. Absolute proof of organic evolution would mean the positive demonstration that all life forms descended naturally from preceding ones, back to a simple beginning. This would require an endless succession of individuals, each with "birth certificates" that can never be supplied. Faunal succession is more than a theory, however, for it shows that life has indeed changed and progressed with the passage of time.

RECAPITULATION

That the universe is governed by law is accepted by all scientists. There are, however, many differences of opinion about what the laws are. A well-founded natural law ought to be universal and timeless in its application and one that can be relied on to govern similar situations in the same way at all times and places. We have learned by experience that many so-called laws are not really as fundamental and reliable as once supposed. For example, the law of the conservation of matter now reads the law of the conservation of matter and energy. Scientists are much more cautious in proposing laws than they were a few decades ago. We may do better by referring to generalizations of an unprovable nature as principles, explanations, rules or beliefs.

In line with this note of caution we refer to the **concept of uniformitarianism** and the **principle of faunal succession,** leaving open the possibility that they are not to be applied as absolute and invariable at all times and places. On the other hand (and the writer's colleagues may not all agree), it is safe to refer to the law of superposition as invariable and changeless. Be this as it may, geologists base their conclusions chiefly on these three rules of thought. So far we have not thereby been led into impossible contradictions or unprofitable avenues of investigation.

SUMMARY

Geology is a derived science; it is essentially physics and chemistry applied to the earth. The study of ancient fossil organisms as such may be thought of as a division of biology. But the study of the unobserved and unrepeatable geologic past also has guides and techniques peculiar to itself. Three principles or generalizations are of utmost importance. Uniformitarianism has been summarized in the saying that the present is the key to the past. It dictates that geological explanations will be based as far as possible upon known processes and principles and upon what can be observed in operation in the present world. Under uniformitarianism we reject the incomprehensible, mysterious or fantastic explanations as long as everyday, natural ones will suffice.

A second important guide is the principle of superposition. Simply stated this is: In any sequence of undisturbed sediments, any bed is older than the one above it and younger than the one below. This concept may be extended to include any situation where it can be determined from physical evidence that one event preceded or succeeded another. Igneous bodies, faults, and surface features can be placed in order of origin.

The third guide in the study of the past is faunal succession: Groups of plants and animals succeed each other in a definite and determinable order, and any period of time can be recognized by its respective fossils. This was discovered to be a fact as fossils were collected over ever-expanding parts of the earth. The same succession of life forms is found on every continent, always in the same order and never repeated in the same area. The application of the principle has made possible world-wide unified mapping and correlation of sediments. Faunal succession is proven also by biotic association, or the fact that certain organisms are found to have lived consistently together at the same time while others have not.

ADDITIONAL READING

Adams, F. D., *The Birth and Development of the Geological Sciences.* New York: Dover Publications, 1954.

Albritton, C. C., ed., *The Fabric of Geology.* San Francisco: Freeman, Cooper and Co., 1964.

Dunbar, C. O., and John Rodgers, *Principles of Stratigraphy.* New York: John Wiley & Sons, 1957.

Krumbein, W. C., and L. L. Sloss, *Stratigraphy and Sedimentation.* San Francisco: W. H. Freeman and Co., 1951.

Low, Julian W., *Geologic Field Methods.* New York: Harper & Row, 1957.

Pettijohn, F. J., *Sedimentary Rocks,* 2nd ed. New York: Harper & Row, 1957.

Shrock, R. R., *Sequence in Layered Rocks.* New York: McGraw-Hill Book Co., 1948.

Weller, J. M., *Stratigraphic Principles and Practice.* New York: Harper & Row, 1960.

16

The Early Paleozoic Periods

This chapter treats the combined Cambrian, Ordovician, and Silurian Periods, or early Paleozoic Era, with a total length of 195 million years. (Best current estimates give the Cambrian a duration of 100 million years, the Ordovician 75 million years, and the Silurian 20 million years. The disparity in length of the periods is a good reason for not treating each in a separate chapter.) The next chapter covers the late Paleozoic (Devonian, Mississippian, Pennsylvanian, and Permian Periods) with a combined duration of 170 million years. The Mesozoic Era, consisting of the Triassic, Jurassic, and Cretaceous Periods, with a combined length of 165 million years, constitutes another convenient unit which we will discuss in Chapter 18.

It is obvious that these three- or four-period intervals are of approximately equal duration; a closer look shows that each interval encompasses a roughly similar sequence of events. At the beginning of a typical major cycle, the continents are relatively high and rugged and the oceans are confined well within their basins. This is also the interval of mountain-building, volcanism, glaciation, aridity, and continental sedimentation. With the passage of time, as earth disturbances subside, erosion slowly eats away the lands, the seas creep inward in shallow floods, climates become mild and more uniform, and sea life and marine sediments dominate the record. After a lengthy and relatively quiet span, conditions gradually change as crustal disturbances elevate the continents and drive out the shallow seas. Climates diversify and glaciers and deserts become common. Continental types of sediment are produced in abundance, and marine deposits are correspondingly restricted. Thus, one cycle ends and the stage is set for the next to commence.

Like most cycles that historians recognize, these geologic repetitions are neither perfect nor universal. They are best thought of as generalized patterns for the earth as a whole. Some geologists refer to the times of greatest emergence as **land periods** and to the times of submergence as **sea periods.** We may consider a combined land-sea interval as a great cycle because it tends to repeat certain events.

European and Russian geologists designate the events of the early Paleozoic as **Caledonian,** those of the late Paleozoic as **Hercynian,** those of the Mesozoic as **Kimmerian,** and those of the Cenozoic as **Alpine.** These names emphasize chiefly physical events such as mountain-building rather than sedimentary rocks or fossils.

The early stages of continental growth have been described in Chapter 13. The ancient continental cores or nuclei which formed during Precambrian time had many important influences upon subsequent history. These pre-existing land areas furnished the erosion products from which later formations are composed and also determined the positions of basins, geosynclines, and mountain ranges that were yet to form. Since each of the major continents had one or more nuclei, there is a certain basis of uniformity with which to begin the story of later time.

BEGINNING OF THE CAMBRIAN

During the latest stages of the Precambrian, the lands appear to have been relatively high and locally mountainous, and the oceans were apparently confined well within their basins. The many clear indications of extensive glaciation near the beginning of Cambrian time that are found in Greenland, Australia, South Africa, India, China, Canada, and the United States have already been mentioned. There appears to be a logical connection between high continents, cold glacial climates, deep contracted oceans, and scarcity of fossils. The underlying cause of all these conditions may have been a period of widespread adjustment in the earth's crust during late Precambrian time. When this disturbance had subsided, the Cambrian began; the continents were lowered by erosion, glaciers melted, the oceans warmed and flooded inland, and marine life flourished and spread widely. The slow rise of sea level may have stemmed from a number of causes, such as the release of water from glaciers, the dumping of sediment from the land, or changes in the shape of the ocean floor.

NORTHWESTERN EUROPE
AND THE CALEDONIAN REVOLUTION

The science of geology had its inception in northwestern Europe, and one phase of the formative period was the designation of the **type,** or first-studied, **sections** of the Cambrian, Ordovician, and Silurian Systems in Great

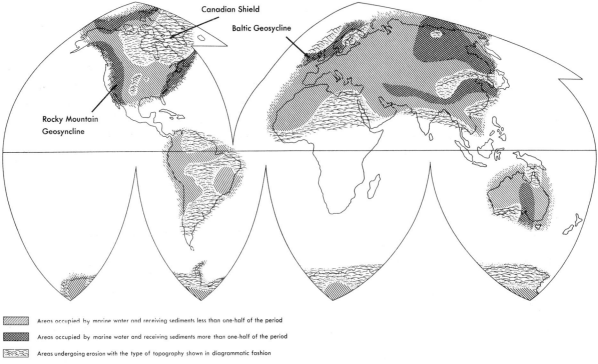

Areas occupied by marine water and receiving sediments less than one-half of the period

Areas occupied by marine water and receiving sediments more than one-half of the period

Areas undergoing erosion with the type of topography shown in diagrammatic fashion

White areas indicate open ocean or geologically unknown areas

Outlines of present land masses are for reference only

Figure 16-1   Generalized paleogeographic map of the Cambrian Period.

Figure 16-2   Signs of the Caledonian mountain-building disturbance, Yorkshire County, England. Horizontal Carboniferous limestone overlies steeply dipping and eroded Silurian beds. (*Crown Copyright Geological Survey photograph. Reproduced by permission of the Controller of H. M. Stationery Office.*)

Britain. The British Isles together with Norway, Sweden and Denmark were part of the subsiding **Baltic**, or **Caledonian, Geosyncline**, which trended northeastward along the northwest border of Europe at this time. At least 40,000 feet of early Paleozoic rocks accumulated in the Welsh segment of the trough.

The type Cambrian System in the Caledonian belt has many fossil trilobites and a variety of rock types appropriate to the varied environments of a subsiding seaway. Unusual by comparison with North America is the presence of considerable volcanic material in the European Cambrian.

The Caledonian Geosyncline continued to subside, and Ordovician and Silurian deposits followed those of Cambrian age. Included are black shale facies with graptolites; shell-bearing facies with abundant corals, brachiopods, and trilobites; facies of mixed sandstone and conglomerate with few fossils; and, finally, thick volcanic facies of ash, tuff, and lava. The grap-

314

tolites have proven to be the best guide fossils for subdividing both the Ordovician and Silurian into zones. Not to be overlooked are the Late Silurian (Ludlovian) beds of northwestern Europe, which yield the best-known remains of early primitive vertebrates and eurypterids.

The Silurian came to an end in northwest Europe with an important and widespread mountain-building episode, the Caledonian Revolution. This was very intense in Norway, where rocks of Precambrian, Cambrian, Ordovician, and Silurian age were metamorphosed almost beyond recognition. Only the finding of rare but diagnostic fossils enabled geologists to interpret the history correctly. Granitic bodies were formed and the area was cut by great thrust faults which further complicate the picture.

Farther south, in Great Britain, the effects were less intense, but faulting and folding give clear indication of mountain building in Wales and Scotland. The land area thus created is

known as the Old Red Sandstone Continent. It extended for an unknown distance beyond the present borders of Europe, and its eastern edge fused with the original Baltic Shield to form a more or less rigid area that has never been invaded by the seas since Silurian time. Similar intensive effects are noted in the Silurian of Greenland.

THE TETHYS SEAWAY TAKES FORM

The long, relatively narrow tract of the earth's crust that includes the Mediterranean Sea and the great ranges of the Alpine-Himalayan chain is the world's most extensive geosynclinal belt; this is called the **Tethys seaway** or simply **Tethys**. It lies between the Baltic and Angara Shields on the north and the African and Indian shield areas on the south. This was a position of instability and unrest, and with the passage of time the belt subsided and accumulated a

Figure 16-3 Generalized paleogeographic map of the Ordovician Period.

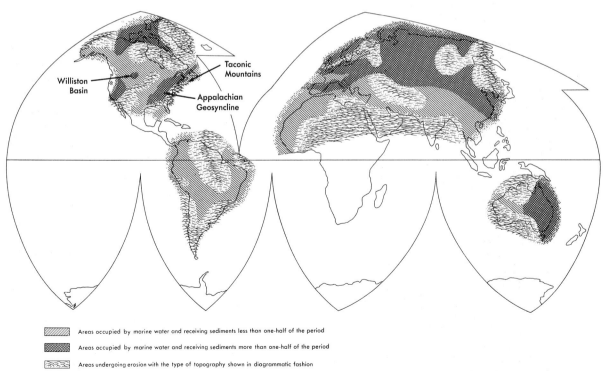

Williston Basin

Taconic Mountains

Appalachian Geosyncline

▨ Areas occupied by marine water and receiving sediments less than one-half of the period

▩ Areas occupied by marine water and receiving sediments more than one-half of the period

▨ Areas undergoing erosion with the type of topography shown in diagrammatic fashion

White areas indicate open ocean or geologically unknown areas

Outlines of present land masses are for reference only

record of all the geologic systems. During the early Paleozoic it was not as active as the Caledonian trough, but deposits of the Cambrian, Ordovician, and Silurian are known across its entire length, stretching from Spain to southeast Asia.

Rocks of the early Paleozoic are widespread in China and contain abundant fossils. The oldest known fossils of Japan and of Indonesia are of Silurian age. There is little or no evidence of sedimentary deposits along the western Pacific or in the East Indies before this time.

EURASIA NORTH OF TETHYS

The vast plains of northern Russia and most of Siberia are underlain by varied formations of Cambrian, Ordovician, and Silurian age. There are many similarities with rocks of the same age in North America, and the fossils prove

occasional shallow-water connections between the northern continents.

The Cambrian of the northwestern Russian platform is described as soft shale or clay, indicating that it has not been disturbed or deeply buried since deposition. In the interior of Asia the Cambrian contains salt and gypsum beds, which are among the earliest deposits of this type known.

The Ordovician System here is usually thicker and is at least as extensive as the Cambrian. Ordovician rocks are found throughout the length of the Urals, indicating geosynclinal subsidences in this area. There were very strong mountain-building movements in the Ordovician along much of the western and southern borders of the Angara Shield. These produced a variety of eruptive rocks and large granitic intrusions. A comparison with similar events in eastern North America is suggested. These disturbances began in the Ordovician and continued into the Devonian and are considered as

Figure 16-4   Generalized paleogeographic map of the Silurian Period.

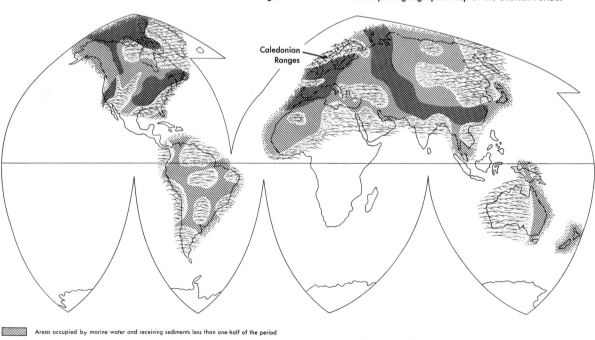

Caledonian Ranges

Areas occupied by marine water and receiving sediments less than one-half of the period

Areas occupied by marine water and receiving sediments more than one-half of the period

Areas undergoing erosion with the. type of topography shown in diagrammatic fashion

White areas indicate open ocean or geologically unknown areas

Outlines of present land masses are for reference only

part of the Caledonian orogenic cycle by Russian geologists.

The Silurian is generally less extensive than the Ordovician, but it reaches a thickness of 12,000 feet in the Ural Mountains and in Turkestan. Silurian volcanic rocks are frequently found, but signs of mountain-building are less evident than in the Ordovician.

NORTH AMERICA

North America has the most complete and extensive record of the Cambrian, Ordovician, and Silurian Periods of any continent. Seas of these Periods spread far inland and at times covered practically all of the Canadian Shield. In addition there were geosynclinal belts which almost encircled the continent. The fossils abundantly preserved in the troughs and shelf areas give a remarkably complete picture of the life of the early Paleozoic.

Commencing with the Cambrian, the North American continent may be thought of as being divided by a sort of "backbone" into two great provinces—one to the southeast, the other to the northwest. The backbone, or **Transcontinental Arch** as it is properly called, extends from the Mojave Desert area of California entirely across the United States to Lake Superior and into Labrador. Across its summit the geologic systems are thin and discontinuous; they thicken away from it in both directions.

EASTERN NORTH AMERICA   That portion of North America lying east and southeast of the Transcontinental Arch displays extensive outcrops of early Paleozoic rocks. The interior regions, chiefly the drainage area of the Mississippi River, are underlain by rocks like those of the Canadian Shield with a thin cover of Paleozoic sediments. A number of broad structural domes and basins surrounded by wide bands of Paleozoic sediments characterize this region. The major uplifts, along with the age of the oldest rocks exposed in their respective central areas, are as follows: Ozark Mountains, Precambrian; Cincinnati Arch, Ordovician;

Wisconsin Dome, Precambrian and Cambrian. The major basins, with the age of youngest rocks in their central regions, are: Illinois Basin, Pennsylvanian; Michigan Basin, Pennsylvanian; and Allegheny Basin, Permian. These domes and basins mostly began to form in Ordovician time and have been accentuated by later forces, not, however, by intensive mountain-building.

Bordering the interior plains are mountain systems born of Paleozoic geosynclines. Along the eastern margin from Newfoundland to Georgia is the **Appalachian geosynclinal belt.** The **Ouachita Mountain system,** now largely buried, arose from a geosyncline that lay along the southern margins of the continental nucleus. These troughs received sediments from the continental interior and occasionally from uplifts within or beyond their outer borders.

The concept of the geosyncline as a great belt of downsinking and deposition came through studies by American geologists in the Appalachian region. The idea has proved a most useful one and has now been applied on all continents. The original picture of a single sinking trough has had to be modified and the geosyncline is now visualized as being divided into two parallel sub-troughs. The outer or seaward trough is called the **eugeosyncline.** It contains chiefly highly siliceous material, mainly volcanic products, coarse and poorly sorted with few fossils. This belt appears chiefly in New England where early Paleozoic siliceous and volcanic rocks reach 15,000 feet in New Hampshire.

By contrast, the inner, or **miogeosynclinal,** belt and shelf areas received mainly nonvolcanic shallow-water deposits such as limestone, dolomite, clean sandstone, and shale. There are many fossils, and coal and oil are present. In the Appalachian miogeosyncline the Early Cambrian is chiefly sandstone. Later in the Cambrian and continuing in the Ordovician came great thicknesses of dolomite and limestone. These calcareous rocks reach a thickness of 10,000 feet in Alabama and 6,000 feet in Oklahoma. The immense number of fossil shells and other organically precipitated carbonates attest to the importance of life in the building of rocks at this time. The early Paleozoic carbonate sheets effectively sealed off, or "armor plated," much of the Precambrian crystalline outcrops so that coarse sandy sediments were not available to erosion until laid bare in the subsequent mountain-building and erosion of late Paleozoic time.

During the Cambrian there was suprisingly little volcanic activity in North America and even the outer (eugeosynclinal) belt was inhabited by a variety of silt-loving trilobites. During the Ordovician, increasing amounts of dark-colored shale with fossil graptolites were laid down. In recognition of the almost world-wide association of dark shale and graptolites in the Ordovician and Silurian Periods, the term "graptolite facies" has come into general use. The term contrasts with "shelly facies" which designates the contemporaneous shell-bearing limy rocks.

As we have already mentioned, the Atlantic border began to show deep-seated unrest in mid-Ordovician time. Earth movement and volcanic activity mounted in intensity and culminated near the close of the period in the **Taconic Disturbance,** so named from effects in the Taconic Range of Vermont and New York. The offshore land masses formed at this time shed coarse-grained sediment westward and brought the great lime-depositing interval to a close. Sandy sediments spread across Penn-

sylvania and New York as the borderland, Appalachia, continued to rise; this series of coarse deposits is known as the **Queenston Delta.**

The high ground created by the Taconic Disturbance continued to supply coarse sediments throughout most of the Silurian, but by the end of the period the seas had cleared again and limestone was deposited. Not to be overlooked are the extensive salt-bearing beds of the eastern interior, which also accumulated near the close of the Silurian. Through a peculiar combination of land-locked basins and restricted seaways, a vast, almost "Dead Sea" type of environment came into being in western New York, Pennsylvania, Ohio, and Michigan. The greatest salt thickness, aggregating 1,600 feet, is in the center of the Michigan Basin. Salt from this formation is extensively mined at many places. The most famous exposure of Silurian rocks is at Niagara Falls; the rocks here are older than the salt-bearing series.

WESTERN NORTH AMERICA During the early Paleozoic the Pacific Ocean washed inland to the margins of the Transcontinental Arch and the Canadian Shield. There was no Rocky Mountain chain but its geological forerunner, the Rocky Mountain Geosyncline, was a dominant feature. This great curving trough begins in southern California, extends into Utah and Idaho, and then back toward the Pacific through Montana, Alberta, and Alaska. By contrast with eastern North America there is practically no evidence of an offshore western borderland analogous to Appalachia in early Paleozoic time. Essentially all of the earlier deposits of the trough came from seawater or from the wearing down of interior lands. The hypothetical borderland of Cascadia evidently is not needed, and for the early Paleozoic, at least, the Rocky Mountain Geosyncline was essentially one-sided. Another significant difference is the almost complete lack of volcanic products in the western trough. Here the sedimentary history of the early Paleozoic was unbroken by strong mountain-building or volcanic effects.

The Cambrian began with the encroachment of shallow seas at the northwest and

Figure 16-5 A specimen of black shale with impressions of graptolites from Ordovician rocks of west-central Nevada. For some reason not fully clear, most graptolite specimens are found in dark-colored fine-grained rock. Scale represents one inch.

southwest parts of the geosyncline. The initial deposits were chiefly clean quartz sands washed from the continental interior. With the passage of time and the steady transgressions of the seas, the sediments became finer and more calcareous. The amount of limestone and dolomite deposited in the inner, or miogeosynclinal, belts is even greater than that of the eastern United States. The combined Cambrian-Ordovician carbonate section reaches 15,000 feet in western Utah. Much of the spectacular mountain scenery of the Alberta Rockies is carved from these rocks. Late in the Cambrian the seas had flooded inward until the Transcontinental Arch was reduced to a number of islands.

During the Ordovician the Rocky Mountain trough shows a clear division into an inner, or miogeosynclinal, carbonate belt and an outer, or eugeosynclinal, siliceous belt. In this period the east and west margins of the continent reached a high degree of symmetry and similarity. In both east and west the inner limestone facies passes into the outer or graptolite facies rather abruptly, but the structural complications are greater in New England than in Nevada. In gen-

eral, throughout the western miogeosyncline, the early Ordovician is limy and the later part is dolomitic. Between them is a widespread sandstone or quartzite phase similar to the better-known formation called the **St. Peter Sandstone** of the mid-continent. Thin deposits record the eastward spread of shallow seas onto and occasionally across the Transcontinental Arch. The Williston Basin in North Dakota and south-central Canada began to form in the Ordovician and received sediments of all the later Paleozoic periods.

The Silurian is a short period and its deposits are correspondingly thin. A single sheet of dolomite in the deeper parts of the Rocky Mountain Geosyncline gives a relatively incomplete record of the time. That the seas did occasionally spread farther inland is known from small isolated patches in Wyoming and Colorado, but it is certain that no very thick or extensive deposits were laid down.

Early Paleozoic rocks are widespread in northern Canada, including the Arctic Islands. Thin deposits on the mainland thicken northward into the Franklyn Geosyncline, where as

Figure 16-6 Restored cross-section of Cambrian formations from southern Nevada into the Grand Canyon, Arizona. Length of section about 150 miles. This section illustrates the encroachment of the Cambrian seas upon the continent. The sandy deposits of the Prospect Mountain and Tapeats represent coarse material eroded from the exposed lands; they were covered later by shale and limestone as seas deepened. The individual formations are younger to the east than to the west, illustrating the fact that formations may transgress time lines so as to be older in one locality than in another.

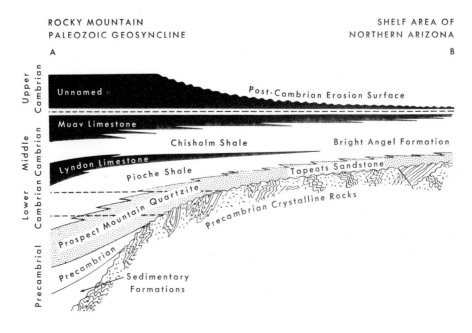

Figure 16-7 An important geologic boundary on Mt. Weaver, Antarctica. The geologist is standing on the contact of late Paleozoic glacial conglomerates (*above*) and granitic rocks of Cambrian or Ordovician age (*below*). (*Courtesy Velon H. Minshew, Ohio State University Institute of Polar Studies.*)

much as 18,000 feet of early Paleozoic marine beds accumulated. Sediments are varied, but carbonates, as elsewhere in North America, are dominant. An outer belt of graptolitic shale correlates with the inner carbonates. Conditions under the Arctic Ocean are not well understood.

THE SOUTHERN CONTINENTS

Compared with North America and Eurasia, the southern continents have a very incomplete and scattered sedimentary record of the early Paleozoic periods. This deficiency is probably due to the relatively emergent conditions of the southern land masses, which favored erosion rather than deposition.

The most complete representation of the Cambrian, Ordovician, and Silurian Systems in the Southern Hemisphere is in Australia. In the eastern part of the continent there was steady deposition in the northerly-trending **Tasmanian,** or **Tasman, Geosyncline.** The types of fossils found in these beds indicate that migration of organisms to and from distant lands was possible. Cephalopods of the Australian Ordovician are much like those of western

North America, and the graptolites of the Ordovician and Silurian are almost identical to those from Wales and the United States. The migration routes which permitted these similarities to exist are still obscure.

No Cambrian, Ordovician, or Silurian rocks have been positively identified in that part of Africa lying south of the equator. The few nondiagnostic fossils that have been found in pre-Devonian rocks do not resemble typical early Paleozoic forms from other places and may be of Precambrian age. South Africa was probably well above sea level in the early Paleozoic, just as it now is. That part of Africa north of the equator has Cambrian, Ordovician, and Silurian rocks laid down in shallow embayments of the Tethys seaway, and these rocks need not be discussed here.

Although the early Paleozoic rock record of South America is much better than that of Africa, it is still less complete than that of North America. Fossiliferous Cambrian deposits are very rare, but deposits in Argentina have yielded Middle Cambrian trilobites almost identical with those of the Baltic region. By contrast, the Ordovician is fairly well represented along the entire Andean belt, in places, by deposits of great thickness. Graptolite-bearing shales are common and many of the forms are related to those of eastern North America and the Baltic region of Europe. A short period of glaciation is recorded during the period in western Argentina.

Figure 16-8 Specimen of fossil alga, *Newlandia frondosa,* showing characteristic concentric, cabbage-like appearance. (*Courtesy U.S. Geological Survey.*)

Early Silurian seas spread across wide areas of South America mainly east of the Andean belt in the Amazon trough and across northern Argentina. In the mid-Silurian the seas retreated to the Andean belt; no late Silurian deposits are known, but glacial deposits of Silurian age are said to be present in northern Argentina and Bolivia.

Although geologic investigations of Antarctica are incomplete, it is fairly well established that no Ordovician or Silurian rocks exist there. The Cambrian, with **archaeocyathids** (see p. 322) and other typical fossils, is present along the central mountain ranges.

LIFE OF THE PALEOZOIC

Plant Life

Layered calcareous structures built by algae are among the oldest known fossils. Bacteria over 3 billion years old have also left unmistakable remains in siliceous rocks and iron ores. Spores are found in Cambrian rocks as are unidentifiable "seaweeds." All these evidences preceded the advent of land vegetation, the first traces of which are from Upper Silurian rocks of eastern Australia. These are mainly small, leafless forms with primitive spore-bearing organs on the ends of the branches. A few have simple forked stems with short scale-like leaves.

The Invertebrates

THE APPEARANCE OF ABUNDANT MARINE FOSSILS　With the beginning of the Cambrian Period, fossils began to be preserved in great numbers. Although we do not understand why fossils of marine invertebrates suddenly became plentiful, we are inclined to suppose that it was at least partly because of the increasing production of shells and skeletons by animals that had formerly been without them.

There was a sudden marked increase in the number of animals that use calcium to build their shells—the **molluscs** and **echino-**

derms which use calcium carbonate almost exclusively; and the **brachiopods** and **arthropods,** which secrete mixtures of calcareous and phosphatic material. The increased use of calcium by shell-building animals seems to coincide with the formation of thick beds of limestone and dolomite. The prevalence of limy formations and calcareous shells during the Cambrian and Ordovician may be related to a general warming of the ocean, for calcite is deposited and secreted more easily in warm water than in cold water.

The Cambrian—Age of Trilobites

The **trilobites** were crawling or swimming arthropods with light, jointed skeletons (Figure 16-9). They are now extinct and have no close living relatives. Their remains are found on all continents, especially in Cambrian rocks, and thousands of species have been described. The typical trilobite "shell," or carapace, is formed of a number of separate articulating pieces which tended to fall apart when the animal

Figure 16-9　Early Cambrian trilobite, Olenellus garretti, *from Crainbrook, British Columbia. (Courtesy V. J. Okulitch.)*

Figure 16-10 *Acrothele, a typical inarticulate brachiopod, from the Middle Cambrian. The small, two-piece shell was preserved as it lay open on the Cambrian sea bed. Each valve is about $\frac{1}{4}$ inch across.*

moulted or died. Perfect specimens are rare but the heads and tails are so diagnostic that an expert can readily distinguish one species from another without the entire fossil. The trilobites were obviously adapted for life in shallow seas, where they swam, floated, crawled, or burrowed, seeking food and protection.

A second important group of Cambrian organisms is the **brachiopods** (Figure 16-10). These, in contrast to trilobites, are immovable and have a two-piece shell that closes to protect the animal inside. The earlier brachiopods resembled two shallow saucers fitted face to face and held together by a system of muscles. They were oval, round, or tongue-shaped, and their shells were mostly phosphatic. The earlier forms are called **inarticulates** because their shells lacked definite hinge structures. More advanced brachiopods developed definite hinge structures and are called **articulates** because their shells can open and close like a lady's compact. All brachiopods, living or extinct, are fixed permanently in one spot by a sort of root or fleshy extension of the body. The trilobites could go wherever food was most abun-

dant, but the brachiopods had to depend on the movement of water to bring food within reach of the feeble inflowing currents that were generated by ciliated coiled structures within their shells. Trilobites squandered some energy dragging their shells about; brachiopods conserved energy by remaining in one spot. But since both animals survived and prospered, each mode of life must have had its particular advantages.

A puzzling group of Cambrian organisms, the **Archaeocyatha** (ancient cups), were the earliest known reef-forming animals. They left conical calcareous fossils up to 4 inches long. The group is confined almost entirely to the Early Cambrian. So far as is known, this may be the first phylum to become extinct.

Trilobites make up about 60 per cent of all Cambrian fossils; brachiopods constitute 10 to 20 per cent; and the remainder includes archaeocyathids, protozoans, sponges, worms, gastropods, echinoderms such as cystoids, cephalopods, and arthropods other than trilobites. The trilobites and brachiopods so completely dominate the Cambrian fossil record that all other forms are interesting chiefly for the information they yield about the primitive beginnings of their respective lines. Among the groups not yet found in Cambrian rocks are bone-bearing animals, **pelecypods, bryozoans, true corals, starfish,** and **sea urchins.**

Ordovician Faunas—
All Major Phyla in Existence

During the Ordovician Period conditions continued to be favorable for marine invertebrates. New groups joined those that had appeared in the Cambrian, and by the close of the Ordovician all major animal phyla capable of leaving fossils were in existence. Calcite continued to be the chief construction material of shells and skeletons, and calcareous shells were locally so abundant that entire formations are composed of them. The first appearance of abundant oil and gas resources in Ordovician rocks may indicate increasing organic productivity of the ocean waters during this period.

Figure 16-11 Typical Ordovician brachiopods, *Platystrophia* (*left*) and *Dinorthis* (*right*). Scale represents one inch.

Trilobites reached the height of their development during the Ordovician and assumed a great variety of shapes and sizes. Ordovician trilobites tended to be either smooth and rounded or bristled with nodes and spines. A number of forms probably took up a free-floating existence at this time. The brachiopods also were numerous and varied (Figure 16-11). Ordovician brachiopods were mostly articulates, less than 1 inch across, and were generally of calcareous composition. The majority lacked spines and ornaments other than simple ribs.

The **bryozoans,** which are unknown in Cambrian rocks, appeared early in the Ordovician and increased tremendously during that period. They are extremely small animals that always grow in composite masses or colonies composed of multitudes of single individuals (Figure 16-12). They construct colonies of calcite or other material in the form of twigs, branches, crusts, mounds, or networks. The individual animals are microscopic, which explains why scientists first thought they were plants and called them bryozoa, or "moss animals." The bryozoans were the first group to

Figure 16-12 Ordovician bryozoa. *Constellaria* (*above*) is named for the small, star-shaped elevations that cover the surface. *Eridotrypa* (*below*) has a twig-like form. The small pores are the living chambers of individual animals that are extremely small. Scale represents one inch.

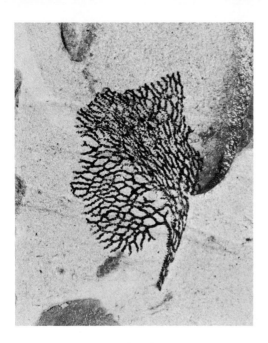

Figure 16-13 Graptolites preserved as thin carbonaceous films on fine-grained shale of Ordovician age. On the left is a branching of dendritic type, on the right is a *Didymograptus*, confined to the Early Ordovician and distributed almost world-wide. (Courtesy Lee Braithwaite.)

exploit thoroughly the possibility of community existence. Existing specimens indicate that their food has always consisted of small particles strained from the surrounding water.

The **graptolites** were another group of colonial animals that became common in the Ordovician (Figure 16-13). Some types were fixed like small shrubs to the sea bottom, and others floated freely in the upper levels or were attached to seaweeds. They are extinct, and we know very little about their relationships to other animals. Their skeletons were composed of chitinous material and were light enough to float but too thin to afford much protection. Graptolites existed in many forms and went through distinctive evolutionary stages during the Ordovician and Silurian.

The **cephalopods,** an important class of molluscs, also flourished during the Ordovician. Their variously shaped, chambered shells were buoyant enough to permit the animals to move about rapidly, and their keen senses probably made them the most advanced of all marine invertebrates.

Another group, the **crinoids,** also began to leave an abundant fossil record during the Ordovician. Crinoids are echinoderms with plant-like stems and roots and a flower-like crown or head. The stem enabled the animals to keep their food-collecting devices well above the ocean bottom, but they were delicate affairs

Figure 16-14 Well-preserved crinoid (*Eucalyptocrinus crassus*) of Silurian age. (Courtesy American Museum of Natural History.)

Figure 16-15 Ordovician "cup," or "horn," corals. The illustration shows several individuals of the common genus *Streptelasma*. The fossils represent only the stony framework in which the soft, polyp-like body of the animal was fixed. Scale represents one inch.

and could easily be broken. Complete crinoid specimens are rare (Figure 16-14). Their heads are composed of many calcite plates that usually fall apart. The most common remains are the round, flat, disc-like structures that make up the stem.

During the Ordovician, **corals** became increasingly common, both colonial as well as solitary types. The corals capture food from the surrounding water with the aid of stinging cells and thread-like structures that they shoot at their prey.

The Silurian—
Heyday of the Brachiopods

The Silurian was a relatively short period, and its life represents an orderly outgrowth from the Ordovician. Shallow seas still spread widely over the continental areas and provided the chief environments for life. Apparently few animals besides the graptolites were adapted to existence in the open oceans, and nonmarine or even brackish-water invertebrates are not positively known.

The chief invertebrates of the Silurian were **brachiopods, trilobites,** and **graptolites.** The molluscs, including **cephalopods, pelecypods,** and **gastropods,** were increasing as were the **corals, bryozoans,** and **crinoids.** Toward the close of the period the **eurypterids** became common.

More families of brachiopods have been identified in the Silurian than in any other period. There was an increase of larger forms with definite complex internal structures and roughly 5-sided outlines (*Pentamerus*). **Spiriferoid** forms with wing-shaped shells appeared

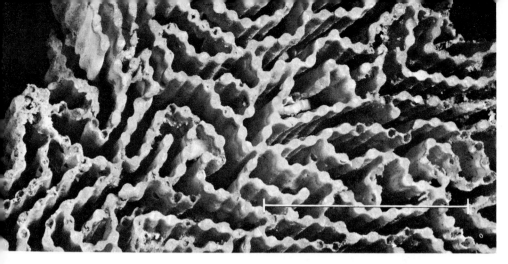

suddenly to launch a long and successful career. Trilobites were still abundant but had definitely passed their zenith and few new genera were produced. Spiny and smooth forms were characteristic.

The graptolites of the Silurian were superficially more simple than their Ordovician predecessors. Most are classed as monograptids with living chambers (**theca**) ranged along one side of a single threadlike support. Corals proliferated and began to build extensive reefs; those of the Late Silurian of the east-central United States are outstanding. Also contributing to the Silurian reef structures were great numbers of the lime-secreting crinoids and bryozoans. A peculiar coral with a chain-like cross-section (*Halysites*) is very characteristic of Silurian rocks (Figure 16-16).

The mobile and predaceous cephalopods increased in importance; the **nautiloids,** with simple, unfolded internal partitions and a variety of shell shapes, represented this group. Judged by their obviously fierce appearance and inferred predaceous habits, the rulers of Silurian seas were the **eurypterids,** or "water scorpions" (Figure 16-17). They were the largest animals of the time, some reaching a length of 6 feet. Another arthropod group, the **ostracods,** with small bivalved shells, was also increasing.

Vertebrates and Possible Kin

Although it is customary to consider vertebrates as more highly organized and specialized than invertebrates, it is impossible to make a fully accurate classification of all animals on

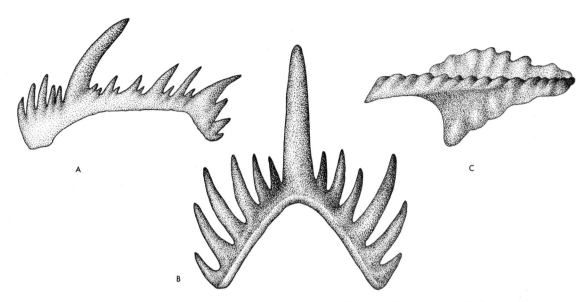

Figure 16-18 Conodonts, small tooth-like objects left by animals of unknown relationships. A: *Metaprionoidus*, Upper Dev—Lower Miss.; B: *Hibbardella*, Mid. Ord.—M. Triassic; C: *Pseudopolygnathus*, Lower Miss. Specimens about ½ inch in maximum dimension.

the basis of whether or not they possess a backbone. Instead of the term "vertebrate," it is more precise to use the term "chordate," which designates not only the vertebrates but also their relatives that are not strictly invertebrates.

Two groups which may be chordates are the **graptolites** and the **conodonts.** We have already described the graptolites as invertebrates in the preceding section, but it is only fair to state that many investigators believe them to be primitive chordates, members of the subphylum Hemichordata to be exact. The conodonts are perhaps the most puzzling of all fossils, for they are represented only by teeth or teeth-like objects. The body shape is entirely unknown. They range from the Cambrian into the Triassic.

If either the graptolite or conodont is a chordate, we can say that this phylum was present in the Cambrian. But if we ignore these problematical forms, the geologic history of vertebrates begins with the appearance of bone. This hard, durable, easily fossilized substance assumes many forms and is ideal for the construction of internal skeletons.

THE EARLIEST VERTEBRATES   The earliest known fossil attributed to a vertebrate is a single small jaw with sharp, pointed teeth that was discovered in rocks of Early Ordovician age in Missouri. Aside from this find, the first really abundant remains occur in the Middle Ordovician Harding Sandstone of Colorado. This formation contains many fragments of bone and enamel, but no complete specimens have yet come to light. The bone fragments occur intermingled with shells of invertebrates and with tiny conodont teeth, which do not appear to belong to the same animals as the bones. It is possible that these early fish-like vertebrates may have lived in fresh water and that their remains were washed into the sea and mixed with ordinary marine forms.

Figure 16-19 Fragment of Harding Sandstone (Middle Ordovician age) with small pieces of fossil bone. Specimen about 3 inches across.

Figure 16-20 Complete specimen of *Rhyncholepis,* a primitive fish, from Upper Silurian rocks near Oslo, Norway. Length about 5 inches. (*Courtesy A. Heintz.*)

So far, Late Ordovician rocks have yielded very little information about vertebrates, but impressive evidences of the group are found in Silurian rocks of northwestern Europe, where a number of strange fish-like forms are represented. Here, for the first time, the real nature of the earliest vertebrates is revealed. They are fish-like, mostly not over a few inches long. Some, known as **ostracoderms,** are partly encased in bone, others are covered with queer scale patterns, and a few were apparently devoid of any protective covering except skin. Ordovician and Silurian fish seem to have been mainly mud-grubbers, for most of them had neither teeth nor jaws.

However obscure their beginnings may have been, these early fish possessed the potential for becoming masters of the sea. By slow degrees and the evolution of many improvements, they achieved a dominant position in the ocean, which has never been successfully contested by the invertebrates. Jaws appear to have developed from gill supports that lay behind and near the mouth, while teeth may have been derived from modified tooth-like structures that are similar to the tiny pointed scales that make the skin of modern sharks feel so rough. Marvelously well-preserved fossils of the brain cavity and nerve canals reveal that their nervous system and sense organs were already well developed by Silurian time, and there can be little doubt that certain other bodily systems were also relatively efficient and highly orga-

nized. In spite of the incomplete fossil record, it is evident that vertebrates made many of their most important advances in early Paleozoic time.

ECONOMIC PRODUCTS OF THE EARLY PALEOZOIC PERIODS

The study and evaluation of economic mineral deposits constitutes an important subdivision of geology (see Chapter 22). For present purposes we must confine our attention to the historical aspects of the subject—that is, to the times and manner in which mineral deposits were formed and their relation to other geologic events. If we disregard building materials and ordinary stone products, which are available almost everywhere, it is here convenient to consider mineral products as (1) those originating by igneous activity, (2) those originating by sedimentary processes and not affected by organic influences, and (3) those originating through the influence of organic materials.

The early Paleozoic is not particularly rich in metallic minerals because igneous action (which is usually connected with their deposition) was not strong. A few important sedimentary deposits with metallic minerals should be noted, however. Economic deposits of sedimentary iron occur in Ordovician and Silurian rocks in northern Norway, Great Britain, Germany, northeast Siberia, Spain, and the eastern United States. The Clinton Formation, which is the chief iron-producer in the Appalachian region, is a sedimentary deposit that extends for hundreds of miles from New York State to Alabama. It is possible that certain bacteria were actively engaged in precipitating iron-rich deposits at this time.

Commercial deposits of copper are found in Late Cambrian and Ordovician sediments of Siberia, and there is phosphate-bearing ore in the Cambrian of central Asia.

Among the deposits associated with intrusive igneous rocks are platinum and gold in the Ural Range; copper, nickel, titanium, and chromium in areas of Caledonian disturbances in northern Norway; gold in New South Wales and Tasmania; and copper and gold in eastern North America. Important commercial deposits of salt are found in the Silurian of the western New York and Great Lakes region and in the Cambrian of central Asia.

Unlike the situation in the other continents, a great deal of oil and gas is derived from Ordovician rocks in North America. As a matter of fact, in the United States the Ordovician ranks third among the systems in known oil and gas yield and reserves. The largest Ordovician fields are in the midcontinent region. Plants had not yet become abundant enough, however, for the formation of significant coal beds.

SUMMARY

The Paleozoic Era began with the appearance of abundant fossils and a slow submergence of the continental margins. During the Cambrian, Ordovician, and Silurian Periods the major geosynclines were occupied almost continually by shallow seas and the shield areas occasionally were flooded. The Cambrian was generally quiet, with volcanism and mountain-building at a low ebb. Sediments from this period are chiefly fine-grained, and there are thick accumulations of limestone, dolomite, and shale.

During the Ordovician the eastern margin of North America was affected by the Taconic mountain-building disturbance. Other areas bordering the north Atlantic were in a state of geologic unrest during the Ordovician and Silurian. Major effects during the Silurian were in northwest Europe, where the previously downfolded Baltic geosyncline was compressed and intruded by granites (Caledonian Revolution). The Southern Hemisphere and Pacific borderlands appear to have been geologically quiet.

The early Paleozoic was an age of marine invertebrates. All the major phyla were in existence and the shallow continental seas were teeming with life. The vertebrates appear as fossils in the Ordovician, and fish multiplied in the seas during the Silurian. The first land vegetation appeared in the Silurian but there were no forests of inland vegetation sufficient to leave coal beds.

ADDITIONAL READING

Augusta, J., and Z. Burian, *Prehistoric Animals.* London: Spring Books, 1956.

Barnett, Lincoln, *The World We Live In.* New York: Time, Inc., 1955.

Clark, Thomas H., and Colin W. Stearn, *The Geologic Evolution of North America.* New York: Ronald Press, 1960.

Dunbar, C. O., *Historical Geology.* New York: John Wiley & Sons, 1960.

Eardley, A. J., *Structural Geology of North America.* New York: Harper & Row, 1951.

Fenton, C. L., and M. A. Fenton, *The Fossil Book.* Garden City, N.Y.: Doubleday, 1958.

Kay, Marshall, *North American Geosynclines.* Geological Society of America, Memoir 48, 1951.

Kay, Marshall, and Edwin H. Colbert, *Stratigraphy and Life History.* New York: John Wiley & Sons, 1964.

King, Philip B., *The Tectonics of Middle North America.* Princeton: Princeton University Press, 1951.

————, *The Evolution of North America.* Princeton: Princeton University Press, 1959.

Kummel, Bernhard, *History of the Earth.* San Francisco: W. H. Freeman and Co., 1961.

Ladd, H. S., ed., *Treatise on Marine Ecology and Paleoecology.* New York: Geological Society of America, Memoir 67, 1957.

Moore, R. C., *Introduction to Historical Geology,* 2nd ed. New York: McGraw-Hill Book Co., 1958.

Raymond, Percy E., *Prehistoric Life.* Cambridge: Harvard University Press, 1939.

Richards, Horace G., *Record of the Rocks—The Geological Story of Eastern North America.* New York: Ronald Press, 1954.

Woodford, A. O. *Historical Geology.* San Francisco: W. H. Freeman and Co., 1965.

17

The Late Paleozoic Periods

The late Paleozoic is divided into four periods whose names and estimated durations in years are: Devonian, 55 million years; Mississippian, 35 million years; Pennsylvanian, 30 million years; and Permian, 50 million years.

Every major land mass of the earth has rocks formed during each of these periods. Among the major events recorded in these rocks are intensive ice ages affecting chiefly the Southern Hemisphere, the growth and burial of widespread coal-forming vegetation, the formation of extensive mountain chains in both the Eastern and Western Hemispheres, and a world-wide time of extermination of plants and animals at the end of the Paleozoic Era.

THE PATTERN OF LANDS AND SEAS

TETHYS The **Mesogean**, or **Tethys**, seaway, greatest of all geosynclinal belts, extended halfway around the world, almost parallel with the equator, and occupied territory that is now within and adjacent to the Mediterranean Sea and the great east-west mountain systems of Europe and Asia. This belt was occupied by a succession of shifting seas, coal-forming swamps, lakes, and sandy lowlands, which received a great variety of sediments. Like geosynclinal areas in general the area was geologically active. By contrast, most of central and southern

Africa and the Baltic and Angara shields remained stable and above water.

The Tethys seaway presented a barrier to the migration of land plants and animals. At the same time, it was frequently possible for marine organisms to migrate along its length from one extremity of the great Eurasian continent to the other. Correlating by fossils along the Tethys seaway is, therefore, fairly easy; correlation across it is difficult.

An offshoot of the Tethys seaway occupied the site of the present Ural Mountains and extended well into the Arctic region. This geosyncline had already received deposits during every early Paleozoic period, and with the passage of time, representative types of Mississippian, Pennsylvanian, and Permian rocks accumulated to give the Urals a fairly complete Paleozoic record. This area is in fact the world's standard of reference for the Permian System of rocks.

Figure 17-1 Generalized paleogeographic map of the Devonian Period.

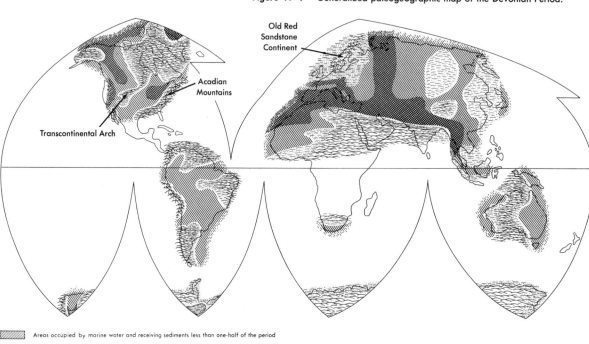

Areas occupied by marine water and receiving sediments less than one-half of the period

Areas occupied by marine water and receiving sediments more than one-half of the period

Areas receiving mainly non-marine sediments during the period

Areas undergoing erosion with the type of topography shown in diagrammatic fashion

White areas indicate open ocean or geologically unknown areas

Outlines of present land masses are for reference only

Figure 17-2 The Late Devonian fish, *Holoptychius flemingi* from the Old Red Sandstone of Dura Den, Fife, Scotland. Slab about 39 inches across. (*Courtesy Charles D. Waterston, Royal Scottish Museum.*)

NORTHWESTERN EUROPE: THE CALEDONIAN FOLDS AND THE OLD RED SANDSTONE   Early in the Devonian Period, land-laid sediments began to fill the depressions between and around the Caledonian folded mountains which had formed in the Late Silurian. The area thus affected included much of northwestern Europe, west-

central Asia, and an unknown amount of territory extending beyond the coastlines of present-day land areas. These land-laid sediments are preserved in several areas of Great Britain, where they are known as the Old Red Sandstone. Although the total area now covered by these beds is small, they are of interest because their study and classification had a significant influence on geological thought. Scattered throughout the Old Red series are beds containing brackish or fresh-water fish, eurypterids, and fragments of land plants. These fossils were among the first to become well known to the general public, and they helped direct attention to the fact that the rocks have a definite story to tell about past conditions.

THE HERCYNIAN OROGENY   During the Late Pennsylvanian and Early Permian a great system of mountains known as the **Hercynian Chain** was formed in Europe and Asia. It seems significant that the dominant trend of

Figure 17-3   Generalized paleogeographic map of the Mississippian Period.

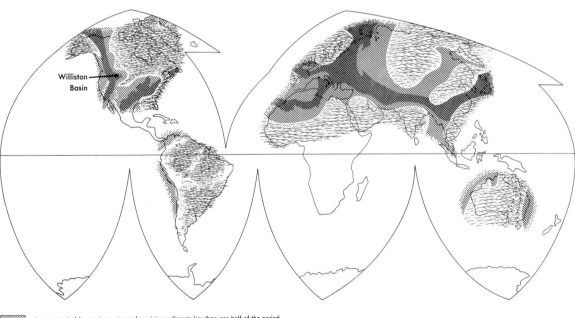

Williston Basin

▨ Areas occupied by marine water and receiving sediments less than one-half of the period

▨ Areas occupied by marine water and receiving sediments more than one-half of the period

▨ Areas undergoing erosion with the type of topography shown in diagrammatic fashion

White areas indicate open ocean or geologically unknown areas

Outlines of present land masses are for reference only

this system was east-west, the same direction taken by nearly contemporaneous structures in North America. The region affected included southern Wales, northern and central France, southern Germany, Bohemia, and parts of the USSR and central Asia. Volcanic outpourings and granitic intrusions accompanied the folding, and many important ore deposits were formed. This ancient mountain chain was subsequently deeply eroded; portions sank and were flooded by Tethys and still later were incorporated in the great Alpine and Himalayan Chains.

Southeastern Australia was affected by a major mountain-building which began during the Mississippian and continued into the Permian. Lava and volcanic products were emitted on a large scale, and glaciers descending from the uplifted ranges dumped their characteristic deposits into adjacent seas. The Devonian of southern Africa is more intensively folded than overlying beds, and we assume that the late Paleozoic orogenies also may have affected this area.

The Urals were compressed and uplifted during the closing stages of the Paleozoic, and the site thereafter was covered only by thin beds mainly of continental origin. At frequent intervals, seas spread northeastward across central Asia through what is now China.

NORTH AMERICA AND THE APPALACHIAN REVOLUTION   After the Taconic disturbance, which culminated near the end of the Ordovician, the Appalachian Geosyncline was in a state of intermittent unrest. The eastern borderland, Appalachia, was apparently alternately uplifted and eroded and gave rise to a number of large river systems that carried sediments westward to the geosyncline. The Catskill Mountains preserve the deeply eroded remnants of a large delta, with coarse sediments to the east and finer ones to the west. Elsewhere in the geosyncline and across most of North America, open seas prevailed during most of the Devonian, and limestone and fine-grained shale beds were deposited.

The close of the Devonian was marked by a localized disturbance, the **Acadian Orogeny**, which affected territory in and adjacent to New England and eastern Canada (Acadia). Intense folding and metamorphism of older rocks, the extrusion of lava, and the intrusion of granite accompanied this activity.

Mississippian time in the Appalachian Geosyncline and over most of the interior of North America was relatively quiet. Extensive shoals and wide mud flats lay over the area affected by earlier disturbances, which would hence-

Figure 17-4   Large quarry in the Salem Limestone, of Mississippian age, near Oolitic, Lawrence County, Indiana. (*Courtesy Indiana Geological Survey.*)

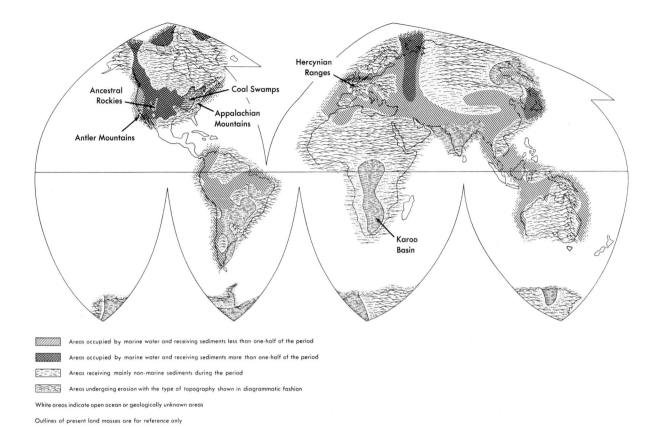

Areas occupied by marine water and receiving sediments less than one-half of the period

Areas occupied by marine water and receiving sediments more than one-half of the period

Areas receiving mainly non-marine sediments during the period

Areas undergoing erosion with the type of topography shown in diagrammatic fashion

White areas indicate open ocean or geologically unknown areas

Outlines of present land masses are for reference only

Figure 17-5   Generalized paleogeographic map of the Pennsylvanian Period.

forth remain dry land. Most of the interior of North America was covered by wide shallow seas in which limestone was the dominant sediment. The period gets its name from the general area near the junction of the Mississippi and Missouri rivers, where the formations are for the most part very limy.

Geologists generally believe that the Appalachian trough turns rather abruptly to the northwest somewhere under the edges of the Gulf of Mexico. Perhaps it reappears again within the continent, for the succession of rocks found in the Ouachita-Wichita uplifts in the Oklahoma-Arkansas region are similar to formations in the Appalachians. In Oklahoma and Arkansas we find evidences of intense orogeny in the Late Mississippian and again at several times during the Pennsylvanian. Another great mountain chain, known as the **Ancestral Rockies,** was formed during the Pennsylvanian in the Utah-Colorado-New Mexico area. The Ancestral Rockies trend in the same general

direction as those in Texas and Oklahoma that came into existence between the Middle Mississippian and Late Pennsylvanian. The entire group is broadly considered by most geologists to have been a product of the Appalachian Revolution.

The western and southwestern parts of the United States were occupied by a succession of shifting seaways and uplifts during the late Paleozoic. Devonian and Mississippian downsinking and deposition followed the northerly trend of the great Rocky Mountain Geosyncline, and there were substantial interior seas in the Williston Basin in the heart of the continent. A major change in the pattern of geologic development took place in the Late Mississippian and Pennsylvanian. Prior to this time, the Appalachian and Rocky Mountain geosynclines had been receiving most of the sediments. In the later Paleozoic periods a number of additional basins came into being in the southwestern part of the continent in connection with the

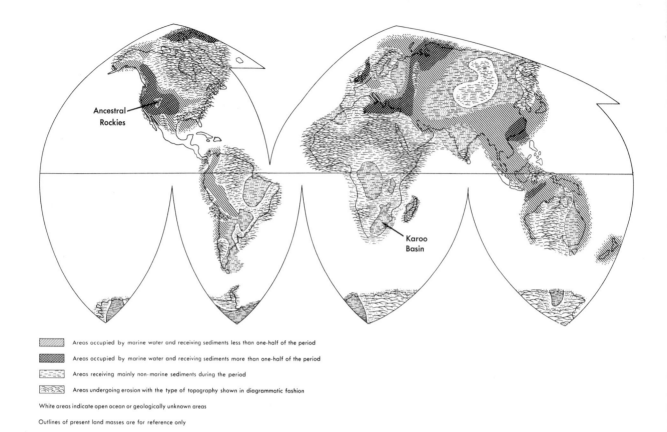

Areas occupied by marine water and receiving sediments less than one-half of the period

Areas occupied by marine water and receiving sediments more than one-half of the period

Areas receiving mainly non-marine sediments during the period

Areas undergoing erosion with the type of topography shown in diagrammatic fashion

White areas indicate open ocean or geologically unknown areas

Outlines of present land masses are for reference only

Figure 17-6   Generalized paleogeographic map of the Permian Period.

Figure 17-7   Monument Valley, Utah. The imposing monoliths are erosional remnants of Permian De Chelly Sandstone resting on red siltstone, also of Permian age. On top of some of the monuments are small remnants of Triassic formations. (*Courtesy Utah Travel Council.*)

Ancestral Rockies, and in these basins, thick Pennsylvanian and Permian deposits were laid down.

Recent exploration of the Arctic regions has shown an extensive rock record of late Paleozoic time. The Devonian reaches great thickness and is chiefly dolomite and shale. The Mississippian, Pennsylvanian, and Permian have less volume. Evaporite (salt and gypsum) deposits occur in the Pennsylvanian and Permian, but coal is not known.

The various orogenic movements that affected the borderlands of the Canadian Shield during the late Paleozoic touched off a distinctive change in sedimentation. Prior to this period, limestone, dolomite, and shale predominated; afterward, the sediments contained a higher proportion of sandstone and conglomerate, both in the marine and continental sediments. It was a time of formation of gypsum, salt, and red beds. The Appalachian Geosyncline ceased to exist as an open seaway during the Pennsylvanian, for the areas of Permian deposition follow a distinctly different pattern.

The Southern Hemisphere

The geologic record of each of the southern continents is remarkably similar, a fact which lends weight to the theory that they were once united in one great land mass. Fossils are relatively few, but, on the other hand, a variety of physical events and processes are clearly recorded that have no counterparts in northern lands.

At the extreme southern tip of Africa a section of marine Devonian rocks about 7,000 feet thick indicates temporary subsidence. About half of South America was covered by Devonian seas, including the present Andes and Amazon Basin. Some of the fossils are related to North America, some to other southern continents. Devonian rocks with brachiopods and primitive plants have been found in Antarctica, indicating shallow, warm seas at that time. Devonian rocks are also widespread in Australia, 20,000 feet thick in the Tasmanian Geosyncline.

Figure 17-8 Aerial view of the Cape Peninsula, Union of South Africa. Stratified rocks of early Paleozoic age make up Table Mountain that rises above Cape Town. (*Courtesy South African Information Service, Pretoria.*)

Ice Age
in the Southern Hemisphere

Abundant evidence proves that a great ice age gripped the Southern Hemisphere during the late Paleozoic. Much of the evidence of ice action is centered in what are now tropical and semitropical regions. Many geologists find it easier to believe that the continents bearing this evidence have "floated" to their present position from a former location near the South Pole, rather than that thick ice caps could have formed and spread in tropical or semitropical lands (see Chapter 21).

Middle Devonian glacial deposits, dated by associated fossils, occur in western Argentina; and evidence of more extensive ice sheets

Figure 17-9 The Dwyka tillite of South Africa is the deposit of a continental ice sheet of late Paleozoic age. Here the bedrock floor striated by the Paleozoic glacier passes beneath the tillite. (*Photo by R. B. Young.*)

occurs in the Pennsylvanian of much of southern South America. In Australia, where marine beds with fossils are found interbedded with glacial deposits, it is possible to distinguish Permian and possible Pennsylvanian glaciations. The **Dwyka Tillite,** which covers many thousands of square miles in South Africa, is regarded by geologists as a product of a large continental glacier and has been dated as Late Pennsylvanian. An extensive tillite resembling the Dwyka has been discovered in Antarctica. Although geologists have not evaluated all the evidence, it appears that continental glaciation in the Southern Hemisphere reached a maximum in the Late Pennsylvanian and Early Permian with some minor effects in evidence both before and after this time.

The trend of scratches and grooves in the bedrock indicates the direction in which the glaciers moved. In South Africa they moved principally from north to south—away from the equator! In central Africa and Madagascar other deposits show that the ice moved northward, well within the tropics. Most surprising has been the discovery of great beds of glacial debris in northern India, where the direction of movement was northward. Evidences of glaciation are widespread, too, in Australia and Tasmania, where the ice moved from south to north. The direction of movement in Brazil and Argentina was toward the west.

The Beginning
of the Karoo Series

The **Karoo,** a geographical part of the Cape Province of South Africa, gives its name to a sequence of rocks that contributes much to an understanding of the geologic history of the Southern Hemisphere and of the land life of the time. The **Karoo Series,** which reaches a thickness of 20,000 feet, was deposited almost entirely under continental conditions. Deposition started early in the Pennsylvanian and continued without interruption through the Permian and Triassic into the Jurassic. At the base is the Dwyka Tillite, the previously mentioned deposit of glacial origin.

Above the Dwyka lies the **Ecca Series,** which contains the best coal of Africa and a variety of fresh-water fossils. Among these remains are the first fossil leaves of the well-known **Glossopteris flora.** Following the Ecca is the much thicker **Beaufort Series,** famous for its fossils of fish, amphibians, and varied reptiles. The Permian-Triassic boundary lies within this series. The Mesozoic portion of the series will be described in the next chapter.

LIFE OF THE LATE PALEOZOIC

The First Forests

The plant kingdom advanced and diversified tremendously during the late Paleozoic. The most important developments took place on the continents, where the spread of vegetation was amazingly rapid, considering how barren the long preceding periods had been. Our knowledge of Early Devonian land plants is rather imperfect, although remains have been discovered in Europe, North America, China, and Australia. These early plants are known collectively as the **psilophytes flora,** from the most common genus, *Psilophyton.* In general, these earliest known plants lacked true roots and leaves and bore spores at the ends of simple branching stems.

More advanced types of vegetation appeared in the Middle Devonian. Two of the best known forms, *Rhynia* and *Hornea,* had no leaves and roots and were only a few inches high (see Figure 17-10). They had spores suitable for dispersal on land and a central strand of conducting tissue. Other Middle Devonian plants such as *Pseudosporochus* and *Duisbergia* grew 7 or 8 feet tall, had swollen stems, and bear the distinction of being the probable ancestors of all later land vegetation except mosses and fungi.

There is a distinct break between the flora of Middle and Late Devonian time, marked by the disappearance of the psilophytes and the rise of a new group called the *Archaeopteris* flora. Fossil remains of *Archaeopteris* have been

Figure 17-10 Model of the Middle Devonian plant *Rhynia.* The simple, leafless stems are about 3 inches high. (*Courtesy Field Museum of Natural History.*)

found in such widely scattered areas as Russia, Ireland, Ellesmere Island to the north of Canada, and Australia. The plant had large fern-like leaves with clusters of spore-bearing organs. As a whole, the dominant Late Devonian plants were larger than their Mid-Devonian relatives and had branching root systems, stronger stems, and better reproductive systems. They were mainly lowland types and grew along shores and valley bottoms. There were scouring rushes, or horsetails (the living *Equisetum* is a descendant), seed ferns (*Archaeopteris, Protopteridium*), and lycopods (spore-bearing plants) such as *Protolepidodendron* and *Archeosigillaria,* which would give rise to immense forests in the following period. The most primitive gymnosperm, *Callixylon,* is found in Late Devonian rocks.

Figure 17-11 Reconstruction of the oldest known fossil forest discovered in Middle Devonian rocks at Gilboa, New York. Background painting depicts the living forest; foreground is actual rock with stumps in place as brought from the quarry. (*Courtesy N.Y. State Museum and Science Service.*)

These Late Devonian plants produced the earliest known **fossil forests.** Near Gilboa, New York, numerous stumps up to 3½ feet in diameter have been uncovered (see Figure 17-11).

The Coal-Forming Swamps

The Pennsylvanian Period was ideal for swamp vegetation and became the great period of coal formation. The fossil record is exceptionally complete because mining operations have yielded a wealth of specimens. Perhaps the most important contributors to the coal beds were the so-called **scale trees,** *Lepidodendron* and *Sigillaria. Lepidodendron* had a slender trunk and a crown of forking branches that soared skyward to heights of over 100 feet. The leaves were lance-shaped and arranged in spirals around the branches. When the leaves were shed, they left a characteristic pattern of scars on the branches, which gives the tree its popular name (see Figure 17-13). Only about 10 per cent of the trunk of *Lepidodendron* was actual woody tissue; it was therefore not as sturdy as most living trees. In *Sigillaria* the leaf scars are in vertical rows.

Figure 17-12 Reconstruction of a coal-forming forest of the Pennsylvanian Period. (*Courtesy Field Museum of Natural History.*)

Also inhabiting the coal forest were many jointed plants called *Sphenopsida.* The leaves of these plants radiated in whorls around the joints, as in the modern horsetail, *Equisetum.* Largest of the jointed plants was *Calamites,* which reached a height of over 100 feet and a diameter of 2 to 3 feet.

In addition to the important coal-forming plants, there were minor types that were destined to give rise to important vegetative groups in later periods. True ferns made up much of the undergrowth and the **gymnosperms,** which were to dominate the Mesozoic, were represented by at least five orders, including the Pteridospermae, Cordaitales, and Bennettitales, which are extinct; the Ginkgoales, represented

by one living species; and the Coniferales (cone-bearers), which make up an important segment of present-day vegetation.

Plants of the Permian Period

The Permian was a time of increasing drought, climatic diversity and extensive glaciation in the Southern Hemisphere. Swamp vegetation was being replaced by upland and desert types. In a general way, the gymnosperms increased while the older groups declined during this interval. Some of the trees show definite annual rings, and leaves are coarser and thicker than they were in the Pennsylvanian. An important group of the late Paleozoic plant world

Figure 17-13 Pennsylvanian plant fossils. The specimen on the left is an impression of the trunk of the scale tree, *Lepidodendron rimosum,* showing the characteristic diamond-shaped scars left by fallen leaves. The specimens on the right are various types of foliage preserved in nodules found at Mazon Creek, Illinois. Six of the specimens represent halves of nodules that can be fitted together. Remains of insects and small vertebrates are occasionally found in the nodules from this locality. (*Courtesy Field Museum of Natural History.*)

Figure 17-14 These leaves of the fossil plant, *Glossopteris*, come from strata of Permian age in Australia. The Glossopteris flora is found also in South America, Africa, India, and Antarctica. The widespread occurrence of this very uniform flora has been used as evidence both by opponents and proponents of continental drift. (*Specimen from Paleobotanical Collections, Princeton University. Photo by Willard Starks.*)

(which we will discuss in connection with continental drift) was the so-called Glossopteris flora, named from the tongue-shaped leaves of the seed fern, *Glossopteris* (see Figure 17-14). Fossil remains of this flora are broadly distributed in South Africa, South America, Australia, India, and in Antarctica, within 300 miles of the South Pole. Some geologists argue that this wide dispersal supports the theory of continental drift, for these plants could probably not have distributed themselves across the vast oceans that now separate their fossilized remains. It also seems impossible that lush vegetation could have lived within 300 miles of the Pole. The presence of the Glossopteris flora on all the southern continents is frequently cited as evidence for Gondwanaland and for continental drift.

Coal as Fossil Vegetation

Coal is the most important by-product of past life known to man. It has accumulated in prodigious quantity at many times and places when the right biologic and physical factors

Figure 17-15 Bituminous coal and peat. On the left is a lump of bituminous coal from Wyoming County, West Virginia. The streaks and layers can be identified as having originated from various types of plant tissue. Peat is the parent material of coal. It begins as a spongy, water-soaked mass of vegetation. The specimen on the right is from Hawk Island Swamp, Manitowoc County, Wisconsin. (*Courtesy U.S. Bureau of Mines.*)

have happened to coincide. All evidence indicates that coal consists of altered plant remains, and every stage in this process of alteration has been thoroughly studied. Commencing with peat, which today is still in the process of formation, the successive ranks of coal are **lignite, sub-bituminous, bituminous,** and **anthracite.** The rank depends on the conditions to which the plant remains were subjected after they were buried—the greater the pressure and heat, the higher the rank of the coal. Higher-ranking coals are denser and contain less moisture and volatile gases and have a higher heat value than low-ranking coals. Obviously, more than a heavy growth of vegetation is required for coal formation. The plant debris must be buried, compressed, and protected from erosion and from intensive metamorphism. The complete story of coal formation involves not only a study of the coal forests themselves but also a consideration of the types of sediment in which the coal is buried and an understanding of the processes acting on the plant material after it has been buried.

A regular sequence of repeating or cyclic sediments of which coal is a normal member is called a **cyclothem.** When fully developed a cyclothem has the following units:

10. Shale with ironstone concretions
9. Marine limestone
8. Black shale with black limestone concretions or layers
7. Impure, lenticular, marine limestone
6. Shale
5. Coal
4. Underclay
3. "Fresh-water" limestone
2. Sandy shale
1. Sandstone, at the base and locally unconformable on underlying beds

A number of possible mechanisms have been proposed to account for the alternate flooding and emergence which produced the cyclothems. All theories agree that there must be a prolonged regional downsinking of coastal areas. One school of thought maintains that the downsinking is not steady, but alternately slows down and speeds up in giant pulsations. During the pauses coal swamps flourish; during more rapid downward movements the sea spreads inland, burying and compressing the vegetation of the former swamps. An opposing school of thought attributes the cyclic effects to the rise and fall of sea level superimposed on the sinking lands. During emergent or low-water periods forests flourish; during flooding they are covered with water. Supporters of this idea point out that the period of coal formation in the Northern Hemisphere was the time of glaciation in the Southern Hemisphere and that alternate periods of freezing (withdrawal of water from the sea) and melting (restoration of water to the sea) could have caused changes in the sea level. The whole problem is in an interesting state of speculation, and no one theory is accepted by all students of coal geology. What we do know is that a peculiar combination of apparently unrelated factors came into existence and operated over a period of many mil-

Figure 17-16 Stripping the over-burden from a coal seam in eastern Sullivan County, Indiana. Where the coal lies near the surface, as it does over large areas of Illinois, it is cheaper to mine the beds from the surface than by underground workings. The stripped land may be smoothed over and reclaimed for other purposes after the coal has been removed. (*Courtesy Indiana Geological Survey.*)

lions of years to produce a large part of the coal resources on which we depend for a great deal of our energy and many raw materials.

INVERTEBRATE LIFE
OF THE LATE PALEOZOIC

The invertebrates of late Paleozoic time show few spectacular advances and reveal less of evolutionary significance than either the plants or vertebrates of the same period. In general, it was a time of intensive competition in the seas, with a consequent gradual elimination of less effective types and a flowering of more progressive ones.

Aquatic animals had already achieved their basic adaptations before the late Paleozoic and had settled down, as it were, to intensive competition involving mainly minor changes. As a rule, there were more relatively mobile creatures in the ocean than there had been in earlier periods. Legs, swimming organs, and fins were more in evidence, and more animals were able to crawl or burrow. Even sluggishly moving animals such as starfish, echinoids, and sea cucumbers gradually replaced the fixed members of their phylum typified by the cystoids and blastoids. Crawling molluscs were on the increase, and the cephalopods already had developed their coiled many-chambered, buoyant shells to high levels of perfection.

At the same time there is a greater evidence of both defensive and offensive mechanisms and structures. Brachiopods were abundant, with a preponderance of thick-shelled and highly spiny types. As if to balance the scales, many species of sharks with heavy, flat teeth, well adapted for shell-crushing, cruised the seas. Slow-moving animals with weak skeletons, such as trilobites, inarticulate brachiopods, and graptolites, were either extinct or in decline as the more mobile or better-protected forms flourished.

Food-gathering and food-protecting techniques improved. Passive feeders, which depended on the vagaries of passing currents for their sustenance, were gradually replaced by

Figure 17-17 A remarkable slab of fossil crinoids from Mississippian rocks near Legrande, Iowa. Preservation of entire individuals such as these is very rare. (*Courtesy Iowa State Department of History and Archives.*)

animals able to move about or at least to gather food by self-generated currents. Virtually all brachiopods of the late Paleozoic possessed more powerful food-gathering mechanisms than their ancestors. Particularly efficient in this respect were the stalked crinoids, whose food-gathering arms branched and subdivided to cover wide areas of water. As the crinoids flourished, their relatives, such as cystoids and blastoids, with less efficient food-collecting systems, declined and disappeared.

Finally, we should mention the evolutionary advances made by the reef-building and colonial animals. These creatures were able to create interlocking structures of great size, in which both plants and animals cooperated. The Permian reefs of Texas are examples. Here, by presenting a sufficiently strong front to the open ocean, organisms could find food and living space that might otherwise go unclaimed.

344

Although late Paleozoic marine species were more advanced than their predecessors, they had still not achieved maximum efficiency or security, as we shall see from the pages that follow.

The late Paleozoic saw the rise and fall of many important groups of invertebrate animals. Important debuts included the **fusulines** in the Mississippian, cephalopods with moderately crinkled septa in the Early Mississippian, cephalopods with highly crinkled septa in the Middle Permian, land gastropods in the Pennsylvanian, spiny brachiopods in the Late Devonian, and insects in the Middle Devonian.

The corals, bryozoans, brachiopods, gastropods, and pelecypods managed to maintain a relatively stable level of existence and were common and abundant during the late Paleozoic. These groups contribute the vast bulk of the marine fossils, and many thousands of species of each have been preserved. Within each group there were significant trends, marked by the extinction and replacement of individual families. Among the important coral genera were *Halysites* (Upper Ord. to Lower Dev.), *Favosites* (Lower Ord.-Perm.), *Chaetetes* (Ord.-Jurassic), and *Syringopora* (Sil.-Penn.). An important group of late Paleozoic bryozoans were the lacy forms, or **fenestellids** (Sil.-Perm.), which left delicate fossils representing colonies of many individual animals; also prevalent was the curious screw-shaped bryozoan, *Archimedes* (Miss.-Perm.) (see Figure 17-18). The most distinctive brachiopods during the late Paleozoic

Figure 17-18 Fossil bryozoans from the Mississippian Period. On the left is an enlarged view of matted remains of many individual colonies of the lacy bryozoans known as fenestelids. On the right are several fragments of the peculiar, screw-shaped fossil, *Archimedes*, which is associated with some fenestellid bryozoans. Specimens about 1 inch long.

Figure 17-19 Spiriferoid brachiopods of late Paleozoic periods. Largest specimens are *Paraspirifer* from the Middle Devonian; medium-size specimens are *Mucrospirifer*, common in the Appalachian region; smaller specimens are *Punctospirifer kentuckiensis* of Pennsylvanian age, common in the mid-continent.

were **spirifers** (Ord.-Triassic), characterized by pointed, wide, and winged shells, and the very spiny **productids** (Dev.-Perm.), some of which reached 12 inches in diameter. Pelecypods were represented by a variety of forms but were still subordinate to brachiopods in late Paleozoic seas. Gastropods of many types abounded locally but made no special advances, except for the evolution of certain air-breathing species that we have already mentioned.

The eurypterids (Ord.-Perm.), which have been aptly described as "sea scorpions," were the largest known arthropods of the late Paleozoic. Their jointed external skeletons ranged in size from a few inches to over 7 feet. They reached the apex of their development in the Silurian and Devonian and gradually declined thereafter. We may assume that they competed with the early fish, especially during the Ordovician and Silurian Periods.

Beginning in the Late Devonian, the coiled cephalopods with complex internal structures (the ammonites) began to be abundant and

Figure 17-20 A mass of spiny shells of the Devonian productid brachiopod, *Productella*. These fossils are silicified and have been freed from the limy matrix by an acid bath. (*Courtesy Field Museum of Natural History.*)

widespread. About 10 world-wide cephalopod zones are recognized in the Devonian, 7 in the Mississippian, 6 in the Pennsylvanian, and 5 in the Permian.

In North America the best guide fossils for marine Pennsylvanian and Permian rocks are the Protozoans called fusulines (Figure 17-21). Their spindle-shaped skeletons superficially resemble grains of wheat, oats, rice, or rye. They have left their skeletons abundantly in limestone, sandstone, and shale, indicating a cosmopolitan type of existence. Although simple in outward appearance, their internal structure is very complex, consisting of numerous coils separated by curving partitions into a great many chambers. The internal details are characteristic for the different species, and since the fusulines evolved rapidly, we can distinguish the fossils of one interval or formation fairly easily from those of succeeding or preceding ones.

Because fusulines are generally quite small and tend to occur packed together in dense masses, they are frequently brought up in cores from wells and are very useful in correlating certain oil-bearing formations.

LATE PALEOZOIC VERTEBRATES

The Devonian Period is known as the Age of Fishes. For the first time, the fossil record reveals the existence of numerous and varied fish forms that represent a distinct evolutionary advance over the contemporary Paleozoic invertebrates.

As the fish diversified, competition began. Among those eliminated were the jawless **ostracoderms,** a few of which had lingered on from the Silurian. These creatures were the first large group of vertebrates to become extinct. Forms that enjoyed a temporary success and then disappeared before the close of the period were the **antiarchs** (spiny sharks) and the **arthrodires** (joint-necked fish). One of the arthrodires, *Dinichthys,* from the Late Devonian rocks of Ohio, was 30 feet long, probably the largest animal of the time.

SUCCESS OF THE FISH During the Late Devonian two classes of fish began to establish their superiority: the **bony fish,** or *Osteichthyes,*

Figure 17-21 Fusulines. On the left is a collection of wheat-shaped specimens of the common fusuline *Triticites.* Notice the pencil point for size comparison. On the right is a highly magnified, thin section showing the complex internal structure. In the center is a specimen cut along the long axis; at the right of it is a specimen cut at right angles to the long axis to show the spiral coiling and chambers.

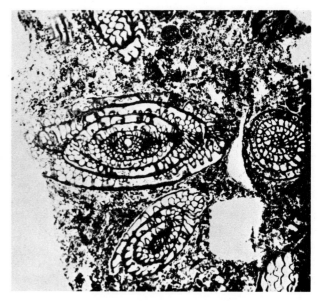

Figure 17-22 Some important representatives of the Age of Fishes. *Coccosteus* (*upper right*), an arthrodire, or joint-necked fish. Although the arthrodires were among the most successful animals of the Devonian time, they were extinct by the close of the period. *Bothriolepis* (*upper left*), a small antiarch, with flattened body, small mouth, head and body cased in armor, and probably functional lungs. Many excellent specimens occur in the Gaspé Peninsula, Quebec. *Cheirolepis* (*lower left*), an ancestral bony fish whose descendants became masters of the seas. *Eusthenopteron* (*lower right*), a progressive crossopterygian, or lobe-finned fish, with a complex pattern of skull and jaw bones that shows a close relationship with the early land-living amphibians. (*Courtesy American Museum of Natural History.*)

and the **cartilage fish,** or *Chondrichthyes.* The bony fish, the most numerous, varied, and successful of the aquatic vertebrates, include the vast majority of living fish and many extinct forms. They are adapted for life in both salt and fresh water and have lived in practically all water environments on earth. Their story is mainly a chapter in later geologic time.

Included in the *Osteichthyes* class is a less numerous and rather unimpressive group, the *Choanichthyes,* or **nostril-bearing fish,** which can take in air through their nostrils as well as their mouths. This group includes the Devonian ancestors of the modern **lungfish,** which are characterized by peculiar teeth and the ability to survive dry periods by burrowing in the moist beds of streams or lakes. The *Choanichthyes* also include the **crossopterygians,** or **lobe-finned** fish, which are in the direct line of evolution from fish to land-living vertebrates and are now represented by the solitary "living fossil," *Latimeria.* In these fish the fin is a solid, muscular structure with a central axis of bones.

OUT OF THE WATER   Late in the Devonian Period certain lobe-finned fishes established themselves on land, a step made possible by a great many structural and functional modifications. The lobe-fin, with its axis of internal bones, had to be converted into a walking limb, the lung was adapted to breathe air just as it now does in the lungfish, and the circulatory and excretory systems were modified along much the same lines as in present-day tadpoles. The earliest known amphibians, called **ichthyostegides,** of which the genus *Ichthyostega* is a typical example, are found in Late Devonian rocks of Greenland. *Ichthyostega* was about 2 feet long and possessed a strange mixture of newly acquired characteristics and older traits inherited from its fish ancestors (see Figure 17-24). The legs were weak, the tail was long and had a fringe-like fin. Its fishlike skull can be compared bone for bone with the skulls of its fish relatives that never left the water. There were many pointed conical teeth with a peculiar structure that occurs also in the crossopterygian ancestors. This tooth structure, known as **labyrinthodont,** is characterized by deep infolding of the enamel. All in all, the fossil record of the skeletal changes that accompanied the important transition from water to land is quite complete.

We cannot be certain just why the crossopterygians invaded the land. Certainly competition in the water had become very severe, and the land offered food and protection to any animals that could live out of water. It seems logical that they made their first approach to land across the moist and sandy beaches where food, cast up by the tides, was generally avail-

able. Here, too, the opportunity or necessity of digging in the moist sand favored the development of stout limbs with toes. The enticement of live food in the forests in the form of various arthropods eventually led the first pioneers to abandon the shores and to forsake the water completely.

SUCCESS OF THE AMPHIBIANS   During the Mississippian and Pennsylvanian Periods, **amphibians** became the dominant land animals. The Mississippian, with its extensive shallow seas, was not so favorable to their expansion as was the succeeding Pennsylvanian, with its

Figure 17-23   The Late Devonian crossopterygian fish, *Eusthenopteron foordii.* About 20 inches long. (*Courtesy Erik Jarvik.*)

Figure 17-24   Ichthyostega, earliest known amphibian. From the uppermost Upper Devonian of East Greenland. Length about 40 inches. (*Courtesy Erik Jarvik.*)

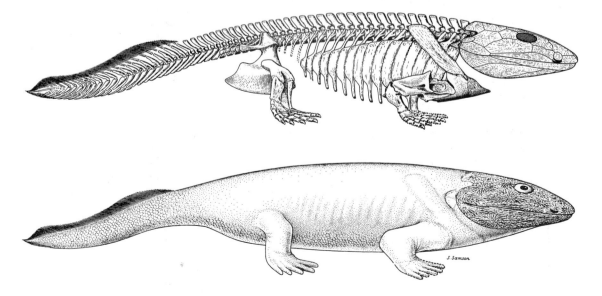

Figure 17-25 A scene in a Pennsylvanian coal swamp. In the shadows of luxuriant forest growth a giant insect attracts the attention of *Diplovertebron,* one of the most highly developed amphibians of the time.

great swamps, mild climates, and luxuriant forests of coal-forming plants. Such surroundings were obviously ideally suited to the amphibians' way of life, and most of our knowledge about Pennsylvanian vertebrates comes from specimens found in coal-bearing rocks. From these remains we can reconstruct many types of amphibians—some with lizard-like shapes, some resembling snakes, and some much larger, with contours resembling crocodiles and salamanders. We find not only the full-grown animals, but also many remains of immature or tadpole stages. And associated with the bones of the amphibians are the fossilized remains of the creatures they preyed on: spiders, centipedes, scorpions, and a variety of winged insects. In the world of the swamp forests, the amphibians ruled supreme, preying on any of the lower forms of life with which they came in contact.

DIFFICULTIES OF LAND LIFE   The gradual drying and cooling that characterized the Permian Period caused a corresponding decline in the number and variety of amphibians. Those that survived were mainly confined to water courses in dry regions, and we find their remains chiefly in red-bed types of sediments. These later amphibians were adapted to a large extent for life out of water, but they were awk-

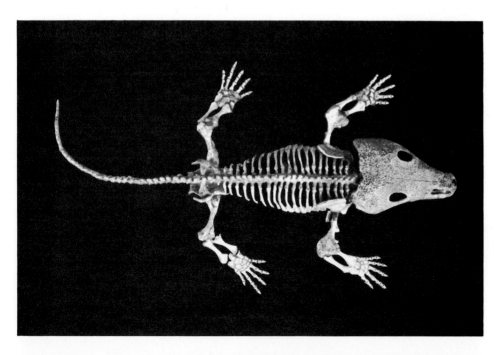

Figure 17-26 Skeleton of *Trematops,* a sprawling, flat-headed amphibian from the Early Permian of Texas. (*Courtesy Field Museum of Natural History.*)

ward and inefficient by comparison with later land animals. As we look at their skeletons, we are impressed by the clumsy sprawling legs, heavy tails, and immense flattened heads. Their skeletons tell us that one of the amphibians' chief foes was the force of gravity. Merely to raise their bodies off the ground must have required intense physical effort, and really rapid locomotion was out of the question.

Many adaptive changes in the structure of the backbone strengthened it for its new role of supporting the weight of the amphibian's body. The changes involved mainly the development of interlocking devices and processes for muscle attachment. These variations in the structure of the backbone serve as a basis for classifying the amphibians. The ancestral amphibians had rather deep, fish-like heads, about as wide as they were high. With the passage of time the skull gradually flattened until the entire head was many times wider than it was thick. This curious adaptation eventually enabled the animal to open its mouth by raising its upper jaws and skull while its lower jaw lay flat on the surface on which the animal rested. The usual method of chewing by lowering and raising the lower jaw is obviously inefficient if an animal must raise its entire body in order to permit the lower jaw to operate.

Since virtually all groups of late amphibians developed broad, flat skulls, we suppose that the same principle of conservation of energy was acting on them all.

The term "**stegocephalian**" (roof-headed) is applied to the larger flattened amphibians of the Pennsylvanian, Permian, and Triassic Periods. Although this type of amphibian lingered on into the Triassic, it was already declining at the close of the Paleozoic. Frogs and toads were products of a later time, and investigators have found no trace of their precise ancestors among Paleozoic fossils.

THE COMING OF THE REPTILES   All evidence indicates that **reptiles** developed from amphibians some time during the Mississippian or Pennsylvanian. A few isolated bones that some geologists assign to reptiles have been found in Mississippian deposits, but the first complete and authentic reptile skeletons have been taken from rocks of Pennsylvanian age. The Permian red beds of Texas have yielded a number of well-preserved skeletons of a small animal that stands almost midway between reptiles and amphibians. This creature, called *Seymouria*, although not the exact reptile ancestor, does indicate what the actual ancestor may have been like.

Figure 17-27 Reconstructed scene with the ancestral reptile, Petrolacosaurus, from the rocks of Late Pennsylvanian age near Garnett, Kansas. Fossils of the other plants and animals depicted in the illustration were found in the same deposit. (*From F. E. Peabody, Courtesy University of Kansas Paleontological Contributions.*)

Figure 17-28 The oldest known vertebrate egg. Although crushed and distorted, this object has been identified as an egg from the structure of the shell material. It was found in Early Permian red beds of Texas. (*Courtesy A. S. Romer, Museum of Comparative Zoology.*)

Another important link in the history of the reptiles was discovered in Late Pennsylvanian rocks near Garnett, Kansas. Here, the complete 24-inch skeleton of a small, lizard-like reptile was found in natural association with a large number of other plant and animal fossils. This animal, called *Petrolacosaurus*, currently lays claim to being the oldest known fairly complete reptile (see Figure 17-27). *Petrolacosaurus* had a delicate, well-constructed skeleton, sharp teeth, and the general appearance of an alert, swift-moving animal. In comparison with contemporary amphibians, *Petrolacosaurus* shows clearly the improved adaptations to land life that the reptiles had by this time achieved.

We must say something here about the one unique and basic feature that separates reptiles from amphibians—the ability to produce an egg that can be laid and hatched out of water. Just how did the reptiles develop this capability? On this point the fossil record is silent, but it is significant that a fossil egg, the oldest known, has been discovered in Permian rocks of Texas (Figure 17-28). The ability to produce an egg complete with food, water, and oxygen supply encased in a protective shell entails

many basic adjustments that involve intricate chemical and mechanical processes.

Long before the Permian Period ended, the amphibians had sharply declined and reptiles were spreading over the continental areas. Remains of late Paleozoic vertebrates are scattered over all the great continents, but the most complete and continuous record is found in the Karoo Basin in South Africa. The most characteristic animals of the Karoo belong to the *Therapsida*, or **mammal-like reptiles.** This group, which includes animals of various sizes, developed adaptations similar to those of later mammals (Figure 17-29). Some had well-differentiated teeth, the limbs were "pulled in" and not sprawling, there were fewer ribs, the tail was smaller, and the whole skeleton was light and well constructed. These were all reptiles, however; the transition to mammals took place during the Triassic, and it took many millions of years before the reptiles yielded their supremacy to the mammals.

ECONOMIC GEOLOGY OF THE LATE PALEOZOIC

Mineral deposits of all types were formed during the late Paleozoic periods. Especially significant are the vast stores of fossil fuels: coal, oil, and gas. Coal of Mississippian age is mined in Russia, Pennsylvanian coal supports heavy industry in the eastern United States, Great Britain, and western Europe. Permian beds are the chief source of coal in India, Australia, South Africa, and China, and are also important in Russia.

Oil and gas are plentiful in late Paleozoic rocks, especially in North America. The Devonian is a major source of oil in Canada, and important Mississippian, Pennsylvanian, and Permian pools are found in interior parts of the United States. It has been estimated that reserves of Paleozoic oil account for about 10 per cent of the world's total, which indicates just how extensive the later Mesozoic and Cenozoic contributions have been.

The extensive mountain-building activity

and granitic intrusions of the late Paleozoic, which we usually call the Hercynian, or Appalachian, orogenies, brought many important metalliferous deposits into existence throughout the affected areas. Tin, lead, zinc, copper, and silver deposits were formed in western Europe, and the iron, copper, chromium, nickel, and chromite ores of the Urals date from this period. Large deposits of sedimentary copper occur in lower Carboniferous rocks of south-central USSR. Gold, lead, silver, and other metals were deposited in central Asia, along with tin and tungsten ores in the Malaya-Burma region and tin, zinc, antimony, and mercury deposits in China. Important ores of various metals also were deposited in Australia and New Zealand.

By contrast, there are apparently very few metal deposits of this age in the Western Hemisphere.

The late Paleozoic was a time of extensive salt deposition, especially in the northern continents. Ordinary table salt, halite, is found in the Pennsylvanian of Colorado and Utah, and in the Permian of Texas, New Mexico, and Kansas. It is accompanied by the more valuable potash salts in the western localities. Salts of various kinds are also mined from Permian rocks in Germany and Russia.

Important reserves of phosphate, which were laid down in Late Permian (**Phosphoria Formation**) rocks in Idaho and adjacent states, support a flourishing mineral-fertilizer industry.

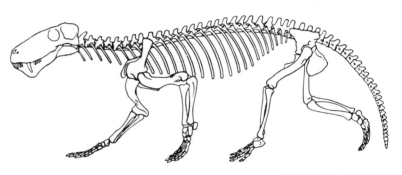

Figure 17-29 Above: reconstruction of the mammal-like reptile *Lycaenops*, from the Permian beds of South Africa. (*Reprinted with permission of Colbert,* Evolution of Vertebrates, *John Wiley & Sons, Inc., 1955.*) The painting, by John German, shows the desert-like landscape and the characteristic *Glossopteris* vegetation. (*Courtesy American Museum of Natural History.*) The skeleton, although mammal-like, exhibits many reptilian characteristics. Notice the presence of two bones in the lower jaw, the small brain case, the absence of external ears, the ribs on the neck vertebrae, the small scapula and pelvis, the absence of a knee-cap, and the long, heavy tail.

SUMMARY

Sediments of late Paleozoic age occur on all the continents, including Greenland and Antarctica. The northern continents were flooded by extensive shallow seas in the Devonian and Mississippian Periods. In the Pennsylvanian and Permian there is a higher proportion of land-laid sediments, including extensive coal beds. The record of marine sedimentation for the Southern Hemisphere is fragmentary except in Australia. Signs of glacial action in the Pennsylvanian and Permian have been found in Africa, Antarctica, Australia, South America, and India. This feature, taken in connection with similarities in fossil forms and igneous activity, is considered by many geologists to indicate that all southern continents were then joined in one super land-mass called Gondwanaland.

The late Paleozoic was a time of evolution and expansion of land life. Forests appeared in the Devonian and became dominant features of the landscape in succeeding periods. Amphibians appeared in the Devonian and were common in the coal swamps. Reptiles appeared in the Late Mississippian or Early Pennsylvanian and had become adapted to life in the continental interiors by the end of the Permian.

The closing stages of the Paleozoic were marked by varied topographic conditions, climatic extremes, and exterminations, especially marine animals such as trilobites, fusulinids and productid brachiopods. Vegetation and land life were less affected.

ADDITIONAL READING

Newell, Norman D., et al., *The Permian Reef Complex of the Guadalupe Mountains Region, Texas and New Mexico.* San Francisco: W. H. Freeman and Co., 1953.

Watson, D. M. S., *Paleontology and Modern Biology.* New Haven: Yale University Press, 1951.

Additional references for the material in this chapter can be found at the end of Chapter 16.

The Mesozoic Era

The Mesozoic, or "time of middle life," which lasted for an estimated 165 million years, is divided into three periods as follows: Triassic Period, 50 million years; Jurassic Period, 45 million years; and Cretaceous Period, 70 million years.

At the beginning of the Triassic Period, the continents were generally well above sea level, remnants of many Paleozoic highlands still were being eroded, and where conditions were favorable, land deposits accumulated in interior basins and alluvial plains. The Triassic was relatively quiet insofar as mountain-building was concerned.

Later in the Triassic and during the Jurassic, as the lands were lowered by erosion, shallow seas spread inward along the geosynclines and on the continental margins. Extensive deposits of interfingering marine and nonmarine sediments were laid down, and a great variety of rocks, including coal beds, was formed. The Cretaceous was a time of even greater flooding, with shallow seas advancing into the continental interiors far beyond the limits reached during the Triassic and Jurassic Periods. Late Cretaceous marine beds, in many places calcareous, were deposited in the seaways while nonmarine beds with coal accumulated in coastal areas.

Toward the close of the Cretaceous, strong crustal movements took place, especially in the Western Hemisphere, and the seas retreated as the lands emerged. The time was critical for life, and many land and sea animals were exterminated.

MESOZOIC OCEANS

Much evidence has been gathered indicating a major breakup of land masses in the mid-Mesozoic. For instance, no marine beds of Triassic or Jurassic age have been discovered along the western margins of Africa or the eastern shores of South America, which suggests that the ocean had not yet penetrated this area. Similarly the oldest rocks of the Indian Ocean are of Cretaceous age; thus this body of water also may not have existed earlier. The Pacific, which was probably correspondingly larger and wider, is definitely known to have existed because of nearshore deposits of Triassic, Jurassic, and Cretaceous age surrounding its margins. Strangely though, no deposits earlier than Cretaceous are known from the Pacific basin or its islands. The Arctic Ocean is a puzzling area, but it is generally agreed that it was present in the Mesozoic, for bordering it in Canada and in Siberia are marine beds that grade outward as though passing into deep water.

TETHYS, THE GREAT LIMY SEAWAY

The greatest geosynclinal belt on earth, known as Tethys, extends across Europe and southern Asia between the Baltic and Angara Shields on the north and the African and Indian Shields on the south. The history of its earlier depositional phase has been outlined in previous chapters; its dramatic elevation into great mountain ranges is yet to come in the Tertiary Period.

During the periods we are considering here, deposition of limy sediment was favored by the warmth of the downsinking Tethys seaway, which lay almost parallel to, and not far from, the equatorial regions. Lime-secreting organisms, both plants and animals, flourished and left their fossil remains and precipitation products in abundance. Great fossil reefs of coral, algae, and sponges are common.

The Tethys seaway appears to have continued across the Himalayan area, southeastward across southeastern Asia and into the East Indies. Scattered exposures of Mesozoic rocks are found from the eastern part of the Celebes and on through Ceram, Tanimbar, and Timor. The geosyncline may have extended as far as western Australia, where it has been called the **Westralian Geosyncline.**

Triassic, Jurassic, and Cretaceous deposits of the Tethys seaway are now uplifted in many great mountain ranges, including the Alps, Pyrenees, Apennines, Atlas, Carpathians, Caucasus, Pamirs, and Himalayas.

EURASIA NORTH OF THE TETHYS SEAWAY

Much of Europe north of the Alps has Mesozoic rocks at or near the surface. The Triassic, with type section in Germany, consists of red beds and limestone; the Jurassic is mixed in nature, with both nonmarine and marine facies. The Cretaceous makes up the famous White Cliffs of Dover and many other calcareous outcrops. Among the mineral resources are salt and gypsum from the Triassic, iron ores from the Jurassic, and gas from the Cretaceous.

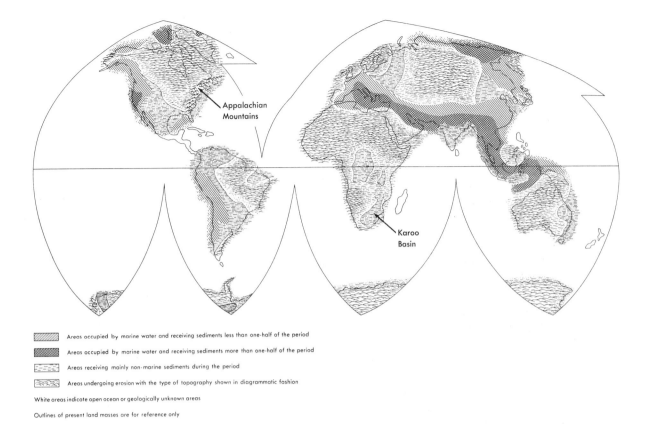

Appalachian
Mountains

Karoo
Basin

	Areas occupied by marine water and receiving sediments less than one-half of the period
	Areas occupied by marine water and receiving sediments more than one-half of the period
	Areas receiving mainly non-marine sediments during the period
	Areas undergoing erosion with the type of topography shown in diagrammatic fashion

White areas indicate open ocean or geologically unknown areas

Outlines of present land masses are for reference only

Figure 18-1   Generalized paleogeographic map of the Triassic Period.

Over most of the area between the Ural Mountains and the east coast of Asia there is no distinct break between the Triassic and Permian rocks. There was, however, an interruption between the Early and Middle Triassic. After this time most of northern Asia was free of marine invasions and received instead a great variety of land-laid sediments. Southward toward the Tethys belt, the amount of marine sediment, chiefly limestone, increases until it makes up whole ranges in the Crimea and Caucasus.

Notable in the Early Triassic of central Siberia are great fields of basaltic lava and

Figure 18-2   Cliffs of chalk on the coast of Selwick's Bay, Yorkshire, England. Glacial deposits overlie the chalk beds. (*Her Majesty's Geological Survey Photographs, Crown Copyright.*)

intrusions of the dark igneous rock, dolerite, or diabase, a type of gabbro. Extensive marine beds of the same age occur in China and eastern Siberia. The Middle and Upper Triassic are poorly represented. The Jurassic was a time of interior lakes and alluvial plains when many important coal beds were deposited in the USSR and China. Cretaceous rocks are unknown in the Siberian Platform, and elsewhere rocks of this age lie upon the Jurassic without significant breaks. Locally they contain coal, bauxite (aluminum-rich rock), and iron ores. In Mongolia the continental beds yield well-preserved dinosaur bones and eggs.

EASTERN NORTH AMERICA

The Triassic and Jurassic are poorly represented in the eastern half of North America. Nonmarine Triassic red beds are found in a dozen downfaulted basins from Nova Scotia to South Carolina. These red formations, known collectively as the **Newark Series,** consist of shale, sandstone, and conglomerate, with great sheets of dark lava and intrusions of dolerite. The famous Palisades of the Hudson is one of these. Fresh-water fish and dinosaur tracks are common fossils in the Newark Series. These rocks are fairly well known because they crop out near centers of population.

No Jurassic is known to appear east of the Mississippi River, but thick formations, some with oil pools, have been found by drilling in states marginal to the Gulf of Mexico. The Cretaceous, though, is well represented as a marginal belt along the Atlantic and Gulf Coasts; this belt lies under the Atlantic from Long Island northward, but is 600 miles wide in the Mississippi Valley. The Cretaceous is mixed marine and nonmarine, and the marine facies die out landward in such a way as to

Figure 18-3   Generalized paleogeographic map of the Jurassic Period.

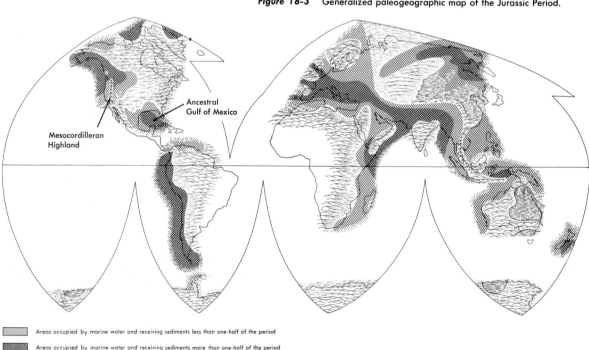

Areas occupied by marine water and receiving sediments less than one-half of the period

Areas occupied by marine water and receiving sediments more than one-half of the period

Areas receiving mainly non-marine sediments during the period

Areas undergoing erosion with the type of topography shown in diagrammatic fashion

White areas indicate open ocean or geologically unknown areas

Outlines of present land masses are for reference only

prove that there was an Atlantic Ocean at this time and that the east coast of North America had essentially its present form.

The Appalachian Mountains, the Canadian Shield, and other central areas, were undergoing erosion throughout the Mesozoic. At the beginning of the Triassic, the Appalachians must have been an imposing mountain range; by the Cretaceous Period, nothing remained but the planed-off, deeply eroded stumps. Most of the material removed in the Triassic and Jurassic was carried beyond the present margins of the Atlantic and Gulf Coasts and may in fact be spread over the ocean bottoms. Material eroded in the Cretaceous is still near at hand in existing formations.

WESTERN AND NORTHERN NORTH AMERICA

A number of shallow marine invasions washed over the western portions of North America during the Mesozoic. Conditions were such that the marine formations alternated with deposits from the interior, and thus a record of both land and sea life is preserved. During the Mesozoic a strip of land up to 400 miles wide was formed by sedimentation and igneous action and welded to the western margin of the pre-existing continental mass.

In Early Triassic time the seas spread inward from the Pacific to central Utah and Wyoming, while broad low flood plains extended well beyond into the central part of the continent. This was the last time marine waters crossed the western United States from the Pacific, because a narrow uplift, the **Mesocordilleran Highland,** arose from the former sea bed in the Middle Triassic to block out the western seas.

For a while the interior protected area behind the highland was the site of accumulation of desert sands on a large scale, but eventually with continued downsinking, the seas entered a pass to the north in Canada or Alaska and again flowed into the west-central parts of the continent. During the Jurassic Period this interior seaway was occupied by at least two

successive shallow embayments up to 800 miles wide. They failed, however, to connect with other embayments that spread inward from the ancestral Gulf of Mexico and from California. One of the last events of the Jurassic was the accumulation of the Morrison Formation, which covers about 750,000 square miles in the Rocky Mountains and western plains. The Morrison is composed of material worn from the Mesocordilleran Highland and spread eastward by sluggish, meandering rivers. Buried in the Morrison are skeletons of the gigantic dinosaurs and other Late Jurassic life forms. This formation supplies most of the uranium ores of the United States.

With continual downsinking during the Cretaceous, shallow seas spread inward on all sides in the greatest flood of the Mesozoic. Although the Mesocordilleran Highland was

Figure 18-4 Sandstone formations of Jurassic age forming vertical walls of the Glen Canyon of the Colorado River, Utah.

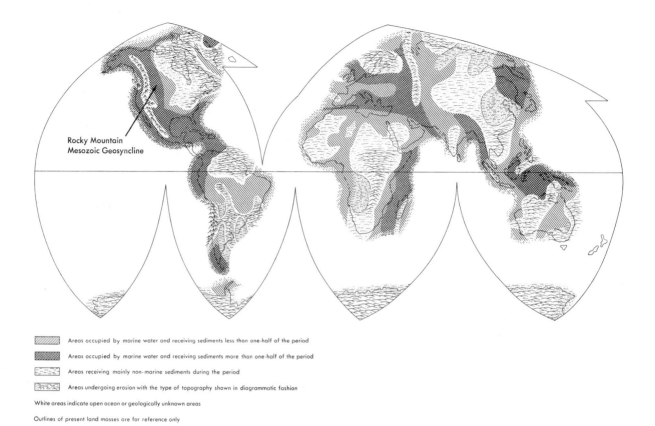

Rocky Mountain
Mesozoic Geosyncline

Figure 18-5   Generalized paleogeographic map of the Cretaceous Period.

not submerged, it was surrounded like an island, as seas from the north connected with seas from the south across the central United States and Canada. In this great Cretaceous seaway many hundreds of cubic miles of silty mud accumulated which now form extensive soft formations from Minnesota to central Utah. On the shallow shelving deltas and flood plains along the western borders of this sea, successive swamps with abundant vegetation gave rise to valuable coal beds.

The Cretaceous came to a close as the central sea was crowded out by its own deposits. Swamps and lakes marked the final phases, and the stage was set for the great Rocky Mountain Revolution, which affected much of the Pacific borderlands.

Northern Canada has a Mesozoic history much like that of the western United States. The Triassic exists in minor amounts with nonmarine red beds and marine shale. The Jurassic has beds of both marine and nonmarine origin,

with little or no lime. The Cretaceous is also well represented by varied sediments. Notable is the presence of basalt flows ranging up to the Cretaceous in age.

Greenland has richly fossiliferous Triassic rocks, a thick and varied Jurassic section, and Cretaceous beds showing alternate retreats and transgressions of the sea. A very large basalt field of Late Cretaceous or Early Tertiary age is found in east-central Greenland.

SOUTH AMERICA AND ANTARCTICA

South America has marine and nonmarine deposits of each of the Mesozoic Eras, but the record is not as extensive as that of North America. Early and Middle Triassic are known only in very small areas along the western margin, but Late Triassic is more widespread, with marine beds in the Andes and nonmarine deposits in eastern Brazil. In the nonmarine formations of Argentina are found land plants and vertebrates comparable to those of South Africa. Near the Triassic-Jurassic transition great floods of basaltic lava covering 380,000 square miles, with an average thickness of 2,000 feet, were extruded in the Parana Basin of Brazil. Similar flows are found in northeastern Brazil also and subsurface in Argentina.

The Jurassic is represented by marine beds in the mountain chains of western South America, with fossils that correlate with the Jurassic of other continents. Only a few small outcrops of nonmarine rocks are known along the east coast.

Cretaceous rocks are far more extensive. All parts of the system are represented, some intervals appear in great thickness in the Andes. The eastern coast and lower Amazon Valley were invaded by shallow seas on several occasions and there were extensive but thin accumulations of continental rock in interior basins. Notable throughout the Mesozoic is the almost total lack of sedimentary rocks in the great eastward bulge of the continent.

Recent explorations in Antarctica have revealed a fairly complete representation of the Mesozoic subdivisions. The Triassic is represented by continental rocks with coal. The Early Jurassic was a time of great intrusive igneous action with huge **diabase sheets** covering thousands of square miles. Basaltic flows also occur, and these in places rest on sedimentary rocks with Early Jurassic plant fossils. The Cretaceous is known chiefly on the Antarctic Peninsula which extends toward South America. Here, thick marine beds with molluscan fossils are found. It may be significant that no land vertebrates have yet been discovered in any of the Mesozoic rocks.

THE PACIFIC OCEAN

Although geologists are confident that there was a Pacific Ocean Basin during the Paleozoic and early Mesozoic, no fossils older than Cretaceous have been found in spite of much dredging, boring, and surface collecting throughout

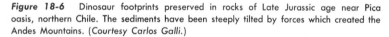

Figure 18-6 Dinosaur footprints preserved in rocks of Late Jurassic age near Pica oasis, northern Chile. The sediments have been steeply tilted by forces which created the Andes Mountains. (*Courtesy Carlos Galli.*)

Figure 18-7 Artist Chesley Bonestell's conception of the topography of the Pacific Ocean bottom. If the water should be removed, the flat-topped seamounts, or guyots, would be revealed. (*Courtesy Edwin L. Hamilton.*)

the Pacific. The best current explanation for this strange circumstance is the hypothesis of sea-floor spreading, according to which all older rocks have been swept into the continents and destroyed by convection currents.

It can scarcely be coincidence that the borderlands of the Pacific became geologically very active about mid-Cretaceous time. Virtually all the ranges that face the Pacific and the island arcs that rise along its margins date from this time. Cretaceous rocks chiefly of igneous derivation abound in Formosa, the Japanese islands, and Korea. Farther south, deposits of the same age occur in the East Indies and New Zealand. The great granitic masses of the Andes and Rockies are also chiefly of Cretaceous age.

Not to be overlooked are the evidences of Cretaceous deposits on many of the 10,000 or so submerged mid-Pacific guyots, or seamounts, which are mostly decapitated volcanoes (Figure 18-7). Cretaceous fossils have been dredged from the tops of these mountains at depths of 6,000 feet. It must be inferred that the fossil-bearing guyots were at or near the surface of the oceans during the Cretaceous Period.

Taking into account the facts just mentioned and the extensive flooding that took place on all continents during the Cretaceous, it seems that geologic activity in and around the Pacific reached a high point at this period. As one geologist put it, "a commotion in the ocean" of some importance is indicated.

Southwestern Pacific

Australia was above sea level during the Triassic, Jurassic, and earliest Cretaceous, but it did receive and retain much continental sediment. The Triassic yields fossils of fresh-water animals and land plants. The Jurassic was a time of extensive swamps and bodies of fresh water, one of which, Lake Wallon, covered at least 300,000 square miles and received deposits over 5,000 feet thick. Fresh-water organisms and land plants are present, together with dinosaurs. Seas invaded Australia in mid-Early Cretaceous and split the continent into two large islands.

New Zealand has a record of Triassic and Jurassic deposition, and in Early Cretaceous time there was a mountain-building episode there which gave rise to intrusions of granite and later to coarse marginal deposits which interfinger outward with marine beds.

AFRICA AND THE COMPLETION OF THE KAROO SYSTEM

Africa, especially that portion south of the Sahara desert, was remarkably stable during the Mesozoic. The northern part bordering on the Mediterranean Sea was a part of Tethys and received thick and varied sediments through all the Mesozoic Periods. During the Cretaceous a shallow arm of the sea spread across the bulge of Africa and connected with the Atlantic. On the east coast, scattered Jurassic marine deposits are found, and Cretaceous sediments extend many miles inland.

Of unusual interest are the continental deposits of the Karoo Basin of south Africa that began to accumulate in the Pennsylvanian

Figure 18-8 Thick sheets of igneous rocks alternate with sediments to form this imposing escarpment of the Drakensburg Mountains in Natal, South Africa. The age of the sediments and igneous rocks is thought to be Early Jurassic or Late Triassic. (*Courtesy South African Information Service.*)

Period and continued into the Early Jurassic without notable interruptions. The Triassic part of the Karoo includes sandstone, shale, and red beds with abundant fossil bones and footprints, including many pertaining to dinosaurs. Fish, crustaceans, and plants also occur.

The closing stages of Karoo history were marked by strong volcanic action which produced the so-called **Drakensberg volcanics.** Both lava (basalt) and intrusive sheets (dolerite) were produced on a large scale. The volcanic rock has been largely removed by erosion, but remnants totaling 10,000 square miles are still preserved in Basutoland. Although fossils are understandably rare, it is concluded that the volcanic activity lasted into Jurassic time. Like other continents, Africa received Cretaceous deposits about its margins.

MESOZOIC DISTURBANCES

Two periods of widespread disturbance, with strongly contrasting structures and rock types took place in the Mesozoic. The first was characterized by the production of dark-colored igneous rock that appeared at the surface as basalt flows and solidified below the surface as dikes and sills of dolerite. Areas affected were chiefly, but not exclusively, in the Southern Hemisphere. South America (Brazil and Argentina), South Africa, Antarctica, and India received vast outpourings of lava. Similar but less extensive flows and intrusions occurred in Siberia, the Arctic Islands, Greenland, and in the Triassic basins of eastern United States and Canada. For some unexplained reason the dark igneous rocks appeared in stable regions of flat-lying sediments and were not associated with mountain-building.

The second notable Mesozoic disturbance affected chiefly the margins of the Pacific Basin.

Figure 18-9 Eroded granite in Yosemite National Park, Mariposa County, California. Age is late Mesozoic (*Photo by Brower, Courtesy U.S. Geological Survey.*)

It produced some of the greatest mountain ranges of the earth, with attendant intrusion of light-colored granitic rock and extrusion of corresponding types of lava, chiefly andesite. Since this disturbance produced the Rocky Mountains, it is sometimes called the **Rocky Mountain,** or **Laramide, Revolution.** Like the basaltic episode, it was spread over several periods, commencing in the Jurassic, culminating in the Cretaceous, and dying down in the Tertiary. Table 18-1 shows the subdivision of this disturbance as suggested for the North American Cordilleran chain. This scheme is arbitrary and cannot be expected to fit all areas. Suffice it to say that the Rocky Mountain Revolution provides a rough division between the Mesozoic and the Tertiary.

Again, with reference to continental drift, it has been speculated that the late Mesozoic disturbance may be due to partial melting of the lower crust as shown by the basaltic outpourings in stable areas. The more active movements and volcanic activity of lands fronting the Pacific might be due to the movement of the continents toward and over the ocean floor. During this whole interval the margins of the Atlantic were quiet and undisturbed. If there was movement outward from the mid-Atlantic ridge, the Atlantic margins were passively dragged or carried along, and consequently were not crumpled and deformed.

LIFE OF THE MESOZOIC

Plants

The Mesozoic was a time of transition and change in the plant kingdom. The typical vegetation of the carboniferous coal forests—**seed-ferns, lycopods,** and **horsetails**—had greatly declined by the Triassic, and a new flora characterized by true ferns, cycads, and conifers dominated the landscape. Ferns, mostly related to living types, flourished even in what are now the cooler latitudes.

Table 18-1 Sequence of Orogenies Making Up the Rocky Mountain Revolution

Period	Mountain stage	Orogeny
Quaternary	Coast Ranges and Great Basin	Late Coast Range Orogeny (Basin and Range Orogeny)
Pliocene	Coast Ranges and Great Basin	Late Coast Range Orogeny (Basin and Range Orogeny)
Miocene	Coast Ranges and Great Basin	Early Coast Range Orogeny (Basin and Range Orogeny)
Oligocene	Coast Ranges and Great Basin	Early Coast Range Orogeny (Basin and Range Orogeny)
Eocene	Rocky Mountains	Late Laramide Orogeny
Paleocene	Rocky Mountains	Mid-Laramide Orogeny
Late Cretaceous	Sierra Nevada and similar mountains	Early Laramide Orogeny
Late Cretaceous	Sierra Nevada and similar mountains	Late Nevadan Orogeny
Early Cretaceous	Sierra Nevada and similar mountains	Mid-Nevadan Orogeny
Jurassic	Sierra Nevada and similar mountains	Early Nevadan Orogeny

Figure 18-10 A cycad trunk, *Cycadeoidea marylandica,* about 13 inches high. Found in Early Cretaceous sediments of Anne Arundel County, Maryland. (*Courtesy F. M. Hueber, Smithsonian Institution.*)

Figure 18-11 Broken sections of fossil logs in the Chinle Formation of Late Triassic age in Petrified Forest National Park, Arizona. (*Courtesy U.S. Park Service.*)

Cycads and related "cycadeoids" abounded. They were cosmopolitan plants, ranging across all the continents. Their distinctive trunks with diamond-shaped indentations and palm-like foliage are locally common fossils (Figure 18-10). Indeed, the Jurassic is sometimes called the **Age of Cycads.** The early Mesozoic was also a high point in the history of the cone-bearing trees. The cool and dry climates of the Permian and Triassic were favorable to this development of primitive conifers. Especially prominent during the early Mesozoic were members of the family Araucariaceae, which now survive only in the Southern Hemisphere. Petrified trunks of Araucarians account for most of the fossil remains in the famous Petrified Forest in Arizona. Here lie trunks as much as 5 feet in diameter and over 100 feet long.

The first true pines appeared in the Late Jurassic and spread widely during the Cretaceous, as their fossilized remains—cones, needles, and wood—indicate. The sequoias, which had a small beginning during the Jurassic, had become very common by the Cretaceous.

A distinct and rather sudden change in the vegetation of the earth took place during the mid-Cretaceous. Earlier, during the Triassic and Jurassic, the most abundant plants had been ferns, various types of cone-bearing plants, and the cycads and their relatives. After the mid-Cretaceous, the chief plants were members of the great group known as the **flowering plants,** or **angiosperms.** The angiosperms, which are pollinated through floral structures and bear seeds enclosed in an ovary or pod, are divided into two groups: the **dicotyledons,** which have

365

Figure 18-12 Fossil angiosperm leaves from Late Cretaceous rocks, Clark County, Idaho. These are typical of the plants that became common during the Cretaceous. (*Courtesy F. M. Hueber, Smithsonian Institution.*)

two "seed leaves" and net-veined leaves; and the **monocotyledons**, with one "seed leaf" and parallel-veined leaves. Estimates indicate that there are about 175,000 species of living flowering plants, and at least 30,000 fossil species have been found. Angiosperms include trees, shrubs, and herbs of all sizes and varieties and they have succeeded in practically all climates.

Flowering plants are important not only because they have become the dominant form of plant life on earth, but also because of the influence they exert on animal life. With the flowering plants came a variety of grains, nuts, and fruits, which furnished a food supply that insured the survival of the plant embryo. The relatively concentrated nature of the food supply and the small size of most seeds, nuts, and fruits made them ideal fare for small land vertebrates and for insects as well. It is unlikely that the large Mesozoic reptiles ate food of this sort.

Figure 18-13 Two types of the chalk-forming fossils, known as coccoliths, from the Taylor Marl of Cretaceous age, Texas. Magnified about 18,000 times. (*Courtesy S. Gartner and W. W. Hay, University of Illinois.*)

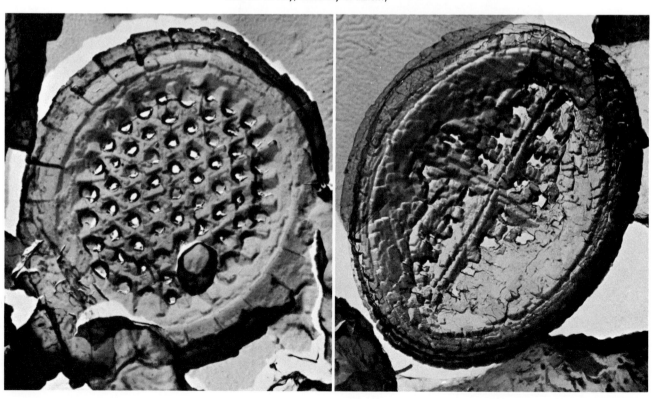

They fed on large quantities of coarse herbage and on succulent water vegetation of various types. The mammals and birds, on the other hand, could and did subsist very nicely on the highly concentrated products of flowering plants (or on the insects that fed on these plants). It is doubtful that mammals and birds could have succeeded without flowering plants.

No less important than the origin and spread of the angiosperms on land was the expansion of lower forms of plant life in marine and fresh water. The small aquatic algae known as **diatoms** are not positively known before the Jurassic, whereas they now number hundreds of species and are the major food source for animal life in the sea. Diatoms secrete skeletons of silica which accumulate to form oceanic ooze, or the sediment called **diatomite** (see Chapter 11).

The chalk beds so characteristic of the Cretaceous are composed largely of extremely small fossils called **coccoliths,** which are generally thought to be remains of very simple floating plants (see Figure 18-13).

NONMARINE INVERTEBRATES

Invertebrates living on dry land and in fresh water were fairly well established by the Mesozoic. Streams and lakes were well stocked with clams, snails, arthropods such as **ostracods** and **branchiopods,** and small, inconspicuous sponges. All these fed chiefly on water plants, with which their remains are usually associated. Air-breathing snails, though, are occasionally found.

The history of insects is particularly important, especially as it relates to the flowering plants. The plants furnish food for the insects in the form of nectar and pollen, in return for which insects serve the vital function of fertilization by transferring pollen from flower to flower. This association undoubtedly evolved gradually over the ages, which suggests that many of the complicated behavior patterns of insects and the myriad forms of flowering plants are the outcome of a long process of adaptation. The earliest evidence of bees or wasps is a

cast of a nest found in the Upper Cretaceous of Utah (Figure 18-14).

The ascendancy of insects and flowering plants during the Mesozoic was greatly aided by this relationship that developed between them. The benefits that accrued to birds, mammals, and ultimately to man are incidental to the process. Most of our fruits, vegetables, ornamental plants, and industrial plants are insect-pollinated. It may be somewhat sobering to some of us to realize that our flowers bloom to please the insects and not us human beings who cultivate them.

Apparently, their small size is the only thing that has prevented insects from becoming the unquestioned rulers of the earth. Their evolution was rapid, but once a group reached a certain level, it tended to stagnate. Fossil ants found preserved in amber 50 million years old are nearly indistinguishable from living forms. They apparently completed all essential phases of their evolution at least that long ago.

Figure 18-14   Fossil wasp nest from Upper Cretaceous rocks of southern Utah. This unique specimen indicates the presence of highly developed insects with social adaptions depending on flowering plants at least as early as the Late Cretaceous. Top and side views are shown. (*Courtesy Roland W. Brown.*)

MARINE INVERTEBRATES

As a group, Triassic marine invertebrates show the effects of the late Paleozoic exterminations. Apparently the Early Triassic seas continued to be unusually cool or otherwise inhospitable to such animals as corals, sponges, bryozoans, and protozoans. The scarcity of carbonate rock in Early Triassic formations except the Tethys seaway is notable. Corals seem to have escaped extinction by a very narrow margin, as few solitary corals and no coral reefs have been found in the Early Triassic. Other groups that were relegated to permanently minor positions were crinoids and brachiopods, which are generally rare in Mesozoic rocks. Two groups that eventually recovered a great deal of the ground they had lost were the protozoans and bryozoans, but the species that became common during the late Mesozoic and Cenozoic were quite different from their Paleozoic predecessors. Protozoans and bryozoans are rare in the Triassic, increase during the Jurassic, and become prolific during the Cretaceous.

The molluscs seem to have weathered the critical late Paleozoic disturbance without great losses and came to be the most important shelled invertebrates of the Mesozoic seas. You will recall that this group includes the coiled, single-chambered gastropods; the bivalved (two-shelled) pelecypods, typified by the clams and oysters (see Figure 18-15); and the coiled many-chambered cephalopods. As a general rule, the molluscs gradually grew more varied and numerous during the Jurassic and Cretaceous. Freshwater clams and gastropods were plentiful, and air-breathing snails were locally abundant. By the time of the Cretaceous, we find entire reeflike structures composed of oysters and oysterlike shells. Of special importance are the large conical or twisted shells of a group of pelecypods known as rudistids, some of which reach a length of 4 feet and a diameter of over 1 foot. Fossil rudistids are distributed in Cretaceous rocks in a world-circling belt along Tethys and in warmer regions of the Western Hemisphere.

The most spectacular, varied, and successful marine invertebrates of the Mesozoic were the cephalopods. Since they were able to swim and crawl when alive and since the shells of some species could float after the animals had died, their remains have been scattered and preserved in many localities. Cephalopod shells make striking fossils, and they are usually beautifully preserved. The coiled varieties range from less

Figure 18-15 Typical Cretaceous pelecypods. *Gryphaea (top); Ostrea (oyster) (middle);* and *Exogyra (bottom).* In these forms the shells are of irregular shape and one valve is larger than the other. Scale represents one inch.

Figure 18-16 Cephalopod specimens illustrating the various type suture patterns. Shell material has been removed to expose the sutures and the rock material filling the spaces between the partitions. *Upper left, Eutrephoceras,* from the Cretaceous of Wyoming, showing the relatively straight nautiloid suture pattern (*Courtesy Julian Maack*); *upper right, Imitoceras,* from the Mississippian of Indiana, showing the goniatitic type pattern, with sharp angular bends (*Courtesy G. Arthur Cooper*); *lower left, Ceratites,* from the Triassic of Germany, with the ceratitic suture line in which small crenulations are beginning to appear on the larger curves (*Courtesy Julian Maack*); *lower right, Placenticeras,* from the Cretaceous of South Dakota, with the complexly developed ammonitic suture patterns (*Courtesy Ward's Natural Science Establishment, Inc.*). Specimens range from 3 to 7 inches in diameter but are shown the same size for comparative purposes.

than an inch across to 4 feet in diameter. Also included in the cephalopod class are the **belemnites,** squid-like forms whose internal skeletons take the form of a solid, stony, cylindrical object shaped like a cigar. Fossilized belemnite skeletons are particularly abundant and resistant to erosion, and have been known for centuries as "thunderbolts."

The **ammonites** (cephalopods whose shells have complex suture patterns) are unequaled as

guide fossils for marine Triassic, Jurassic, and Cretaceous rocks (see Figure 18-17). Individual species ranged widely, lived short lives, were independent of ocean-bottom conditions, and, of course, are usually well preserved. Ammonites successfully weathered the critical Permian-Triassic transition, and descendents of Paleozoic forms blossomed in Mesozoic seas over the entire world. Although the group suffered a serious setback at the close of the Tri-

Figure 18-17 Fossil shells of *Scaphites*, a common Late Cretaceous ammonite of the western United States. For some little-understood reason, ammonites frequently occur by the hundreds in compact concretionary masses. This concretion is about 6 inches across. (*Courtesy Karl Waage.*)

Figure 18-18 Lobster-like crustacean, *Eryon*, from the Upper Jurassic Solnhofen limestone, Bavaria. About 6 inches long. (*Courtesy Field Museum of Natural History.*)

assic and again at the close of the Jurassic, the surviving members recovered rapidly, and each time succeeded in repopulating the seas with their descendents. Only at the close of the Cretaceous did the race suffer final extinction.

The extent to which ammonites have been useful in world-wide correlation is indicated by their selection as guides to many zones and stages. European authorities recognize 29 zones in the Triassic, based mainly on collections from the Alps. A recent summary of the North American Triassic formations shows 30 ammonite guide species. Since geologists estimate that the Triassic spanned approximately 30 million years, we can theoretically correlate a million-year segment of time over the entire earth if the necessary ammonite fossils can be found.

The Jurassic ammonites are even more diagnostic and have been studied more thoroughly than the Triassic ammonites. You will recall that the striking shells in the Jurassic rocks of England strongly influenced the early development of the science of stratigraphy and correlation. On the basis of their numerous and excellent collections of ammonites, British geologists recognize from 40 to 50 zones. The North American Jurassic is relatively incomplete, with only about 10 zones having been established so far in the United States and 24 in Mexico. Under favorable conditions, then, intervals of less than a million years may be correlated by Jurassic ammonites.

The Cretaceous rocks of Europe cannot be as easily zoned by ammonites as the Jurassic and Triassic. Other types of invertebrates, such as echinoids and brachiopods, are used in conjunction with the ammonites. Perhaps 20 to 30 ammonite zones can be recognized in Europe. Twenty-nine fossil zones have been tentatively recognized in the late Cretaceous of the United States, of which 26 are based on ammonites. The relative length of recognizable intervals again approaches a million years.

During the Mesozoic the arthropods evolved and spread in the oceans, as well as on land and in the air. The living space vacated by the trilobites was taken over at least in part by a variety of other crustaceans. The group

Figure 18-19 Numerous specimens of the starfish *Austinaster mccarteri* from the Cretaceous Austin Formation of Austin, Texas. (*Courtesy Texas Memorial Museum.*)

that includes the familiar shrimps, crabs, crayfish, and lobsters appeared in the Triassic. Over 8,000 species of this group have been identified. The first true crabs especially adapted for life along the beaches and shallow offshore areas appeared during the Jurassic.

Mesozoic echinoderms were represented by a variety of forms, including starfish, sea urchins, crinoids, and sea cucumbers. It is significant that the majority of these creatures were capable of some degree of locomotion.

Protozoans were at a very low ebb in the Triassic but increased in the Jurassic and reached spectacular numbers in the Cretaceous. A recent survey shows 9 families in the Triassic, 24 in the Jurassic, and 36 in the Cretaceous. An important development of the Cretaceous was the appearance and spread of floating forms such as Globigerina, a lime-secreting form living in open oceans.

THE VERTEBRATES

The Mesozoic was a time of abundant land life. It is popularly known as the **Age of Reptiles** because of the dominant position this group achieved on land, in the air, and in the seas. Although mammals and birds appeared during the Mesozoic, they were not particularly abundant. Fish continued to evolve and became better adapted to their special ways of life, but the amphibians sank to a level of comparative insignificance and have never recovered.

Fish and Amphibians

Fossil fish are common in many Mesozoic formations of both fresh-water and marine origin. The most important advances were

Figure 18-20 Fourteen-foot skeleton of *Portheus*, a giant Cretaceous fish uncovered in the chalk beds of western Kansas. Not visible in this view is a 6-foot skeleton of another fish inside the stomach cavity. (*Courtesy American Museum of Natural History.*)

made by the bony fish, especially the **actinopterygians,** or **ray-finned** forms. During the early stages of the Mesozoic most fish belonged to the **Chondrostei,** a group characterized by heavy diamond-shaped scales, asymmetrical tails, somewhat scaly fins, and considerable cartilage in their skeletons. Toward the middle of the era these fish were gradually replaced by the **Holostei,** which had heavy scales but more symmetrical tails, fins supported by flexible rays, and relatively more bone in their skeletons. This group was in turn displaced during the Cretaceous by the **Teleostei,** flexible-scaled fish with completely bony skeletons and powerful, well-formed fins and tails. This is the group that dominates present-day seas and rivers.

The sharks were poorly represented during the early Mesozoic but gradually expanded dur-

Figure 18-21 Graveyard of *Buettneria,* the giant amphibian, as found in Triassic beds near Santa Fe, New Mexico. The massed remains of many specimens probably record the drying up of a pond or lake. The skulls are about 2 feet long. (*Courtesy U.S. National Museum.*)

ing the Jurassic and Cretaceous to regain the ground they had lost during the critical late Paleozoic period. The crossopterygians and lungfish held a subordinate position in out-of-the-way surroundings, just as they now do. The Mesozoic was a period of decline for the amphibians. All the large flat-headed stegocephalians became extinct early in the Triassic, and the group thereafter is represented by the familiar toads, frogs, salamanders, and the legless, wormlike apoda. The first true frogs are found in Triassic rocks of Madagascar, but ancestral forms from which they could have evolved have been discovered in the preceding period. The first known salamanders come from the Late Jurassic Morrison Formation.

Reptiles

Although the amphibians as a group never achieved complete sway over the land, their descendents, the reptiles, became rulers of the earth. About a dozen orders of reptiles were present during the Late Triassic and Early Jurassic; only four orders exist today. Their basic adaptations permitted them to expand into hitherto unoccupied territory and even to re-enter the ocean, where they became successful competitors of the fish.

The Triassic Period was marked by the decline and disappearance of certain of the older orders of reptiles and by the appearance of new and vigorous stocks. Among the Permian holdovers that disappeared in the Triassic were the **protosaurs** and certain mammal-like reptiles, the **therapsids.** The exact nature of these animals need not concern us here, but the newly evolved groups merit more detailed attention. The first turtles appeared during the Triassic and quickly achieved their typical form. The **plesiosaurs** and **ichthyosaurs,** adapted to life in the ocean, also appeared at this time, along with the first crocodiles. Most notable from the viewpoint of evolutionary progress were the **thecodonts:** lightly built, relatively small reptiles adapted to land life. As a group, they are confined to the Triassic, but they gave rise to a remarkable array of descendents that dominated the Jurassic and Cretaceous Periods. Crocodiles, dinosaurs, flying reptiles (**pterosaurs,** or **pterodactyls**), and birds all sprang from thecodont ancestors. One short-lived line of thecodonts, the **phytosaurs,** resembled the crocodile in size, shape, and mode of life, so nearly in fact that they are called "ecological ancestors" of the crocodiles, meaning that they occupied a similar place in nature but are only very distantly related (Figure 18-22).

Dinosaurs

The term **"dinosaur"** is popularly applied to members of two orders of reptiles, both of which achieved gigantic size and occupied similar environments. The group first appeared during the Triassic as certain slender two-legged forms belonging to the order **Saurischia.** A typical genus is *Coelophysis,* a carnivore found in

Figure 18-22 *Rutiodon, a Triassic phytosaur, whose general shape and mode of life suggest the modern crocodile. The two are only distantly related. Rutiodon is an "ecological ancestor" of the crocodile, fitted by adaption for the same general environment. (Courtesy American Museum of Natural History.)*

Late Triassic rocks of New Mexico and adapted for life on dry uplands (Figure 18-23). *Coelophysis* was the forebear of a host of saurischian dinosaurs that adapted to many different terrestrial environments. Some, which increased in size, reverted to the four-footed stance, eventually giving rise to the gigantic, long-tailed, long-necked sauropods. The **sauropods** were most common in the Jurassic but existed in restricted localities until the very end of the Cretaceous. Among the well-known sauropods are the ancestral form *Plateosaurus*, from the Late Triassic of Germany; *Diplodocus*, a slender, whip-tailed type from the Jurassic Morrison Formation in the western United States (Figure 18-24); *Brontosaurus*, a heavier contemporary of Diplodocus; and *Brachiosaurus*, the long-necked but short-tailed form, perhaps the greatest land animal of all time.

Those saurischians that retained their two-legged pose and carnivorous habits continued to live side by side with the sauropods and perhaps eventually began to prey on them. This group includes the well-known *Allosaurus*, from the Morrison Formation; *Tyrannosaurus rex*, the greatest land carnivore of all time and perhaps the best known of all the dinosaurs; and *Gorgosaurus*, which lived shortly after *Tyrannosaurus* on the Late Cretaceous plains of Canada.

Figure 18-23   Reconstruction and skeleton of the primitive dinosaur *Coelophysis*, from the Late Triassic rocks of northwestern New Mexico. This lightly built and obviously active animal was about 8 feet long. (*Courtesy American Museum of Natural History.*)

Figure 18-24 *Diplodocus,* a giant sauropod dinosaur from the Morrison Formation. *(Courtesy U.S. National Museum.)*

Figure 18-25 An endless supply of teeth. This view of the inner side of the lower jaw of a duck-billed dinosaur shows some of the 2,000 teeth that were in the mouth at one time. Notice that fully formed new teeth are pushing up from below, while old and worn down teeth are disappearing along the grinding surface. The succession appears to have been endless as long as the dinosaur lived. *(Courtesy American Museum of Natural History.)*

The second order of dinosaurs, the **Ornithischia,** was not very prominent in the Triassic, but its members grew numerous and varied during the Jurassic and Cretaceous. Here again there are two-legged types, but few members of the group lost the use of their forelimbs to the extent that the saurischian bipeds did. All ornithischians were herbivores, and the group adapted to environments ranging from arid deserts to marshes and lagoons. The suborder **Ornithopoda** (bird foot) included many large water-loving plant-eaters with "duck-billed" faces. That they existed on tough, woody vegetation is indicated by the numerous closely-

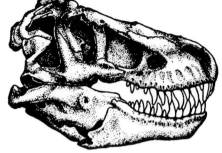

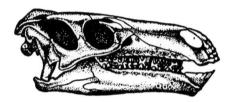

Figure 18-26 A variety of dinosaur skulls. *Upper left, Euparkeria, a small, ancestral form; upper right, the great flesh-eater, Tyrannosaurus; lower left, Diplodocus, a long-necked sauropod; lower right, Stegosaurus, the plated dinosaur. The adaptations to varied types of food are obvious.*

Figure 18-27 An ichthyosaur, *Stenopterygius quadricissus,* with the outline of the body preserved. The specimen is from the Lower Jurassic, Holzmaden, Germany, and is 9 feet long. (*Courtesy Field Museum of Natural History.*)

packed teeth that were set in their strong jaws. The duck-bills were most plentiful during the Cretaceous. The suborder **Stegosauria** included heavy four-legged herbivores armed with various types of spikes, plates, and bony protuberances; they were mainly of Jurassic age. The suborder **Ankylosauria** were heavily armored types known only from the Cretaceous. A fourth order, **Ceratopsia,** included large quadrupedal specimens that had tremendous skulls and a sort of collar or frill that extended backward across the neck and shoulders. Most of the later ceratopsians had one or more forward-pointing horns. This group is known only from the Cretaceous. Geologists believe that it originated in Asia and reached North America late in the Cretaceous.

Sea Monsters

During the Mesozoic a number of reptilian groups adapted to life in the seas. There were fishlike forms, appropriately called **ichthyosaurs;** paddle-swimmers with short tails and long necks, called **plesiosaurs;** gigantic long-tailed marine lizards, the **mosasaurs;** and large **sea turtles.** Of these, only the sea turtles survive; the rest become extinct at or before the close of the Cretaceous, 60 million years ago.

The ichthyosaurs were the first large reptiles to invade the seas and they became the most fishlike in their adaptations (Figure 18-27). The earliest known members of the group are of Triassic age, and they became very common

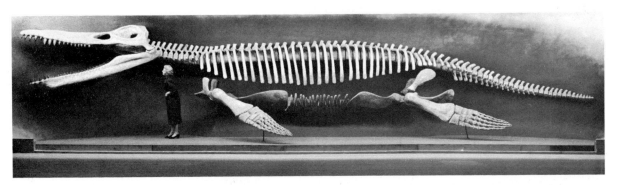

Figure 18-28 Gigantic 42-foot-long reconstructed skeleton of *Kronosaurus*, a short-necked plesiosaur from the Cretaceous of Australia. (*Courtesy Harvard University News Service.*)

during the Jurassic and Cretaceous. They had fishlike limbs and a forked tail and unusually large eyes, indicating that they may have lived in the dimly lighted depths of the ocean. Their jaws were lined with many sharp teeth; and stomach contents, which have been found petrified inside the body of some specimens, indicate that the animals lived on a diet of fish and cephalopods. The largest specimens reached a maximum length of about 15 feet. All evidence indicates that the ichthyosaurs hatched their young internally and brought them forth into the sea fully formed.

The plesiosaurs appeared in the Triassic and had vanished by the close of the Cretaceous. There were two chief lines of evolution. One, typified by *Alasmosaurus*, had long necks and small heads; the other, including the remarkable *Kronosaurus* (Figure 18-28), had short necks and large heads. The plesiosaurs had wide oarlike flippers, or paddles, and evidently preyed on fish. Since they could not move as quickly as the contemporaneous ichthyosaurs, they probably depended heavily on their flexible necks to capture prey. The number of vertebrae in the long-necked group increased steadily during their evolutionary history. The last form had 76 neck vertebrae, which added up to over half the animals total length.

The 25-foot-long marine lizards, the mosasaurs, appeared in the Late Cretaceous but had vanished by the close of the period. With their long, flat tails and sinuous bodies, they were undoubtedly excellent swimmers, and their numerous conical teeth were well suited for capturing large, active prey.

Archelon, the giant sea turtle found in the Cretaceous chalkbeds of Kansas, had a flattened body, 12 feet long from its nose to the tip of its tail. The bones of the "shell" were very small, and most of the covering must have been of a leathery nature.

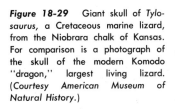

Figure 18-29 Giant skull of *Tylosaurus*, a Cretaceous marine lizard, from the Niobrara chalk of Kansas. For comparison is a photograph of the skull of the modern Komodo "dragon," largest living lizard. (*Courtesy American Museum of Natural History.*)

Snakes and Lizards

The first lizards made their debut during the Jurassic but have left few remains. The large marine forms we have already mentioned. The snakes, which are the last major group of reptiles to appear, are first found in Cretaceous rocks. They are obviously highly modified lizards, with which they are grouped to constitute the single order, *Squamata*. Lizards and snakes have succeeded in both arid and humid regions.

Figure 18-30 Fossil skeleton of the oldest known aerial vertebrate, named *Icarosaurus*. There were no wings; the flight membrane was stretched between extensions of the ribs. The specimen was found in Triassic rocks of New Jersey. (*Courtesy American Museum of Natural History.*)

Flying Reptiles

For many millions of years in the late Paleozoic, the only animals capable of flight were the insects. This aerial monoply was broken in the Triassic when vertebrates took to the air. A gliding reptile from the Newark Series of New Jersey, which has been named *Icarosaurus*, is the oldest known aerial vertebrate (Figure 18-30). In the succeeding Jurassic Period, the feathered birds and leathery-winged **pterosaurs** became airborne and highly successful. The pterosaurs appear in the fossil record slightly before the birds, and may have outnumbered them in the Jurassic and Early Cretaceous. The remains of both pterosaurs and birds are rare, since both had light and delicate skeletons and were apt to live and die in forests, which are generally not favorable for fossilization.

The pterosaurs ranged from sparrow size (Figure 18-31) to giants with a wingspread of 27 feet. In general, Jurassic forms were smaller than their Cretaceous descendents and had many small teeth, long tails, and heavier skeletons. *Rhamphorhynchus*, represented by well-preserved skeletons from the Solnhofen quarries in Bavaria, is typical of the group. Later species, such as the well-known Cretaceous form *Pteranodon*, were generally larger and toothless and had short tails and thin, delicate bones (Figure 18-32). The remains of pterosaurs were preserved only under very special conditions, usually in extremely fine-grained rocks that accumulated in quiet, shallow water. Paleontologists generally agree that the pterosaurs were gliders, for their remains show no signs of attachments for powerful wing muscles. The finding of well-preserved footprints with impressions of both the hind feet and fore feet has led some investigators to speculate that they could walk when necessary and could take to the air after climbing trees or cliffs. The wing membrane was stretched between the elongated "little finger" and the sides of the body; damage to such a structure would be difficult to repair and would perhaps permanently disable the animal.

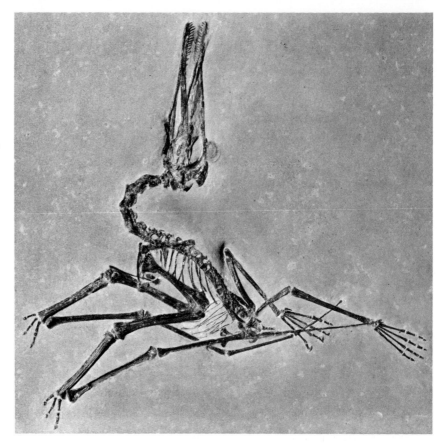

Figure 18-31 Skeleton of Ptero-dactylus elegans preserved in fine-grained Jurassic limestone from the Solnhofen quarries. The specimen is not much larger than a sparrow. (Courtesy American Museum of Natural History.)

Figure 18-32 Skeleton and restored body outline of the great Cretaceous pterodactyl, Pteranodon, from the chalk beds of Kansas. A mounted specimen of the condor, largest living bird, is shown for comparison. (Courtesy American Museum of Natural History.)

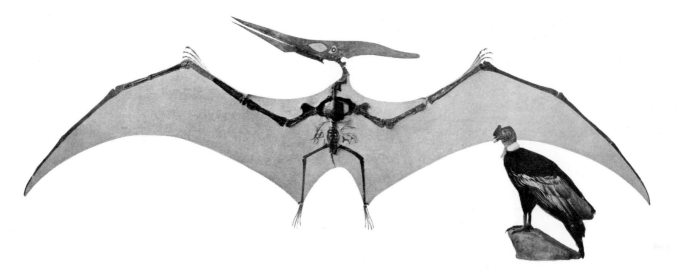

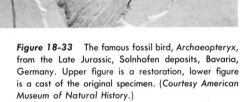

Figure 18-33 The famous fossil bird, *Archaeopteryx*, from the Late Jurassic, Solnhofen deposits, Bavaria, Germany. Upper figure is a restoration, lower figure is a cast of the original specimen. (*Courtesy American Museum of Natural History.*)

Birds

Birds appear in the fossil record during the Late Jurassic. Two well-preserved skeletons with imprints of feathers have been found in the Solnhofen quarries. These remains belong to two genera, *Archaeopteryx* and *Archaeornis*, and pertain to animals the size of a crow. In anatomy, *Archaeopteryx* stands about midway between thecodont reptiles and later birds. These

earliest birds had entered many new environments, but their fossils are nevertheless rare. A 6-foot-long bird from the Cretaceous chalk beds of Kansas is *Hesperornis;* it still had a good set of teeth but no trace of wings. It was probably a powerful diver and swimmer.

A comparison of the wings plainly reveals why birds succeeded and pterodactyls failed. The pterodactyl's wing, as we have already mentioned, was formed of membrane and so was difficult to repair, and it was adapted solely for gliding; but a bird's wing is composed of many individual feathers that can be renewed and replaced as needed to keep the wing in a state of constant efficiency and permit true flight.

Mesozoic Mammals

The fossils of Mesozoic mammals are of great evolutionary importance, although they are small, scattered, and almost insignificant in comparison with reptile remains. You will recall that many mammal-like reptiles had already appeared and flourished during the Permian, only to decline in the Triassic. One of the Permian lines, the **ictidosaurs,** achieved a combination of superior characteristics and gave rise to the true mammals late in the Triassic. Their anatomy places the ictidosaurs almost midway between reptiles and true mammals—they fill the requirements for linking the two groups almost perfectly.

The remains of Jurassic mammals have been found both in Europe and North America, but the fossils are relatively rare and consist only of partial skulls, jaws, and teeth. All are rodent-like, about the size of mice and rats. Several distinct orders are represented. The teeth are variously modified and differentiated into incisors, canines, and molars; the animals seem to have subsisted on a high-energy diet of insects, seeds, and fruit. The typical Jurassic mammal inhabited the undergrowth or branches of trees and was ever on the alert for predatory reptiles with which it could not hope to compete in open combat.

Figure 18-34 Jaw and teeth of *Triconodon*, a primitive mammal from the Late Jurassic of England. The specimen is about 1 inch long. (*Crown Copyright Geological Survey photograph. Reproduced by permission of the Controller of H. M. Stationery Office.*)

Mammals continued to be scarce during the Cretaceous, and some of the Jurassic forms even disappeared. The best-known late Mesozoic remains are from the Upper Cretaceous of Mongolia and the western United States. Late in the period true **marsupials** (pouched mammals) and **placentals** (advanced mammals) appeared, and some grew to the size of a beaver. All in all, the mammals were quite rare during Mesozoic time, but they had already developed the potential to replace the reptiles when the time arrived.

CLOSE OF THE MESOZOIC

No single dramatic event marks the end of the Mesozoic Era. Although a number of gradual changes occurred near the Mesozoic-Cenozoic time boundary, geologists have found no evidence of a rapid, simultaneous, world-wide change. In general, the oceans withdrew during this interval, converting former sea bottoms into swamps, flood plains, and tidal flats. At places this withdrawal was accompanied by mountain-building. In western North America the Rocky Mountain ranges were in the process of formation, a disturbance referred to as the Rocky Mountain Orogeny, or Laramide Orogeny. We know, however, that the evolution of the Rockies was spread out over millions of years on both sides of the time boundary.

In the biological sense there were a number of significant changes near the end of the Mesozoic Era. Almost all fossiliferous areas indicate that large and important groups were being exterminated both on the land and in the oceans. Dinosaurs and pterodactyls vanished from the lands, and in the ocean the last plesiosaurs, mosasaurs, and icthyosaurs disappeared. Of even greater significance to paleontologists was the extinction of the ammonite cephalopods, the belemnites, and the large rudistid pelecypods, and certain ancient lineages of oys-

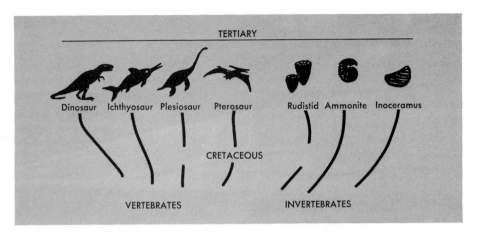

Figure 18-35 Animals exterminated at or near the close of the Mesozoic Era.

terlike pelecypods. Although all these groups did not disappear simultaneously everywhere, their extinction does provide a guide to the end of the Mesozoic Era. In practice, the line between the Cretaceous and Tertiary is placed above the highest or last occurrence of dinosaurs, ammonites, or other key forms.

ECONOMIC PRODUCTS OF THE MESOZOIC

Mineral resources of Mesozoic age are critically important to our modern industrialized civilization. On an average, Mesozoic rocks are richer in oil than either Paleozoic or Cenozoic rocks. According to a recent survey, almost one-fifth of all the world's oil fields tap Mesozoic rocks, and these rocks contain 52.7 per cent of the world's known reserves. The prolific Middle East fields draw oil chiefly from Jurassic and Cretaceous rocks. Other areas of Mesozoic production are the Rocky Mountains, Upper Gulf Coast, western Venezuela, and Argentina.

Coal is found in rocks of each Mesozoic period: Triassic coal occurs in the eastern United States, South Africa, and China; important Jurassic coal deposits are found in China and Siberia; and Cretaceous coal is so abundant in the United States and Canada that the system ranks second only to the Pennsylvanian in amount of total reserves. Cretaceous coal is also important economically in northeast Asia.

Metallic mineral products were formed in many places in connection with Mesozoic igneous activity and sedimentation. Copper occurs in scattered deposits in Triassic sandstone and shale in Germany, Russia, and the United States. Jurassic rocks contain important reserves of sedimentary iron ore in England and Alsace-Lorraine; Cretaceous sedimentary iron ore is mined in Siberia. Both Triassic and Jurassic rocks in the western United States contain important reserves of uranium. The **salt plugs,** or **domes,** in the Gulf Coast area, which yield sulfur in addition to salt, arose from Jurassic beds thousands of feet beneath the surface. The diamond-bearing "pipes" of South Africa are probably of Cretaceous age, and those of Siberia are thought to belong to the Triassic and Jurassic. The diamonds they contain, however, may have been formed at an earlier time and, of course, may have been freed from their original matrix and redeposited in later rocks. Evidence indicates that the gold of the mother lode belt of the Sierra Nevada in California is of Cretaceous age, and there may be other deposits originating in the same period at various places in the mountains of North and South America.

SUMMARY

The Mesozoic Era dawned with the lands relatively high and with few seas in the interiors of the continents. The Triassic Period was geologically rather quiet, and large volumes of red continental sediments were laid down on the land area. The succeeding Jurassic Period was without extensive mountain-building, the oceans spread more widely over the continents, and a variety of marine and nonmarine sediments accumulated. The Triassic and Jurassic were marked by widespread intrusion and extrusion of basic igneous rocks, especially in the Southern Hemisphere. Proponents of continental drift maintain that the breakup of Gondwanaland was accomplished chiefly in the mid-Mesozoic.

During the Cretaceous, interior seas spread across the continents in one of the greatest floods of all times. Commencing in mid-Cretaceous time, the margins of the Pacific became geologically active; igneous masses were intruded and older geosynclinal deposits were folded and uplifted. The era closed with the continents being elevated and eroded.

Mesozoic life was in transition. Plants became better adjusted to dry-land environments and to seasonal changes. Pines, ferns, and cycads were dominant during most of the era. In mid-Cretaceous time the flowering plants appeared in considerable numbers. Marine organisms slowly recovered from the critical late Paleozoic period. Pelecypods, gastropods, and coiled cephalopods multiplied, and toward the end of the era, floating organisms of various kinds increased. On land, the reptiles, represented by dinosaurs, were the dominant vertebrates. Mammals appeared in the Triassic and birds in the Jurassic, but neither group succeeded in becoming dominant during the Mesozoic.

ADDITIONAL READING

Arkell, W. J., *Jurassic Geology of the World.* New York: Hafner Publishing Co., 1956.

Colbert, E. H., *The Dinosaur Book.* New York: McGraw-Hill Book Co., 1951.

Other references for material in this chapter can be found at the end of Chapter 16.

19

The Tertiary Period

This chapter deals with a single period, the Tertiary. The abundantly preserved rocks and fossils of this period indicate that the physical conditions under which they originated were much like those of today. Indeed, most present-day life forms have their obvious ancestors among the fossils that are found in profusion in rocks of Tertiary age.

The Tertiary began with the continents well out of water. Of the many Cretaceous sea-

Figure 19-1 The Alps of the Bernese Oberland, Switzerland. The Alpine chain is a product of Tertiary mountain-building. (*Courtesy Swiss National Tourist Office.*)

ways, only Tethys and its embayments remained. Even this feature was largely obliterated during the mid-Tertiary, or Alpine, disturbances that elevated the great east-west mountain chains of Europe and Asia. During the middle and late Tertiary the other continents were practically free of interior seas. The borders of the Pacific continued to be geologically active, and the East and West Indies took on their modern appearance.

Although the Tertiary was a time both of extensive migrations of plants and animals and of great diversification into orders and lesser categories, no large or radically new groups of plants or animals made their appearance or were exterminated during the period.

OCEANS AND SEAWAYS

The major ocean basins were all in existence in the Tertiary and have in fact changed hardly at all since the end of the Cretaceous. Limited areas adjacent to the continents have risen or sunk, many volcanic islands have been built up and eroded, and narrow but important land bridges have occasionally appeared to connect the major continents. It was, in fact (as will be pointed out in the following pages), the areas between neighboring continents that experienced the greatest changes during the Tertiary.

Tethys: From Subsiding Trough to Mountain Ranges

Although the wide and lengthy Tethys seaway was still in existence at the beginning of the Tertiary, the downsinking and sedimentation phases of the geosynclinal cycle were drawing to a close. Mountain range after mountain range began to appear in Europe and Asia as compressive and volcanic processes disturbed the area. The effect was to create from the area of deepest sediments the highest mountain ranges. The whole **Alpine Revolution,** as it is generally called, culminated in the Miocene. A number of residual seas in the late Miocene and Pliocene encircled the previously formed mountains and received extensive deposits of sediment from the newly formed ranges. These deposits later became involved in secondary movements and foldings.

385

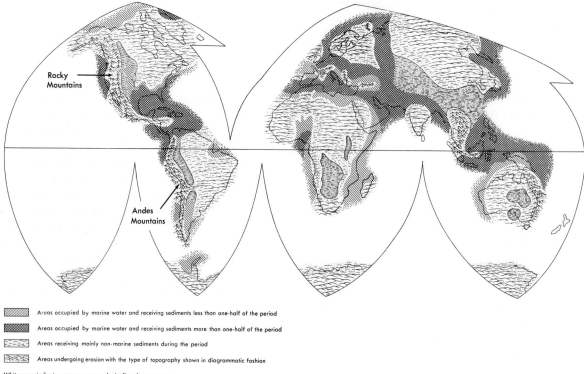

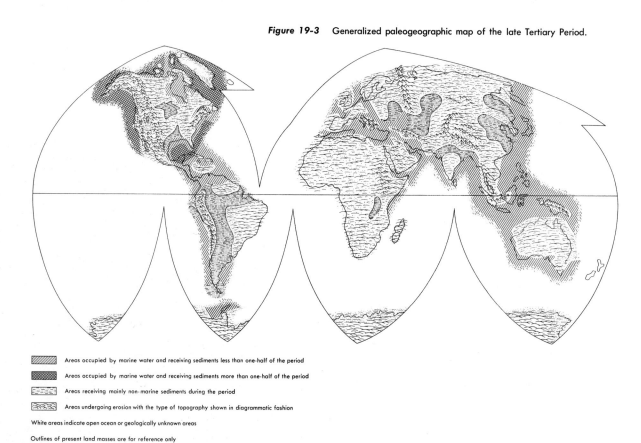

Figure 19-2 Generalized paleogeographic map of the early Tertiary Period.

Areas occupied by marine water and receiving sediments less than one-half of the period

Areas occupied by marine water and receiving sediments more than one-half of the period

Areas receiving mainly non-marine sediments during the period

Areas undergoing erosion with the type of topography shown in diagrammatic fashion

White areas indicate open ocean or geologically unknown areas

Outlines of present land masses are for reference only

Figure 19-3 Generalized paleogeographic map of the late Tertiary Period.

Areas occupied by marine water and receiving sediments less than one-half of the period

Areas occupied by marine water and receiving sediments more than one-half of the period

Areas receiving mainly non-marine sediments during the period

Areas undergoing erosion with the type of topography shown in diagrammatic fashion

White areas indicate open ocean or geologically unknown areas

Outlines of present land masses are for reference only

Much of the actual folding and mountain-building of the Tethyan belt took place at or below sea level. Later effects served to elevate the mountains as well as surrounding areas on a broad or **epirogenic** scale, so that the seas were permanently expelled and broad tracts bordering the ranges became dry land. The Mediterranean and other isolated bodies of water remain as remnants of Tethys, but erosion has been the dominant geologic activity during the last few million years.

Eurasia North of the Tethys

Most of Europe between the Tethys seaway and the Baltic Shield was occupied by a series of shallow Tertiary seas or lagoons. There was a discontinuous barrier between the northern lagoons and the Tethys in the form of the eroded remnants of the Hercynian ranges. The famous succession of deposits in the Paris Basin, where Lyell conceived the subdivisions of the Tertiary, represents deposition in shallow embayments from the Atlantic and contrasts sharply with contemporaneous deposits in Tethys.

Eastward, the Tertiary seas were less extensive. They did not reach Moscow, but covered much of southern Russia. For a short period in the Oligocene, a narrow seaway lying east of the Urals extended from the Arctic Ocean to Tethys. In northern and eastern Asia many large basins that came into existence trapped continental sediments from adjacent ranges. In these basins are well-preserved fossils of contemporary mammals and plant life.

EASTERN NORTH AMERICA

A relatively narrow belt of Tertiary sediments fringes the Atlantic and Gulf Coasts of North America. The visible part of the belt begins at Cape Cod, widens southward to include all of Florida, and is up to 200 miles wide in the lower Mississippi Valley. The interior regions, including the stumps of the Appalachian Range, supplied much of the sediments. Since the coastal plain has been little deformed and its sediments can be related directly to their source areas, we know that the Tertiary of eastern North America was relatively quiet and uneventful.

As would be expected, the Tertiary rocks become thinner toward the land and contain more and more marine fossils as they are traced seaward. Coarse sands and silts characterize the northern outcrops, but limy rocks reflecting warmer seas increase southward. Florida, for instance, has many limy formations with masses of shells and even coral reefs. The oldest formation seen at the surface in Florida is of Eocene age, and the whole state is essentially a product of shallow Tertiary seas.

WESTERN NORTH AMERICA

The Tertiary brought extensive changes along the Pacific Coast of North America, the Coast Ranges being principally a product of this interval. At the beginning of the Tertiary, the

Figure 19-4 Columbia River Basalt, Franklin-Whitman Counties, Washington. Successive flows are exposed as cliffs in the canyon walls. (*Courtesy U.S. Geological Survey.*)

Figure 19-5 Peaks of the Grand Teton Range, Wyoming. The central higher portions are ancient Precambrian rocks. The range was uplifted during the Rocky Mountain revolution early in the Tertiary Period. (*Courtesy Hal Rumel.*)

of the land. The Sierra Nevada was eroded nearly to sea level by the middle Miocene, but was then rejuvenated, supplying additional sediments westward to the nearby basins. With the passage of time, by the addition of sediment and general uplift, a fringing strip of land including the Coast Ranges became a part of the continent. The Cascade Range was uplifted in the late Pliocene, about 4 million years ago. The famous volcanic cones capping the Cascades came later, during the Pleistocene.

The Rocky Mountains continued to grow during the early Tertiary. The Great Basin, with its peculiar north south-trending ranges, began to form in the Oligocene, as great numbers of parallel faults cut the area. The region between the Sierra Nevada and Wasatch Ranges subsided unevenly to create basins for the lakes that ultimately formed in the more humid phases of the Pleistocene Ice Age.

Tertiary deposits are widespread in Alaska but rare in Northern Canada and the Arctic Islands. In Alaska, coal beds and fossil plants are common, but no Tertiary vertebrates have yet been found, hinting that climates were not as favorable as they were farther south.

Pacific extended inward over the site of the present Cascade Range and to the foothills of the Sierra Nevada. Great outpourings of lava, especially in the Miocene, spread widely in Washington, Idaho, and Oregon. The Columbia River basalts cover at least 200,000 square miles and are up to 10,000 feet thick.

In California, a succession of temporary embayments accompanied the uneasy shifting

Figure 19-6 Reconstructed stages in the development of the Medicine Bow Mountains, Wyoming. Drawn by S. R. Knight. (*Courtesy Wyoming Geological Association.*)

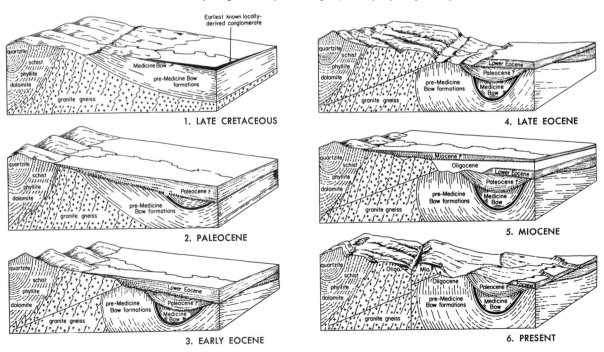

Figure 19-7   Eroded cliffs of the Green River Formation of Eocene age, near Rifle, Moffat County, Colorado. Rich beds of oil shale, which yields up to 80 gallons of oil per ton of rock, make up part of the higher cliffs. (*Courtesy Colorado Department of Public Relations.*)

CONTINENTAL SEDIMENTS   The most complete sequence of Tertiary land deposits known is found in the western United States. Deposits of the Paleocene Epoch accumulated mainly in the interior basins lying between the ranges created by the Laramide Orogeny. There are also many thousands of square miles of Paleocene rocks in the plains of Montana and the Dakotas. The fossil vegetation and animal life indicate that a generally humid semitropical climate prevailed over the western interior of the United States at this time. Apparently the whole region was several thousand feet lower than it is at present.

The Eocene is represented by formations in at least a dozen separate Rocky Mountain basins, but there are virtually no sediments of this age in the plains area. The sediments that filled the individual basins were obviously derived from the adjacent uplifted ranges and show considerable variety. Among the most common rock types are thick conglomerates and coarse sandstones laid down by powerful streams. An unusual feature of the Eocene was a system of large interior lakes that formed in the adjoining parts of Colorado, Utah, and Wyoming. This water body, called the **Green River Lake System,** covered about 40,000 square miles. Its waters teemed with plant and animal life whose remains have become incorporated in the fine-grained bottom sediments. These organic-rich deposits constitute the world's greatest oil reserve, and the delicate fossils of insects, leaves, and fish that are found in the Green River Formation are world-famous.

With the coming of the Oligocene Epoch, the geologic quiet was broken by volcanic outbursts that blanketed large areas of the American West with a thick covering of ashes and dust. Explosive volcanoes erupted in many places and were particularly active in the Yellowstone Park area of Wyoming and the San Juan Mountains of Colorado. Although the volcanic deposits were originally hundreds of feet thick, they have since been eroded away to the point where the topography that existed before the eruptions now lies exposed. There is rela-

389

Figure 19-8 Eroded badland topography cut in the White River Formation of Oligocene age in the Badlands National Monument, South Dakota. The area is famous for the well-preserved mammalian fossils that frequently come to light. (*Courtesy National Park Service.*)

Figure 19-9 Basins with Tertiary sediments within and near the Rocky Mountains. From these basins come most of the fossil remains that are the basis for reconstructing the early Tertiary life of North America. Areas occupied by lakes for significant periods of time are indicated by wavy lines. (*Modified from P. B. King*, The Evolution of North America. *Princeton, N.J.: Princeton University Press, 1959. Reprinted by permission.*)

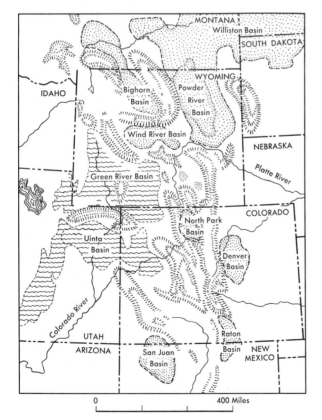

tively little Oligocene sediment preserved within the Rocky Mountains proper. The most complete record of this epoch is in the foothills and plains areas of Colorado, Wyoming, Nebraska, and South Dakota. Here we find the famous White River Beds, from which come the most perfect and complete fossil mammals to be found anywhere in the world (Figure 19-8). From the White River badlands have come remains of at least 150 species of fossil animals, including types ancestral to forms still alive and others that are completely extinct. The Oligocene climate was evidently somewhat cooler and drier than the preceding Eocene.

The succeeding Miocene Epoch witnessed a general uplift over a large part of North America. The entire Rocky Mountain area was raised bodily several thousand feet, and the climate became drier and cooler. Miocene deposits are mainly spread out over thousands of square miles between the Rocky Mountains and the Mississippi River. Here are found ancient stream channels, lake beds, flood plains, and soils composed of sediments derived from the rejuvenated mountain ranges to the west. Mammal remains are abundant, but the warmth-loving semitropical forms are no longer in evidence. The animal life suggests that extensive grassy plains were spreading over the area, replacing forested sections.

Pliocene deposits are found over much of the same area as are those of the Miocene. The chief source of sediment was still the Rocky Mountain ranges, and the place of deposition was the western plains. Animal and plant remains and the types of sediment deposited indicate that climates were even cooler and drier than they were during the Miocene. Mammals adapted to moist, warm climates were no longer represented. Some had migrated elsewhere and some had become extinct. The stage was set for the great Pleistocene Ice Age, which we shall discuss in the next chapter.

SOUTH AMERICA AND ANTARCTICA

A fairly complete and varied rock record of the Tertiary Period is found in South America. All epochs are represented and some portions are extremely fossiliferous. Volcanic rocks and intrusions are abundantly represented, especially in the southern part of the Andes; in fact, much of the southern tip of the continent is a product of Tertiary activity.

Continental deposits are much more extensive in South America than are marine deposits. Most of the land-laid sediments came directly from the Andes, which were already present in the Late Cretaceous and continued to rise throughout the Tertiary. In places there are abundant deposits of fossil mammals not unlike those of the plains of North America. The belt of sedimentation along the east border of the Andes widened and deepened with time and in the Pliocene extended from Venezuela to Patagonia, with extensions down the Amazon Valley.

West Antarctica has a geologic history much like that of southern South America, especially that of the Andean Chain. Volcanic eruptions broke forth intermittently, and there was intensive faulting and folding. Fossils are chiefly those of plants and marine molluscs. Mild climates are indicated by the vegetation and by the fossil molluscs and brachiopods. No land vertebrates have been found. There is evidence of close connections with South America early in the Tertiary, but similarities diminish with time. The problem of how Antarctica became isolated in a south polar position is not entirely solved.

Figure 19-10 Cliffs of Tertiary conglomerate, sandstone, and volcanic tuff, Province of Tarapaca, Chile. (*Courtesy U.S. Geological Survey.*)

AFRICA

That portion of Africa bordering the Mediterranean Sea belongs to the Tethys geosynclinal belt. Its general history is not greatly different from that of southern Europe, which has already been discussed. All epochs of the Tertiary are represented by marine deposits, those of the earlier Tertiary being marked by abundant nummulites (see p. 396). Egypt and Libya were inundated by successive shallow seas, marginal to which the widespread Nubian sandstone, which covers much of the eastern Sahara, was laid down. Northeastern Africa was little affected by the Alpine disturbances.

The marine Tertiary deposits of the remainder of Africa occur chiefly as a marginal band of variable width. An embayment several hundred miles long entered Nigeria in the early Tertiary, but elsewhere the seas did not penetrate the continent, which was generally well above sea level.

Chad Basin

Congo Basin

Kalahari Basin

Figure 19-11 Continental Tertiary deposits of Africa. Chief basins only are named. Many patches of loose, drifting sand are included in the Kalahari and Sahara deserts.

A number of extensive and important interior basins received land-laid sediment during various intervals of the Tertiary. The Congo Basin and its great river system was created in the late Pliocene, and it has extensive deposits of this age. The enormous Chad Basin in and adjacent to the southern Sahara was occupied by a succession of fluctuating lakes and received mixed late Tertiary and Quaternary deposits, including desert sands and volcanic dusts. The fossil record proves many humid intervals with abundant animal life.

Much of Africa south of the Congo, especially the Kalahari desert, is covered by the unusual Kalahari beds, which are mainly loose-to-partly-consolidated red sands. The age is uncertain and the sands may have been deposited, blown about, and redeposited a number of times. Stone artifacts are frequently found in the shifting sands.

Most important of the continental formations of Africa are those found in and near the rift valley systems. The rift valleys are elongate, steep-sided depressions, lowered by parallel faults and bordered by large volcanoes. Large lakes, such as Lake Albert, Lake Nyasa, and Lake Tanganyika, occupy these depressions, and even larger ones are recorded from the

past. In the Miocene, Pliocene, and Pleistocene, a remarkable variety of fossils was entombed, including the best-known specimens of early prehuman and human creatures. The famous **Olduvai Gorge,** which is discussed in Chapter 20, is near the rift valleys.

AUSTRALIA, THE EAST INDIES, AND NEW ZEALAND

The Tertiary geologic history of the numerous islands making up Indonesia is very complex; it contrasts with that of Australia, and both are different from nearby New Zealand. The three are included together here merely for convenience.

Australia has marine, nonmarine, and volcanic rocks of Tertiary age. Outcrops are concentrated chiefly on the southeast quarter of the continent and cover relatively little area. The marine beds are at the margins of the continent and chiefly of Oligocene and Miocene age. Many scattered lake and river deposits are known; some of these contain important coal beds and many species of fossil plants. The record of vertebrate life is very scanty and casts little light on the early history of the peculiar marsupial fauna.

The East Indies as they now exist are essentially the result of Tertiary geologic events; about three-fourths of the surface of the islands consists of sediments and volcanic deposits of Cenozoic age. The sedimentary rocks being mostly marine, limy deposits rich in corals, algae, and foraminifera are common. On a few of the larger islands, continental beds with coal are found. There are tremendous volcanic accumulations consisting of flows, tuffs, and breccias, some of which solidified below sea level.

The history of the region is one of unstable, rapidly changing landscapes. Local oblong basins that filled rapidly and were then uplifted without intensive deformation seem to have been typical. The Tertiary deposits are very thick; measurements of from 18,000 to 50,000 feet are common.

Figure 19-12 Craters on the island of Java, Indonesia. Volcanic activity and crustal unrest have characterized the southwestern Pacific for many geological periods. (*Courtesy Indonesian Information Office.*)

The most abundant fossils are molluscs, corals, and foraminifera, many of the latter being nummulites in the broad sense and correlating with distant European formations. Vertebrate fossils are known from scattered localities; Pithecanthropus or "Java Ape Man" is from the Pleistocene of central Java.

Tertiary rocks make up about half the surface of New Zealand. All parts of the period are present and volcanic rocks are abundant. Intense mountain-building occurred in the Miocene and Pliocene and produced the New Zealand Alps. Many similarities with the Tethyan belt can be noted. Some geologists regard New Zealand as a youthful continental nucleus.

THE WEST INDIES

The Caribbean Sea, with adjacent lands and islands, presents many geologic problems. The rock record begins in the Mesozoic, and the vast bulk of exposed material is of Cretaceous or Tertiary age. Volcanic products are common and limestone is the prevalent sediment. Since there has been continual geologic unrest, most of the structures are very complex. Although the Isthmus of Panama is clearly a part of the great "backbone" of North and South America, it is of fairly recent origin, and is lacking in older configurations.

The curving West Indian island arcs have much in common with the Pacific borderlands, specifically in the age and type of rocks involved. There is good evidence of a large eastward movement of the crust and surface between North and South America away from the Pacific. This shift could be explained by the theory of ocean-bottom spreading, which is discussed in Chapter 21. Another feature of the area is the close relationships of the Cretaceous and Tertiary fossil forms with those of the Tethyan seaway of the Old World. Obviously many warm-water organisms, including large foraminifera, echinoids, corals, and molluscs, were able to travel across the Atlantic, which may have been narrower at this time. Land life of the West Indies shows little similarity to that of the Old World, however.

LIFE OF THE TERTIARY PERIOD

In a general but unmistakable way, the life of the Tertiary was modified in response to new and rigorous conditions. As shown by the preceding review of the physical environments, the continents became relatively high and rugged while the interior and marginal seas withdrew. It seems safe to say that there has been greater diversity in living conditions during the last 60-million-year interval than in any other

Figure 19-13   Fossil ginkgo leaf on a slab of Miocene shale from southwestern Montana compared with the leaves from a living tree.

Figure 19-14   Fossil nuts and seeds from the Clarno Formation of Oligocene age, Washington. *Upper left, Bursericarpum* (elephant tree); *upper right,* unidentified *Vitaceae* (grape); *lower left, Meliosma* (no modern counterpart); and *lower right, Juglandaceae* (walnut). All except the last named are about $\frac{1}{3}$ inch in diameter. (*Specimens collected and photographed by Thomas J. Bones.*)

equivalent span of the earth's history. New environments were created, most of which could be successfully utilized only by plants and animals that could adapt to the changed conditions. In general, the story of Tertiary life is one of response to climatic extremes and topographic diversity, with a premium on adaptations that could overcome cold and seasonal changes.

Plants

All major groups of plants are represented by fossils in Tertiary rocks. Even soft and unsubstantial forms, such as mosses, fungi, molds, and bacteria, have left actual remains or indirect evidence of their existence at this time. The descendents of earlier important groups, such as club mosses, horsetails, ferns, ginkgoes (Figure 19-13), and cycads, also continued to leave a few scattered fossils. Cone-bearing plants have left more numerous remains, including sequoia, pine, juniper, cypress, fir, and cedar.

The **angiosperms,** or flowering plants, are preserved in great profusion. This large group had become well established in the Cretaceous, and all modern families appear to have evolved by Miocene time. Remains include trunks, branches, leaves, flowers, and pollen grains. Under favorable conditions, Tertiary plants accumulated to form coal, lignite, and peat.

Grass is the most important angiosperm of the Tertiary. The first fossil grass seeds appear late in the Cretaceous; today the family includes about 500 genera embracing 5,000 species, and there are scarcely any areas where grass will not grow. Among the important items of food furnished by the grass family are rice, wheat, barley, oats, rye, corn, and millet. Although all these plants have been modified by man, their ancestors provided food for plains-living mammals throughout the Tertiary epochs. The grazing habits of many of our large mammals evolved in response to the availability of grass. The grains also sustain many rodents, birds, and insects. Indeed it is difficult to appreciate how important this one group was to Tertiary life.

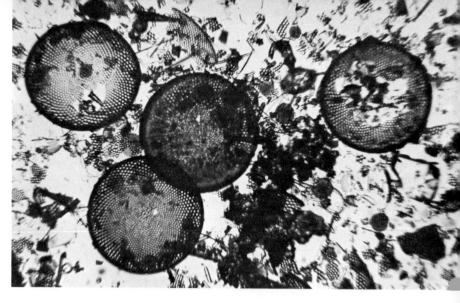

Figure 19-15 A highly enlarged view of diatomaceous ooze collected from the ocean bottom northwest of Honshu, Japan. (*Courtesy Scripps Institution of Oceanography, photo by Taro Kanaya.*)

During the Tertiary, plant groups migrated extensively in response to climatic changes. In general, these migrations were marked by a withdrawal of tropical and semitropical vegetation toward the equator as the climate of the continents grew cooler and drier. The uplifting of mountain ranges such as the Alpine-Himalayan chain and the American Cordillera profoundly affected these migrations. As seasonal changes grew more pronounced, only those forms of vegetation that could shed their leaves and live through cold seasons in a resting stage were able to survive. In the seas and oceans, plant life also continued to evolve. The diatoms expanded in importance to become the basic food source in the marine world ever since the mid-Mesozoic (Figure 19-15).

Marine Invertebrates

The chief marine invertebrates of the Tertiary, arranged roughly in order of decreasing importance to paleontologists, are foraminiferal protozoans, pelecypods, gastropods, corals, bryozoans, crustaceans, and sea urchins. Of course, any such arrangement is somewhat arbitrary and is not evident in all places at all times. Missing at the dawn of the Tertiary were ammonites, rudistids, inoceramus pelecypods, and certain types of oysters.

The pelecypods and gastropods have been especially successful. The shells cast up on the beach or buried in the sediments reveal the amazing variety of shape and size these creatures have attained. Although most of the modern families of pelecypods and gastropods appeared in the Mesozoic, their great expansion occurred during the Tertiary. All the shelled cephalopods except the ancestors of the pearly nautilus had disappeared by the Paleocene, but the subclass continued to be well represented by squids, cuttlefish, and the octopus.

The importance of the protozoans during the Tertiary is indicated by the number of species that appeared, by the extent to which they contributed their shells and skeletons to the formation of rocks and deep-sea oozes, and by their practical value as guide fossils in correlating oil-bearing rocks. Many forms have been discovered, but the most important guide

Figure 19-16 Two common Tertiary marine molluscs. *Pecten* (left), a pelecypod, is more popularly known as the scallop. *Turritella* (right) is a high-spired gastropod. Specimens are from the Tertiary beds of California.

fossils are the large varieties commonly called **nummulites** (Figure 19-17). Some nummulites may be more than an inch across, and they occur locally in such profusion that they often make up large masses of rock. These "coin" fossils are common in Egypt and other Mediterranean lands.

The nummulites lived mainly in warm waters and are highly characteristic of the Eocene and Oligocene of the Tethys seaway. They swarmed over the coral and algae reefs and contributed their shells to the building of thick limestone formations. They are also found in deposits laid down in the warmer waters of the Western Hemisphere, chiefly adjacent to the Gulf of Mexico and Caribbean Sea.

No new major groups of invertebrates appeared, and it may even be that Tertiary marine life was somewhat less prolific than it was during the Cretaceous. The relative uplift of the land masses during the Tertiary stimulated erosion and flooded the offshore waters with heavy loads of mud and silt. Such organisms as sponges, corals, brachiopods, bryozoans, crinoids, and other fixed forms cannot survive in muddy water, and even pelecypods, gastropods, starfish, and sea urchins do not thrive in it. Elimination of interior seas and unfavorable living conditions on continental shelves may have forced many species into deeper waters; certainly these events restricted their living space.

Vertebrates

The Cenozoic is commonly referred to as the **Age of Mammals,** in recognition of the group that contributed the dominant land forms during the period. But in giving due credit to the mammals we should not overlook the fact that birds also progressed during this same period and became adapted to a great variety of conditions. Likewise, in the seas the modernized bony fish achieved a supremacy equal to the mammals' on land. We would therefore be more correct in characterizing the Tertiary as the **Age of Mammals, Birds, and Teleost Fish.** The reptiles had been reduced to relative insignificance at the end of the Mesozoic, joining the amphibians among the ranks of the dispossessed.

MAMMALS Conditions at the beginning of the Tertiary were ideal for mammals, which were quick to seize their opportunities. Their ancient reptilian enemies were gone, food was abundant, and living space was almost unlimited. Mammals are characterized by such obvious physical traits as warm blood, hairy covering, efficient reproductive systems, milk glands, strong teeth, and sturdy skeletons. But more important than any of these in the fight for survival was the gradual enlargement of the mammalian brain (see Figure 19-18), which became an organ capable of storing and retaining impressions that could be used in directing subsequent intelligent action.

Aided by superior brains, mammals are able to compete successfully with animals that are much stronger than they, to escape unfavorable environments, and to survive during periods of danger and stress. Circumstances forced the mammals to "live by their wits" during the Mesozoic. During the Tertiary, as they came to compete with one another and with an unfriendly environment, they became even more intelligent and adaptable.

Figure 19-17 Nummulites from the Eocene Giza limestone of Egypt.

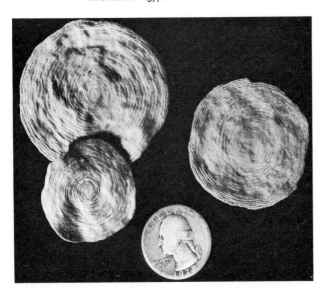

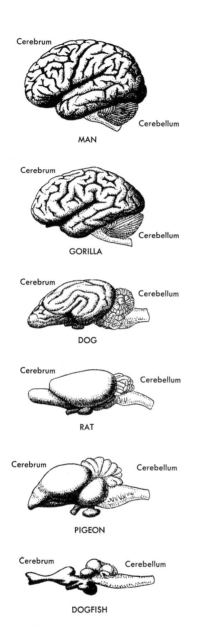

Figure 19-18 The brain, from fish to man. The diagram shows the increase in size of the cerebrum and the complex foldings that characterize the more advanced forms of life. Not intended to show true relative sizes. (*Courtesy Scientific American.*)

Figure 19-19 Scene in western Colorado during the Paleocene Epoch. The animal is *Barylambda*, a large hoofed mammal that has no living descendants. This picture of a well-watered, semitropical landscape is based on study of the sediments and fossil vegetation associated with the vertebrate remains. (*Courtesy Field Museum of Natural History.*)

Mammals of the Paleocene were primitive, unspecialized, and relatively small. Of the 15 orders of mammals known from Paleocene rocks, 5 have been found in the preceding Cretaceous, and only 6 are alive today. The orders in existence before the Paleocene include the **multituberculates, marsupials, condylarths, primates,** and **insectivores.** Among the primitive Paleocene forms, we perceive possible ancestors of many succeeding orders, but the differences by which we distinguish living carnivorous types and the various orders of hoofed animals were not yet clearly evident. The Paleocene life of Europe and North America was similar, indicating that a land bridge probably connected the two continents.

Nature continued to favor the mammals during the Eocene Epoch. The descendants of the archaic Mesozoic and Paleocene forms lived side by side with the newly evolved and more progressive ancestors of modern families. Ten new orders were added to the 15 that had carried over from the Paleocene. The multituberculates disappeared at the end of the epoch, after having lived through at least 2 geologic periods. They may have been pushed aside by the more efficient rodents. There were a number of clumsy primitive herbivores such as **Coryphodon** and **Phenacodus**, which had teeth adapted for eating vegetation but also some carnivorous characteristics such as claws, long tails, and short limbs. Among the important groups that took on recognizable characteristics during the Eocene were the carnivores and the hoofed animals. For the first time, in fact, we find true hoofed animals. There were odd-toed

forms (**perissodactyls**), including the famous "dawn horse," **Eohippus**, as well as ancestral tapirs and rhinoceroses. The even-toed hoofed animals (**artiodactyls**) spread tremendously during the late Eocene; among those appearing on the scene were the ancestors of the deer, pig, and camel, although all were small and very much alike. Rabbits were present in a recognizable form, and other small mammals such as rodents, insectivores, and primates were gaining in importance. There were bats in the air and whales in the ocean, but the history of these two groups is obscure.

South America was now completely separated from the other continents and supported a number of odd herbivorous groups. The Eocene climate was temperate and equable and the lands were generally lower than at present. Migration between North America and Europe appears to have been possible during the early Eocene but not late in the epoch.

Although no drastic changes mark the close of the Eocene, there was a transitional period in which the archaic mammals were rapidly eliminated and modernized forms began to spread. Thus, the Oligocene faunas are notably different from Eocene types. A few apparently indestructible forms, such as the opossum, moles, and shrews, continued to survive and were joined by other small animals such as beavers, rats, and mice. New families appeared among the artiodactyls and perissodactyls: horses, deer, tapirs, rhinoceroses, camels, and antelopes, as well as true cats and dogs were all clearly recognizable.

Among other forms that disappeared during the Oligocene were the gigantic **titanotheres**, typified by **Brontops**, which was as large as an elephant but had weak teeth and a small brain. Another common Oligocene mammal was the **oreodont**, a grazing animal about the size of a modern sheep.

The climates of the northern land masses were becoming cooler and drier, and the semi-tropical forests were retreating southward during the Oligocene. The warmth-loving primates that had been plentiful in North America during the Paleocene and Eocene now disappeared from the continent. There was a marked increase in the number of animals adapted to subsist on grass.

During the Miocene, as we have seen, there was a general uplift of the northern continents and considerable mountain-building along the Tethys belt. With the uplift came cooler and drier climates and corresponding changes in the plant and animal world. Grasslands expanded, forests retreated, and the time grew favorable for animals that could exist by grazing on open plains. It is not surprising that the hoofed animals, able to travel widely over rough ground, should multiply considerably. There were many species of 3-toed horses, rhinoceroses, giant pigs, camels, ancestral deer, primitive antelopes, mastodons, and the last survivors of the oreodonts and chalcotheres. Also making their appearance were large panther- and tiger-like cats, the first bears and raccoons, and a host of lesser flesh-eaters, such as weasels, wolverines, skunks, and otters.

Uplift had brought Eurasia into contact with North America, and Africa was connected with Europe and Asia, but not all types of mammals found and crossed the available land

Figure 19-22 Mammals of the early Miocene of Nebraska. Foreground, *Parahippus;* 3-toed horse; *center right, Dinohyus,* giant pig-like mammal; *near center left, Stenomylus,* small camel; *center left, Promerychoerus,* oreodont; *under the tree, Diceratherium,* rhinoceros; *upper right, Oxydactylus,* long-legged camel; horned artiodactyl, *Syndyoceras,* is near horses. (Courtesy U.S. National Museum, mural by Jay H. Matternes.)

Figure 19-23 Mammals of the early Pliocene as reconstructed from fossils from the southern High Plains. *Center and center left* is the shovel-toothed mastodon *Amebelodon; lower left* is the short-legged rhinoceros, *Teleoceros;* and in the *lower right* is a characteristic 3-toed horse, *Hipparion.* (Courtesy U.S. National Museum, mural by Jay H. Matternes.)

bridges. South American life continued to evolve in isolation from the rest of the world, and Miocene deposits of the southern continent contain abundant fossils of the edentates, ground sloths, armadillos, and other bizarre native herbivores. In many ways the Miocene was a high point in mammalian evolution. Conditions were ideal for land life, and wholesale exterminations had not yet begun.

The Pliocene Epoch has been called the autumn of the Cenozoic, for its climate heralded the coming of the ice and cold of the Pleistocene. Pliocene mammals were clearly adapted to cool conditions and seasonal changes. Warmth-loving mammals, such as the primates, which formerly had been widespread, now lived only in restricted tropical areas. The open plains of the northern continents were inhabited by numerous highly specialized forms, many of which grew quite large. A variety of bears, dogs, cats, wolves, antelopes, camels, horses, and mastodons roamed North America and Eurasia. There appears to have been inter-

mittent migration between the northern land masses and Africa, but South America still remained cut off from the rest of the world until near the end of the epoch. When the land bridge between the two Americas was elevated, a lively exchange of land mammals commenced. The competition was disastrous for the less adaptable South American forms, many of which were exterminated.

The Pliocene Epoch on the whole produced few new types of mammals. The time of rapid expansion and diversification had passed, and an increasingly harsh and unhospitable environment was beginning to eliminate the stupid and inefficient. This weeding-out process would continue during the Pleistocene.

MINERAL RESOURCES OF THE TERTIARY

Although it was a relatively short period, many important mineral deposits were formed during the Tertiary, including coal, oil, and gas

400

deposits in widely scattered areas of the world, and rich deposits of metallic minerals in the Western Hemisphere.

According to a recent statistical survey, 50 per cent of the world's oil fields tap Tertiary rocks and are responsible for 38.2 per cent of the world's total oil reserves. The Oligocene and Miocene are especially prolific in the rich Middle East fields. Other Tertiary oil and gas fields have been discovered along the Gulf Coast and in California, Venezuela, Colombia, the East Indies, and Russia. We should also mention here the great Eocene oil-shale deposits in the western United States. Large reserves of coal and lignite occur in Paleocene rocks of Montana and the Dakotas, and there are important deposits of Oligocene brown coal in Germany and France.

Although geologists cannot always positively determine when deep-seated ore deposits were formed, most of the metal-bearing ores of western North America and South America are considered to be products of Tertiary activity. Deposits of mercury, gold, silver, lead,

zinc, and copper are widespread in and adjacent to the great Rocky Mountain-Andes Cordillera. These deposits are mainly associated with intrusive igneous rocks, and many, out of the hundreds that have been discovered, are bonanzas of the richest type. Similar Tertiary deposits occur around the western margin of the Pacific Ocean and in Japan, the Philippines, the East Indies, and Australia. Almost everywhere these Tertiary deposits have been more or less eroded, and native metals such as gold, platinum, and tin have been released to form placer deposits (see Chapter 22).

A variety of metallic deposits—gold, silver, lead, zinc, copper, mercury, and other rarer metals—came into being in southern Europe during the Alpine Orogeny. Similar deposits were also formed in the mountain ranges of southern Asia.

Nonmetallic minerals such as clay, diatomaceous earth, gypsum, salt, phosphate rock, and building stone are mined in great quantities from Tertiary rocks at many scattered localities around the earth.

Figure 19-24 Drilling a test well in oil-rich Saudi Arabia. In the general vicinity of the Persian Gulf, Tertiary rocks are prolific sources of oil and gas. (*Courtesy Arabian-American Oil* Co.)

SUMMARY

During the Tertiary Period the continents were elevated, topography was rugged, and rigorous climatic conditions prevailed. The Alpine-Himalayan Chain was elevated, and disturbances of various kinds affected the margins of the Pacific Ocean. The East Indies and West Indies also underwent modifications. Sediments produced during the period chiefly reflect the accelerated erosion of the continents—coarse conglomerates, sandstone, and shale were produced in abundance and fine muds and limestone were rare.

The fringing continental shelves were considerably enlarged, and the rate of marine deposition also appears to have speeded up. All types of reefs expanded, especially the ones attached to Pacific volcanic isles.

Few new major groups of plants and animals appeared during the Tertiary, but many species evolved in response to changed conditions. Mammals were the dominant form of land life. Birds and teleost fish continued to evolve in their respective environments and became highly specialized. Plants migrated widely and there was a general withdrawal of warmth-loving vegetation toward the equator. Grass became the dominant vegetative form in temperate regions. Marine life was somewhat restricted, but all forms that could adapt to life in the open ocean increased.

Many important raw materials came into existence; oil, gas, and coal were formed in connection with Tertiary sedimentation, and many deposits of metallic minerals were formed in association with igneous activity.

ADDITIONAL READING

Osborn, Henry F., *The Age of Mammals in Europe, Asia, and North America.* New York: Macmillan, 1910.

Scott, W. B., *A History of Land Mammals in the Western Hemisphere.* New York: Macmillan, 1937

Additional references to the material of this chapter can be found at the end of Chapter 16.

20

Man and the Great Ice Age

At first glance the two topics combined in the above chapter title may seem to bear no close relationship to each other. We shall see, however, that there are many reasons for considering man and the Ice Age together. Man is essentially a product of the Ice Age and we cannot understand his evolutionary development apart from the subjects of climatic change and glacial chronology.

Early man lived close to nature and was largely at the mercy of the elements. Climate and weather controlled his comings and goings and dictated the nature of his food, clothing, and shelter. His chief enemies were the large Pleistocene animals which shared the earth with him. The ice-age environment was harsh and inhospitable and life was full of challenges. Since constant vigilance was necessary merely to stay alive, there were definite advantages to be gained by the exercise of intelligence, by inventiveness, and by adaptability. Man, more than any other creature, was shaped by the rigors of climatic change.

CONCEPT OF THE PLEISTOCENE ICE AGE

The effects of the last glacial period, or the Great Ice Age, were first recognized in Europe. The active glaciers of the Alps provide vivid examples of ice in action and the effects created by them led naturally to intelligent understanding of the analogous but more widespread continental ice caps. An early student of the Ice Age was Louis Agassiz who is known also for his contributions in zoology. You may recall the account of how the glacial theory was conceived, developed, and finally accepted as given in Chapter 10.

Once geologists, geographers, and biologists were convinced of the validity of the glacial theory, they searched for proof of its past extent. When the exact outlines of the ice masses were carefully charted, it became clear that nearly half of Europe had been submerged by an ice cap which radiated from the Scandanavian highlands to cover 1,650,000 square miles. This sheet pushed across the North Sea and joined with local ice masses to cover all of Great Britain except a narrow strip along the southern part of the island. The Alps supported much larger glaciers than at present, and these flowed onto adjacent lowlands but did not merge with the main sheet which came down from the north.

Figure 20-1   Glacier-filled valley in the Alps. The study of Alpine glaciers laid a foundation for understanding the Pleistocene Ice Age. (*Courtesy Swiss National Tourist Office.*)

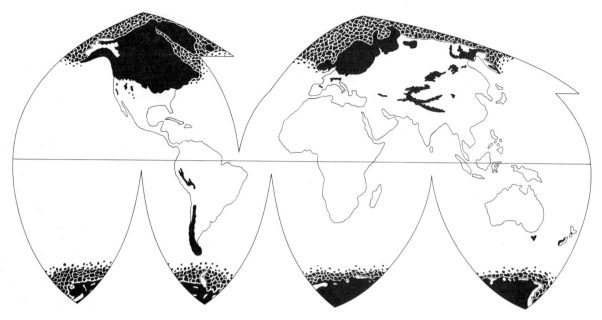

Figure 20-2 World of the Pleistocene Ice Age. Major continental and mountain glaciers shown in black and areas of oceanic pack ice in broken patterns.

About 1,600,000 square miles of northern Asia were covered by another ice cap which moved from a center in Northwestern Siberia. This sheet eventually coalesced with the Scandanavian ice in the vicinity of Moscow. The higher ranges of Asia supported glaciers even larger than those of the Alps; ice streams from the Himalayan ranges descended to within 3000 feet of sea level.

The North American continental ice sheet covered no less than 4,500,000 square miles. Unbroken ice blanketed nearly all of Canada and much of the northwestern United States as far south as the Ohio and Missouri rivers. Large independent mountain glaciers came into being in the Rocky Mountains as far south as New Mexico and also in the Sierra Nevada. The Greenland ice cap was much larger than it now is; in fact, solid ice connected it with the Canadian mainland. Floating pack ice covered the Atlantic as far south as Iceland and the surface of the entire Arctic ocean was probably frozen solid.

The great ice cap of Antarctica may be regarded as a reminder of the Ice Age. It is even now almost as thick and extensive as it could possibly be for it reaches the ocean almost everywhere and shows no clear evidence of being on the decline and, in fact, it may be expanding. Elsewhere in the Southern Hemisphere the story is one of diminishing glacial action. South American glaciers were confined chiefly to the Andes, but along the narrow southern tip, ice spread from the highlands eastward onto the Argentine Pampas and westward into the Pacific Ocean. Africa had no extensive ice masses but the glaciers of Mt. Kenya descended 5,400 feet below the limits of the present shrunken remnants.

The glaciers of New Zealand descended below present sea level and Tasmania supported a sizable ice cap where none exists today. Mountainous islands in the open ocean, such as New Guinea and Hawaii, also had large glaciers.

It is estimated that 27 per cent of the land surface of the earth, a total of 15 million square miles, was covered by ice during the last glacial stage.

MULTIPLE GLACIATIONS AND SUBDIVISION OF THE PLEISTOCENE

The fact of a great Pleistocene Ice Age is now accepted by all students of the past, but they disagree about its duration in years and the

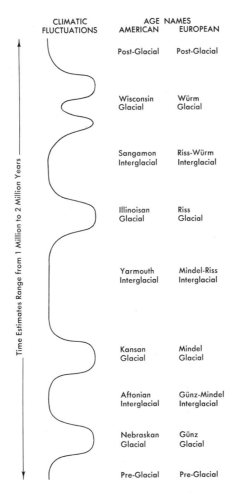

CLIMATIC FLUCTUATIONS	AGE NAMES

	AMERICAN	EUROPEAN
	Post-Glacial	Post-Glacial
	Wisconsin Glacial	Würm Glacial
	Sangamon Interglacial	Riss-Würm Interglacial
	Illinoisan Glacial	Riss Glacial
	Yarmouth Interglacial	Mindel-Riss Interglacial
	Kansan Glacial	Mindel Glacial
	Aftonian Interglacial	Günz-Mindel Interglacial
	Nebraskan Glacial	Günz Glacial
	Pre-Glacial	Pre-Glacial

Time Estimates Range from 1 Million to 2 Million Years

Figure 20-3 Terminology of the subdivisions and correlation of the Pleistocene as commonly accepted in North America and Europe. Because of the intensified study of glacial geology, the terminology and subdivisions are subject to constant revision.

glacial stage, because the length of time since the disappearance of the continental ice sheet from the United States is shorter than the time assigned to any of the previous major interglacial stages.

Glaciations are recognizable by ice-deposited materials, varved clays, scratched and polished rock surfaces, and fossils of cold-adapted organisms. Interglacials are indicated by old soil horizons, deep chemical weathering of rocks in place, some types of wind-blown deposits, and fossils of warmth-loving organisms.

In both Europe and America the Pleistocene has usually been subdivided into four glaciations and three intervening interglaciations. These subdivisions are shown in Figure 20-3. Many minor retreats and advances of the ice are recognized and details differ from place to place. Much effort is being expended in correlating the record of the Ice Age that is preserved in the ocean with that of the lands. Deep sea cores from the Atlantic are thought to indicate a greater number of possible ice advances than do the lands. In areas far from the actual ice sheets, it is even more difficult to correlate with the advances and retreats of the ice. In such areas the current practice is to refer correlations to the Early, Middle and Late Pleistocene. Continued detailed studies of fossils and the application of various dating methods will eventually provide a reliable framework for identifying the subdivisions of the Pleistocene wherever they are found.

DURATION OF THE PLEISTOCENE

The Pleistocene is generally regarded as having commenced with the first great ice advance. In theory this might appear to be a satisfactory clear-cut milepost but in practice it is not easy to determine, especially in areas hundreds or thousands of miles from major ice masses. At least for the present, it is agreed that fossils give the best evidence for fixing the base or beginning of the Pleistocene in both glacial and nonglacial areas. For land areas the best guides are the mammals, for oceans small floating organisms are best.

number of subdivisions that should be recognized. It became known rather early that the Ice Age was not one lengthy unbroken cold period. Evidences of successive retreats and advances of both continental and mountain glaciers can be seen in countless places. Periods of ice formation (technically called **glaciations**) alternate with ice-free periods (called **interglaciations**) on a grand, possibly world-wide, scale. The interglaciations were as long or longer than the glaciations; as a matter of fact, it is generally thought that the earth is now in an inter-

It is one thing to determine the beginning of Pleistocene deposition in sediments and it is another thing to assign an age in years to the deposits. It has long been customary to date the commencement of the Pleistocene about 1,000,000 years ago. Now, with the advent of more reliable radiometric methods, the evidence is that this estimate should be doubled to at least 2,000,000 years. Clearly a great deal of work must be done before the recorded events of the Pleistocene are unified by a good dating system. The information included in Figure 20-3 is the best currently available.

Figure 20-4 Ancient beaches of Pleistocene Lake Bonneville in the Terrace Mountains near Great Salt Lake, Utah. Water stood at the highest levels about 20,000 years ago. (*Courtesy Peter B. Stifel.*)

BEYOND THE ICE

There is more to an ice age than just ice. Glaciers are an essential feature, it is true, but attendant climatic influences go far beyond the ice caps. Because of the effects of the ocean and atmosphere in transporting heat and cold, it is impossible to extensively alter the weather or climate of one area without affecting other areas as well. We see a good example of this in present-day Antarctica, which is called the "weather factory of the world."

Wind and Storm Patterns

Many attempts have been made to reconstruct the weather and climate of an ice age. It may seem paradoxical that it is the weather which brings in glaciation and yet the weather is, in turn, profoundly influenced by the ice sheets once they are formed. We may ask if glaciers are a cause or a result of an ice age. For the present we must leave this question unanswered and attempt to portray the climatic conditions of the earth during a time when the glaciers were near maximum size.

Since cold air sinks and warm air rises, we would expect the great ice sheets to be centers of dispersal of outflowing cold air. Opposing the colder and heavier air from the glaciers would be warm air from the equatorial regions. The belts or zones where cold and warm air meet would be the places of storms and high precipitation. They would in general follow the

edge of the ice cap and would be pushed ahead of a continental glacier as it expands. Another effect of glaciation would be to compress and intensify the climatic zones between the ice and the equatorial regions. This shifting and intensification of storm belts must have resulted in increased precipitation in areas that were previously relatively dry if not actually desert-like.

LAKES AND RIVERS

The ice age brought great changes to lakes and river systems of the world. Lakes expanded in arid and semi-arid latitudes. In the western United States, Lake Bonneville (Figure 20-4) and Lake Lahonton appeared in the Great Basin, and in the Sahara, Lake Chad expanded to cover thousands of square miles. Permanent water bodies such as the Caspian Sea and the Dead Sea also oscillated in size with glacial conditions.

Other lakes were formed by direct ice action. In these the water was held in check by glaciers which dammed up the normal drainage ways. Such lakes would invariably disappear as the ice melted. The greatest known ice-dammed body of water was **Lake Agassiz**, which inundated over 100,000 square miles in north-central Canada and adjacent parts of the United States. Since the water was held in check mainly by the Canadian ice cap, when this disappeared so did the lake. Other lakes, num-

Figure 20-5 Undrained depressions and lakes in the area where the continental glacier melted away. Scene is on the west side of Coteau des Prairies, east of Aberdeen, South Dakota. (*Courtesy John S. Shelton.*)

bering in the tens of thousands, occupy depressions formed by continental ice sheets. The characteristic appearance of much of Canada and the Baltic region of Europe is due to abundant glacial lakes.

Mountain glaciers left lakes of 2 kinds: those occupying basins gouged out at the head and along the upper courses of the ice streams and those dammed up by the moraines at their lower ends.

Ice ages affected rivers in many ways. Some systems were completely obliterated by being overridden by ice. Some were forced to empty into entirely different bodies of water from what they did before the ice age. All of the upper Missouri drainage flowed to Hudson Bay in preglacial times; now it flows into the

Gulf of Mexico. In a few cases, rivers were actually reversed, as in the famous Finger Lake region of New York.

THE OCEANS

The ocean is the great thermal regulator of the earth. Water warms and cools slowly, and as it circulates in the massive currents of the ocean, it carries warmth to northern regions and coolness toward the equator. A peculiar physical property of water is that it expands as it freezes; thus ice will float and not accumulate on the bottoms of water bodies. Water cooled to the freezing point is nevertheless heavier than warm water so that it sinks in polar regions and flows toward the equator beneath the warmer higher layers. Oceanic circulation is very complicated, but the tendency is always to equalize the temperature, pressure, and salinity throughout.

The bearing of the above facts on our present subject is that a lengthy period of glaciation will tend to cool the oceans. Cold water derived from polar ice caps and cooled by radiation in the open ocean will tend to sink to lower levels so that, given ample time, the ocean will be cooled from the bottom up. This cooling will have drastic effects upon sea life and may drive many species to migration or actually to extinction. The impact of cold oceans on the weather and climate of the continents will be somewhat delayed but inevitably the temperature and precipitation must be lessened.

The Pleistocene Ice Age brought drastic world-wide changes in sea level. As glaciers accumulated on land, the level of the oceans fell; as glaciers melted, sea level rose. It has been calculated that 14,000,000 cubic miles of

water, or about 5 per cent of all the water on earth, was locked in glaciers at the height of the last Ice Age. At the period of maximum withdrawal, the ocean was 350 feet below present levels. Obviously, from the persistence of the Greenland and Antarctic ice caps, all the ice did not melt. In fact, if all existing ice should melt there would be an additional sea-level rise of 150 to 200 feet.

Remember that changes of level due to the addition or withdrawal of water are superimposed upon other effects, such as those due to the rise and fall of land masses, movements in the ocean basins, sedimentation, and changes in the shape or motion of the earth. It is known, for instance, that the submergence of the New Jersey Coast has been about 5 feet per thousand years for the past 2,600 years, before which it was about 10 feet per thousand years. An independent study of the Connecticut coast shows a submergence of 9 feet in the last 3,000 years and 33 feet in the last 7,000 years. If continued, this submergence could flood most of the major cities of the world; New York,

Figure 20-6   Abandoned beaches on James Bay, Canada. Since this water body connects with the ocean by way of Hudson Bay, the beaches represent either a general fall of sea level or a relative rise of the land. All evidence favors the latter mechanism as the one responsible. (*Courtesy Department of Energy, Mines and Resources, Canada.*)

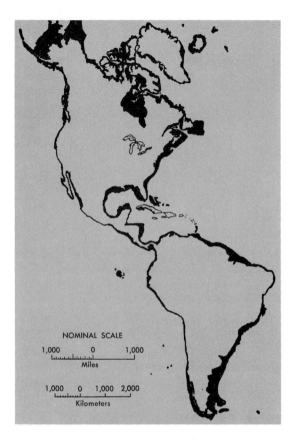

Figure 20-7 Extent of the continental shelves, shown in black, about the margins of North and South America. The shallow, submerged shelves have a combined area of 2,220,000 square miles for North America and 981,000 square miles for South America. (*Courtesy, U.S. Geological Survey, reproduced from Bulletin 1067.*)

NOMINAL SCALE

Miles

Kilometers

sion alternates between denizens of the ocean and the inhabitants of the land. As far as land animals, including man, are concerned, these tracts had to be abandoned as seas rose and recolonized as they retreated. Also affected were many shallow banks and islands which are not only valuable in themselves but are also migration routes between major land masses. A sea-level drop of 300 feet unites the Old and New World by converting the Bering Straits to dry land; Ireland joins England and both became part of Europe. A shallowly submerged ridge also appears across the mid-Mediterranean to join Italy with Africa. Literally thousands of East Indian islands would become elevations on a vast low-lying plain extending southeastward from mainland Asia. Examples are endless; an examination of any good map showing elevations of land and depths of water illustrates what can happen and, in fact, has happened with relatively minor rises and falls of sea level.

Tokyo, Paris, Berlin, and many others are within a few hundred feet of sea level. Marine installations and port facilities everywhere would have to be abandoned or rebuilt. A reverse trend of falling sea level might appear to be less dangerous, but it would be an ominous sign that glaciers were again building up to devastate the lands.

Although we are individually not likely to be greatly disturbed by either rising or falling sea level, the effects have been drastic and far-reaching in the past. Great tracts of low-lying land equal in total area to a good-sized continent were alternately laid bare and inundated with each glacial-interglacial interval. By any standard this territory was and is choice living space for plants and animals. Its posses-

EFFECTS OF THE ICE AGE ON PLANTS AND ANIMALS

The extensive changes of climate and physical geography which came with the Ice Age were responsible for corresponding great changes in the biological realm. Although no radically different forms of life, except modern man, appeared during the Pleistocene, there were notable evolutionary changes at all levels. The really significant impact of the Ice Age occurred through the enforced **migration, mixing,** and **isolation** that developed as ice sheets contracted and expanded. New living space became available as low-lying lands and islands were laid bare of ice or water. Corresponding contractions resulted as the sea level rose during interglaciations. Migration routes were opened and closed on a scale unknown under nonglacial conditions. Tropical regions, far from actual ice, were affected by changes in precipitation and by variations in the volume and capacity of rivers. Even the depths of the ocean were stirred by influx of cold water or by changes in current directions.

Each advance of glacial ice totally depopulated millions of square miles of the earth's surface. Although most plant and animal species were able to escape extermination by retreating before the ice, their living space was drastically reduced. To put it another way, the total food production of glaciated lands was greatly curtailed and fewer individuals, though not necessarily fewer species, were able to exist. Organisms were not forced to adapt to climatic conditions for which they were entirely unsuited; rather, the climatic zones themselves were greatly compressed. Thus, the tundra belt, now perhaps a thousand miles wide in North America, was narrowed to a few miles adjacent to the expanded ice fields. During the glacial advances, for example, species that are now confined to Canada were found in the United States, together with those that are now here.

ENFORCED MIGRATIONS OF MAMMALS It is not unusual to find fossils of cold- and warmth-loving animals alternating with one another in the sediments of glaciated areas. Thus, in central and western Europe the glacial deposits contain woolly rhinoceroses, mammoths, lemmings, reindeer, arctic foxes, and moose—forms now extinct or confined to more northern lands. The interglacial deposits of the same area contain fossils of the lion, rhinoceros, hippopotamus, and hyena, now characteristic of African climates.

The island of Malta, now isolated in the Mediterranean, has yielded reindeer, arctic fox, mammoth, bison, horse, and wolf, recording not only much cooler climates but also land connections with the European mainland. Similar less spectacular faunal changes occurred in North America. Reindeer and woolly mammoths reached southern New England, and moose lived in New Jersey during the glacial stages. During warmer periods fossil sea cows, now found in coastal waters off Florida, ranged as far north as New Jersey, and the tapir and peccary roamed Pennsylvania. Ground sloth remains have been found as far north as Alaska. Elephants were isolated on the Channel Islands off the coast of California.

Figure 20-8 The musk ox, a survivor from the Ice Age. Scattered remains prove that the musk ox migrated widely as the ice sheets advanced and retreated in the Northern Hemisphere. (*Courtesy Field Museum of Natural History.*)

The history of the musk ox during the Ice Age is particularly significant (Figure 20-8). Its bones have been found in Iowa, Nebraska, and Minnesota, recording a time when tundra conditions prevailed in the north-central United States. Today, the musk ox lives only in the far northern reaches of continental Canada, the Arctic Archipelago, and northern Greenland. The animal has evidently moved with its customary environment as the environment has shifted with the ice front across a distance of about 2,000 miles.

DISPLACEMENTS OF PLEISTOCENE VEGETATION Pleistocene plants belong mostly to still-living species, but there has been great displacement and mingling of plant groups. Indeed, the present distribution of plants is difficult to explain without reference to the Ice Age. In Europe the forests of hardwood that characterized the Tertiary were considerably reduced by the advancing Scandinavian and Alpine ice sheets. In North America, where the mountain ranges trend north-south, the hardwood forests advanced and retreated across open lowlands and were not imprisoned as they were in Europe. As glaciers retreated, the arctic floras followed the margin of the ice and also ascended mountains where favorable cool conditions still prevailed. Thus, once-continuous plant populations became more and more widely separated, one group retreating north-

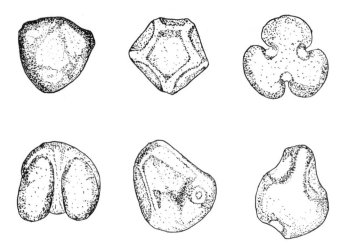

Figure 20-9 Pollen grains that are useful in determining climatic conditions in Pleistocene deposits. *Upper row, from left to right:* birch, alder, and oak; *lower:* pine, corn, and grass. All are greatly enlarged.

ward and the other ascending available mountains. Some plants that now grow along the highest slopes of the White Mountains in New Hampshire and on Labrador have disappeared from the intervening lowlands. On Greenland grow species that are found elsewhere only in the Alps and Himalayas. The great vegetational flux of the Pleistocene is still going on, and is of tremendous importance to man.

The study of pollen grains has thrown considerable light on climatic fluctuations and plant migration during the Pleistocene. Pollen is produced in great quantities by many plants, and is so resistant to decay that it remains recognizable for extremely long periods. Experts can identify the grains produced by specific plants, and are thus able to reconstruct the general composition of the vegetation of particular times and places (see Figure 20-9). Since plants are very sensitive to environmental factors such as temperature and moisture conditions, the analysis of pollen offers perhaps the best means of discovering what the climates of the past were really like.

Such species as birch, spruce, and fir indicate cold and moist conditions; pine signifies warmth

and dryness. Oak, alder, and hemlock suggest warm, moist surroundings; and an absence of tree pollen coupled with an increase of pollen from arctic herbs would indicate a tundra environment. Pollens of grass and drought-resistant shrubs are a sign of dryness. Even the pollens of cultivated plants such as corn yield important clues about the agricultural and food habits of early man.

Fate of the Giant Mammals

The Pliocene and Pleistocene were characterized by giant mammals. Almost every group of mammals produced one or several colossal members. These are abundantly preserved on all continents, occasionally in great "graveyards" such as the La Brea Tar Pits in Los Angeles, California, or the Big Bone Lick

Figure 20-10 Skull of the great saber-toothed cat *Smilodon,* whose bones are common in the La Brea tar pits. Notice that the lower jaw can be pulled far back to free the great canine teeth for use. (*Courtesy American Museum of Natural History.*)

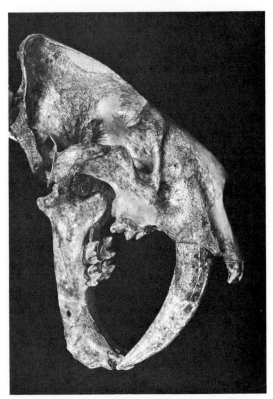

in Kentucky. Some of the fossils are so recent that their unpetrified, dried, mummified, frozen, or embalmed remains are still to be found.

Among the most common and well-known giants of the Pleistocene were the mammoths and the mastodons. The Imperial Mammoth attained an average height of 13 to 14 feet at the shoulders and had great curving tusks reaching up to 13 feet in length. Mammoth and mastodon bones are surprisingly abundant; over 100 mastodon skeletons have been recorded from New York State alone. Another famous Pleistocene animal is the saber-toothed "tiger," Smilodon, of which hundreds of individuals left their bones in the La Brea Tar Pits (Figure 20-10). There were true lions much larger than the present "king of beasts," and bears more

massive than the grizzly. The giant beaver, large as the black bear, could topple the largest trees, and there were other rodents of proportionally large size. Several kinds of bison roamed the American West; one species had a horn spread of over 6 feet. Large camels, pigs, and dogs lived in North America, together with the huge ground sloth, heavy as an elephant, which reared clumsily on its hind legs to browse on foliage 20 feet above the ground.

Other continents also had their giants. In Africa there were pigs big as a present-day rhinoceros, sheep that stood 6 feet at the shoulders, giant baboons larger than the gorilla, and ostrich relatives over 12 feet tall. From South America come fossils of the giant anteater, the glyptodon, and the sloth, together

Figure 20-11 Diagrammatic illustration of a Pleistocene bog deposit with fossil mammoth skeleton. This mode of preservation is common in the glaciated portions of the United States. (*Courtesy New York State Museum and Science Service.*)

Figure 20-12 Skull of the giant Pleistocene beaver (*top*) compared with the skull of the living form. The history of the beaver is typical of the history of many mammals in that the living forms are smaller than their Pleistocene predecessors. In general, it is the larger members of any fauna that disappear in times of stress. (*Courtesy American Museum of Natural History.*)

with rodents big as calves. Here also were abundant large, flightless, flesh-eating birds, up to 8 feet tall and with 15-inch beaks. Even Australia had giant kangaroos and other marsupials.

Most of the giant Pleistocene land animals can be traced to smaller ancestors in preceding epochs of the Tertiary. The gradual increase in size is a tendency that is observed many times in the history of land life and presents no particular problems. It is puzzling, however, to find that most of the giants survived the repeated glacial onslaughts, only to disappear within the last few thousand years. This condition is particularly true of North America, where glaciation was both extensive and intensive. A recent survey gives the following estimated dates of extermination of some key forms in North America: saber-tooth cat, 14,000 years ago; woolly mammoth, 10,500 years ago; ground sloth, 9,500 years ago; horse, 8,000 years ago; Columbian mammoth, 7,800 years ago; and mastodon, 6,000 years ago.

Man has been blamed for the destruction of many giant mammals, but such a charge is difficult to prove and can scarcely be true for those animals that disappeared before his arrival. Available evidence suggests that man accomplished by indirect means what he could not

do with the primitive weapons then at his disposal. His probable ally was fire which, by accident or design, he applied to forest and prairie with catastrophic results. We know that burning out forests to clear agricultural plots was a common practice among early inhabitants of northern Europe, and certain American Indians also were arsonists when necessary.

The "big game" that ranges over America today is but a pitiful remnant of small and medium-sized mammals left over from the Ice Age. Africa today suggests, but does not duplicate, the teeming life that was characteristic of other continents during the Tertiary and Pleistocene.

MAN IN THE ICE AGE SETTING

Although many highly advanced primates have been found in pre-Pleistocene deposits, none of these is assigned to the hominidae, or family of man. The history of Homo and his immediate predecessors is therefore a story of the Ice Age. That man as such should emerge at this time is not entirely coincidental, for the challenge of the environment placed a premium on just such characteristics as were needed to put the "final touches" on the human race.

The Pleistocene was a time of accelerated climatic change and unsettled conditions. In the plant world there was a general retreat and destruction of jungle-like tropical and subtropical forests. Grasslands and tundra expanded at the expense of trees; large grazing animals with herd instincts were favored over browsers and tree dwellers. There was therefore more opportunity for life on the ground and in the open. Man himself has followed this line of development. The scarcity of forest foods that monkeys and apes find desirable forced man and his immediate ancestors to adapt to other sources. The shift to an increasingly carnivorous diet was natural. At first only small, easily killed creatures were taken—lizards, birds, tortoises, and fish. The enticement of larger game led to the development of weapons and traps. More

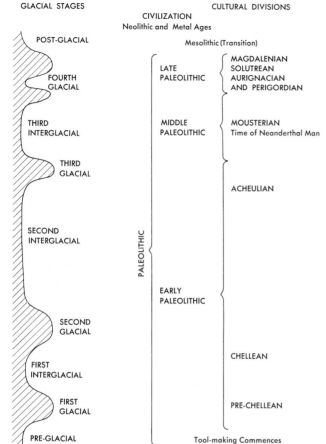

GLACIAL STAGES		CULTURAL DIVISIONS

CIVILIZATION
Neolithic and Metal Ages

POST-GLACIAL

Mesolithic (Transition)

FOURTH GLACIAL

LATE PALEOLITHIC — MAGDALENIAN / SOLUTREAN / AURIGNACIAN / AND PERIGORDIAN

THIRD INTERGLACIAL

MIDDLE PALEOLITHIC — MOUSTERIAN / Time of Neanderthal Man

THIRD GLACIAL

ACHEULIAN

SECOND INTERGLACIAL

PALEOLITHIC

EARLY PALEOLITHIC

SECOND GLACIAL

FIRST INTERGLACIAL

CHELLEAN

FIRST GLACIAL

PRE-CHELLEAN

PRE-GLACIAL

Tool-making Commences
1,750,000 Years Ago

← WARM
COLD →

Figure 20-13   Relation of glacial and interglacial stages to the prehistoric cultural stages of man.

Figure 20-14   Side view of *Australopithecus transvalensis*, discovered in 1947 at Sterkfontein, South Africa. (*Courtesy American Museum of Natural History.*)

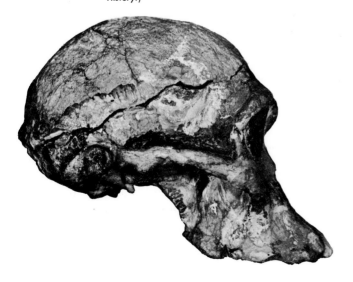

than artificial aids were needed; raw courage, skill, and daring became matters of survival. The need for cooperative effort and family groupings are also obvious.

Climatic changes insured that no place or mode of existence became permanent. Cold taught man the comforts of clothing and the benefits of fire. Life in caves, where available, fostered the accumulation of material culture and community existence. Competition on many fronts weeded out the weak and inefficient and drove the survivors to further efforts, which at length reached the plane of conscious and purposeful planning and premeditated action. Some of the chief advances as now known are briefly described in the following pages.

AUSTRALOPITHECINES— "SOUTHERN APES"

Fossils of man-like creatures began to turn up in early Pleistocene deposits of South Africa in 1925. These were variously termed "ape-men," "man-apes," and "half-men" in popular terminology, but the name **Australopithecines**, meaning "southern apes," has become well established. Recently (since 1960) additional remains of this group have been found in the Republic of Tanzania, chiefly at Olduvai Gorge. As the individual discoveries were made, there was an understandable tendency on the part of their discoverers to regard each as being different enough to warrant a new generic name. The present attitude favors a more simplified classification; thereby all the "southern apes" are placed in one of three species of the genus *Australopithecus*.

The Australopithecines were relatively small animals up to 100 pounds in weight with a brain capacity between 435 and 600 cubic centimeters. They were strictly bipedal, all bodily requirements for the erect posture having been acquired by the early Pleistocene. The head was not very man-like, however; the brow sloped sharply backward, the lower jaw receded, and the teeth protruded. If the Australopithecines made tools or weapons at all, these were simple and rudimentary. No artifacts can be positively credited to them.

Remains of the Australopithecines are fortunately fairly abundant. There are over 600 teeth, several good skulls and lower jaws, as well as miscellaneous skeletal parts. It is generally believed that the Australopithecines are not in the immediate family line of modern man. They appear in the early Pleistocene and continue into the middle Pleistocene at which time they disappear from the record. During this period of time they show some humanizing advances but not in the proper direction to lead to modern man. This is not to say that there is no relationship between modern man and the Australopithecines, for there was a common ancestor to both in the late Pliocene.

"HOMO HABILIS"—FIRST MAN

Olduvai Gorge in Tanzania, East Africa, first became famous as a site for Australopithecine remains. Here Dr. L. S. B. Leakey discovered a well-preserved skull which he named *Zinjanthropus*. Later, as work by the Leakey family progressed, remains of an even more important creature came to light. To this hominid the name *Homo habilis* has been applied. The specific name "habilis" means "able, handy, mentally skillful, vigorous," and the use of the generic name Homo signifies a close kinship

with modern man. The remains reported so far (1966) consist of parts of 5 individuals and include some 40 teeth, two fairly good lower jaws, parts of upper jaws, braincases, hand and foot bones, and a collarbone.

From a study of these significant remains, *Homo habilis* has been reconstructed as a pygmy-size hominid with a relatively large brain (450–750 cc), small narrow teeth, and man-like limbs. There is no doubt that he is more humanized than any of the most advanced Australopithecines of South and East Africa.

It is significant to note that *Homo habilis* lived at the same time and in close association with the Australopithecines. There can be little doubt that the two were competing for the same local food supply, but *habilis* seems to have had an advantage in the use of simple tools and weapons. He also seems to have built crude shelters in the open, but there are no evidences of use of fire. *Homo habilis* ranged in time from about the middle of the early Pleistocene into the early part of the middle Pleistocene. During the three-quarters of a million years during which they lived, the habilines became more man-like while at the same time the Australopithecines drew near to extinction in the middle Pleistocene.

"HOMO ERECTUS"— MAN OF THE MIDDLE PLEISTOCENE

One of the most famous fossils ever discovered, the so-called **Java "ape-man,"** long known as *Pithecanthropus erectus*, was unearthed in 1890 near Trinil, Java. Because of its obviously intermediate status between man and ape, this find gave rise to intensive and often bitter debate, and its study laid the foundations for modern ideas about the origin of man.

The original discovery consisted of a skull cap, thighbone, and a few teeth. Additional material from Java found 40 to 50 years later include skull and skeletal material from a number of individuals. Olduvai Gorge has also contributed a good cranium of the same type; the discovery comes from a higher level than that

Figure 20-15   Mrs. L.S.B. Leakey directs operations at one of the excavations at Olduvai Gorge, Tanganyika. *(Courtesy George H. Hansen.)*

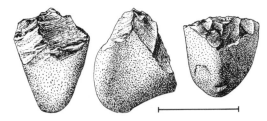

Figure 20-16 Tools of the earliest men. These simple artifacts, formed by shaping one edge of a rough pebble, are from Bed 1, Olduvai Gorge, Tanganyika. These implements belong to the pre-Chellean stage of culture. Scale represents three inches. (*Courtesy British Museum [Natural History], from "Man the Toolmaker."*)

Figure 20-17 Skull of *Pithecanthropus* as reconstructed by Dr. Franz Weidenreich from all available material. (*Courtesy American Museum of Natural History.*)

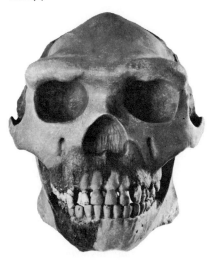

southwest of Peking. Charcoal layers, suggesting the use of fire, and crude stone implements are associated with the bones.

After comparing all remains of the Pithecanthropines, paleontologists have made a satisfactory reconstruction. The cranial capacity is 700 to 800 cubic centimeters, the brain case is low, the forehead flat, and the eyebrows heavy and protruding. The upper jaw is very large and protrudes forward, the lower jaw is also heavy and lacks a chin. The teeth are large, but the canines project only slightly beyond the level of the other teeth. *Homo erectus* is almost certainly a descendent of *Homo habilis*, the transition from one species to another having taken place near the beginning of the middle Pleistocene.

The earlier Pithecanthropines appear to have overlapped in time and territory with the Australopithecines, and they may have survived to within 400,000 years of the present. Their distinctly hominid features would permit them to be the ancestors not only of Neanderthal man, but also of modern *Homo sapiens.* Thus, they constitute a distinct and essential stage in evolution, just as was suspected when the first "ape man" was found.

Neither Australopithecines nor Pithecanthropines have been positively identified in Europe, which was probably too cool for primates during the early Pleistocene. There are, however, a number of tantalizing, less-well-known finds of hominids, as old as Java or Peking man, which show that the Continent

which contained *Zinjanthropus* and *Homo habilis.* No artifacts have been found with the Java specimen but some are associated with the Olduvai remains. Another specimen, known for a time as *Telanthropus,* comes from Swartkrans in South Africa and is assigned to this group. Significantly this specimen is associated with what may be the last of the Australopithecines.

Equally important to an understanding of this group is the so-called **Peking Man,** formerly known as *Sinanthropus erectus.* Remains of over 50 individuals were found, chiefly at a locality near the village of Chou-k' ou-tien, 30 miles

Figure 20-18 Reconstruction of head and skull of *Sinanthropus* woman by Dr. Franz Weidenreich. (*Courtesy American Museum of Natural History.*)

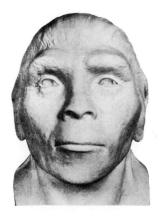

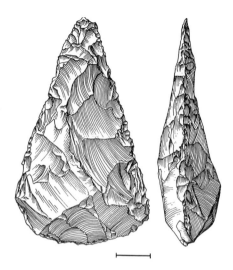

Figure 20-19 Hand axes found in association with the Swanscombe skull. Artifacts of this type are characteristic of the Acheulian cultural stage. Scale represents one inch. (*Courtesy British Museum [Natural History], from "Man the Toolmaker."*)

and Great Britain were inhabited by men or near-men in the second to third interglacials. A large, heavy jaw with 16 teeth intact, discovered near Heidelberg, Germany, in 1907, is one of these. **Heidelberg man** is regarded as the earliest hominid of Europe, since the associated animals point to an early middle Pleistocene age. Also from Germany is **Steinheim man,** represented by a skull found in 1933 near Stuttgart. The age is the second interglacial. From England there is **Swanscombe man,** represented by skull fragments found in 1935–36 near Kent. The brain capacity is estimated at 1,350 cubic centimeters, and there are well-formed hand axes associated with the bones (Figure 20-19). France has contributed **Fontechevade man,** found in 1947, 26 miles east of Angouleme. Two skull caps buried in a cave deposit of the third interglacial represent this man.

Chinese scientists have reported several human fossils intermediate between *Sinanthropus* and modern *Homo sapiens* in age and morphology. Some of these have neanderthaloid characteristics (to be discussed shortly), but others resemble *Homo sapiens* and the just-mentioned European forms.

Java has yielded the so-called **Solo man,** who some consider intermediate between *Pithecanthropus* and Neanderthal man. With the 11 skulls attributed to Solo man were a number of skillfully formed artifacts.

Africa has contributed a full share of intermediate middle Pleistocene hominids. **Kanjera man,** from Kenya, East Africa, is regarded as of middle Pleistocene age, and was a tool maker of about the same age as Swanscombe man in England. These fragmentary hominids seem to bridge the gap between *Pithecanthropus* and Neanderthal man on one hand and *Pithecanthropus* and modern man on the other. Further study and better specimens are needed to settle exact classifications.

NEANDERTHAL MAN

Second in interest only to *Homo sapiens sapiens,* or modern man, is the **Neanderthal man,** *Homo sapiens neanderthalensis.* His skeletal remains are relatively abundant, and we know a great deal about the implements and weapons he used. Many paintings and reconstructions have been made of him, and these renditions have given rise to the popular notion of a crude, hairy, cave-dwelling race that was somehow pushed aside or superseded in the struggle for existence. Many theories have grown up around Neanderthal man, but we are still far from understanding his true evolutionary position in relation to ourselves. For a long time after his discovery, he was regarded as an ancestor of modern man or as a distinct evolutionary stage through which man had progressed. Later on, fossil specimens were discovered that combined the characteristics of modern man and Neanderthal man, suggesting hybrids that had arisen from a mingling of the two types. Still later, and most revealing of all, remains of modern man at least as old as, and perhaps even older than, Neanderthal man, were found, proving that the two types had existed simultaneously over long periods and that Neanderthal was probably not an ancestor of modern man.

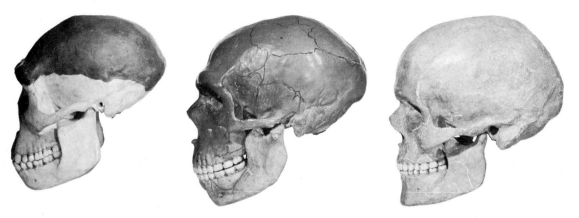

Figure 20-20 Skull of Neanderthal man (*center*) compared with *Pithecanthropus* (*left*) and Cro-Magnon (*right*). (*Courtesy American Museum of Natural History.*)

The first Neanderthal skull was found in 1848 in a cave in the Rock of Gibraltar. This specimen was laid aside and ignored for nearly 20 years until a more complete specimen was found in the Neander Valley near Düsseldorf, Germany. This second specimen was accidentally uncovered in 1856 by workmen clearing out a cave; a large portion of the skeleton was recovered and preserved, but no associated artifacts or other bones were found in the cave. A fierce debate soon arose over the Neander Valley remains. Some investigators held that the bones were the skeleton of an idiot or an individual afflicted with rickets. Others claimed that the skeleton was the re-

mains of a normal being of a type different from modern man, and they gave it the name *Homo neanderthalensis*. The argument was settled in 1886 when additional specimens, particularly 2 well-preserved skeletons from the Spy Caverns of Belgium, were found mingled with mammal fossils of the glacial fauna. The Gibraltar skull was re-examined and recognized as neanderthaloid in 1906.

Since then, many Neanderthal remains have been discovered. A recent catalogue shows that in Germany 6 authentic finds have been made, and in other localities as follows: Belgium, 3; France, 15; Hungary, 1; Italy, 3; Romania, 1; Gibraltar, 2; Channel Islands, 2; Malta, 1; and

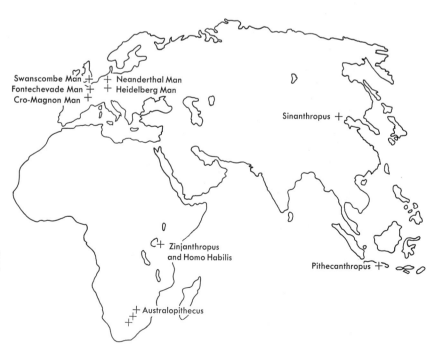

Figure 20-21 Discovery sites of important Old-World fossil men and pre-men mentioned in the text.

Swanscombe Man
Fontechevade Man
Cro-Magnon Man
Neanderthal Man
Heidelberg Man
Sinanthropus
Zinjanthropus and Homo Habilis
Pithecanthropus
Australopithecus

Iran, 1. Many of these finds consist of more than one individual, and accompanying them are abundant artifacts and animal remains. From these discoveries we learn that Neanderthal man lived in Europe and nearby regions during the third interglacial interval and that he hunted and killed a variety of animals, including the great cave bear and the hairy mammoth. He used well-formed, stone-tipped spears, and is responsible for the cultural evidences we know as the **Mousterian.** He also used fire and buried his dead.

Neanderthal man was rough and brutish in appearance. His skeletal remains reveal very distinct features. He had a squat body with a barrel chest, bowed legs, and flat feet, suggesting a slight slouch and shuffling gait. He had a long, low skull with big, jutting-brow ridges, a flat nose, a protruding, muzzle-like mouth, and a retreating chin; but his brain, as the cranial capacity of 1,200 to 1,600 cubic centimeters indicates, was just as large as, or larger than, modern man's.

MODERN MAN

In spite of the many significant discoveries of the past few decades, the origin of modern man is still uncertain. True, some former candidates for his ancestry have been eliminated and their places taken by better ones, but the species ancestral to *Homo sapiens sapiens* has eluded the scholars. As usual we need new, or at least more complete, fossils to settle this important question.

The first and best-known representative of *Homo sapiens sapiens* is **Cro-Magnon man,** who takes his name from a French rock-shelter where his remains were first discovered in 1868. Cro-Magnon remains are widespread in western and central Europe, and over 100 individual specimens have been recovered. The race dates to the waning stages of the last glacial advance, from 35,000 to 8,000 years B.C.

The average Cro-Magnon was rather large and massively built; many of the men were 6 feet tall or more. There are no traces of

Neanderthaloid characteristics in the typical Cro-Magnon skeleton. The forehead and skull vault are high, the brow ridges are small, the nose narrow and prominent, the chin highly developed. His brain capacity averaged 1,700 to 1,800 cubic centimeters, probably more than the average of living men.

Cro-Magnon was progressive and adaptable. During his period of existence he developed at least 5 distinct successive cultures and became an expert at shaping stone tools and weapons. By 8,000 B.C. he had learned to fashion bone and antler and to make awls, saws, needles, and delicately fashioned weapons. He apparently did not learn to domesticate animals, but he was a mighty hunter, as bones of his prey and his cave art indicate. Use of fire and clothing enabled him to withstand the elements and to establish more or less permanent settlements.

MAN IN THE NEW WORLD

The history of primates in the New World is discontinuous and incomplete. North America, lying farther from the equator than any other large continent, became too cold for primates early in the Tertiary, and there are no known fossil remains of the group between the early Oligocene and the late Pleistocene. Even in South America, where we might expect the record to be more abundant, evolution seemingly did not progress past the monkey stage. As far as primates are concerned, the New World was effectively separated from the Old World until late in the Pleistocene, when modern man successfully migrated from one hemisphere to the other. Paleontologists generally agree that America's oldest human inhabitants probably reached North America from Asia via the Bering Straits area, which occasionally formed a dry-land bridge between the two continents.

Evidence for human occupancy of North America 30,000 years ago is indicated by a few apparently good carbon-14 dates. Another series of more numerous and reliable dates commences 12,000 to 10,000 years ago. Perhaps two invasions are represented.

Figure 20-22 Folsom man hunts the giant bison by killing it with a spear-thrower or driving it over a cliff. (*Courtesy Alfred M. Bailey, Denver Museum of Natural History.*)

Paleontologists are most interested in the period beginning with the arrival of man and ending about 5,000 years ago. During this interval, ancient Americans lived in association with many large mammals that are now extinct, and pursued a nomadic existence governed by climatic conditions and the distribution of food sources. It seems unrealistic to call these early people Indians, for they may not have been ancestors of the inhabitants Columbus encountered in the 15th century. Following the anthropologists, we will call these earliest Americans **paleo-Indians.**

Paleo-Indians are known to have hunted a variety of now-extinct mammals, because many stone projectile points and bones of these animals have been found mingled together. Among the animals we know were positively associated with early man in the Americas are several types of extinct bison, the ground sloth, the extinct horse, the mammoth, the camel, the mastodon, and various antelopes. The most common source of meat appears to have been the bison, of which many varieties, mostly larger than the type with which we are familiar, have been found.

America's oldest humans knew how to use fire, and their stone work is distinctively unlike anything that was produced in Europe. They created a characteristic type of projectile point with wide, shallow grooves or channels on one or both faces. This artifact, best typified by the well-known **Folsom point,** is not the only distinctive American contribution, however, for other types of arrow and spear points, both older and younger than that, have also been discovered.

Modern Indians and their direct ancestors are comparatively well known. They were associated with animals that still exist and lived under climatic conditions much like those of the present.

SUMMARY

During the last 1 to 2 million years there have been drastic climatic changes which caused advance and retreat of continental glaciers over at least one-fourth of the land area. Simultaneous effects include rise and fall of sea level, cooling of the oceans, filling of interior basins by freshwater lakes, permanent freezing of rock and soil, and heightening of wind action. All parts of the earth were directly or indirectly affected.

The Ice Age caused great disturbances in the biologic realm. Plants and animals were forced to migrate with changing climates and there was an over-all reduction of organic productivity of the lands. There were notable exterminations, especially among the larger mammals, but the greatest extinctions seem to have occurred after the last glaciation was over.

Man is in a sense a product of the Ice Age. The first erect, 2-legged primates (the Australopithecines and *Homo habilis*) lived about 2 million years ago in East and South Africa. During successive glacial and inter-glacial stages, more advanced hominids appeared in the Old World. The Pithecanthropines (*Homo erectus*, including the Java "ape man" and the "Peking man") inhabited southeast Asia and parts of Africa in the middle Pleistocene. From the early and middle Pleistocene of Europe came Heidelberg man, Steinheim man, Swanscombe man, and Fontechevade man, all near the *Homo sapiens* ancestral line.

Glacially-adapted Neanderthal man lived in Europe, Asia, and Africa during the middle Pleistocene and left relatively abundant cultural remains. Modern man (*Homo sapiens sapiens*) appeared in the second inter-glacial stage and was contemporary with, rather than subsequent to, Neanderthal man. Cro-Magnon man is the best-known fossil representative of modern man.

Man colonized the New World at a relatively late date. In the Americas he lived with and hunted a variety of giant mammals that are now extinct.

ADDITIONAL READING

Brooks, C. E. P., *Climate Through the Ages*, 2nd ed. New York: McGraw-Hill Book Co., 1949.

Butzer, K. W., *Environment and Archeology: An Introduction to Pleistocene Geography*. Chicago: Aldine Publishing Co., 1964.

Charlesworth, J. K., *The Quaternary Era*, 2 vols. London: Edward Arnold, 1957.

Clark, W. E. L., *History of the Primates*. London: British Museum (Natural History), 1950.

———, *The Fossil Evidence for Human Evolution*. Chicago: University of Chicago Press, 1955.

Flint, Richard Foster, *Glacial and Pleistocene Geology*. New York: John Wiley & Sons, 1957.

Greene, J. C., *The Death of Adam*. Ames, Iowa: Iowa State University Press, 1959.

Howell, F. Clark, and Francois Bourliere, *African Ecology and Human Evolution*. Chicago: Aldine Publishing Co., 1963.

Leakey, L. S. B., *et al*, *Olduvai Gorge 1951–61, Vol. 1, A preliminary report on the geology and fauna*. New York: Cambridge University Press, 1965.

Oakley, K., *Frameworks for Dating Fossil Man*. Chicago: Aldine Publishing Co., 1964.

Washburn, Sherwood, ed., *Classification and Human Evolution*. Chicago: Aldine Publishing Co., 1963.

Woodbury, D. O., *The Great White Mantle*. New York: The Viking Press, 1962.

Wormington, H. M., *Ancient Man in North America*. Denver: Denver Museum of Natural History, 1957.

Wright, H. E., ed., *The Quaternary of the United States*. Princeton: Princeton University Press, 1965.

Zeuner, F. E., *The Pleistocene Period, Its Climate, Chronology, and Faunal Succession*. London: The Ray Society, 1959.

21

The Stimulating Problem
of Continental Drift

Anyone who has experienced an earthquake or witnessed a volcanic eruption knows with certainty that extremely powerful forces reside beneath his feet. Aside from the unsettled feelings of the moment, there is the disturbing afterthought that we haven't seen the worst and that earth's hidden forces might be capable of truly cataclysmic violence. Although a geologist tries to take a detached, objective view of earthquakes and volcanoes, he too wonders about what could be (or what has been) accomplished by the long-continued release of energy from within the earth. To satisfy this curiosity, and hopefully to acquire greater security from natural violence, the geologist examines not only the written accounts of past disturbances but also the record of the rocks as far as he can decipher them.

From the almost universal occurrence of faults cutting the outer shell of the earth and from the presence of igneous rocks of all ages, it is obvious that earthquakes and igneous activity have been taking place for a very long time and that the earth's surface has been significantly shaped by them. It is the possibility that these are but superficial manifestations of even greater and more deep-seated dislocations that concerns us in this chapter.

A PROBLEM EMERGES

One of the dramatic results of early Antarctic exploration was the discovery by Scott's expedition in 1901 of fossil leaves within 300 miles of the South Pole. Later findings including large logs and beds of coal up to 5 feet thick prove that ice-bound Antarctica once supported lush vegetation. No less surprising was the discovery of undoubtable evidence of the past existence of large glaciers in central and southern Africa and in warm portions of South America and India. Drastic geographic changes thus are indicated, and intelligent thinkers, if they try to reason on the subject, may soon find themselves taking sides in one of the most important scientific controversies of modern time—the problem of continental drift. There are two choices: Either the climates of the polar and equatorial regions have been altered in drastic fashion, or Antarctica and Africa have been displaced bodily from former climatic zones to the positions they now occupy.

Although climates have definitely changed, it is inconceivable that climatic factors alone could allow lush vegetation in polar lands or massive continental glaciers under the equator. Many geologists would rather believe that the continents have been displaced from former climatic zones, bearing their fossil evidence with them into the positions they now occupy. Yet this explanation is not a particularly easy way out of the situation. Far from it, continental displacement, or "drift," raises problems of such complexity that the combined efforts of many minds over a half century of intensive effort have not yet solved them.

THE CONTINENTAL JIG–SAW PUZZLE

The idea that continents now separated were once in contact can be traced as far back as 1620 when Francis Bacon speculated about the meaning of the parallel shores of Africa and South America which map-makers were begin-

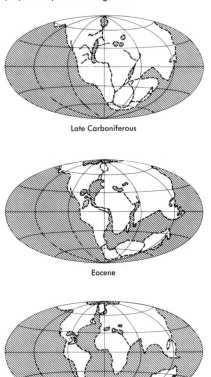

Figure 21-1   Concept of the original great land mass Pangaea and its break-up into present continents as proposed by Alfred Wegener.

Late Carboniferous

Eocene

Early Pleistocene

Figure 21-2 The suggested fitting together of Africa and South America. The present coastlines, shown by the thin lines, do not fit as well as the contours of the continents at a depth of about 6,500 feet below sea level, as shown by the heavier lines.

SOUTH AMERICA

AFRICA

Present
Coastline

Contour Line
6,500 Feet
Below Sea
Level

ning to depict. In 1858 Antonio Snider published the first map showing these coasts united. Significantly, Snider intended his reconstruction to explain the similarity of coal vegetation in Europe and America. The first really scientific treatments of the subject were books by F. B. Taylor in America (1908) and Alfred Wegener in Germany (1910). Wegener's treatment was the more thorough; he began by assembling all the land areas of the globe into one super-continent called **Pangaea.** This arrangement is shown in Figure 21-1.

Wegener pictured Pangaea as rifting apart and its fragments drifting westward and toward the equator. This movement, Wegener thought, would account for the formation of crumpled mountains along the forward edges—as, for example, the Rockies and Andes fronting the Pacific. Small pieces left behind became the islands of the West Indies and of the Scotia Arc between South America and Antarctica. Many other facts also went into his presentation, some of which will be mentioned in the following discussion.

Wegener's reconstructions were immediately subject to intensive criticism, mostly of an adverse nature. His paper was the forerunner of literally thousands of subsequent presentations of evidence for or against continental drift. We shall give here an outline of these arguments, but for those who are interested more extensive summaries are listed in the references on p. 440.

THE GEOGRAPHIC ARGUMENT

Aside from the very obvious fit of the coasts of Africa and South America (Figure 21-2), the closing of the Atlantic would produce other good, but less perfect, fits. Thus, the bulge of Africa and western Europe would adjoin the east coast of North America in a ragged way. Another good match is that between eastern India and northwestern Australia. But if this fit is maintained, it is difficult to get Antarctica into the picture. The best position for this piece of the puzzle would be southwest of Africa and southeast of Australia, as shown by Figure 21-3. This reconstruction does not bring the southern lands in actual contact but it does relate significant geologic features. The conti-

425

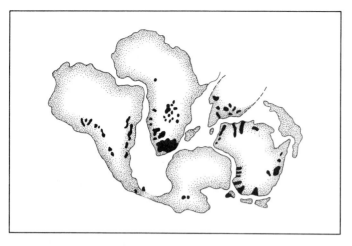

Figure 21-3 Possible assembly of the Gondwanaland masses which brings the areas of Paleozoic glaciers, shown in black, into rough proximity.

Figure 21-4 Evidence of Carboniferous glaciation in Antarctica. The parallel groovings on the rock floor were formed by glacial ice moving across it. The glacial formation is the Buckeye tillite; locality, Wisconsin Range, Antarctica. (*Courtesy V. H. Minshew.*)

nent created by the assembly of the southern lands and India is called **Gondwanaland,** that of the northern lands, **Laurasia.**

GEOLOGIC ARGUMENTS

Gondwanaland

Anyone who has assembled a jig-saw puzzle knows that not only must the pieces fit according to shape but also the patterns of lines and colors must match. The same applies to the game of assembling ancient lands. Here again we look to South America and Africa, and we find that many striking similarities appear. With regard to the geology of the opposing lands, a recent student, H. Martin, has reported (1961) that for the time from the Silurian to the Cretaceous, a period of some 200 million years, the stratigraphic and lithologic columns "have become almost identical." In general, the oldest rocks are of similar type and age, and both compose extensive "shield areas" (Figure 13-7). Evidence of a Precambrian glaciation, an early Devonian glaciation, and a Pennsylvanian glaciation occur on both lands. Among other similarities too numerous to mention is the presence of similar great fields of lava of Triassic and Jurassic age. Similar economic products occur; in fact, it has been said that the gold and diamonds of Brazil may have come from Africa.

Insofar as structures are concerned, it is probably not coincidental that the Cape Range of South Africa is made of the same type and age of rocks as the Sierra de la Ventana in Argentina, that both trend easterly, and that both are abruptly cut off at the coast.

As for India and Australia, on the opposing coasts there are similar iron- and gold-bearing Precambrian rocks. The most striking likenesses are Permian beds of similar thickness with identical fossils, almost bed for bed.

The general similarity of the Paleozoic sequence in all the proposed pieces of Gondwanaland is most impressive. At bottom is an ancient basement of Precambrian rocks. Generally there is little record of the Cambrian, Ordovician, or Silurian, except in Australia. Devonian formations with a peculiar marine fauna are found in Africa, Antarctica, Australia, South America, and the Falkland Islands. Most significant is the presence of Carboniferous glacial deposits on all the southern lands and India. These are known as the Dwyka in South Africa, the Talchir in India, the Itarare and Tupe in South America, and the Buckeye in Antarctica. It was one of the successes of Wegener's assembly of the continents that all these glaciated areas were brought into reasonable space relationships.

426

Figure 21-5 Edge of the Drakensburg Plateau, Natal, South Africa, where over 4,000 feet of lava of Jurassic age is exposed. These outpourings terminated the Karoo series. (*Courtesy South African Information Service.*)

cline in western Europe. The Appalachians terminate abruptly at the coast of Newfoundland and rocks of similar age emerge from the Atlantic in Great Britain. Mountain-building episodes roughly coincide—one in the Ordovician and Silurian, the other in the Mississippian and Pennsylvanian. Coal periods and vegetation are almost identical, and the Permian consists of red beds on both sides of the Atlantic.

Greenland is not particularly troublesome, since it can be fitted between North America and Eurasia as a geologic link between the two. And Iceland, being chiefly volcanic, probably

Figure 21-6 Possible relative positions of North America and Europe at a time when they were closer together. Belts of pre-Mesozoic mountain-building which may have been continuous are shown. Black symbols represent belt of Hercynian (Carboniferous-Permian) disturbances, stippled symbols represent belt of Caledonian (Ordovician-Devonian) disturbances.

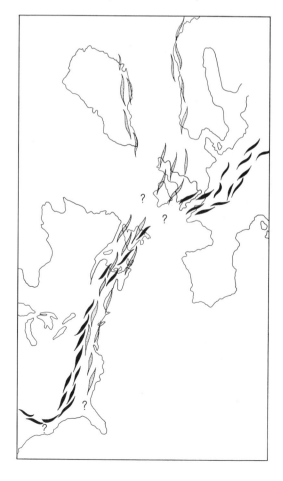

Above the glacial deposits is a series of continental red sediments with fossils of land animals, some coal, and the well-known *Glossopteris* flora. The Karoo System of South Africa is the best known and most extensive remnant of this red series. Simultaneous deposition of similar continental sediments with similar fossils on four separate land masses is one of the strongest points in favor of the drift theory.

A final expression of similarity among the southern lands relates to the production of great flows of basalt and the intrusion of dolerite. These igneous rocks produced in the Triassic and Jurassic, cover thousands of square miles in South Africa and Brazil. The break-up of Gondwanaland is thought to have come during and following the igneous episode.

Laurasia

Although the fit of Europe and eastern North America is not smooth, proponents of the drift theory point out the many striking geologic similarities between the Appalachian geosyncline in America and the Baltic geosyn-

originated since the breakup occurred. The drift theory requires no special fitting together of coasts fronting on the Pacific.

BIOGEOGRAPHICAL ARGUMENTS

Plant and animal species are adapted to spread from their places of origin into additional territory whenever it is available. When we find similar or identical organisms in two separate areas we are led to inquire how they reached these areas. There are no difficulties if the areas are continuous or if there are suitable avenues between them. If, however, the living areas are separated by geographic barriers such as deep oceans, the problem is not easily solved. This is the situation with many plants and animals of the Gondwana continents. It is difficult to account for the occurrence of similar fossil

Figure 21-7   Some common leaf forms of the Glossopteris flora extensively distributed on the southern continents and India. A: *Glossopteris.* B: *Merianopteris.* C: *Schizoneura.* D: *Gangamopteris.* (From Aber, 1905.)

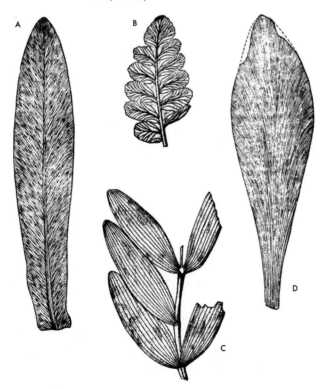

forms in the several southern continents now separated by thousands of miles of deep ocean; if these areas were once in contact, however, the distribution is easier to explain.

The first clear proof of similarity of fossil forms in the Southern Hemisphere is in the Devonian formations, which yield the same peculiar collection of invertebrates in southern South America, the Falkland Islands, Antarctica, Australia, and South Africa. At a higher level, in Permo-Triassic continental sediments, we find the *Glossopteris* flora, often cited as positive proof of continental drift. No matter what the means of dispersal may have been, it is almost inconceivable that *Glossopteris* and the other plants which accompany it could spread across wide oceans such as now separate the southern lands.

A small, fresh-water, fish-eating reptile, *Mesosaurus,* is also found in beds of the same age on both sides of the Atlantic. It is not considered possible that the forms on the two continents could have developed independently, and it is not likely that *Mesosaurus* could have survived a trip across a wide ocean or that it could have followed thousands of miles of shoreline from one hemisphere to another without leaving fossil evidence.

There are many sides to the subject of the distribution of organisms in relation to the drift hypotheses. Thus, drift can be called upon to explain why fossils of certain times are similar on a number of continents and also why they are different at other times on these same continents. If the continents did split sometime during the middle Mesozoic, their life forms should have been more similar before this time and less similar afterward. And this does indeed seem to be the case; for at present there are many differences and few similarities in the life of the Gondwana fragments. For instance, South America has none of the large land mammals of Africa; and there are, in the Old World, no hummingbirds or cacti which are common in the New World. There are exceptions, of course: The sea cow and ostrich are found on both sides of the South Atlantic.

On the basis of existing life forms, everyone agrees that there has been little natural ex-

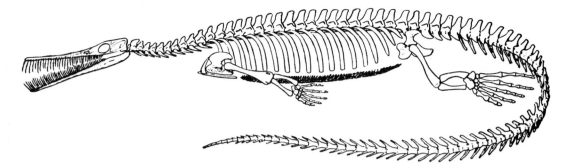

Figure 21-8 Restoration of the small, fish-eating, fresh-water reptile, *Mesosaurus*, from Triassic rocks of Brazil. Closely related species are found in South Africa suggesting former proximity of the continents.

change or migration across the Atlantic for a very long time. We may summarize, then, by saying that the theory of continental drift conveniently explains the similarity of life on the southern continents before the middle Mesozoic and the dissimilarity afterward.

NEW LIGHT ON THE PROBLEM

What we have said so far with regard to continental drift is mainly a summary of arguments brought forth when the theory was first proposed. Additional evidence that has come to light, mostly in the last decade, should be briefly noted as well. The fresh information comes chiefly from the new science of **paleomagnetism,** from the intensified study of the ocean basins, from the study of ancient climates, and from exploration of Antarctica.

PALEOMAGNETISM

As man has known from ancient times, some iron minerals, such as hematite and magnetite, are strongly magnetic. As a matter of fact, all rocks are magnetic to some degree. Magnetism is a property of individual mineral grains and so can be measured not only for rocks in which magnetic minerals are abundant but also for those in which they are sparse or widely dispersed. How a rock becomes magnetized depends on its history. Magnetism may be acquired by minerals during the cooling of igneous lava or magma; this is called **thermoremanent mag-**

netism (TRM). Or it may be acquired during the formation of iron minerals at low temperatures; this is **chemical remanent magnetism (CRM).** It may also occur as small mineral grains settle out during sedimentation; this is called **depositional remanent magnetism (DRM).** But the main point is that, no matter what its origin, magnetism is controlled by the orientation of the earth's general field at the time of formation. Obviously, although all types of rock will be magnetized, those with a high content of iron minerals will be most affected; they are thus better for study.

In order to determine the magnetic orientation under which a particular sample was deposited, we must carefully note its position in the earth before it is removed. In the laboratory it is cut to standard size and rotated at high speed near an induction coil. If this operation is successful, the result gives a basis for calculating the position of the pole at the time of formation of the rock. The study of ancient pole positions or changes is known as **paleomagnetism.** Thousands of determinations, based on rocks of all ages and from all continents, have been made and are being added to constantly.

Results
of Paleomagnetic Studies

At this point you should clearly understand the assumptions that are made in paleomagnetic studies. First, the earth is assumed to have had a dipole field like the present one. In other words, the solid earth has always reacted as though it contained a giant bar magnet with

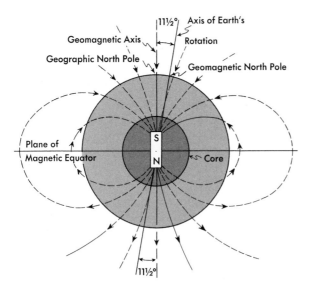

Figure 21-9 The geomagnetic poles are defined by an imaginary magnetic axis passing through the earth's center and inclined 11½° from the axis of rotation. This magnetic axis is determined by a hypothetical, earth-centered bar magnet positioned to best approximate the earth's known magnetic field.

well-defined positive and negative poles. A second assumption is that the axis of the magnetic field has been essentially the same as the axis of rotation. This would mean that the magnetic pole has always had climatic significance. At present the magnetic and rotational axes are 1,100 miles apart. Clearly the two poles do not coincide today. Why don't they, and why should we assume that they did in the past?

A partial answer lies in the dynamo theory of earth magnetism. The generally accepted model of the earth pictures an iron core that is fluid in its outer part. This core therefore is not only an excellent conductor of electrical currents but also exists in a physical state in which motion can easily occur. Electromagnetic currents, therefore, can be generated and then amplified by motion within the current-conducting liquid. The dynamo theory further requires that the random convective motions and their accompanying electromagnetic fields be ordered to produce a single united magnetic field. It is thought that the rotation of the earth can impose such an order. According to this theory, then, the magnetic and geographic poles should coincide.

Observational data support the theoretical considerations. When we plot the virtual geomagnetic poles of changing fields over long periods at magnetic observatories around the world, we find a tendency for these poles to group around the geographic pole.[1] More convincing are the paleomagnetic poles calculated on the basis of magnetic measurements of rocks of Pleistocene and Recent age. These materials, including lava flows and varves, reveal pole positions clustered around the present geographic pole rather than the present geomagnetic pole (Figure 21-10).

As a result of theoretical and observational data, therefore, most authorities feel that the apparent, present-day discrepancy between magnetic and rotational poles would disappear if measurements were averaged out over a span of approximately 2,000 years. The same principle would apply for any 2,000-year period throughout geologic time. Thus, when we speak of a paleomagnetic pole we have some confidence that it had essentially the same location as the true geographic pole of the time.

Paleomagnetic data derived from rocks of Tertiary age indicate, fairly conclusively, no significant shift of the geomagnetic poles from the Oligocene to the present.

The farther back we go in time beyond the Oligocene, however, the more convincing becomes the case for a shifting magnetic pole. Results are fairly consistent for the following pole positions, given in relation to present geographic features (see also Figure 21-11): Middle Precambrian, southwestern United States or nearby Pacific; Late Precambrian, near the Hawaiian Islands; Cambrian, central Pacific southwest of Hawaiian Islands; Ordovician and Silurian, near the Marianas; Devonian and Carboniferous, moving northwesterly so as to lie in

[1] The pole consistent with the magnetic field as measured at any one locality is the virtual geomagnetic pole of that locality. It differs from the geomagnetic pole because it refers to the field direction of a single observational station, whereas the geomagnetic pole is the best fit of a geocentric dipole for the entire earth's field. Inasmuch as it is impossible to describe the entire earth's field at various times in the past, the virtual geomagnetic pole is commonly used in expressing paleomagnetic data.

the Pacific off the east coast of Japan and Kamtchatka; Triassic and Jurassic, on the mainland of southeast Siberia; Cretaceous and early Tertiary, approaching the Arctic Ocean. The pole evidently reached essentially its present position in the middle Tertiary. This postulated migration of the magnetic pole has carried it over a distance of 13,000 miles across the earth's surface.

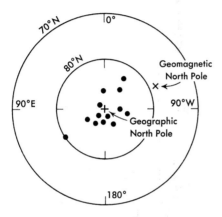

Figure 21-10 The virtual geomagnetic poles determined by magnetic measurements of earth materials of Pleistocene and Recent age cluster around the modern geographic pole rather than around the present geomagnetic pole. (*Redrawn from Allan Cox and R. R. Doell, "Review of Paleomagnetism," Geol. Soc. Am. Bull., LXXI (1960), 734, Fig. 17.*)

Figure 21-11 Paleomagnetic measurements of rocks from North America and Europe show the paths followed by the magnetic poles of these two continents from Precambrian times to the present. (*Redrawn from Cox and Doell, ibid., p. 758, Fig. 33.*)

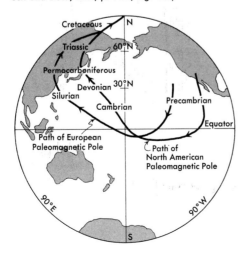

A Number of Possibilities

There is no natural longitudinal standard comparable to the latitudinal one provided by the poles and the equator. Paleomagnetism can locate a position in the north-south direction, but east-west locations must be plotted in relation to other continents, usually Africa which is assumed in theory at least to be stable.

It was not long before students of paleomagnetism realized that there are several ways in which a continent might shift with respect to the poles: (1) Individual continents might move through the underlying dense material; (2) major earth blocks, continental as well as oceanic, might move along major transverse faults—the San Andreas fault as an example; (3) there might be an actual shift of the earth's rotational axis in space; or (4) the entire outer earth shell (crust plus perhaps some outer mantle) might shift or slide over the interior while the rotational axis remained fixed in space. To this list we should add the possibility of the expansion of the earth, which would increase the distance between the continents but would not displace them with regard to climatic belts.

Continental drift, the movement of crustal blocks, and the apparent polar movement all require a decoupling or loosening mechanism between the moving external part and the underlying substratum. This loosening might take place just beneath the continental blocks, at the crust-mantle boundary, or somewhere in the mantle. Heat is the most probable agent to determine the level of such a zone; consequently, the decoupling level might rise or fall with changing heat relations.

Polar Wandering and Continental Drift

The postulated slow migration of the north pole across the Pacific and northeast Asia to its present position—this so-called "polar wandering"—is regarded as a fact by many geologists and geophysicists. It is generally taken to mean that, while the axis of rotation has remained steadily pointing in the same direction, the outer shell of the earth has shifted as a whole over the inner part so as to bring successive areas into polar positions. Note that no movement of individual continents is involved—they all move together. If this were true, however, then the geographical pole would be the same for each continent at any one time and the paleomagnetism of each continent would give the same results—there would be a single "polar-wandering path" for all of them. The truth of the matter is that each continent has its own peculiar path. Considerably different paths are obtained from Europe and North America, as shown by Figure 21-11. Yet these can be made to coincide if we assume that the two continents were together up to the time when the lines converge in the middle Mesozoic. Obvi-

ously, this explanation requires continental drift or relative movements between the two continents of exactly the nature required by other evidence.

The movements indicated for other continents are not as simple or easy to explain as those of Europe and North America, and many complicated drift patterns have been proposed. One rule of the game is, of course, that no two continents can occupy the same space at the same time. Figure 21-12 is one of the latest reconstructions of the Gondwana continents, one that is based on paleomagnetism.

The only satisfactory explanation for the data of paleomagnetism is that there has been relative movement, or actual drifting, of individual continents as well as a shift of the outer shell as a whole. At present it is impossible to decide how these two movements have operated; actually an infinite number of possibilities exists. Plainly, paleomagnetism has thrown much light on the subject of continental movements, but it has also added new complexities.

It is only fair to state that many geologists are not convinced of the validity of paleomagnetic results. They point out that there is no proof that the earth has always had magnetic poles—these may have developed gradually as the core was formed, or they may come and go with obscure internal changes. At times, the critics say, the earth may have had several poles, maybe one for each continent. There is also the possibility that the magnetic poles may move about independently of the geographic poles, in which case there would be no true relations between climatic zones and paleomagnetic polar positions. The whole problem is in an interesting state of development.

Reversals of the Earth's Magnetic Field

A sidelight of paleomagnetic studies was the somewhat startling discovery that the earth's main magnetic field changes its polarity (so that the north pole instead of being negative

Figure 21-12 Recent reconstruction of the Gondwana land masses as based on paleomagnetic data. (*Modified from E. Irving, Paleomagnetism and its Application to Geological and Geophysical Problems. New York: John Wiley and Sons, 1964.*)

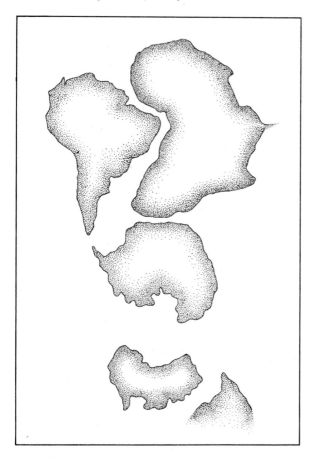

TIME IN MILLIONS OF YEARS

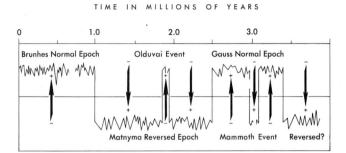

Figure 21-13 Changes in the earth's polarity over the last 3½ million years. The present or normal magnetic field has existed for about 1 million years. This and preceding intervals of reverse and normal polarity are shown by following the diagram from left to right.

Figure 21-14 Present-day climatic boundaries are arranged concentrically around the poles and thus are approximately parallel to lines of latitude.

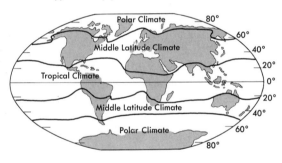

as it now is becomes positive). The possibility of such reversals is consistent with assumed conditions in the earth's core and is theoretically sound. And in fact, thousands of rock specimens that have been studied show magnetism that is reversed 180 degrees from the present field.

Of course, since any such reversal is world wide, the time of its occurrence, if related to sediments, fossils, lava flows, or earth movements, constitutes a valuable datum plane for correlation.

Reversals appear to be rare events: There have been about a half-dozen in the past 4

million years. The last reversal, which is verified in many localities on several continents, took place about 1 million years ago. For the interval from 1 million to about 2.5 million years ago, reverse magnetism prevailed, except for one short return to conditions like the present about 1.9 million years ago.

The study of "polarity epochs" can be correlated with radiometric dating. For instance, if the radiometric age of a reversal can be determined at one point, this age should coincide with the same reversal everywhere. By cross-references of this sort it is evident that the potassium-argon dating of volcanic rocks is very accurate. In other words, age-dates by the potassium-argon method of rocks associated with a specific reversal are essentially the same all over the earth.

PALEOCLIMATOLOGY

Climate dictates the types of plants and animals that can exist on any part of the earth. If we understood this relationship completely, we could know by studying a collection of life forms just what climates they represent. And since climate also leaves its imprint on the earth's soils and landscapes, we should be able to determine through geological studies something about the climates under which certain formations were laid down. The study of ancient climates (paleoclimatology) relies heavily on the principle of uniformitarianism, the concept that past conditions can be interpreted by study of the present.

There are many good guides to ancient climates. The presence of coal, for example, means a humid environment. We are not justified, though, in concluding that the environment was necessarily warm, because vegetation can accumulate in cool as well as warm areas. The types of plants in the coal give important clues, however, and we can usually detect tropical, subtropical, temperate, or cold-tolerant floras. As we go back to the Carboniferous with its extinct and unfamiliar plants, we can be less

Figure 21-15 Rock surface polished and grooved by ice of the late Paleozoic glaciation of South Africa. View at Noostgedacht Farm, near Kimberly. (*Courtesy George W. Bain.*)

Figure 21-16 Cross-bedding in wind-deposited Jurassic sandstone of the Colorado Plateau. The dominant wind which formed the cross-beds was blowing from left to right. This type of evidence is of much use in study of ancient climates.

sure about their climatic meaning. As for other evidence, petrified wood with well-marked rings suggests seasonal effects and is more appropriate to temperate regions than to tropics; and leaves that are large, thick and rounded reflect warm conditions, whereas small, thin, serrated forms indicate the cooler environments.

The effects of glacial ice are relatively easy to interpret. The presence of unsorted, heterogeneous coarse and fine materials (tillite) resting on a polished or striated surface is regarded as evidence of a moving glacier (see Figure 21-15). Seasonally banded sediments (varves) lend additional support. This is not to say that we can always detect glacial tillites for there are many masses of unsorted material which are not glacial in origin. These others generally lack the underlying smoothed and striated floor, however.

Sand dunes are usually associated with arid deserts, but again, when conditions are right sand dunes can build up in humid climates or wherever the wind can pick up sufficient sand.

The interpretation of marine environments, or the "climate" of the oceans, is particularly difficult because water stands as a buffer between the sediments and the atmosphere. We are interested especially in the temperature and salinity of seawater as indicators of prevailing conditions. The problem of organic reefs is relevant here. On the basis of present-day reefs, we would probably place fossil reefs generally near the equator in warm shallow seas of average salinity. This might lead to erroneous conclusions, however, for there are corals capable of living in cool water; furthermore, Paleozoic corals belong mostly to groups that are totally unrepresented in modern seas. Incidentally, it has been noted that corals of certain formations show growth "rings" while similar species of other places do not. The first type is thought to have lived in areas of seasonal change, the other perhaps near the equator where seasonal effects are weak.

Paleoclimatology has many ramifications; we are here concerned with its bearing on the problem of continental drift. Can we gather

434

Figure 21-17 Fossil coral of Mississippian age. The prominent ridges which circle the specimen represent yearly additions of calcareous material. Such evidence proves seasonal effects and suggests an environment in the temperate zone.

from rocks and fossils any clues to the climatic zone in which they were formed? Without going into lengthy details, we can say that it is generally agreed that the following types of sediments or deposits have some value as climatic indicators or, in other words, show some dependence on latitude.

Dolomite and limestone—more common in warm water

Red beds—more common in warm, arid, continental regions

Sandstones with wind cross-bedding—more common in arid regions

Evaporites (salt and gypsum)—more common in warm, arid regions

Coal—indicates humid conditions

Tillite—indicates moving ice, more common in polar regions

Laterite—(soil from which silica has been leached, leaving concentrations of iron, aluminum, and manganese) more common in tropical and subtropical climates

Very few of these criteria, when taken alone, are considered sufficient to prove absolutely a certain paleoclimate, but when several occur together and in connection with appropriate types of fossils, the conclusions become fairly certain.

Results of Paleoclimatic Investigations

No one has denied the climatic implications of coal forests at the south pole and glaciers under the equator. These facts are strongly in favor of continental drift, especially when taken in connection with paleomagnetic results. Equally certain on the basis of climatological data is the absence of glaciers in the northern hemisphere while ice dominated southern lands.

For the period between the Gondwanaland glaciation to the time of disruption in the mid-Mesozoic, paleoclimatology tells a fairly consistent story. The Permian and Triassic are marked by abundant red beds and evaporite deposits, and these extend through wide zones of latitude, avoiding only the polar regions. Land life of this interval was dominated by amphibians and reptiles. The distribution of these coincides closely with the evaporites and red beds and thus argues for warm, equable climates on both northern and southern lands.

Between the beginning of continental break-up and the Tertiary Period, the paleoclimatological record is not always clear. We would like to know what conditions were like on Antarctica and India, for these lands presumably drifted greater distances than did others, cross-

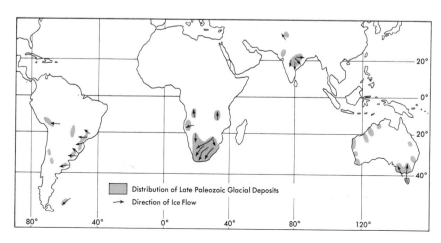

Figure 21-18 Direction of movement of late Paleozoic ice sheet and distribution of known late Paleozoic tillites.

Distribution of Late Paleozoic Glacial Deposits
Direction of Ice Flow

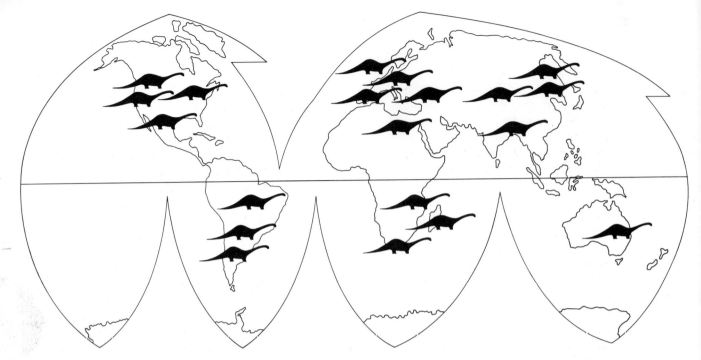

Figure 21-19 Distribution of sauropod dinosaurs during the Jurassic and Cretaceous Periods. The presence of these specialized reptiles on practically all continents is evidence of land connections over which they could travel and of mild, warm climates over most of the earth.

ing climatic belts in the process. Unfortunately, the stratigraphic record is deficient here. For other continents which moved along east-west lines, such as the Americas and Australia there is a better record, one that continues to tell of warm, equable climatic conditions. For example, in the Jurassic and Cretaceous, the giant dinosaurs, almost surely requiring warm climates, lived on all major continents (they are not recorded, however, on Antarctica), well into the present temperate zones.

Paleoclimatology, therefore, has contributed heavily to the solution of the problem of continental displacement. The data on past climates seem to favor—almost require—at least one period of extensive drifting and to impose restraints on extensive lateral movements since that time.

CLUES FROM THE OCEAN BASINS

Intensive exploration of the ocean basins, especially during the last decade, has produced a wealth of information bearing on the history of the earth. As usual, the information has led to a number of diverse hypotheses. The most striking oceanic feature, and one of which there can be no doubt, is a world-circling system of mid-oceanic ridges. This is essentially a 40,000-mile-long submarine mountain system totally unlike anything found on land. The ridge is composed of rugged volcanic flows with a thin veneer of oceanic ooze. The opposing step-like slopes rise toward a central summit that is cut by a narrow trench or trough called the mid-

Figure 21-20 Configuration of the Atlantic basin along a line from Cape Henry to Rio de Oro. Maximum depth of ocean about 18,000 feet. The mid-Atlantic Ridge and trench are well shown. (*Modified from a paper by Bruce C. Heezen, et al., The Floors of the Oceans, Geol. Soc. America Special Paper 65, 1959.*)

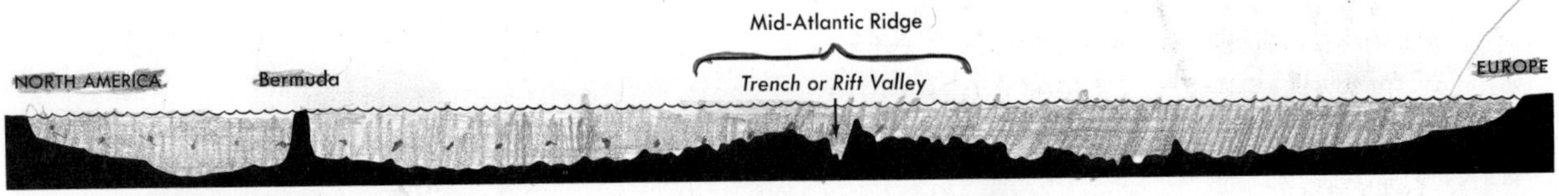

Mid-Atlantic Ridge

NORTH AMERICA   Bermuda   Trench or Rift Valley   EUROPE

ridge graben. This depressed zone on top of the ridge is the site of intensive earthquake activity and is bordered by many volcanoes, some of which rise above sea level. Iceland sits on the ridge and is sliced by active faults in line with the central depression of the oceanic ridge.

The mid-ridge trench is clearly a zone of tension; in other words, the floor of the ocean is splitting apart with the formation of an ever-widening fracture. This opening does not extend indefinitely downward, however; it is "healed," or filled with lava that has risen from below. From the fact that newly formed rock lies in and near the trench with progressively older parallel bands on either side, it is concluded that the ocean basin is continually widening and being renewed by material flowing into the central trench. The Red Sea shows similar activity and perhaps gives a picture of what the Mid-Atlantic Ridge was like at an earlier time.

A recent study of rocks dredged from the ocean bottom in and adjacent to the Mid-Atlantic Ridge indicates that there has been little or no spreading since the Miocene. The indicated rate of drift, which is about 1.6 cm per year, would place the separation of Africa and the Americas somewhere in Jurassic time.

The evidence of the mid-ocean ridge system to some geologists indicates an expanding earth; to others it is evidence for convection currents. According to the first idea, the earth is growing from within and the world-circling fracture system is the result. Carried to an extreme this could mean that the area of the present continents is the area of the original earth, and that the ocean basins have been formed by splitting the lands. According to the other concept, the ridge lies above an ascending column of hot material which divides to flow outward from the ridge, carrying the ocean floor with it toward the continents.

Obviously, as seen in Figure 21-21, the system is not as simple as our abbreviated explanation might indicate. Although the Mid-Atlantic Ridge almost precisely divides the Atlantic, the East Pacific Rise does not divide the Pacific. In fact—and this is most significant

for the United States—the East Pacific Rise approaches northwestern Mexico, enters the Gulf of California, continues inland under the Great Basin-Rocky Mountains, and reappears from the Canadian coast. The ridge system of the western Indian Ocean also turns and intersects the land and is apparently intimately related to the widening of the Red Sea and the African Rift System.

The evidence from the Mid-Atlantic system supports, and in the minds of many workers virtually requires, continental drift. Europe and Africa parted from North and South America along the Mid-Atlantic Ridge and have moved to their present positions with the aid of slowly moving currents in the viscous substratum. This appears to have been a passive process, for the western coasts of the Atlantic are not geologically active, as might be expected if the current system were impinging on the continent. The story is evidently much different on the opposite coast. We get the distinct impression that western North America has been forced upon and across the ridge system. Violent geologic activity, including volcanism, faulting and mountain-building commenced in the Triassic and eventually created the Rocky Mountains from Alaska to Tierra del Fuego.

Although it appears that the continent has actively over-ridden the Pacific border, the action may have been just the opposite; the ocean may have actively moved under the land. This concept is elaborated in the theory of **ocean-spreading**. According to this view it is the actual ocean bottom and not a deeper

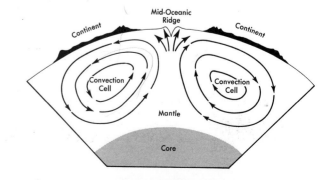

Figure 21-21 Diagrammatic representation of convection currents in the mantle which are rising and diverging beneath the mid-oceanic ridge and carrying the continents in opposite directions.

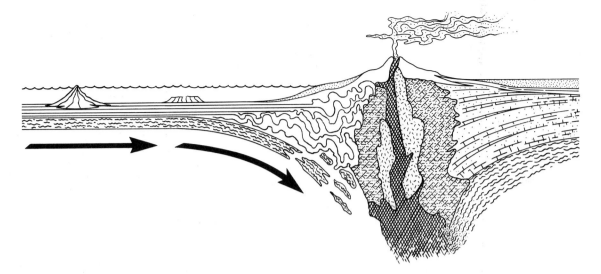

Figure 21-22 Geologic conditions at the margin of a continent according to the concept of spreading ocean bottoms. The ocean floor (*left*) is moving toward and beneath the continent (*right*) where its rocks are being metamorphosed, melted, and welded to the continent.

layer which moves by convection currents toward the land. This conveyor-belt action brings the ocean bottom with its layers of basalt and ooze toward the land where the whole mass sinks or is forced downward into zones of higher temperature. The melting of an ocean bottom made of basalt and water-saturated oceanic oozes is considered capable of generating the granitic material and other products that have risen to create mountain systems along the continental borders. The theory of ocean-bottom spreading explains the curious fact that nowhere in the true ocean basins have rocks older than the Cretaceous been found. What has happened to deposits that must have formed in earlier periods? That they might have been remelted and welded to the continent seems a good possibility. Unfortunately, we cannot review all the interesting points for and against the different theories we have mentioned. But the unfolding of the evidence will continue to make news in scientific circles for a long time to come.

ANTARCTICA

Over 95 per cent of Antarctica is under ice, but the exposures of bedrock around the margins and protruding above the glaciers gives us a reliable sample of the continent as a whole.

Explorations have progressed so rapidly during the last decade that enough is known to permit comparisons with the other major land masses. Interest in results has been high, because Antarctica was in a very real sense the last major piece to be fitted into the giant jig-saw puzzle of Gondwanaland. How does it fit? Do its rocks and fossils favor the drift hypothesis or do they deal it a fatal blow?

As a matter of fact, the geology of Antarctica shows an amazing similarity to that of South Africa, South America, Australia, and even India. The early Paleozoic is represented by fossiliferous Cambrian deposits with fossils similar to those of Australia. No Ordovician or Silurian fossils are known, recalling the scanty record of these periods in other southern lands. The Devonian has marine fossils of the widespread southern fauna, and there are fish appropriate to the Age of Fishes. Most significant is the presence of the Buckeye Tillite, an undoubted glacial deposit, in rocks of Carboniferous age. Above this, in the Permian and Triassic, are coal beds and numerous *Glossopteris* leaves. Still higher, in the Jurassic, are sheets of intrusive dolerite. The sequence—tillite at the base, land sediments with the Glossopteris flora next, and capped by dark igneous rock—is identical to that found on other southern continents, and its occurrence strengthens the case for former close associations.

438

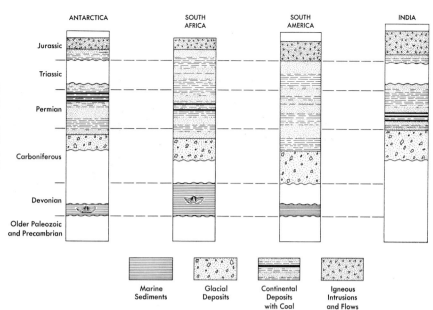

Figure 21-23 Late Paleozoic and early Mesozoic rock units of the chief land masses of the Gondwana assemblage. Shows the broad similarities which prove parallel development and possibly close geographic proximity. Sections from 10,000 to 20,000 feet thick are represented.

The record of Cretaceous and Tertiary rocks is confined chiefly to those parts of Antarctica nearest South America. From these we get a picture of temperate vegetation on the land and warm-water invertebrates in the sea. Evidently the present ice age did not settle on Antarctica until late in the Cenozoic.

NO FINAL ANSWERS

Although textbook writers are often inclined to present their material as the final word on the topic at hand, this procedure is usually not possible. The subject of the history of continents and ocean basins is no exception; it would be misleading to say that solutions to any of the really fundamental problems have been found. One renowned authority on the structure of the earth, after writing on such topics as polar wandering, continental drift, and convection currents concludes "that something is wrong with each and every one of the theories." Another respected student in reviewing a large volume devoted exclusively to continental drift concludes that: "the probability of drift seems fairly high, but many of the arguments, both geological and geophysical, involved too much special pleading for comfort. Both geologist and geophysicist must go considerably farther before the theory can be considered either firmly established or disproved."

The authors of this textbook must confess to being believers in continental displacement. Too many lines of evidence seem to indicate that it has taken place. It has not been possible here to present all the arguments for and against the idea but other material is available from your instructor or the readings cited at the end of this chapter.

SUMMARY

Problems related to the origin and distribution of the continents and ocean basins are currently receiving much attention, particularly the hypothesis of continental drift, which maintains that the major land masses were once part of 1 or 2 super-continents that split apart and that the pieces moved to their present locations sometime in the Mesozoic. Geographic evidence is the parallel configuration of many coastlines, especially those fronting the Atlantic. Geologic evidence includes similar structures and stratigraphic sequences on the supposed once-continuous areas, particularly in the Southern Hemisphere. Especially notable are signs of exten-

439

sive contemporaneous glaciers on Africa, Australia, South America, Antarctica, and India, which together constitute the hypothetical or actual Gondwanaland. The fossil forms of the disrupted lands show many similarities up to the mid-Mesozoic. Whether or not the plants and animals represented could cross oceans of existing widths is doubtful.

New light on the history of continents comes from paleomagnetism, the study of magnetism preserved in the rocks. These data indicate that the magnetic and probably the geographic poles have shifted with time, not by an actual change in the axis of rotation in space, but by slipping of the entire outer shell of the earth so that different areas came successively into polar positions. Paleomagnetism also indicates that the continents moved independently, thus strengthening older arguments for the drift hypothesis.

Detailed, world-wide study of ocean basins reveals a world-circling mountain system which approximately divides the ocean basins and is the site of a split or rift where the outer shell of the earth has been actively pulled apart and healed by lava from below. The spreading movements related to the rift system are those expected under the theory of continental drift.

Although evidences for displacement of large segments of the crust, for drift of continents, and for slipping of the entire outer shell of the earth have been steadily accumulating, there is as yet no known activating force for such movements. The most popular idea favors heat-driven, slowly-moving, deep-seated convection currents.

Active research on all aspects of the problem is continuing.

ADDITIONAL READING

Ballard, E. C., "Continental Drift," *Quarterly Journal of the Geological Society of London,* vol. 120 (1964), 1–33.

Blackett, P. M. S., E. Ballard, and S. K. Runcorn (organizers), *A Symposium on Continental Drift.* London Royal Society, 1965.

Holmes, Arthur, *Principles of Physical Geology.* New York: Ronald Press, 1965.

Irving, E., *Paleomagnetism and Its Application to Geological and Geophysical Problems.* New York: John Wiley & Sons, 1964.

Nairn, A. E. M., ed., *Descriptive Paleoclimatology.* New York: Interscience Publishers, 1961.

———, ed., *Problems in Paleoclimatology.* New York: Interscience Publishers, 1964.

Schwarzbach, Martin (translated by Richard O. Muir), *Climates of the Past.* Princeton: D. Van Nostrand Co., 1963.

Toit, A. L. du, *Our Wandering Continents.* Edinburgh: Oliver and Boyd, 1937 (reprinted 1957).

Wegener, A. L., *The Origin of Continents and Oceans,* translation of 3rd ed. London: Methuen, 1924.

22

Natural Resources

All living things depend on the physical resources of the earth for their existence. Man is no exception; indeed, he has, more than any other organism, learned to exploit the materials of the earth. His ability to find and use mineral and energy sources have allowed him to control and modify his environment; yet at the same time he is ultimately dependent on a continuing and usually expanding supply of energy and mineral materials.

A study of the earth's economic resources, then, involves geology. But it also involves the technology of exploration, extraction, and fabrication, as well as the economics and the very fabric of man's social systems. Space here demands that we focus our attention on the geologic aspects of natural resources, but some understandings here may prove useful in considering the technological and human aspects.

The processes by which nature has produced minerals and mineral fuels useful to man are not unique; rather they are the same processes involved in all other geologic phenomenon. For example, the sand shoveled from a sand deposit for mixing with cement to form concrete was laid down by some common agent such as a stream or the seawater sloshing on a beach. The gold in a lady's pin may have been concentrated in veins of quartz during the final stages of a period of igneous activity. The ore that provided aluminum for your soft-drink can may have been mined from a deposit formed by long-continued weathering that produced a soil-related deposit high in bauxite, an oxide of aluminum. All that is unique about these deposits is that man finds them of value.

ORE DEPOSITS

Minerals of use to man can be grouped into two broad categories: (1) **metals,** such as aluminum, copper, gold, silver, iron, tin, platinum, chromium, nickel, lead, and zinc, and (2) **nonmetals,** such as diamond, salt, limestone, cement, sulfur, and asbestos. Most of these can be found in some quantity, in some form, almost anywhere. But not all deposits can be used, either because methods of separating the desired mineral from associated minerals are not available, or because the deposit is too small or inaccessible. When minerals occur so that they can be worked at a profit, they are called **ore deposits.**

Although a mineral is more concentrated in an ore deposit than elsewhere, it still is mixed with unwanted material from which it must be separated. Gold, for instance, in sugar-sized grains spread through a gravel deposit has to be separated from the other minerals in the gravel. The separation is accomplished by **amalgamation,** taking advantage of the strong tendency for gold to combine with mercury. Gold-bearing gravel is poured onto a tilted table with closely spaced ridges across it and a surface coated with mercury. The table is shaken rapidly. Grains of gold work down through the gravel; and when they come into contact with the mercury, they cling to it while the gravel slides on.

Some sulfide minerals are desired for the metal they contain. But most sulfides are not found alone; they are often associated in rocks with valueless minerals. In order to retrieve the sulfides, the rocks are all ground up, then separated by a process called **flotation.** Finely ground sulfides have an affinity for air, whereas other minerals such as quartz have an affinity for water. In a thoroughly stirred mixture of water and finely ground minerals, with air bubbling up through it, sulfides cling to the air bubbles and rise while the other minerals sink. The sulfide-coated air bubbles form a froth on top of the liquid. This is allowed to overflow the tank; then it is gathered and strained to drain the water and to collect the sulfides. These are heated in a process called **smelting,** to burn off the sulfur and melt the metal.

A convenient way of discussing mineral deposits is to classify them on the basis of the geologic processes that have created them: igneous activity, weathering, sedimentation, and the formation of the original rock masses.

Concentration by Igneous Activity

You will remember that in Chapter 3 we discussed the formation of igneous rocks from a mixture of elements in a solution called a magma. Some magmas, however, also contain elements that, because of the size of their ions, do not combine readily with the common rock-forming minerals. Sometimes these elements crystallize early in the cooling of the magma and settle out of the solution. Sometimes they form late and are trapped in the crystallized magma. But more often they become mixed with hot volatiles, including water, and are injected into the surrounding rocks.

Diamond is most familiar to us as a precious gem. But it is also widely used in industry as an abrasive, for it is the hardest mineral known. Diamond is found only where carbon has been trapped under terrific pressure. Consequently, we cannot expect to find diamond deposits where these conditions have not prevailed. Most diamonds have been discovered in old volcanic necks, where the cooling magma formed the rock peridotite at depths of several miles beneath the surface. Diamonds may be crystallizing out of magma at this very moment, deep below Mauna Loa or in other places in the world where igneous activity persists. But these diamonds will not be found until the volcano has become dormant, and until erosion has stripped away both the volcano itself and miles of the earth materials on which it stands.

Deposits of **chromium, nickel,** and **platinum** occur in formations of simatic rocks all around the world. At Sudbury, Ontario, for example, there are valuable deposits of nickel in rock of this sort. Apparently these minerals somehow became concentrated in the cooling magma; and since they were heavier than the rock-forming minerals, they settled out during crystallization.

Although the chromium and nickel that make up the deposits have combined with other elements to form compounds, the platinum occurs in an uncombined state. The chief source of chromium is **chromite,** $FeCr_2O_4$. Most of the chromium produced in the United States comes from Shasta County, California, but much greater quantities are imported from Oceania and Turkey. Chromium is used chiefly to form an alloy with steel that has extreme hardness, toughness, and resistance to chemical attack. It is also used for plating hardware, plumbing fixtures, and automobile accessories.

About half of the chromite consumed in the United States goes into metallurgical uses of this sort. The other half is used in the con-

Figure 22-1 Abandoned pit of Kimberley diamond mine in the rock of a volcanic neck near Kimberley, South Africa. (*Photo by Cornelius S. Hurlbut, Jr.*)

struction of furnaces and other equipment where heat resistance is required, and in various chemical processes.

Although nickel is a relatively rare element in the earth's crust, it is extremely important in modern industry. It is used in the manufacture of a strong, tough alloy known as **nickel steel** (2.5 to 3.5 per cent nickel) and in the preparation of **monel metal** (68 per cent nickel) and **nichrome** (35–85 per cent nickel). It is also used in various plating processes, and it forms 25 per cent of the United States five-cent coin. Finally, its low expansion tendency makes it an ideal metal for watch springs and other delicate instruments. An important ore of nickel is **pentlandite** $(Fe, Ni)_9S_8$. Large deposits of this mineral at Sudbury, Ontario, and elsewhere make it the world's most valuable source of nickel.

Platinum also occurs in association with the nickel deposits at Sudbury. The value of platinum in industry results from its high melting point, 1,755°C, and its resistance to chemical attack. These properties make it especially useful in laboratory equipment such as crucibles, dishes, and spoons, and for the contact points of bells, magnetos, and induction coils. Platinum also finds special uses in the manufacture of jewelry, in dentistry, and in photography.

Gold, copper, tin, and **silver** are deposited from the hydrothermal solutions that penetrate into the rock surrounding a magma during igneous activity. Deposition is a result of a drop in temperature and pressure as well as reaction with the wall rock.

Gold is a rare element used principally in coinage and jewelry. It occurs normally in the uncombined state in sialic igneous rocks, particularly those that are rich in quartz. About half of the gold that is mined in California, the leading gold-producing state, comes from the Mother Lode, a series of hydrothermal veins lying along the western slope of the Sierra Nevada. The rest comes from placer deposits (see below, "Concentration by Sedimentary Processes").

Copper is second only to iron among the important metals used in modern technology. It is used extensively for electrical equipment, mostly as wire, and also in the manufacture of metal sheets and nails. In combination with other metals, it forms several useful alloys: Brass is an alloy of copper and zinc; bronze is an alloy of copper, tin, and zinc; and German silver is an alloy of copper, zinc, and nickel.

The only important ore of tin is **cassiterite,** SnO_2. A good bit of tin occurs in original hydrothermal deposits, but 75 per cent of the world's supply comes from placers. Tin is used principally as a coating on steel to form **tin plate** for food containers.

Native silver has been deposited from hydrothermal solutions, as has another ore of silver —**argentite,** Ag_2S, silver sulfide. Argentite as an ore may also be of secondary origin when it has been concentrated by weathering processes. For centuries, silver was used in jewelry and

Figure 22-2 Native silver. The specimen, approximately 3 inches long, came from Kongsberg, Norway. (*Harvard Mineralogical Collection. Photo by Harry Groom.*)

coins. By 1940, however, it had become an important industrial metal. It is extensively used in photography, in laboratory and electrical goods, for medical and dental work, as an alloy in bearings, solders, and brazing compounds.

Lead and **zinc** deposits have been created mainly by the process of metasomatism (see Chapter 6), in which hydrothermal solutions

444

and magmatic gases have replaced some of the original components of the rock surrounding a magma. Limestone exposed to igneous activity is particularly susceptible to metasomatism. In the Tristate District of Missouri, Oklahoma, and Kansas, for example, the magmatic solutions have replaced whole layers in a nearly horizontal series of limestone and chert beds.

The principal ore of lead is **galena**, PbS; the principal ore of zinc is **sphalerite**, ZnS. Lead is used in the manufacture of bullets, cable coverings, foil, pipes, storage batteries, weights, and a gasoline additive. It forms an alloy with tin to make solder, with antimony to make type-metal, and with bismuth and tin to make metals that melt at low temperatures. Large quantities of lead are used every year in the preparation of paint pigment. Zinc is used chiefly for galvanizing iron, as an alloy with copper in making brass, and in the manufacture of batteries.

Concentration by Weathering

So far, we have been discussing deposits that were originally created by igneous activity in about the same form in which they now appear. But other important deposits have been built up by the action of weathering on pre-existing rocks. There are three important weathering processes in the formation of ore deposits:

(1) *The chemical alteration of compounds from which desired elements cannot otherwise be extracted economically.*

Aluminum, although it is one of the most common elements in the earth's crust, almost always occurs in feldspars and other silicates from which it cannot be extracted economically by any process now known. Fortunately, however, under tropical conditions, weathering breaks the feldspars down into clay minerals; they in turn become hydrous oxides of aluminum and iron. The soils produced by this activity are sometimes known as "**laterites**" and the aluminum ore is called **bauxite**. The principal deposits of bauxite in the United States occur in Arkansas.

Aluminum is a very light, strong metal used extensively in the manufacture of cooking utensils, furniture, household appliances, automobiles, airplanes, railway cars, and machinery. It is becoming increasingly popular as an insulating material in buildings.

(2) *The removal of undesired components, leaving the desired compounds more concentrated than they were originally.*

Iron, the most widely used metal in our industrial civilization, has been concentrated by this weathering process in many areas of the world—in the extremely important deposits around Lake Superior, for example. In Minnesota and Michigan, iron-bearing formations underlie thousands of square miles; but for years, only where percolating ground water had removed enough silica from the parent rock was the iron (in the form of Fe_2O_3) sufficiently concentrated to make mining praticable.

(3) *The solution and redeposition of desired elements in useful concentrations, a process sometimes called secondary or supergene enrichment.*

In some regions, igneous activity has built up original deposits of copper, but not in great enough concentrations to be worked. Sometimes, though, ground water has dissolved the copper and has carried it down to be deposited in an enriched zone. At Bingham Canyon, Utah (see Figure 22-3), there is a spectacular open-

Figure 22-3   Copper mine at Bingham Canyon, Utah. The benches are 50 to 70 feet high, and not less than 65 feet wide. (*Photo by Rotkin, P.F.I.*)

pit mining operation that recovers at a profit an ore containing as little as four-tenths of 1 per cent of metal. The ore is sialic porphyry that contains finely disseminated primary sulfides. The benches of the mine range from 40 to 50 feet in height and are not less than 65 feet in width. The operation covers 878 acres and contains about 160 miles of rail and truck roads, most of which are moved continually to meet operating needs. At Morenci, Arizona, the impoverished zone is as deep as 220 feet, but beneath it the enriched zone extends about 1,000 feet farther down. Underlying the enriched zone is the unaltered bedrock, which is often too low-grade to be worth mining.

Concentration by Sedimentary Processes

Some of the geologic agents described in Chapters 9, 10, and 11 pick up the products of weathering and ultimately deposit them below

Figure 22-4   Panning for gold. The prospector partly fills the pan with water and throws in a shovelful of dirt. He picks out the pebbles and stirs the mass until clay-sized particles are dislodged and can be sloughed away in the muddied water. He then partly fills the pan with water again and gives it a slightly eccentric circular motion to build up a wave to slop over the edge each time, carrying with it a little sand. He continues this process until only the specks of gold, which have greater specific gravity, remain in the pan. On the Anderson River, tributary to the Fraser River, British Columbia's Sierra Cascade Mts. (*Photo by Elliott A. Riggs.*)

base level. Both mechanical and chemical processes are involved in the transportation and deposition of the weathered rock.

Flowing water moves great quantities of mineral material along the channels of streams, particularly in mountainous regions. The heavier minerals—harder for the water to transport, yet resistant to chemical decay—tend to accumulate in the channel basins, in a deposit called a **placer** (rhymes with "passer"). Gold is exceptionally well adapted to placer deposition. Weathering breaks it from the rocks and veins where it originally crystallized from hydrothermal solutions, but its malleability prevents it from being finely pulverized. Moreover, its high specific gravity (ranging from 15 to 19, depending on the percentage of impurities present) causes it to settle readily from agitated mixtures of water, sand, and lighter materials. The gold discovered in 1848 on the western slopes of the Sierra Nevada in California was concentrated in placers so rich that great fortunes were made simply by panning it out by hand (see Figure 22-4). Less concentrated placer deposits can now be worked by modern hydraulic giants, which wash away the barren material that overlies the pay dirt, and sluice the gold-bearing gravels into boxes where the gold is trapped.

Even deposits of gold in gravel below groundwater or ocean level can be worked by specially designed dredges that recover at a profit gold so thinly dispersed that there are only a few cents' worth in each cubic yard. The world's greatest gold deposits are in the Witwatersrand District of South Africa, on a plateau standing 6,000 feet above sea level about 700 miles northeast of Cape Town. ("Witwatersrand" means white divide, so called because of a prominent white quartzite that resists erosion and stands forth as a "water ridge" or "divide.") The deposits in this rich area occur in conglomerates, themselves formed from ancient placer deposits, according to some geologists. Others think that permeable channels in the original rock were invaded by gold-bearing hydrothermal solutions. Approximately

Figure 22-5 Cassiterite from Cornwall, England. Waterworn pebbles from a placer deposit. (*Photo by Benjamin M. Shaub.*)

40 per cent of the world's gold is produced by the Union of South Africa.

Nearly 75 per cent of the world's tin production comes from placer deposits. Most of the ore is in the form of cassiterite, or tin dioxide (SnO_2), which has a specific gravity of 7 (Figure 22-5).

Initially, the world's greatest deposits of iron ores were built up by chemical precipitation in sediments. But most of the deposits could not be worked commercially until weathering processes had increased the concentration by secondary enrichment.

About nine-tenths of the iron ore in the United States occurs as hematite (Fe_2O_3). In the Lake Superior District, the zone that has still not been leached by weathering consists of a mineral assemblage called **taconite**, containing chert with **hematite, magnetite** (Fe_2O_4), **siderite** ($FeCO_3$), and **hydrous iron silicates.** The iron content of taconite averages about only 25 per cent. But in the zone that has been leached, most of the iron has been oxidized to hematite, which produces ores of from 50 to 60 per cent iron. Recently, however, commercial methods

Figure 22-6 Magnetite from Magnet Cove, Arkansas. (*Photo by Benjamin M. Shaub.*)

Figure 22-8 Outcrop of Clinton iron ore near Birmingham, Alabama. The ore is the thick bottom layer. (*Photo by Aloia Studio. Courtesy Republic Steel Corp.*)

have been developed for recovering iron even from the taconite of this district. So great stretches of original unleached rock have been added to our iron reserve (Figure 22-7).

The newest reserves of iron ore on the North American continent, near 55°N., 67°W., on the Labrador-Quebec border, also consist of deposits enriched by weathering. Other deposits are being worked in sedimentary formations of Silurian age, known as the Clinton beds, which outcrop across Wisconsin and New York, and along the southern Appalachians. These beds are also being mined extensively in Alabama, in the Birmingham District (see Figures 22-8, 22-9). The primary unleached ores from the Clinton beds are often high in $CaCO_3$ and contain 35 to 40 per cent iron. But after the $CaCO_3$ has been leached out by weathering, they may contain as much as 50 per cent iron.

Concentration during Rock Formation

Many rock materials are valuable in their original condition, produced by rock-forming processes, without undergoing any additional

448

Figure 22-9 Underground mine in Clinton iron ore near Birmingham, Alabama (see Figure 22-8). (Courtesy Tennessee Coal and Iron Division, United States Steel Corporation.)

enrichment or concentration. Stone, of course, has been used for several thousand years as a building material. But its importance has grown tremendously during the last half century, with the discovery of new techniques for removing it from the ground by blasting, and for crushing it into usable sizes (see Figure 22-10). Every mode of transportation in the modern world depends in some degree on crushed or broken stone: It provides the basis for countless miles of modern highways, ballast for railways, bases for landing fields, and jetty stone for harbor facilities.

Other rocks have commercial value because of their chemical properties. **Limestone,** for example, is used to neutralize acids in the processing of sugar, to correct the acidity of soil, and to supply calcium to plants. Limestone

Figure 22-10 Modern methods break over 200,000 tons of rock from a quarry face with 53,377 pounds of explosive. (Courtesy New York Trap Rock Corporation.)

that contains limited amounts of impurities serves as the raw material in the manufacture of cement; the impurities give cement its characteristic hardness. The type known as Portland cement consists of 75 per cent calcium carbonate (limestone), 13 per cent silica, and 5 per cent aluminum oxide, along with the silica and alumina that are normally present in clays or shales. Some manufacturers add the right percentages of impurities to the limestone; others use deposits called **cement rock,** in which the impurities occur naturally.

Phosphate rock is a popular term used for sedimentary rocks that contain high percentages of phosphate, usually in the form of mineral **apatite,** calcium fluorophosphate. The rock is extremely important as a source of agricultural fertilizer. The Rocky Mountain states have phosphate reserves estimated at 6 billion tons, enough to last for many centuries; the reserves in Idaho run close to 5 billion tons. Other deposits are being mined in Florida and Tennessee.

Asbestos is a general term applied to certain minerals that form soft, silky, flexible fibers in metamorphic rocks (see Figure 22-11). The most common asbestos is **chrysotile,** a variety of the mineral **serpentine,** a magnesium silicate. The longer fibers are woven into yarn for use in brake linings and heat-resistant tapes and cloth. Asbestos materials are extremely versatile, for they withstand fire, insulate against heat and sound, are light in weight, can be made into pliable fabrics, and resist soil, corrosion, and vermin. The United States, the greatest user of asbestos, imports up to 90 per cent of its needs from Canada, where there is an important belt of serpentine in Quebec.

Salt, **NaCl,** essential to life, and fortunately one of the most abundant substances in the world, is derived commercially both from sea water and from rocks that were formed by the natural evaporation of sea water. Rock salt is produced by about half the states of the United States.

The primary use of salt is in the chemical industries, but it is also valuable in the preparation and transportation of foods, in various manufacturing processes, and in the treatment of icy highways.

Figure 22-11 Chrysotile asbestos, a fibrous variety of serpentine from Thetford, Quebec. (*Photo by Benjamin M. Shaub.*)

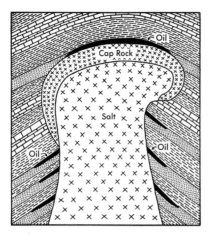

Figure 22-12   Schematic diagram of a salt dome.

Under the pressure of a few thousand feet of sediments, rock salt flows plastically. In some regions it has been pushed up into overlying sediments in great plugs known as **salt domes.** Although the details of shape and history vary a good bit from one dome to another, they all tend to have a cylindrical shape with a top diameter of about a mile. They may rise to within a few hundred feet of the surface, or they may get no nearer than a few thousand feet. Some of them have forced their way upward from the original salt bed through 20,000 feet of overlying sediments. Reservoirs for oil and gas are often formed by salt domes as they rise (see Figure 22-12).

SOURCES OF ENERGY

The chief sources of harnessable energy available to man today are liquid petroleum, natural gas, coal, water power, and fissionable material. As the United States entered the final third of the 20th century, natural gas and liquid petroleum accounted for about 75 per cent of the energy used in the country. About 21 per cent came from coal and 4 per cent from water power. Fissionable material providing so-called atomic power was becoming competitive—but accounted for less than 1 per cent of the energy consumed.

Coal, Oil and Gas

These 3 fuels represent energy that has been concentrated by the decay of organic material and are often referred to as **fossil** fuels, for obvious reasons. During the decay process, the less combustible components are driven off, leaving behind the highly combustible elements carbon, hydrogen, and oxygen.

When organic fuels are burned, great quantities of stored chemical energy are released in the form of heat energy. This heat may either be used directly or converted into other forms, such as electrical energy.

COAL   Coal, as we have seen in Chapter 17, is the end product of vegetable matter that accumulated in the swamplands of the earth millions of years ago. The size of a coal bed depends on the extent of the original swamp and the amount of vegetable matter that collected in it.

We distinguish among varieties of coal on the basis of their carbon content, which increases the longer the material has undergone decay. The plant matter from which coal has

Figure 22-13   Coal seams form part of a series of sedimentary rocks. The darkest layers are coal and shale; the lightest are limestone. Near Cokedale, Colorado. (*Photo by Tozier.*)

developed contains about 50 per cent carbon. Peat, the first stage in the decay process, contains about 60 per cent; anthracite, the final stage, contains 95 to 98 per cent. Although carbon is by all odds the most important element in coal, as many as 72 elements have been found in some deposits. Over 1 per cent of the ash formed by the bituminous coals of West Virginia consists of sodium, potassium, calcium, aluminum, silicon, iron, and titanium. And there are 26 metals present in concentrations ranging down to .01 per cent, including lithium, rubidium, chromium, cobalt, copper, gallium, germanium, lanthanum, nickel, tungsten, and zirconium.

Coal is also important as the source of coke used in the steel industry. In fact, one-fourth of the coal produced every year is used for this purpose. The coke is burned in blast furnaces, where it supplies carbon, which combines with the oxygen of iron ores to free the metallic iron. In the future, coal may become even more valuable as a source of coke than as a direct source of heat.

OIL AND GAS   Coal is rapidly being replaced as a fuel by more efficient, easier-to-handle oil and gas. Fortunately, there are also large supplies of these fuels in the United States, and it is to them that we owe much of our industrial progress and high standard of living. Great Britain, on the other hand, although her coal and iron ore enabled her to pioneer the industrial revolution, now has to buy large quantities of oil and gas reserves in other countries. Her own resources do not include the large sedimentary basins where oil and gas accumulate.

Oil and gas are the remains of living matter that has been reduced by decay to a state in which carbon and hydrogen are the principal elements. These elements are combined in a great variety of ways to form molecules of substances called **hydrocarbons.** The distinguishing feature of the molecule of each hydrocarbon is the number of carbon atoms it contains. One carbon atom combined with 4 hydrogen atoms, for example, forms a molecule of a gas called methane, CH_4. Two carbon atoms combined with 6 hydrogen atoms form a molecule of a gas called ethane, C_2H_6.

Natural deposits of oil contain many kinds of hydrocarbons mixed together. They are separated by an industrial process called **fractional distillation,** based on the principle that light molecules are volatilized more readily than heavy molecules. As early as 600 B.C., Nebuchadnezzar, king of Babylon, was building roads that consisted of stones set in asphalt. The asphalt was nothing more than the hydrocarbons left behind where natural oil has seeped to the surface and lost its lighter components by evaporation.

Source Beds. Most petroleum (from the Latin *petra*, "rock," and *oleum*, "oil"; hence, "rock oil") and natural gas have developed from organic remains originally deposited in a marine sedimentary environment. A modern example of such an environment is the Black Sea. Here the water circulates very slowly, and the bottom sediments contain as much as 35 per cent organic matter, in contrast to the 2.5 per cent that is normal for marine sediments. When the putrefaction of the organic remains takes place in an environment of this sort, the product is a slimy black mud known as **sapropel** (from Greek *sapros*, "rotten," and *pelagos*, "sea"). Petroleum and natural gas are believed to develop from the sapropel through a series of transformations not unlike the stages in coal's development from peat.

Three conditions are required for the development of a deposit of petroleum or natural gas: (1) source beds where the hydrocarbons can form, (2) a relatively porous and permeable reservoir bed into which they can migrate, and (3) a trap at some point in the reservoir bed where they can become imprisoned.

The most important source beds are generally believed to be marine shales, although certain limestones, particularly if they form a reef, may also serve the purpose (see Figure 22-14). There are also extensive beds of shales formed from fresh-water deposits, such as the Eocene lake deposits in Utah, Colorado, and Wyoming. These **oil shales** have yielded from 10 to 80 gallons of oil per ton and constitute important fuel reserves.

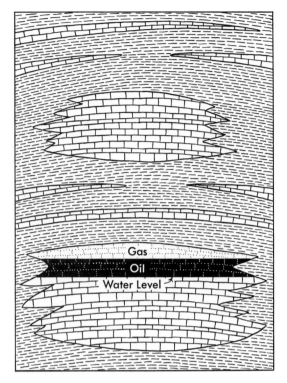

Figure 22-14   Oil and gas trapped in an ancient coral reef, surrounded by impermeable shales. Some reefs are believed to have contributed animal remains as a source material for petroleum as well as reservoir rocks for storing the naturally distilled hydrocarbons.

Figure 22-15   Symmetrical anticlinal trap for oil and gas separated from water by differences in specific gravity. The oil and gas move upward above the water associated with them in a permeable reservoir rock (shown here as a sandstone) until they encounter an impermeable shale folded into an anticline and can rise no further. There they accumulate, with gas above the oil.

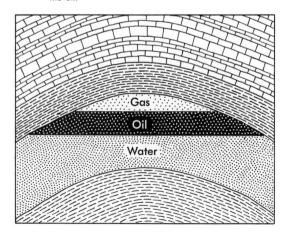

Location of Reservoir Beds. Just where we will find a reservoir of petroleum or natural gas depends on the laws that govern the migration of these substances to reservoir rocks. Unfortunately, we do not yet understand just what these laws are, although several empirical relationships have been established.

Simple gravity seems to explain the location of many occurrences. According to the **gravitational theory,** if oil, gas, and water are present in a reservoir bed, the oil and gas, being lighter than water, will rise to the top, with the gas uppermost. If the reservoir is trapped in a dome or an anticline capped by an impermeable formation, the oil and gas will accumulate along the crest of the anticline or dome (see Figures 22-15, 22-16). This **anticlinal theory** of accumulation, one aspect of the gravitational theory, has proved to be a valuable guide to prospectors and has led to a substantial volume of production. A corollary of the gravitational theory is that if no water is present, the oil will gather in the trough of a syncline with the gas above it.

Another structure that is important in the gravitational theory is the **stratigraphic trap,** formed when oil and gas in the presence of water are impeded by a zone of reduced per-

Figure 22-16   Distorted anticlinal trap for oil. If the anticlinal fold is slightly steeper on one side than on the other, its crest at the surface (outcrop of the axial plane) will not be vertically above its crest at the depth where oil and gas have accumulated.

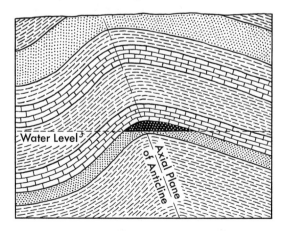

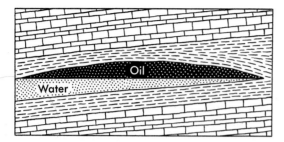

Figure 22-17 Stratigraphic trap for oil. If old shore-lines or sandbars developed conditions in which sand graded into clay, the rock equivalents of these deposits will show permeability for the sand and none for the clay. If oil migrating upward in the sand is trapped by a sudden change to impermeable shale, without structural deformation, a stratigraphic trap develops.

meability as they migrate upward (see Figure 22-17). This situation may develop, for example, along old shorelines or in ancient sandbars, where facies change horizontally from sand to clay. Or the upward progress of the oil and gas through a permeable reservoir bed may be blocked by an impermeable bed at an uncomformity, or at a fault.

Water Power

The energy of moving water is all important in the transportation of material from the continents to the ocean basins and in the sculpturing of the world's landscape. For over 2,000 years man has captured and turned some of this energy to his own ends. In the United States the total amount of energy generated from water power has increased through the years, although as a portion of the total energy supply it has remained between 3 and 4 per cent since the turn of the century.

Nuclear Energy

Nuclear energy will undoubtedly be our greatest source of energy in the future. Coal, oil, and gas yield only the chemical energy stored in the electrons of atoms; atomic fuels release the much greater energy that is locked in atomic nuclei. Since mass and energy are interchangeable, the nucleus of an atom, which contains 99.95 per cent of its mass, contains almost all of its total energy. In fact, if atomic nuclei could interact with one another in a way that would release their inner sources of energy, the reaction would produce a million times more energy than is released by ordinary energy-producing chemical reactions.

So far, however, this great store of nuclear energy has been released from the atoms of only a few elements. One of these is uranium, a naturally unstable element. In 1938, it was discovered that when the isotope uranium-235 captures a neutron to form uranium-236, its nucleus becomes unstable and splits apart. Two other elements are produced whose protons total the 92 of uranium, but whose mass numbers do not total 236. Clearly, some of the neutrons have escaped, carrying with them tremendous amounts of energy. When this process is initiated in a pile of uranium, the neutrons that have escaped from one atom hit the nuclei of other atoms and set up a chain reaction. It was a large-scale reaction of this sort that produced the first atomic bomb explosion on July 16, 1945. Since then, scientists have been developing methods of controlling the reaction so that the energy released can be used for constructive purposes. In fact, nuclear energy is now driving submarines and producing electric power, and in the near future it will be used to propel airplanes.

Uranium deposits have been built up by igneous activity, and they occur in igneous rocks, pegmatite dikes, and vein deposits. The primary ore of uranium is the mineral **uraninite,** an oxide sometimes called **pitchblende.** Another oxide, containing smaller amounts of uranium, is the soft, yellow mineral **carnotite,** found in the sandstones of the Colorado Plateau. It constitutes an important source of uranium in the United States. Uranium in this form has gone through several steps, including solution from igneous rocks, transportation in underground solutions, and redeposition.

Most of the world's supply of uranium comes from primary deposits at Great Bear Lake, Canada, in the Congo, and in Czechoslovakia. But important quantities are found in sedimentary rocks such as those of the Colorado Plateau, the Blind River, Canada, and Witwatersrand conglomerates in Africa.

SUMMARY

An ore deposit is a mineral deposit that can be mined at a profit. Ore deposits can be classed as either metals or nonmetals.

The concentration of minerals into an ore takes place by geological processes. The concentration may be the result of igneous activity, of weathering, of sedimentary processes, or of the processes forming the rock itself.

Coal, oil, and gas are organic accumulations and form our chief source of energy today. Nuclear energy promises to replace these sources in the future as the most important source of controlled energy.

ADDITIONAL READING

Bateman, Alan M., *Economic Mineral Deposits* (2nd ed.). New York: John Wiley & Sons, 1950.

Levorsen, A. I., *Geology of Petroleum.* San Francisco: W. H. Freeman and Co., 1958.

McKinstry, Hugh E., *Mining Geology.* Englewood Cliffs, N.J.: Prentice-Hall, 1948.

Park, Charles F., Jr., and Roy A. MacDiarmid, *Ore Deposits.* San Francisco: W. H. Freeman and Co., 1964.

Van Royen, William, and Oliver Bowles, *Atlas of the World's Resources:* Vol. II, *The Mineral Resources of the World.* Englewood Cliffs, N.J.: Prentice-Hall, Inc., 1952.

23

Astrogeology

Astronomy and geology are usually considered as separate sciences, but the distinctions between them are being rapidly broken down as explorations of space bring us nearer to actual physical contact with the so-called "heavenly bodies." It may be debated whether or not the study of the solid matter of other planets is really geology. As a compromise, the term **astrogeology** seems to be gaining favor, since it combines elements of both astronomy and geology and signifies the application of geologic techniques to the solid parts of astronomical bodies of any sort.

In keeping with this point of view, the present brief chapter will be confined to the astrogeology of the members of the solar system which are known or thought to be solid or rock-like in character.

EARTH AND MOON—
PARTNERS IN SPACE

Although the earth and its satellite, the moon, are closely associated in space, they show many puzzling and significant differences. By a study of comparisons and contrasts we can expect to learn more about both of these bodies. In the first place, their surface features stand in sharp contrast; the lunar landscape is marked by innumerable craters; flat plains; rough, ill-defined mountains; long, narrow "rills"; and shining "rays." There are obviously no bodies of water. The earth, in contrast, is characterized by extensive oceans and, topographically, by long, curving mountain chains, vast, sloping plains and countless erosion-carved valleys. Many, but not all, of the surface differences can be attributed to the fact that the earth has an atmosphere and plentiful water while the moon does not.

It has been argued that the earth has had its full share of meteoritic impacts but that the craters have been erased by erosion or covered by water and water-laid sediment almost as fast as they formed. But there are other features that cannot be explained by presence or absence of water erosion. The differences between the two bodies are "more than skin deep" so to speak. The internal structures and composition are almost certainly so different that dissimilar histories are required. In the first place, the mean density of the moon is only 3.3 times that of water; the corresponding figure for the earth is 5.5. This divergence points to a real difference in composition—the moon contains a higher proportion of light material and is deficient in metallic constituents. As additional evi-

dence, we know that the moon has very weak magnetic and electrical fields.

The earth has a very dense core, but even if the heavier constituents were not concentrated around the center it would still have greater density than the moon. Since the earth has a core and the moon evidently has none, we may assume that the moon has never been entirely molten. This is a most significant clue to the differences between the two bodies. The melting of the earth is probably due to a higher content of radioactive material, which provided not only heat but other forms of energy to shape the interior and to keep the surface in a state of unrest and change. Water and an atmos-

Figure 23-1 Crater-scarred surface of the moon is thought to preserve a record of events up to 2 billion years old. Most of the craters are due to impact of infalling meteorites; a few appear to be volcanoes. (*Courtesy Mount Wilson and Palomar Observatories.*)

phere are merely incidental by-products of the melting. The moon apparently never passed through this process. Of course, its low gravity would not long retain water or an atmosphere even if they had been present at one time.

Although the surface and most of the interior of the earth have cooled and solidified, there are manifestations of continuing internal unrest that have important surface effects. The high-standing continents, linear mountain chains, elevated fault blocks, depressed basins, and abundant volcanic fields all tell of internal forces. Thus, even if the earth had no water and no atmosphere its surface would still be different from that of the moon. Only the occasional impact craters that are found on earth appear to be of entirely external origin.

The Topography of the Moon

The surface of the moon exhibits two chief types of topography; one is rough and mountainous, the other is lower and relatively smooth. The rough areas are light in color and were called *terrae* (land) by the early astronomers; the smooth areas are relatively dark and were called *maria* (seas). The mountains of the moon are not organized in chains or ranges and present no discernible preferred directions or patterns. The maria are flat and apparently almost smooth; they display a number of features not clearly seen in the highlands or mountains. On them we discern low folds; traces of faults along which one side has risen or fallen; long, narrow ditch-like depressions without tributaries called rifts; and occasional volcanic cones.

Pockmarking the entire surface and superimposed upon all types of topography, high as well as low, are thousands of circular craters ranging in size from a few inches to many miles in diameter. In the view of most authorities, most of the craters originated from the impact of infalling meteorites. The effects of a major collision are truly spectacular: The circular rims raised by the impacts are ragged moun-

Figure 23-2 View of the surface of the moon from 258 miles above the surface. Photograph by Ranger IX, March 24, 1965. The large crater, Alphonsus, is marked by rills and ridges of unknown origin. The smooth surface on the left is a part of Mare Numbrium. Area represented is 121 by 109 miles. (*Courtesy NASA.*)

Figure 23-3 Portion of the Sea of Tranquility, one of the smoother portions of the moon. Photo by Ranger VIII spacecraft, February 20, 1965; elevation above surface, 151 miles. Shows two large flat-bottomed craters, a number of cone craters, and unexplained trench-like depressions. (*Courtesy NASA.*)

tains up to 20,000 feet high and the central plains within the rims are up to 60 miles across. Ringing the larger craters are chaotic fields of debris only a little lower than the rims. Still farther out are radiating furrows and numerous secondary craters made by pieces thrown out by the impact. Radiating out to still greater distances, extending even for hundreds of miles, are great systems of shining "rays" that are obviously made of fine pulverized or melted material literally splashed out of the parent crater.

The Origin of the Maria— a Lunar Milestone

One feature of the lunar surface apparently was produced during a specific relatively short interval. This event was the formation of the mare plains by the melting of rock and production of lava. This episode, which broke the monotony of continuing crater formation, provides a most important reference point for deciphering the history of the moon.

We have cited evidence that the earth was completely melted at least once. The moon, by contrast, was apparently only partly melted. At this time large volumes of rock material were converted to lava, which rose to the surface where it spread out to engulf and obliterate the surface features. It is plain to see that the lava destroyed or partly obliterated an earlier "moonscape" which was already marked by large craters and other typical lunar features. The mare lava fields make up a great deal of the side of the moon which faces the earth. Strangely, the pictures of the other side of the moon obtained by orbiting space probes show no maria. This mystery remains to be explained.

After the maria were formed, the moon continued to be bombarded by meteorites, with consequent cratering. Craters were blasted in the newly formed mare material, and the associated systems of rays criss-cross much of the surface. The rays furnish a method of estimating the ages of the newer generations of craters, for it has been noted that where ray systems from different craters cross or intersect, the brighter

Figure 23-4   Near view of the moon's surface as shown by a photograph taken by Surveyor I spacecraft, June 2, 1966. Shows a moon rock six inches high and twelve inches long. A small crater lies in the background. (*Courtesy NASA.*)

Figure 23-5   Impact area of Surveyor I spacecraft. The depression made by one of the footpads is clearly shown. The depth of penetration indicates that the material is somewhat loose and fragmental. (*Courtesy NASA.*)

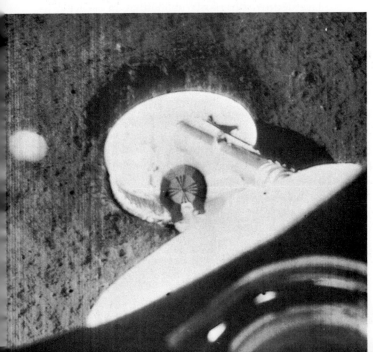

ones always overlie the fainter ones. The oldest craters are rayless, which indicates that the ray material is temporary and is probably obliterated with the passage of time.

Working backward from the more recent craters, with due regard for major events such as formation of the maria, geologists have already produced a tentative history of the lunar surface. It should be noted that the principle of superposition has guided this reconstruction just as it has guided the study of earthly geology.

Surface Material of the Moon

All plans for landing of men or machines on the moon must take serious account of the characteristics of the surface materials. After a great amount of long distance instrumental study and photography, we have obtained concrete evidence of what at least a portion of the surface is like. An amazing series of over 10,000 close-up photographs televised to earth by Surveyor I mooncraft, which landed undamaged on the moon June 2, 1966, shows details of the nearby surface and also more distant features of the terrain.

The general area of the landing is a typical mare region which is seen to be gently rolling, pitted with craters and littered with fragments from sand to boulder size. The local surface is seen to be composed of fine dust-like rock material which has aggregated into lumps and fragments of various size. The footpads of the mooncraft made shallow indentations in the material which is obviously loose but relatively firm—comparable in certain ways to wet beach sand. Needless to say the Surveyor I photographs are most encouraging for future landings.

A reasonable origin for the dust or soil-like material is the pulverizing of rock by the long-continued impact of meteoritic fragments. There is good evidence that the surface layer has been shifted and worked over many times in this way. It is also considered possible that solar radiation might also "erode" the surface to smooth out the smaller features.

Still needed are actual specimens of moon material for geological examination and chemical analysis. These should be forthcoming and astrogeology will then enter a new era.

MARS—THE RED PLANET

Great popular and scientific interest centers on the planet Mars. Its surface has been studied telescopically for many years so that certain characteristic features are known to exist, even though their nature and origin are open to speculation. About three-fourths of the surface is made up of "bright areas," the other one-fourth by "dark areas." These contrasting areas are of varied shape and size. Many configura-

tions have been observed to change in outline, and there are marked variations in color tones as shown by careful study of the light reflected and emitted from the surface. There is an overall reddish cast to both the dark and light areas —hence the appropriate appellation the "red planet." Another unmistakable feature is the presence of white polar caps which expand and contract with the Martian seasons. These polar caps are almost certainly shallow layers of water-ice. A thin atmosphere containing water vapor and carbon dioxide is present. Within this atmosphere move "storms" of some sort and surface-derived dust clouds.

Beyond these generally accepted facts there has been great disagreement about what the surface of Mars is really like. It is not

Figure 23-6 Views of Mars from the earth. A, B, and C show rotation. (*Courtesy Mount Wilson and Palomar Observatories.*)

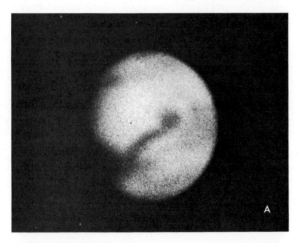
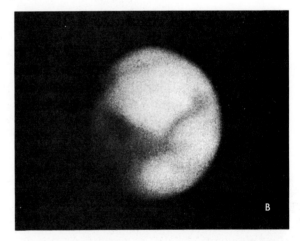
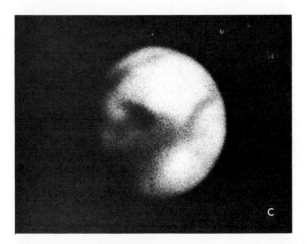
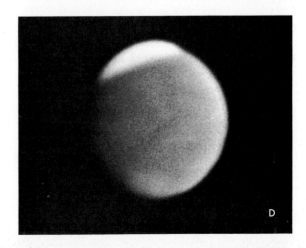

Figure 23-7 Surface of Mars as shown by digital data transmitted by Mariner IV spacecraft, July 1965. Area shown is 170 by 150 miles. The moonlike, cratered topography is well shown. (*Courtesy NASA.*)

known, for example, whether the bright areas are higher or lower than the dark areas, nor are the reasons for the unmistakable changes in color understood. Many observers have mapped complex systems of so-called canals in greater or lesser detail, and these have been popularly interpreted as possible engineering works of intelligent beings. The very vagueness of the finer details and the difficulty of making unbiased observations undoubtedly accounts for the differences of opinion about the true shapes and distribution of the "canals" and other markings.

Much of the previous speculation came to an abrupt end when 21 close-up photographs from the U.S. spacecraft Mariner IV reached the earth in August, 1965. These photographs showed that the surface of Mars is pitted with numerous craters similar to those of the moon. The photographs also prove that the "canals" of Mars are to a large extent optical illusions. Naturally, the images of the photographs are not as clear as those taken of the moon, and only a small fraction of the surface is portrayed; nevertheless, it is clear that river valleys, water-eroded plains, folded mountains, fault scarps, volcanic fields, and ocean basins are not in evidence. The topography of Mars is moon-like, not earth-like.

The similarity of their cratered landscapes strongly suggests that Mars and the moon have had similar histories. In fact, the first conclusion was that the Mars landscape is, like that of the moon, a very old one, dating back several billion years. Some students believe, however, that there are not as many craters on Mars as there should be. It is calculated that with a reasonable rate of crater formation Mars should show 220 craters over 20 kilometers in diameter in the area photographed rather than the 37 that were observed. Since the visible craters are only about one-sixth as abundant as they should be if they are as old as those on the moon, the explanation of the low frequency may be that they are only one-sixth as old (300 to 800 million years). This suggestion does not deny that older ones were formed—they have supposedly been obliterated. If they were destroyed through erosion by running water, we would expect to find that the early history of Mars was like that of the earth, perhaps even with plants and animals. But if, as seems likely, the erosion has occurred through wind action the prospects of finding life are much less promising.

VENUS—THE VEILED PLANET

Venus is sometimes called a "sister planet" of the Earth. The two have nearly the same size, mass, and density. Venus rotates in 243 days and revolves in 440 days, compared with the 24 hours and 365 days for the earth. Beyond these gross comparisons the similarities are few. The atmosphere of Venus, which contains carbon dioxide and water, is so thick that the solid surface beneath is not visible. Recently (1965) the cloud cover has been penetrated by radar, leading to the discovery of extensive mountain chains on the surface of the planet. The significance of this discovery remains to be determined. The upper atmosphere is an excellent reflector, which accounts for the great brilliance of the planet.

The temperature of the surface has been measured at 600 degrees F., but drops in the higher levels of the atmosphere to about −40 degrees F. No one knows the meaning of these great variations, but they may be due to a "greenhouse" effect which traps the solar heat within the lower atmosphere. The surface of Venus may be extremely hot and dusty with no surface bodies of liquid of any kind.

The Mariner II spaceship passed within 21,600 miles of Venus on Dec. 14, 1962 and transmitted scientific data back to Earth from across 37,000,000 miles of space. The magnetic field in the vicinity of Venus was found to be less than $\frac{1}{10}$ as powerful as that of the earth and no belts of energetic particles were discovered. These findings may indicate that Venus has no metallic core and hence may not have passed through the molten state, with consequent production of water. It is difficult to understand how Earth and Venus can be so similar and yet so unlike. Certainly the prospects of finding life on our sister planet are not particularly bright.

MERCURY

Mercury, the innermost planet of the solar system, is so close to the sun that it is difficult to study. It is known to be a solid body with about the same density as the Earth. Its period of revolution, as recently determined (1965) is 586 earth days. Vague surface markings are reported and it is generally thought that the topography is similar to that of the moon. The temperature reaches 780 degrees F., which exceeds the melting point of lead and tin. The atmosphere, if one exists at all, is thin. No one seriously believes that life as we know it can exist on Mercury.

JUPITER—THE GIANT PLANET

Jupiter is the greatest of the planets; if it were much larger it might shrink by gravitation to become a self-luminous star. It rotates with great speed: The day is only 10 hours long.

Figure 23-8 Jupiter, showing banded atmosphere and the large "Red Spot." (*Courtesy Mt. Wilson and Palomar Observatories.*)

Figure 23-9 The planet Saturn. Photo by Mt. Wilson Observatory's 100-inch telescope. (*Courtesy Mt. Wilson and Palomar Observatories.*)

Ammonia, methane, and hydrogen exist in its atmosphere, which must be enormously thick. Bands of ever-changing clouds lie parallel to the equator, apparently blown about by wind systems like those of earth.

Deep in the interior is a heavy central core which rotates as a solid. This core is probably partly rock and there is some evidence that it is producing and radiating heat. As a good approximation, the planet's composition might be 80 per cent hydrogen with the rest heavier "earthy" material.

Jupiter has 12 moons; the whole family is a miniature of the solar system. Two of the satellites, Io and Europa, are similar to the moon in size, mass, and density. Two others, Ganymede and Callisto, are larger than the moon but only about twice as dense as water. These four large satellites are good reflectors of light and may be covered with layers of ice or other frozen gases. Little is known about the fainter moons —they are too small for meaningful study.

SATURN—THE RINGED PLANET

Saturn, the most spectacular of the planets, has an extremely low mean density, being only .71 as dense as water. Even so, it probably has a good-sized core of earthy material buried under thick layers of gas, vapor, and ice. There is more methane and less ammonia than on Jupiter. Because of the low temperature, the ammonia might exist in frozen form at deeper levels.

Saturn has 10 satellites. Titan, the sixth outward, is unusual in possessing an obvious atmosphere. Since all of the measurable satellites have a density of less than 2.4, they must consist of ice, frozen ammonia, and other light compounds mixed with lesser amounts of stony or earthy material. There is little hope of finding life in this system.

URANUS AND NEPTUNE—FAR-OUT GIANTS

The two planets Uranus and Neptune are so similar that they may well be called planetary twins. Methane is abundant and ammonia is absent in the atmospheres of both. The density of Uranus is 1.53, of Neptune 2.41. Both rotate rapidly, Uranus in $10\frac{3}{4}$ hours, Neptune in $15\frac{4}{5}$ hours. From the densities and theoretical considerations, astrogeologists believe that both planets have cores of heavy material, but this idea has not been proven.

Uranus has 5 satellites and Neptune 3; all are small with diameters in the order of a few hundred miles. Triton, the largest of Neptune's satellites, moves in a retrograde orbit.

PLUTO—THE OUTERMOST PLANET

The outermost planet yet discovered is Pluto and it appears to be in a class by itself. We know that it is $39\frac{1}{2}$ times as far from the sun as is the earth. Because of its low temperature, many common gases would be liquids on its surface and it may possess oceans of oxygen or nitrogen. It appears to be somewhat larger than the earth with perhaps about the same density. Pluto may be rocky in character, more like the inner planets than the other outer ones.

THE ASTEROIDS

Numerous relatively small bodies that move in a wide belt between the orbits of Jupiter and Mars are called asteroids. These are commonly regarded as fragments of one or several planets that were somehow disrupted and scattered after having passed through a considerable part of their planetary evolution. Over 1,500 asteroids have been catalogued, and many more— perhaps several hundred thousand—are estimated to exist. The largest is Ceres, 770 kilometers in diameter. The vast majority are pebble- to boulder-sized, hence are undetectable by the telescope.

Inasmuch as the asteroids are widely distributed, there can be no doubt that many of them have been captured by other members of the solar system. The craters on Mars and the moon are evidence of the fate of a goodly number. Many have fallen to earth too; indeed, it is from these fragments that we learn most of

what we know about the physical characteristics of extraterrestrial bodies. Meteorites will
be discussed below and what we say about them
also applies to asteroids.

COMETS

Comets are in many ways the most spectacular
bodies to circle the sun. Most of them move in
exceedingly elongate orbits and are near the
sun for only a short time in each revolution. It
is during these close approaches that they blaze
into prominence. The heat of the sun vaporizes
a part of the nucleus or head and converts it
into the lengthy, ever-changing tail.

Although comets show great variation and
individuality, it is assumed that all are funda-
mentally aggregations of ice, dust, and rock.
Many of the meteorites that crash to earth
(including chunks of ice) are undoubtedly parts
of disintegrated comets. The break-up of known
comets into incoherent swarms of meteoritic
fragments has been well authenticated. In the
earlier stages of the solar system, comets may
have been much more abundant; many have
fallen into the planets, adding considerable substance to them.

METEORITES

A meteorite is a solid object larger than a molecule and smaller than a planet that passes
through the atmosphere and reaches the surface
of the earth without being vaporized. Meteorites are currently being sought after and studied
in an intensive way, for they give our most
direct clues to the composition, age, and origin
of extraterrestrial matter. As we saw in Chapter 7, meteorites are classified into two chief
groups according to composition: the irons, and
the stones.

The irons are almost pure metal, iron being
the chief constituent. They are characterized by
a lattice-like crystalline pattern thought to have
resulted from slow cooling under high pressure,
such as might be reached in the central core of
a fairly large earth-like body. On the basis of
structure and composition, it is thought that
most meteorites are derived from one or more
disrupted planets that occupied an orbit between Mars and Jupiter.

The stony meteorites, which are far more
numerous than the irons, could likewise be
accounted for as fragments of an earth-like

Figure 23-10   Arend-Roland comet, showing changes from April 26 to May 1, 1957.
(*Courtesy Mt. Wilson and Palomar Observatories.*)

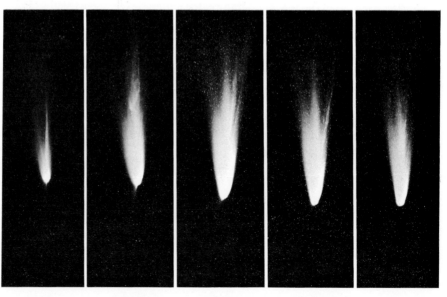

| April 26 | April 27 | April 29 | April 30 | May 1 |

Figure 23-11   Iron meteorite from Henbury, Australia. Length of specimen 7½ inches. (Courtesy Center for Meteorite Studies, Arizona State University.)

planet. Many of them look so much like rocks native to the earth that they escape notice and are not collected. The most common type of stony meteorite comprises the chondrites, so-named because they contain small, rounded, drop-like inclusions called chondrules. Chondrules have a rather uniform chemical composition similar to the heavier basic rocks of the earth and may be samples of the original swarm of particles that aggregated to form the earth-like planets. In support of this theory is the discovery that they show a surprisingly uniform age of about 4.6 billion years, a figure close to that calculated for the earth.

The supposed similarities of meteorites and the earth have been mentioned several times. Although the inner shells of the earth cannot be sampled directly and although it cannot be proven that the asteroids and most meteorites did indeed come from a shattered planet, the sum total of circumstantial and indirect evidence supports the idea that the core of the earth is like the iron meteorites and the mantle is like the stony ones. This concept called the "meteorite analogy," is the basis for much of our thinking about the history and composition of the solar system.

TEKTITES

Tektites are small pieces of glassy material resembling the natural rock obsidian. Although they are generally regarded as a type of meteor-

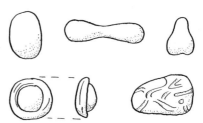

Figure 23-12   Tektites showing varied shapes. One-half natural size.

ite, none have actually been observed to fall. In shape they resemble teardrops, spheres, buttons, dumb-bells, and other rounded objects. Their surfaces show clear evidence of melting, and there are internal indications of very rapid cooling. In chemical composition, they resemble soil or sedimentary rocks and are very unlike ordinary meteorites.

Thousands of tektites have been collected, but they are not distributed uniformly. Eight distinct areas of the earth yield tektites which are designated accordingly as Australites, Indochinites, Philippenites, and so on. The origin of these bodies is a mystery, though several theories have been proposed. Some investigators claim they are of earthly origin, others believe them to be material splashed out of the moon by large meteorites. The prevailing hypothesis of lunar origin seems to explain most of the known facts, but we need actual samples of the moon to test this idea.

SUMMARY

The term *Astrogeology* is coming into use to designate the application of geologic concepts and techniques to solid astronomical bodies. Currently the moon and Mars are receiving much attention and they are being compared and contrasted with each other and with the earth. The dominant features of the moon are craters formed by impact of infalling meteorites; in the absence of active erosion, craters of all ages, up to possibly 4.0 billion years old, are preserved. One episode of igneous activity, the production of the extensive mare plains is attributed to partial melting and outflow of lava. Close-up photographs reveal that some of the surface is composed of loose but firm dust or soil-like material, probably repeatedly broken by infalling fragments.

Mars has been shown by photographs to have a cratered, moon-like surface. There is a light atmosphere, and erosion by air currents and shifting of dust is actively taking place. Not much can be said of the topography and composition of the solid parts of the other planets.

A vital link with extra-terrestrial bodies is provided by the meteorites, of which there are both stony and metallic (iron) varieties. Most meteorites are supposed to have originated at the disruption of an earth-like planet which moved in an orbit between Mars and Jupiter. Meteoritic material resembles earth material in both composition and age. Some meteorites probably come from the disintegration of comets; those suspected of having this origin again reveal a chemical unity with the rest of the system.

Tektites are small glassy objects of uncertain origin. They have obviously been subjected to heat and their distribution suggests that they have fallen in "swarms" through the atmosphere. They may have been propelled from the moon by powerful impacts or "splashed" from the earth when it was struck by large meteorites or asteroids.

ADDITIONAL READING

Baldwin, R. B., *The Measure of the Moon.* Chicago: University of Chicago Press, 1963.

————, *The Moon—A Fundamental Survey.* New York: McGraw-Hill Book Co., 1965.

Hawkins, G. S., *Meteors, Comets and Meteorites.* New York: McGraw-Hill Book Co., 1964.

O'Keefe, John A., *Tektites.* Chicago: University of Chicago Press, 1963.

Page, T., and L. W. Page, eds. *Neighbors of the Earth: Planets, Comets, and the Debris of Space.* New York: Macmillan, 1965.

Richardson, R. S., *Mars.* New York: Harcourt, Brace & World, 1964.

Whipple, F. L., *Earth, Moon and Planets.* Cambridge: Harvard University Press, 1963.

Other references to the material of this chapter can be found at the end of Chapters 1 and 7.

Appendixes

Appendix A

ELECTRONIC CONFIGURATION OF THE FIRST 30 ELEMENTS

(These elements constitute 99.6 per cent of the earth's crust)

Atomic Number (Protons)	Name of Element	Symbol	1-shell s	2-shell s p	3-shell s p d	4-shell s p d f	Mass Number (Protons + Neutrons) of Stable Isotopes in Order of Abundance	Parts Per Million in Earth's Crust
1	Hydrogen	H	1				1, 2	1,400.
2	Helium	He	2 Inert Gas				4, 3	.003
3	Lithium	Li	2	1			7, 6	65.
4	Beryllium	Be	2	2			9	<.001
5	Boron	B	2	2 1			11, 10	3.
6	Carbon	C	2	2 2			12, 13	320.
7	Nitrogen	N	2	2 3			14, 15	46.
8	Oxygen	O	2	2 4			16, 18	466,000.
9	Fluorine	F	2	2 5			19	300.
10	Neon	Ne	2	2 6 Inert Gas			20, 22, 21	<.001
11	Sodium	Na	2	2 6	1		23	28,300.
12	Magnesium	Mg	2	2 6	2		24, 25, 26	20,900.
13	Aluminum	Al	2	2 6	2 1		27	81,300.
14	Silicon	Si	2	2 6	2 2		28, 29, 30	277,200.
15	Phosphorus	P	2	2 6	2 3		31	1,180.
16	Sulfur	S	2	2 6	2 4		32, 34, 33, 36	520.
17	Chlorine	Cl	2	2 6	2 5		35, 37	314.
18	Argon	A	2	2 6	2 6 Inert Gas		40, 36, 38	.04
19	Potassium	K	2	2 6	2 6	1	39, 41	25,900.
20	Calcium	Ca	2	2 6	2 6	2	40, 42, 43, 44, 46, 48	36,300.
21	Scandium	Sc	2	2 6	2 6 1	2	45	5.
22	Titanium	Ti	2	2 6	2 6 2	2	48, 46, 47, 49, 50	4,400.
23	Vanadium	V	2	2 6	2 6 3	2	51	150.
24	Chromium	Cr	2	2 6	2 6 5	1	52, 53, 50, 54	200.
25	Manganese	Mn	2	2 6	2 6 5	2	55	1,000.
26	Iron	Fe	2	2 6	2 6 6	2	56, 54, 57, 58	50,000.
27	Cobalt	Co	2	2 6	2 6 7	2	59	23.
28	Nickel	Ni	2	2 6	2 6 8	2	58, 60, 62, 61, 64	80.
29	Copper	Cu	2	2 6	2 6 10	1	63, 65	70.
30	Zinc	Zn	2	2 6	2 6 10	2	64, 66, 68, 67, 70	132.

(Elements 21–29 marked as "Transition Elements")

996,108.
(99.61 per cent)

Number of Electrons in

Atomic Number (Protons)	Name of Element	Symbol	1-shell s	2-shell s p	3-shell s p d	4-shell s p d f	5-shell s p d f	6-shell s p d f	7-shell s p d f
31	Gallium	Ga	2	2 6	2 6 10	2 1			
32	Germanium	Ge	2	2 6	2 6 10	2 2			
33	Arsenic	As	2	2 6	2 6 10	2 3			
34	Selenium	Se	2	2 6	2 6 10	2 4			
35	Bromine	Br	2	2 6	2 6 10	2 5			
36	Krypton	Kr	2	2 6	2 6 10	2 6 Inert Gas			
37	Rubidium	Rb	2	2 6	2 6 10	2 6	1		
38	Strontium	Sr	2	2 6	2 6 10	2 6	2		
39	Yttrium	Y	2	2 6	2 6 10	2 6 1	2		
40	Zirconium	Zr	2	2 6	2 6 10	2 6 2	2		
41	Niobium (Columbium)	Nb (Cb)	2	2 6	2 6 10	2 6 4	1		
42	Molybdenum	Mo	2	2 6	2 6 10	2 6 5	1		
43	Technetium	Tc	2	2 6	2 6 10	2 6 6	1		
44	Ruthenium	Ru	2	2 6	2 6 10	2 6 7	1		
45	Rhodium	Rh	2	2 6	2 6 10	2 6 8	1		
46	Palladium	Pd	2	2 6	2 6 10	2 6 10			
47	Silver	Ag	2	2 6	2 6 10	2 6 10	1		
48	Cadmium	Cd	2	2 6	2 6 10	2 6 10	2		
49	Indium	In	2	2 6	2 6 10	2 6 10	2 1		
50	Tin	Sn	2	2 6	2 6 10	2 6 10	2 2		
51	Antimony	Sb	2	2 6	2 6 10	2 6 10	2 3		
52	Tellurium	Te	2	2 6	2 6 10	2 6 10	2 4		
53	Iodine	I	2	2 6	2 6 10	2 6 10	2 5		
54	Xenon	Xe	2	2 6	2 6 10	2 6 10	2 6 Inert Gas		
55	Cesium	Cs	2	2 6	2 6 10	2 6 10	2 6	1	
56	Barium	Ba	2	2 6	2 6 10	2 6 10	2 6	2	
57	Lanthanum	La	2	2 6	2 6 10	2 6 10	2 6 1	2	
58	Cerium	Ce	2	2 6	2 6 10	2 6 10 1	2 6 1	2	
59	Praseodymium	Pr	2	2 6	2 6 10	2 6 10 2	2 6 1	2	
60	Neodymium	Nd	2	2 6	2 6 10	2 6 10 3	2 6 1	2	
61	Promethium	Pm	2	2 6	2 6 10	2 6 10 4	2 6 1	2	
62	Samarium	Sm	2	2 6	2 6 10	2 6 10 5	2 6 1	2	
63	Europium	Eu	2	2 6	2 6 10	2 6 10 6	2 6 1	2	
64	Gadolinium	Gd	2	2 6	2 6 10	2 6 10 7	2 6 1	2	
65	Terbium	Tb	2	2 6	2 6 10	2 6 10 8	2 6 1	2	
66	Dysprosium	Dy	2	2 6	2 6 10	2 6 10 9	2 6 1	2	
67	Holmium	Ho	2	2 6	2 6 10	2 6 10 10	2 6 1	2	
68	Erbium	Er	2	2 6	2 6 10	2 6 10 11	2 6 1	2	
69	Thulium	Tm	2	2 6	2 6 10	2 6 10 12	2 6 1	2	
70	Ytterbium	Yb	2	2 6	2 6 10	2 6 10 13	2 6 1	2	
71	Lutetium	Lu	2	2 6	2 6 10	2 6 10 14	2 6 1	2	
72	Hafnium	Hf	2	2 6	2 6 10	2 6 10 14	2 6 2	2	
73	Tantalum	Ta	2	2 6	2 6 10	2 6 10 14	2 6 3	2	
74	Wolfram (Tungsten)	W	2	2 6	2 6 10	2 6 10 14	2 6 4	2	
75	Rhenium	Re	2	2 6	2 6 10	2 6 10 14	2 6 5	2	
76	Osmium	Os	2	2 6	2 6 10	2 6 10 14	2 6 6	2	
77	Iridium	Ir	2	2 6	2 6 10	2 6 10 14	2 6 7	2	
78	Platinum	Pt	2	2 6	2 6 10	2 6 10 14	2 6 8	2	
79	Gold	Au	2	2 6	2 6 10	2 6 10 14	2 6 10	1	
80	Mercury	Hg	2	2 6	2 6 10	2 6 10 14	2 6 10	2	
81	Thallium	Tl	2	2 6	2 6 10	2 6 10 14	2 6 10	2 1	
82	Lead	Pb	2	2 6	2 6 10	2 6 10 14	2 6 10	2 2	
83	Bismuth	Bi	2	2 6	2 6 10	2 6 10 14	2 6 10	2 3	

Note: Elements 39–47 are bracketed "Transition Elements"; elements 57–71 are bracketed "Rare Earths"; elements 57–78 are bracketed "Transition Elements."

Number of Electrons in

Atomic Number (Protons)	Name of Element	Symbol	1-shell s	2-shell s	2-shell p	3-shell s	3-shell p	3-shell d	4-shell s	4-shell p	4-shell d	4-shell f	5-shell s	5-shell p	5-shell d	5-shell f	6-shell s	6-shell p	6-shell d	6-shell f	7-shell s	7-shell p	7-shell d	7-shell f	
84	Polonium	Po	2	2	6	2	6	10	2	6	10	14	2	6	10		2	4							
85	Astatine	At	2	2	6	2	6	10	2	6	10	14	2	6	10		2	5							
86	Radon	Rn	2	2	6	2	6	10	2	6	10	14	2	6	10		2	6		Inert Gas					
87	Francium	Fr	2	2	6	2	6	10	2	6	10	14	2	6	10		2	6			1				
88	Radium	Ra	2	2	6	2	6	10	2	6	10	14	2	6	10		2	6			2				
89	Actinium	Ac	2	2	6	2	6	10	2	6	10	14	2	6	10		2	6	1		2				
90	Thorium	Th	2	2	6	2	6	10	2	6	10	14	2	6	10	1	2	6	1		2				
91	Protactinium	Pa	2	2	6	2	6	10	2	6	10	14	2	6	10	2	2	6	1		2				
92	Uranium	U	2	2	6	2	6	10	2	6	10	14	2	6	10	3	2	6	1		2				
93	Neptunium	Np	2	2	6	2	6	10	2	6	10	14	2	6	10	4	2	6	1		2				
94	Plutonium	Pu	2	2	6	2	6	10	2	6	10	14	2	6	10	5	2	6	1		2				
95	Americium	Am	2	2	6	2	6	10	2	6	10	14	2	6	10	6	2	6	1		2				
96	Curium	Cm	2	2	6	2	6	10	2	6	10	14	2	6	10	7	2	6	1		2				
97	Berkelium	Bk	2	2	6	2	6	10	2	6	10	14	2	6	10	8	2	6	1		2				
98	Californium	Cf	2	2	6	2	6	10	2	6	10	14	2	6	10	9	2	6	1		2				
99	Einsteinium	En	2	2	6	2	6	10	2	6	10	14	2	6	10	10	2	6	1		2				
100	Fermium	Fm	2	2	6	2	6	10	2	6	10	14	2	6	10	11	2	6	1		2				
101	Mendelevium	Me	2	2	6	2	6	10	2	6	10	14	2	6	10	12	2	6	1		2				
102	Nobelium	No	2	2	6	2	6	10	2	6	10	14	2	6	10	13	2	6	1		2				

(Elements 89–102: Transition Elements)

ALPHABETICAL LIST OF THE ELEMENTS

Element	Symbol	Atomic Number	Element	Symbol	Atomic Number	Element	Symbol	Atomic Number
Actinium	Ac	89	Gold	Au	79	Promethium	Pm	61
Aluminum	Al	13	Hafnium	Hf	72	Protactinium	Pa	91
Americium	Am	95	Helium	He	2	Radium	Ra	88
Antimony	Sb	51	Holmium	Ho	67	Radon	Rn	86
Argon	A	18	Hydrogen	H	1	Rhenium	Re	75
Arsenic	As	33	Indium	In	49	Rhodium	Rh	45
Astatine	At	85	Iodine	I	53	Rubidium	Rb	37
Barium	Ba	56	Iridium	Ir	77	Ruthenium	Ru	44
Berkelium	Bk	97	Iron	Fe	26	Samarium	Sm	62
Beryllium	Be	4	Krypton	Kr	36	Scandium	Sc	21
Bismuth	Bi	83	Lanthanum	La	57	Selenium	Se	34
Boron	B	5	Lead	Pb	82	Silicon	Si	14
Bromine	Br	35	Lithium	Li	3	Silver	Ag	47
Cadmium	Cd	48	Lutetium	Lu	71	Sodium	Na	11
Calcium	Ca	20	Magnesium	Mg	12	Strontium	Sr	38
Californium	Cf	98	Manganese	Mn	25	Sulfur	S	16
Carbon	C	6	Mendelevium	Me	101	Tantalum	Ta	73
Cerium	Ce	58	Mercury	Hg	80	Technetium	Tc	43
Cesium	Cs	55	Molybdenum	Mo	42	Tellurium	Te	52
Chlorine	Cl	17	Neodymium	Nd	60	Terbium	Tb	65
Chromium	Cr	24	Neon	Ne	10	Thallium	Tl	81
Cobalt	Co	27	Neptunium	Np	93	Thorium	Th	90
Columbium (or Niobium	Cb Nb)	41	Nickel	Ni	28	Thulium	Tm	69
Copper	Cu	29	Niobium (or Columbium	Nb Cb)	41	Tin	Sn	50
Curium	Cm	96	Nitrogen	N	7	Titanium	Ti	22
Dysprosium	Dy	66	Nobelium	No	102	Tungsten (or Wolfram)	W	74
Einsteinium	En	99	Osmium	Os	76	Uranium	U	92
Erbium	Er	68	Oxygen	O	8	Vanadium	V	23
Europium	Eu	63	Palladium	Pd	46	Wolfram (or Tungsten)	W	74
Fermium	Fm	100	Phosphorus	P	15	Xenon	Xe	54
Fluorine	F	9	Platinum	Pt	78	Ytterbium	Yb	70
Francium	Fr	87	Plutonium	Pu	94	Yttrium	Y	39
Gadolinium	Gd	64	Polonium	Po	84	Zinc	Zn	30
Gallium	Ga	31	Potassium	K	19	Zirconium	Zr	40
Germanium	Ge	32	Praseodymium	Pr	59			

MASS AND ENERGY

It has been found that the mass of an atomic nucleus is less than the total mass of its components as separate particles. This is explained by the fact that when a nucleus forms, a small amount of mass disappears by changing into energy, which is radiated away. The energy represented by this mass defect is called the *binding energy*. It is the amount of energy that must be supplied in order to break the nucleus into its component particles again.

The discovery of the equivalence of mass and energy is one of the most fundamental and significant events in the history of mankind.

Consider, for example, a helium nucleus of 2 protons and 2 neutrons:

1 proton	1.00758 mass units
1 proton	1.00758 mass units
1 neutron	1.00893 mass units
1 neutron	1.00893 mass units
Total 4 particles	4.03302 mass units
Helium nucleus	4.00280 mass units
	.03022 mass units deficiency converted to energy when nucleus was formed

In 1905, Albert Einstein expressed the equivalence of mass and energy by the now-famous equation

$$E = mc^2$$

where E is the energy in ergs, m is the mass in grams, and c is the velocity of light in centimeters per second.

It was not until 1932 that experimental proof of this relationship was obtained. When $_3Li^7$ was bombarded with high-speed protons ($_1H^1$), alpha particles ($_2He^4$) were ejected from the lithium:

Lithium + Hydrogen yielded Alpha Particles

$$_3Li^7 + {_1H^1} \longrightarrow {_2He^4} + {_2He^4}$$

Mass: 8.0241   8.0056

The lost mass was 8.0241 − 8.0056 = .0185, which the two alpha particles were found to possess in the form of velocity of motion.

The quantities of energy released in reactions of this kind are almost inconceivably greater than those released by any other type of reaction involving similar quantities of material. For example, 1 kilogram (2.2 pounds) of matter, if converted entirely into energy, would give 25 billion kilowatt hours of energy. This is equal to the energy that was generated during approximately a two-month period by the total electric power industry existing in the United States in 1939. In contrast, the burning of an equal amount of coal gives 8.5 kilowatt hours of heat energy.

It is now generally believed that a series of nuclear changes maintains the energy of the sun. If the conversion of mass into energy can be accomplished under controlled conditions by man, an almost limitless source of energy in vast quantities will be provided.

Figure A-1 Equivalence of mass and energy. Two protons plus 2 neutrons as separate particles (left-hand scale pan) total 4.03302 mass units. When they are combined to form an alpha particle, mass disappears in the form of energy, so the alpha particle has only 4.00280 mass units (right-hand scale pan). This lost energy (or mass) is called the binding energy and must be applied to the alpha particle to break it up into separate particles again.

Appendix B

POWERS OF TEN

We need a special vocabulary to describe the size of things ranging from invisible atoms to the vast reaches of space around us. Such a vocabulary is supplied by the *powers of ten*.

$10^0 = 1$	1 with decimal point moved zero places
$10^1 = 10$	1 with decimal point moved 1 place to right
$10^2 = 100$	1 with decimal point moved 2 places to right
$10^3 = 1,000$	1 with decimal point moved 3 places to right
$10^4 = 10,000$	1 with decimal point moved 4 places to right
$10^5 = 100,000$	1 with decimal point moved 5 places to right
$10^6 = 1,000,000$ (1 million)	1 with decimal point moved 6 places to right
	etc.

In other words, the exponent of 10 indicates the number of places the decimal point is moved to the right (or the number of zeros following 1).

For numbers smaller than 1, a negative exponent is used.

$10^{-1} = .1$	1 with decimal point moved 1 place to left
$10^{-2} = .01$	1 with decimal point moved 2 places to left
$10^{-3} = .001$	1 with decimal point moved 3 places to left
	etc.

In other words, the negative exponent of 10 indicates the number of places the decimal point is moved to the left of the number 1.

In comparing the sizes of things expressed in powers of 10, we need to recall certain laws of exponents taught in school algebra:

Multiplication. Add exponents. Examples:

$$10^3 \cdot 10^3 = 10^{3+3} = 10^6$$
$$\text{or} \quad 1,000 \cdot 1,000 = 1,000,000 \ (1 \text{ million})$$
$$10^{21} \cdot 10^6 = 10^{27}$$

(That is, 10^{27} is 10^6 or one million times as large as 10^{21}.)

Division. Subtract exponents. Examples:

$$10^6/10^3 = 10^{6-3} = 10^3$$
$$10^{27}/10^{21} = 10^{27-21} = 10^6$$

Some Distances and Sizes Expressed in Powers of Ten

	Centimeters
1 light-year	10^{18}
	10^{17}
	10^{16}
	10^{15}
	10^{14}
Distance from earth to sun ($1.5 \cdot 10^{13}$ cm)	10^{13}
	10^{12}
	10^{11}
	10^{10}
Diameter of earth ($1.3 \cdot 10^9$ cm)	10^9
	10^8
	10^7
Distant view	10^6
	10^5
Lengths of radio waves	10^4
	10^3
Meter stick (approximately 1 yard)	10^2
Width of hand	10^1
Width of pencil 1(cm = .39 in.)	10^0
	10^{-1}
Thickness of sheet of paper	10^{-2}
	10^{-3}
	10^{-4}
Wave length of visible light	10^{-5}
Diameter of some molecules	10^{-6}
X-rays	10^{-7}
Diameter of atom (1 angstrom)	10^{-8}
	10^{-9}
	10^{-10}
	10^{-11}
Diameter of atomic nucleus	10^{-12}
	10^{-13}
	10^{-14}

THE METRIC SYSTEM

Prefixes: Mega = 1,000,000; Kilo = 1,000; Centi = 0.01; Milli = 0.001; and Micro = 0.000001.

Metric units compared with each other and with other systems:

Units of Length

Meter	Foot	Kilometer	Mile (Statute)
1	3.28083	1.0×10^{-3}	6.21372×10^{-4}
0.30480	1	3.0480×10^{-4}	1.8939×10^{-4}
1000	3280.83	1	0.621372
1609.3	5280	1.6093	1

Units of Area

Sq. Meter	Sq. Foot	Sq. Kilometer	Acre (U.S.)	Sq. Mile
1	10.76387	1.0×10^{-6}	2.47104×10^{-4}	3.86101×10^{-7}
0.092903	1	9.2903×10^{-8}	2.2957×10^{-5}	3.58699×10^{-8}
1.0×10^{6}	1.076387×10^{7}	1	247.104	0.386101
4046	43,560	4.04687×10^{-3}	1	1.5625×10^{-3}
2.59000×10^{6}	2.7878×10^{7}	2.59000	640	1

Units of Volume

Cubic Meter	Cubic Foot (U.S.)	Acre Foot	Barrel	Gallon (U.S., Liquid)
1	35.314	8.1070×10^{-4}	6.2898	264.17
2.8317×10^{-2}	1	2.2957×10^{-5}	0.17811	7.4805
1233.5	43,560	1	7758	3.2585×10^{5}
0.15899	5.6146	1.2889×10^{-4}	1	42
3.7854×10^{-3}	0.13368	3.0689×10^{-6}	2.3810×10^{-2}	1

Units of Pressure, PSI

Kilogram/Sq. Centimeter	Lb./Sq. In.	Atmospheric	Lb./Sq. Ft.
1	14.223	0.9678	2048.1
7.0307×10^{-2}	1	6.8046×10^{-2}	144
1.0333	14.696	1	2116.2
4.8824×10^{-4}	6.9444×10^{-3}	4.7254×10^{-4}	1

Units of Weight

Kilogram	Lb. (Avoirdupois)	Ton (Short)
0.4535924	1	0.0005
1	2.20462	1.1023×10^{-3}
907.185	2000	1

Units of Density

Kilogram/Meter^3	Lb./Ft.^{3}	Gram/Centimeter^3
16.018	1	1.6018×10^{-2}
1	6.2428×10^{-2}	0.001
1000	62.428	1

Appendix C

MINERALS

Many of the most common minerals may be identified in hand specimens by their physical properties. Among the characteristics useful for this purpose are (1) hardness, (2) specific gravity, (3) streak (sometimes color), (4) shape (that is, crystal form, cleavage, and fracture), and (5) response to light as indicated by luster and transparency.

Hardness

The hardness of a mineral is determined by scratching the smooth surface of one mineral with the edge of another. In making a hardness test, be sure that the mineral being tested is actually scratched. Sometimes particles simply rub off the specimen, suggesting that it has been scratched, even though it has not been.

Ten common minerals have been arranged in the Mohs scale of relative hardness.

Mohs Scale of Hardness

Softest	1	Talc	
	2	Gypsum	
	3	Calcite	$2\frac{1}{2}$ Fingernail
			3 Copper coin
	4	Fluorite	
	5	Apatite	
			$5\frac{1}{2}$–6 Knife blade or plate
	6	Orthoclase	glass
			$6\frac{1}{2}$–7 Steel file
	7	Quartz	
	8	Topaz	
	9	Corundum	
Hardest	10	Diamond	

Each of these minerals will scratch all those lower in number on the scale and will be scratched by all those higher. In other words, this is a *relative scale*. In terms of absolute hardness, the steps are nearly, though not quite, uniform up to 9. Number 7 is 7 times as hard as 1, and number 9 is 9 times as hard as 1. But number 10 is about 40 times as hard as 1.

Luster

Luster is the way a mineral looks in reflected light. There are several kinds of luster.

Metallic, the luster of metals.
Adamantine, the luster of diamonds.
Vitreous, the luster of a broken edge of glass.
Resinous, the luster of yellow resin.
Pearly, the luster of pearl.
Silky, the luster of silk.

Fracture

Many minerals that do not exhibit cleavage (see Chapter 4) do break, or fracture, in a distinctive manner. Some of the types of fracture are:

Conchoidal: along smooth, curved surfaces like the surface of a shell (*conch*). Commonly observed in glass and quartz.

Fibrous or **splintery:** along surfaces roughened by splinters or fibers.

Uneven or **irregular:** along rough, irregular surfaces.

Hackly: along a jagged, irregular surface with sharp edges.

477

Mineral	Chemical Composition and Name	Specific Gravity	Streak	Hardness	Cleavage or Fracture	Luster
Actinolite (An asbestos; an amphibole)	$Ca_2(Mg,Fe)_5Si_8O_2(OH)_2$ Calcium iron silicate	3.0–3.3	Colorless	5–6	See Amphibole	Vitreous
Albite	(See Feldspars)					
Amphibole	(See Hornblende)				Perfect prismatic at 56° and 124°, often yielding a splintery surface	
Andalusite	Al_2SiO_5 Aluminum silicate	3.16	Colorless	$7\frac{1}{2}$	Not prominent	Vitreous
Anhydrite	$CaSO_4$ Anhydrous calcium sulfate	2.89–2.98	Colorless	$3–3\frac{1}{2}$	3 directions at right angles to form rectangular blocks	Vitreous; pearly
Anorthite	(See Feldspars)					
Apatite	$Ca_5(F,Cl)(PO_4)_3$ Calcium fluophosphate	3.15–3.2	White	5	Poor cleavage, one direction; conchoidal fracture	Glassy
Asbestos	(See Actinolite, Chrysotile, Serpentine)					
Augite (A pyroxene)	$Ca(Mg,Fe,Al)(Al,Si_2O_6)$ Ferromagnesian silicate	3.2–3.4	Greenish gray	5–6	Perfect prismatic along two planes at nearly right angles to each other, often yielding a splintery surface	Vitreous
Azurite	$Cu_3(CO_3)_2(OH)_2$ Blue copper carbonate	3.77	Pale blue	4	Fibrous	Vitreous to dull, earthy
Bauxite	Hydrous aluminum oxides of indefinite composition; not a mineral	2–3	Colorless	1–3	Uneven fracture	Dull to earthy
Biotite (Black mica)	$K(Mg,Fe)_3AlSi_3O_{10}(OH)_2$ Ferromagnesian silicate	2.8–3.2	Colorless	$2\frac{1}{2}–3$	Perfect in one direction into thin, elastic, transparent, smoky sheets	Pearly, glassy
Bornite (Peacock ore; purple copper ore)	Cu_5FeS_4 Copper iron sulfide	5.06–5.08	Grayish black	3	Uneven fracture	Metallic
Calcite	$CaCO_3$ Calcium carbonate	2.72	Colorless	3	Perfect in 3 directions at 75° to form unique rhombohedral fragments	Vitreous
Carnotite	$K_2(UO_2)_2(VO_4)_2$ Potassium uranyl vanadate	4		Very soft	Uneven fracture	Earthy
Cassiterite (Tin stone)	SnO_2 Tin oxide	6.8–7.1	White to light brown	6–7	Conchoidal fracture	Adamantine to submetallic and dull
Chalcedony	(See Quartz)					
Chalcocite (Copper glance)	Cu_2S Copper sulfide	5.5–5.8	Grayish black	$2\frac{1}{2}–3$	Conchoidal fracture	Metallic

Color	Transparency	Form	Other Properties
White to light green	Transparent to translucent	Slender crystals, usually fibrous	A common ferromagnesian metamorphic mineral.
			A group of silicates with tetrahedra in double chains; hornblende is the most important; contrast with pyroxene.
Flesh-red, reddish brown, olive-green	Transparent to translucent	Usually in coarse, nearly square prisms; cross section may show black cross	Found in schists formed by the middle-grade metamorphism of aluminous shales and slates. The variety *chiastolite* has carbonaceous inclusions in the pattern of a cross.
White; may have faint gray, blue, or red tinge	Transparent to translucent	Commonly in massive fine aggregates not showing cleavage; crystals rare	Found in limestones and in beds associated with salt deposits; heavier than calcite, harder than gypsum.
Green, brown, red	Translucent to transparent	Massive, granular	Widely disseminated as an accessory mineral in all types of rocks; unimportant source of fertilizer; a transparent variety is a gem, but too soft for general use.
			A general term applied to certain fibrous minerals that display similar physical characteristics although they differ in composition. The most common asbestos mineral is *chrysotile,* a variety of serpentine.
Dark green to black	Translucent only on thin edges	Short, stubby crystals with 4- or 8-sided cross section; often in granular crystalline masses	An important igneous rock-forming mineral found chiefly in simatic rocks.
Intense azure blue	Opaque	Crystals complex in habit and distorted; sometimes in radiating spherical groups	An ore of copper; a gem mineral; effervesces with HCl.
Yellow, brown, gray, white	Opaque	In rounded grains; or earthy, clay-like masses	An ore of aluminum; produced under subtropical to tropical climatic conditions by prolonged weathering of aluminum-bearing rocks; a component of *laterites;* clay odor when wet.
Black, brown, dark green	Transparent, translucent	Usually in irregular foliated masses; crystals rare	Constructed around tetrahedral sheets; a common and important rock-forming mineral in both igneous and metamorphic rocks.
Brownish bronze on fresh fracture; quickly tarnishes to variegated purple and blue, and finally black	Opaque	Usually massive; rarely in rough cubic crystals	An important ore of copper.
Usually white or colorless; may be tinted gray, red, green, blue, yellow	Transparent to opaque	Usually in crystals or coarse to fine granular aggregates; also compact, earthy; crystals extremely varied—over 300 different forms	A very common rock mineral, occurring in masses as limestone and marble; effervesces freely in cold dilute hydrochloric acid.
Brilliant canary yellow	Opaque	Earthy powder	An ore of vanadium and uranium.
Brown or black; rarely yellow or white	Translucent; rarely transparent	Commonly massive granular	The principal ore of tin.
Shiny lead-gray; tarnishes to dull black	Opaque	Commonly fine-grained and massive; crystals rare; small, tabular with hexagonal outline	One of the most important ore minerals of copper; occurs principally as a result of secondary sulfide enrichment.

Mineral	Chemical Composition and Name	Specific Gravity	Streak	Hardness	Cleavage or Fracture	Luster
Chalcopyrite (Copper pyrites; yellow copper ore; fool's gold)	$CuFeS_2$ Copper iron sulfide	4.1–4.3	Greenish black; also greenish powder in groove when scratched	$3\frac{1}{2}$–4	Uneven fracture	Metallic
Chlorite	$(Mg,Fe)_5(Al,Fe'')_2$ $Si_3O_{10}(OH)_8$ Hydrous ferromagnesian aluminum silicate	2.6–2.9	Colorless	2–$2\frac{1}{2}$	Perfect in 1 direction like micas, but into in-elastic flakes	Vitreous to pearly
Chromite	$FeCr_2O_4$ Iron chromium oxide	4.6	Dark brown	$5\frac{1}{2}$	Uneven fracture	Metallic to submetallic or pitchy
Chrysotile (Serpentine asbestos)	(See Serpentine)					
Clay	(See Kaolinite)					
Corundum (Ruby, sapphire)	Al_2O_3 Aluminum oxide	4.02	Colorless	9	Basal or rhombohedral parting	Adamantine to vitreous
Diamond	C Carbon	3.5	Colorless	10	Octahedral cleavage	Adamantine; greasy
Dolomite	$CaMg(CO_3)_2$ Calcium magnesium carbonate	2.85	Colorless	$3\frac{1}{2}$–4	Perfect in 3 directions at 73°45′	Vitreous or pearly
Emery	(See Corundum)					
Epidote	$Ca_2(Al,Fe)_3(SiO_4)_3(OH)$ Hydrous calcium aluminum iron silicate	3.35–3.45	Colorless	6–7	Good in 1 direction	Vitreous
Feldspars	Alumino silicates	2.55–2.75		6	Good in 2 directions at or near 90°	
Orthoclase	$K(AlSi_3O_8)$ Potassic feldspar	2.57	White	6	Good in 2 directions at or near 90°	Vitreous
Plagioclase	Soda-lime feldspars, a continuous series varying in composition from pure albite to pure anorthite					
Albite	$Na(AlSi_3O_8)$ Sodic feldspar	2.62	Colorless	6	Good in 2 directions at 93°34′	Vitreous to pearly
Anorthite	$Ca(Al_2Si_2O_8)$	2.76	Colorless	6	Good in 2 directions at 94°12′	Vitreous to pearly
Fluorite	CaF_2 Calcium fluoride	3.18	Colorless	4	Good in 4 directions parallel to the faces of an octahedron	Vitreous
Galena	PbS Lead sulfide	7.4–7.6	Lead-gray	$2\frac{1}{2}$	Good in 3 directions parallel to the faces of a cube	Metallic

Color	Transparency	Form	Other Properties
Brass-yellow; tarnishes to bronze or iridescence, but more slowly than bornite or chalcocite	Opaque	Usually massive	An ore of copper; distinguished from pyrite by being softer than steel while pyrite is harder than steel; distinguished from gold by being brittle while gold is not; known as "fool's gold," a term also applied to pyrite.
Green of various shades	Transparent to translucent	Foliated massive, or in aggregates of minute scales	A common metamorphic mineral characteristic of low-grade metamorphism.
Iron-black to brownish black	Subtranslucent	Massive, granular to compact	The only ore of chromium; a common constituent of peridotites and serpentines derived from them; one of the first minerals to crystallize from a cooling magma.
Brown, pink, or blue; may be white, gray, green, ruby-red, sapphire-blue	Transparent to translucent	Barrel-shaped crystals; sometimes deep horizontal striations; coarse or fine granular	Common as an accessory mineral in metamorphic rocks such as marble, mica schist, gneiss; occurs in gem form as *ruby* and *sapphire;* the abrasive emery is black granular corundum mixed with magnetite, hematite, or the magnesian aluminum oxide *spinel.*
Colorless or pale yellow; may be red, orange, green, blue, black	Transparent	Octahedral crystals, flattened, elongated, with curved faces	Gem and abrasive; 95 per cent of natural diamond production is from South Africa; abrasive diamonds have been made in commercial quantities in the laboratory in the United States.
Pink, flesh; may be white, gray, green, brown, black	Transparent to opaque	Rhombohedral crystals with curved faces; coarse-grained cleavable masses, or fine-grained compact	Occurs chiefly in rock masses of dolomitic limestone and marble, or as the principal constituent of the rock named for it; distinguished from limestone by its less vigorous action with cold hydrochloric acid (the powder dissolves with effervescence, large pieces only if the acid is hot).
Pistachio-green, yellowish to blackish green	Transparent to translucent	Prismatic crystals striated parallel to length; usually coarse to fine granular; also fibrous	A metamorphic mineral often associated with chlorite; derived from metamorphism of impure limestone; characteristic of contact metamorphic zones in limestone.
			The most common igneous rock-forming group of minerals; weather to clay minerals.
White, gray, flesh pink	Translucent to opaque	Prismatic crystals; most abundantly in rocks as formless grains	Characteristic of sialic rocks.
			Important rock-forming minerals; characteristic of simatic rocks.
Colorless, white, gray	Transparent to translucent	Tabular crystals; striations caused by twinning	Opalescent variety, *moonstone.*
Colorless, white, gray, green, yellow, red	Transparent to translucent	Lath-like or platy grains, tabular crystals; striations caused by twinning; lath-like or platy grains	A unique and beautiful play of colors is common on plagioclase feldspars intermediate between albite and anorthite in composition, as with *andesine* (70 to 50 per cent albite) and *labradorite* (50 to 30 per cent albite).
Variable; light green, yellow, bluish green, purple, etc.	Transparent to translucent	Well-formed interlocking cubes; also massive, coarse or fine grains	Some varieties fluoresce; a common, widely distributed mineral in dolomites and limestone; an accessory mineral in igneous rocks; used as a flux in making steel.
Lead-gray	Opaque	Cube-shaped crystals; also in granular masses	The principal ore of lead; so commonly associated with silver that it is also an ore of silver.

THE COMMON MINERALS (Cont.)

Mineral	Chemical Composition and Name	Specific Gravity	Streak	Hardness	Cleavage or Fracture	Luster
Garnet	$R''_3R'''_2(SiO_4)_3$ R'' may be Calcium, Magnesium, Iron, or Manganese. R''' may be Aluminum, Iron, Titanium, or Chromium. Ferromagnesian silicates	3.5–4.3	Colorless	$6\frac{1}{2}$–$7\frac{1}{2}$	Uneven fracture	Vitreous to resinous
Graphite (Plumbago; black lead)	C Carbon	2.3	Black	1–2	Good in one direction; folia flexible but not elastic	Metallic or earthy
Gypsum	$CaSO_4 \cdot 2H_2O$ Hydrous calcium sulfate	2.32	Colorless	2	Good cleavage in one direction yielding flexible but inelastic flakes; fibrous fracture in another direction; conchoidal fracture in a third direction	Vitreous, pearly, silky
Halite (Rock salt; common salt)	NaCl Sodium chloride	2.16	Colorless	$2\frac{1}{2}$	Perfect cubic cleavage	Glassy to dull
Hematite	Fe_2O_3 Iron oxide	5.26	Light to dark Indian-red; becomes black on heating	$5\frac{1}{2}$–$6\frac{1}{2}$	Uneven fracture	Metallic
Hornblende (An amphibole)	Complex ferromagnesian silicate of Ca, Na, Mg, Ti, and Al	3.2	Colorless	5–6	Perfect prismatic at 56° and 124°	Vitreous; fibrous variety often silky
Kaolinite (Clay)	$Al_2Si_2O_5(OH)_4$ Hydrous aluminum silicate	2.6	Colorless	2–$2\frac{1}{2}$	None	Dull earthy
Kyanite	Al_2SiO_5 Aluminum silicate	3.56–3.66	Colorless	5 along, 7 across crystals	Good in one direction	Vitreous to pearly
Limonite (Brown hematite; bog iron ore; rust)	Hydrous iron oxides; not a mineral	3.6–4	Yellow-brown	5–$5\frac{1}{2}$ (Finely divided, apparent H as low as 1)	None	Vitreous
Magnetite	Fe_3O_4 Iron oxide	5.18	Black	6	Some octahedral parting	Metallic
Mica	(See Biotite and Muscovite)					
Muscovite (White mica; potassic mica; common mica)	$KAl_3Si_3O_{10}(OH)_2$ Nonferromagnesian silicate	2.76–3.1	Colorless	2–$2\frac{1}{2}$	Good cleavage in one direction, giving thin, very flexible and elastic folia	Vitreous, silky, pearly
Olivine (Peridot)	$(Mg,Fe)_2SiO_4$ Ferromagnesian silicate	3.27–3.37	Pale green, white	$6\frac{1}{2}$–7	Conchoidal fracture	Vitreous

Color	Transparency	Form	Other Properties
Red, brown, yellow, white, green, black	Transparent to translucent	Usually in 12- or 24-sided crystals; also massive granular, coarse or fine	Common and widely distributed, particularly in metamorphic rocks; brownish red variety *almandite*, $Fe_3Al_2(SiO_4)_3$, used to define one of the zones of middle-grade metamorphism; striking in schists.
Black to steel-gray	Opaque	Foliated or scaly masses common; may be radiated or granular	Feels greasy; common in metamorphic rocks such as marble, schists, and gneisses.
Colorless, white, gray; with impurities, yellow, red, brown	Transparent to translucent	Crystals prismatic, tabular, diamond-shaped; also in granular, fibrous, or earthy masses	A common mineral widely distributed in sedimentary rocks, often as thick beds; *satin spar* is a fibrous gypsum with silky luster; *selenite* is a variety which yields broad, colorless, transparent folia; *alabaster* is a fine-grained massive variety.
Colorless or white; impure: yellow, red, blue, purple	Transparent to translucent	Cubic crystals; massive granular	Salty taste; permits ready passage of heat rays (i.e., diathermanous); a very common mineral in sedimentary rocks; interstratified in rocks of all ages to form a true rock mass.
Reddish brown to black	Opaque	Crystals tabular; botryoidal; micaceous and foliated; massive	The most important ore of iron; red earthy variety known as *red ocher*; botryoidal form known as *kidney ore*, micaceous form *specular*; widely distributed in rocks of all types and ages.
Dark green to black	Translucent on thin edges	Long, prismatic crystals; fibrous; coarse- to fine-grained masses	Distinguished from augite by cleavage; a common, rock-forming mineral which occurs in both igneous and metamorphic rocks.
White	Opaque	Claylike masses	Usually unctuous and plastic; other clay minerals similar in composition and physical properties, but different in atomic structure, are *illite* and *montmorillonite*; derived from the weathering of the feldspars.
Blue; may be white, gray, green, streaked	Transparent to translucent	In bladed aggregates	Characteristic of middle-grade metamorphism; compare with andalusite, which has the same composition and is formed under similar conditions, but has a different crystal habit; contrast with sillimanite, which has the same composition but different crystal habit and forms at highest metamorphic temperatures.
Dark brown to black	Opaque	Amorphous; mammillary to stalactitic masses; concretionary, nodular, earthy	Always of secondary origin from alteration or solution of iron minerals; mixed with fine clay, it is a pigment, *yellow ocher*.
Iron-black	Opaque	Usually massive granular, coarse or fine in grain	Strongly magnetic; may act as a natural magnet, known as *lodestone;* an important ore of iron; found in black sands on the seashore; mixed with corundum, it is a component of *emery*.
Thin: colorless; thick: light yellow, brown, green, red	Thin: transparent; thick: translucent	Mostly in thin flakes	Widespread and very common rock-forming mineral; characteristic of sialic rocks; also very common in metamorphic rocks such as gneiss and schist; the principal component of some mica schists; sometimes used for stove doors, lanterns, etc., as transparent *isinglass;* used chiefly as an insulating material.
Olive to grayish green, brown	Transparent to translucent	Usually in imbedded grains or granular masses	A common rock-forming mineral found primarily in simatic rocks; the principal component of peridotite; actually, a series grading from *forsterite*, Mg_2SiO_4, to *fayalite*, Fe_2SiO_4; the most common olivines are richer in magnesium than in iron; the clear green variety *peridot* is sometimes used as a gem.

Mineral	Chemical Composition and Name	Specific Gravity	Streak	Hardness	Cleavage or Fracture	Luster
Opal	(*See* Quartz)					
Orthoclase	(*See* Feldspars)					
Peridot	(*See* Olivine)					
Pitchblende	(*See* Uraninite)					
Plagioclase	(*See* Feldspars)					
Pyrite (Iron pyrites; fool's gold)	FeS_2 Iron sulfide	5.02	Greenish or brownish black	$6-6\frac{1}{2}$	Uneven fracture	Metallic
Pyroxene	(*See* Augite)					
Quartz (Silica)	SiO_2 Silicon oxide but structurally a silicate, with tetrahedra sharing oxygens in 3 dimensions	2.65	Colorless	7	Conchoidal fracture	Vitreous, greasy, splendent
Rock salt	(*See* Halite)					
Ruby	(*See* Corundum)					
Salt	(*See* Halite)					
Sapphire	(*See* Corundum)					
Serpentine	$Mg_3Si_2O_5(OH)_4$ Hydrous magnesium silicate	2.2–2.65	Colorless	2–5	Conchoidal fracture	Greasy, waxy, or silky
Siderite (Spathic iron; chalybite)	$FeCO_3$ Iron carbonate	3.85	Colorless	$3\frac{1}{2}-4$	Perfect rhombohedral cleavage	Vitreous
Silica	(*See* Quartz)					
Sillimanite (Fibrolite)	Al_2SiO_5 Aluminum silicate	3.23	Colorless	6–7	Good cleavage in 1 direction	Vitreous
Sphalerite (Zinc blende; black jack)	ZnS Zinc sulfide	3.9–4.1	White to yellow and brown	$3\frac{1}{2}-4$	Perfect cleavage in 6 directions at 120°	Resinous
Staurolite	$Fe''Al_5Si_2O_{12}(OH)$ Iron aluminum silicate	3.65–3.75	Colorless	$7-7\frac{1}{2}$	Not prominent	Fresh: resinous, vitreous; altered: dull to earthy
Taconite	Not a mineral					

Color	Transparency	Form	Other Properties
Brass-yellow	Opaque	Cubic crystals with striated faces; also massive	The most common of the sulfides; used as a source of sulfur in the manufacture of sulfuric acid; distinguished from chalcopyrite by its paler color and greater hardness; from gold by its brittleness and hardness.
			A group of silicates with tetrahedra in single chains; augite is the most important; contrast with amphibole.
Colorless or white when pure; any color from impurities	Transparent to translucent	Prismatic crystals with faces striated at right angles to long dimension; also massive forms of great variety	An important constituent of sialic rocks; coarsely crystalline varieties: *rock crystal, amethyst* (purple), *rose quartz, smoky quartz, citrine* (yellow), *milky quartz, cat's eye;* cryptocrystalline varieties: *chalcedony, carnelian* (red chalcedony), *chrysoprase* (apple-green chalcedony), *heliotrope* or *bloodstone* (green chalcedony with small red spots), *agate* (alternating layers of chalcedony and opal); granular varieties: *flint* (dull to dark brown), *chert* (like flint but lighter in color), *jasper* (red from hematite inclusions), *prase* (like jasper, but dull green).
Variegated shades of green	Translucent	Platy or fibrous	Platy variety, *antigorite;* fibrous variety, *chrysotile,* an asbestos; an alteration product of magnesium silicates such as olivine, augite, and hornblende; common and widely distributed.
Light to dark brown	Transparent to translucent	Granular, compact, earthy	An ore of iron; an accessory mineral in taconite.
Brown, pale green, white	Transparent to translucent	Long, slender crystals without distinct terminations; often in parallel groups; frequently fibrous	Relatively rare, but important as a mineral characteristic of high-grade metamorphism; contrast with andalusite and kyanite, which have the same composition but form under conditions of middle-grade metamorphism.
Pure: white, green; with iron: yellow to brown and black; red	Transparent to translucent	Usually massive; crystals many-sided, distorted	A common mineral; the most important ore of zinc; the red variety is called *ruby zinc;* streak lighter than corresponding mineral color.
Red-brown to brownish black	Translucent	Usually in crystals, prismatic, twinned to form a cross; rarely massive	A common accessory mineral in schists and slates; characteristic of middle-grade metamorphism; associated with garnet, kyanite, sillimanite, tourmaline.
			Unleached iron formation in the Lake Superior District, consists of chert (*see* Quartz) with hematite, magnetite, siderite, and hydrous iron silicates; an ore of iron.

THE COMMON MINERALS (Cont.)

Mineral	Chemical Composition and Name	Specific Gravity	Streak	Hardness	Cleavage or Fracture	Luster
Talc (Soapstone; steatite)	$Mg_3Si_4O_{10}(OH)_2$ Hydrous magnesium silicate	2.7–2.8	White	1	Good cleavage in 1 direction, gives thin folia, flexible but not elastic	Pearly to greasy
Topaz	$Al_2SiO_4(F,OH)_2$ Aluminum fluosilicate	3.4–3.6	Colorless	8	Good in 1 direction	Vitreous
Tourmaline	Complex silicate of boron and aluminum, with sodium, calcium, fluorine, iron, lithium, or magnesium	3–3.25	Colorless	$7-7\frac{1}{2}$	Not prominent; black variety fractures like coal	Vitreous to resinous
Uraninite (Pitchblende)	Complex oxide of uranium with small amounts of lead, radium, thorium, yttrium, nitrogen, helium, and argon	9–9.7	Brownish black	$5\frac{1}{2}$	Not prominent	Submetallic, pitchy
Wollastonite	$CaSiO_3$ Calcium silicate	2.8–2.9	Colorless	$5-5\frac{1}{2}$	Good cleavage in 2 directions at 84° and 96°	Vitreous or pearly on cleavage surfaces

Reference: Cornelius Hurlbut, Jr., *Dana's Manual of Mineralogy*, 16th ed. New York: John Wiley and Sons, Inc., 1952.

Color	Transparency	Form	Other Properties
Gray, white, silver-white, apple-green	Translucent	Foliated, massive	Of secondary origin, formed by the alteration of magnesium silicates such as olivine, augite, and hornblende; most characteristically found in metamorphic rocks.
Straw-yellow, wine-yellow, pink, bluish, greenish	Transparent to translucent	Usually in prismatic crystals, often with striations in direction of greatest length	Represents 8 on Mohs scale of hardness; a gem stone.
Varied: black, brown; red, pink, green, blue, yellow	Translucent	Usually in crystals; common: with cross section of spherical triangle	Gem stone; an accessory mineral in pegmatites, also in metamorphic rocks such as gneisses, schists, marbles.
Black	Opaque	Usually massive and botryoidal (i.e. like a bunch of grapes)	An ore of uranium and radium; the mineral in which helium and radium were first discovered.
Colorless, white or gray	Translucent	Commonly massive, fibrous, or compact	A common contact metamorphic mineral in limestones.

MINERALS ARRANGED ACCORDING TO SPECIFIC GRAVITY

Specific Gravity	Mineral	Specific Gravity	Mineral	Specific Gravity	Mineral
2.00–3.00	Bauxite	3.00–3.25	Tourmaline	3.90–4.10	Sphalerite
2.16	Halite	3.00–3.30	Actinolite	4.00	Carnotite
2.20–2.65	Serpentine	3.15–3.20	Apatite	4.02	Corundum
2.30	Graphite	3.16	Andalusite	4.10–4.30	Chalcopyrite
2.32	Gypsum	3.18	Fluorite	4.60	Chromite
2.57	Orthoclase	3.20	Hornblende	5.02	Pyrite
2.60	Kaolinite	3.20–3.40	Augite	5.06–5.08	Bornite
2.60–2.90	Chlorite	3.23	Sillimanite	5.18	Magnetite
2.62	Albite	3.27–3.37	Olivine	5.26	Hematite
2.65	Quartz	3.35–3.45	Epidote	5.50–5.80	Chalcocite
2.70–2.80	Talc	3.40–3.60	Topaz		
2.72	Calcite	3.50	Diamond	6.80–7.10	Cassiterite
2.76	Anorthite	3.50–4.30	Garnet		
2.76–3.10	Muscovite	3.56–3.66	Kyanite	7.40–7.60	Galena
2.80–2.90	Wollastonite	3.60–4.00	Limonite		
2.80–3.20	Biotite	3.65–3.75	Staurolite		
2.85	Dolomite	3.77	Azurite		
2.89–2.98	Anhydrite	3.85	Siderite	9.00–9.70	Uraninite

MINERALS ARRANGED ACCORDING TO HARDNESS

Hardness	Mineral	Hardness	Mineral	Hardness	Mineral
1	Talc	$3\frac{1}{2}$–4	Siderite	6	Magnetite
1–2	Graphite	$3\frac{1}{2}$–4	Sphalerite	6	Orthoclase
1–3	Bauxite			6–$6\frac{1}{2}$	Pyrite
		4	Azurite	6–7	Cassiterite
2	Gypsum	4	Fluorite	6–7	Epidote
2–$2\frac{1}{2}$	Chlorite			6–7	Sillimanite
2–$2\frac{1}{2}$	Kaolinite	5	Apatite	$6\frac{1}{2}$–7	Olivine
2–$2\frac{1}{2}$	Muscovite	5	Kyanite (along crystal)	$6\frac{1}{2}$–$7\frac{1}{2}$	Garnet
2–5	Serpentine	5–$5\frac{1}{2}$	Limonite		
$2\frac{1}{2}$	Galena	5–$5\frac{1}{2}$	Wollastonite	7	Kyanite (across crystal)
$2\frac{1}{2}$	Halite	5–6	Actinolite	7	Quartz
$2\frac{1}{2}$–3	Biotite	5–6	Augite	7–$7\frac{1}{2}$	Staurolite
$2\frac{1}{2}$–3	Chalcocite	5–6	Hornblende	7–$7\frac{1}{2}$	Tourmaline
		$5\frac{1}{2}$	Chromite	$7\frac{1}{2}$	Andalusite
3	Bornite	$5\frac{1}{2}$	Uraninite		
3	Calcite	$5\frac{1}{2}$–$6\frac{1}{2}$	Hematite	8	Topaz
3–$3\frac{1}{2}$	Anhydrite			9	Corundum
$3\frac{1}{2}$–4	Chalcopyrite	6	Albite		
$3\frac{1}{2}$–4	Dolomite	6	Anorthite	10	Diamond

ROCK-FORMING MINERALS

Igneous		Metamorphic		Sedimentary		Ore Minerals	
ESSENTIAL	ACCESSORY	REGIONAL	CONTACT	ESSENTIAL	CEMENTS	Azurite	Galena
Quartz	Apatite	Actinolite	*Thermal*	Quartz	Silica	Bauxite	Hematite
Feldspars	Corundum	Andalusite	Corundum	Feldspars	Calcite	Bornite	Magnetite
Micas	Garnet	Asbestos	Garnet	Kaolinite	Hematite	Carnotite	Siderite
Augite	Hematite	Chlorite	Graphite	Calcite	Limonite	Cassiterite	Sphalerite
Hornblende	Magnetite	Garnet		Dolomite		Chalcocite	Uraninite
Olivine	Pyrite	Graphite	*Hydrothermal*	Gypsum		Chalcopyrite	
		Kyanite	Epidote	Anhydrite		Chromite	
		Serpentine	Garnet	Halite			
		Sillimanite	Olivine				
		Staurolite	Ore minerals				
		Talc	Quartz				
			Tourmaline				
			Wollastonite				

Appendix D

TOPOGRAPHIC MAPS*

The term *topography* refers to the shape of the physical features of the land. A *topographic map* is the representation of the position, relation, size, and shape of the physical features of an area. In addition to hills, valleys, rivers, and mountains, most topographic maps also show the culture of a region—that is, roads, towns, houses, political boundaries, and similar features.

Topographic maps are used in the laboratory for the observation and analysis of the effects of the several geologic processes that are constantly changing the face of the earth.

Definitions

Relief of an area is the difference in elevation between the tops of hills and the bottoms of valleys.

Height is the vertical difference in elevation between an object and its immediate surroundings.

Elevation or **altitude** is the vertical distance between a given point and the datum plane.

Datum plane is the reference surface from which all altitudes on a map are measured. This is usually mean sea level.

Bench mark is a point of known elevation and position, which is usually indicated on a map by the letters B.M., with the altitude given to the nearest foot.

Contour line is a map line connecting points representing places on the earth's surface that have the same elevation. It thus locates the intersection with the earth's surface of a plane at any arbitrary elevation parallel to the datum plane. Contours

---

* Adapted by permission from Sheldon Judson and Margaret Skillman Woyski, *Laboratory Manual for Physical Geology.* Dubuque: Wm. C. Brown Co., 1950.

represent the vertical or third dimension on a map, which has only two dimensions. They show the size and shape of physical features such as hills and valleys. A hachured contour line indicates a depression. It resembles an ordinary contour line except for the hachures, or short dashes, on one side pointing toward the center of the depression.

Contour interval is the difference in elevation represented by adjacent contour lines.

Scale of a map is the ratio of the distance between two points on the ground and the same two points on the map. It may be expressed in three ways:

1. *Fractional scale.* If two points are exactly one mile apart, they may be represented on the map as being separated by some fraction of that distance, say one inch. In this instance, the scale is one inch to the mile. There are 63,360 inches in a mile, so this scale can be expressed as the fraction or ratio 1:63,360. Actually, many topographic maps of the United States Geological Survey have a scale of 1:62,500.

2. *Graphic scale.* This scale is a line printed on the map and divided into units that are equivalent to some distance, such as one mile.

3. *Verbal scale.* This is an expression in common speech, such as "an inch to a mile," or "two miles to the inch."

Conventional Symbols

An explanation of the symbols used on topographic maps is printed on the back of each topographic sheet, along the margin or, for newer maps, on a separate legend sheet. In general, culture (works of man) is shown in black. All water features, such as streams, swamps, and glaciers, are shown in blue. Relief is shown by contours in brown. Red may be used to indicate main highways, and green overprints may be used to designate areas of woods, orchards, vineyards, or scrub.

The United States Geological Survey distributes free of charge (apply to The Director, Geological

Survey, Washington 25, D.C.) a single sheet entitled "Topographic Maps" that includes an illustrated summary of topographic map symbols.

Locating Points

Any particular point or area may be located in several ways on a topographic map. The three most commonly used are:

1. *In relation to prominent features.* A point may be referred to as being so many miles in a given direction from a city, mountain, river mouth, lake, or other easily located feature on the map.

2. *By latitude and longitude.* Topographic maps of the United States Geological Survey are bounded on the north and south by parallels of latitude, and on the east and west by meridians of longitude. These intersecting lines form the grid into which the earth has been divided. Latitude is measured north and south from the equator, and longitude is measured east and west from the prime meridian that passes through Greenwich, England. Thus, maps in the United States are within north latitude and west longitude.

3. *By township and range.* The greater part of the United States has been subdivided by a system of land survey in which a square six miles on a side forms the basic unit, called a township. Not included in this system are all the states along the eastern seaboard (with the exception of Florida), West Virginia, Kentucky, Tennessee, Texas, and parts of Ohio. Townships are laid off north and south from a base line, and east and west from a principal meridian. Each township is divided into 36 sections, usually a mile on a side. Each section may be further subdivided into half-sections, quarter-sections, or sixteenth-sections. Thus, in Fig. D-1 the point "X" can be located as in the northeast quarter of the northwest quarter abbreviated as NE¼ NW¼ Sec 3, T9N, R5W, or NW NE Sec 3–9N–5W.

Figure D-1 Subdivision by township and range. See text for discussion.

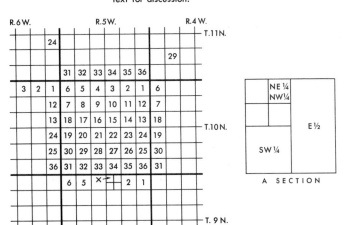

Contour Sketching

Many contour maps are now made from aerial photographs. Before this can be done, however, the position and location of a number of reference points, or bench marks, must be determined in the field. If the topographic map is surveyed in the field rather than from aerial photographs, the topographer first determines the location and elevation of bench marks and a large number of other points that are selected for their critical position. Such points may be along streams, or hilltops, on the lowest point in a saddle between hills, or at places where there is a significant change in slope. On the basis of these points, contours may be sketched through points of equal elevation. Preferably, the contours are sketched in the field, in order to include minor irregularities that are visible to the topographer.

Because contours are not ordinary lines, certain requirements must be met in drawing them to satisfy the definition of contour lines. These are listed below.

1. All points on one contour line have the same elevation.

2. Contours separate all points of higher elevation than the contour from all points of lower elevation.

3. The elevation represented by a contour line is always a simple multiple of the contour interval. Every contour line that is a multiple of 5 times the contour interval is heavier than the others. (Exception: 25-foot contours, in which every multiple of 4 times the interval is heavier.)

4. Contours never cross or intersect one another.

5. A vertical cliff is represented by coincident contours.

6. Every contour closes on itself either within or beyond the limits of the map. In the latter case, the contours will end at the edge of the map.

7. Contour lines never split.

8. Uniformly spaced contour lines represent a uniform slope.

9. Closely spaced contour lines represent a steep slope.

10. Contour lines spaced far apart represent a gentle slope.

11. A contour line that closes within the limits of the map indicates a hill.

12. A hachured contour line represents a depression. The short dashes or hachures point into the depression.

13. Contour lines curve up a valley but cross a stream at right angles to its course.

14. Maximum ridge and minimum valley con-

tours always go in pairs. That is, no single lower contour can lie between two higher ones, and vice versa.

Topographic Profiles

A topographic profile is a cross section of the earth's surface along a given line. The upper line of this section is irregular and shows the shape of the land along the line of profile or section.

Profiles are most easily constructed with graph paper. A horizontal scale, usually the map scale, is chosen. Then a vertical scale sufficient to bring out the features of the surface is chosen. The vertical scale is usually several times larger than the horizontal—that is, it is exaggerated. The steps in the construction of a profile are as follows:

1. Select a base (one of the horizontal lines on the graph paper). This may be sea level or any other convenient datum level.
2. On the graph paper, number each fourth or fifth line above the base, according to the vertical scale chosen.
3. Place the graph paper along the line of profile.
4. With the vertically ruled lines as guides, plot the elevation of each contour line that crosses the line of profile.
5. If great accuracy is not important, plot only every heavy contour and the tops and bottoms of hills and the bottoms of valleys.
6. Connect the points.
7. Label necessary points along the profile.
8. Give the vertical and horizontal scales.
9. State the vertical exaggeration.
10. Title the profile.

VERTICAL EXAGGERATION. The profile represents both vertical and horizontal dimensions. These dimensions are not usually on the same scale, because the vertical needs to be greater than the horizontal to give a clear presentation of changes in level. Thus, if the vertical scale is 500 feet to the inch and the horizontal scale is 5,280 feet to the inch—or say 1:62,500—the vertical exaggeration is about ten times, written $10\times$. This is obtained by dividing the horizontal scale by the vertical scale. Note that both horizontal and vertical scales must be expressed in the same unit (commonly feet to the inch) before dividing.

GEOLOGIC MAPS

Geologic maps show the distribution of earth materials on the surface. In addition, they indicate the relative age of these materials and suggest their arrangement beneath the surface.

Definitions

Formation. The units depicted on a geologic map are usually referred to as formations. We define a formation as a rock unit with upper and lower boundaries that can be recognized easily in the field and that is large enough to be shown on the map. A formation receives a distinctive designation made up of two parts. The first part is geographic and refers to the place or general area where the formation is first described. The second refers to the nature of the rock. Thus, *Trenton limestone* is a formation composed dominantly of limestone and is named after Trenton Falls in central New York State, where it was first formally described. *Wausau granite* designates a body of granite in the Wausau, Wisconsin, area. If the lithology is so variable that no single lithologic distinction is appropriate, the word "formation" may be used. For instance, the *Raritan formation* is named for the area of the Raritan River and Raritan Bay in New Jersey, and its lithology includes both sand and clay.

Dip and Strike. The dip and strike of a rock layer refers to its orientation in relation to a horizontal plane. In Chapter 16 we found that the dip is the acute angle that a tilted rock layer makes with an imaginary plane. We also found that the strike is the compass direction of a line formed by the intersection of the dipping surface with an imaginary horizontal plane. The direction of strike is always at right angles to the direction of dip. The dip-and-strike symbol used on a geologic map is in the form of a topheavy T. The cross bar represents the direction of the strike of the bed. The short upright represents the direction of the dip of the bed. This sometimes, but not always, has an arrow pointing in the direction of dip. Very often the angle of dip is indicated alongside the symbol.

Example:

T 30   Strike E-W; Dip 30° S.
⊥ 25   Strike N 45° E; Dip 25° SE.

Note: In this example, the top of the page is considered to be north.

Contact. A contact is the plane separating two rock units. It is shown on the geologic map as a line that is the intersection of the plane between the rock units and the surface of the ground.

Outcrop. An outcrop is an exposure of rock material that crops out at the surface through the cover of soil and weathered material. In areas of abundant rainfall, soil and vegetation obscure the underlying rock material and only a small fraction of 1 per cent of the surface may be in outcrop. In

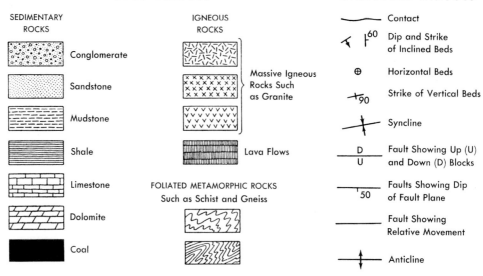

SEDIMENTARY
ROCKS

Conglomerate

Sandstone

Mudstone

Shale

Limestone

Dolomite

Coal

IGNEOUS
ROCKS

Massive Igneous
Rocks Such
as Granite

Lava Flows

FOLIATED METAMORPHIC ROCKS
Such as Schist and Gneiss

Contact

Dip and Strike
of Inclined Beds

Horizontal Beds

Strike of Vertical Beds

Syncline

Fault Showing Up (U)
and Down (D) Blocks

Faults Showing Dip
of Fault Plane

Fault Showing
Relative Movement

Anticline

Figure D-2 Symbols commonly used on geological maps.

dry climates where soils are shallow or absent and the plant cover is discontinuous, bedrock usually crops out much more widely.

Legend and Symbols. A legend is an explanation of the various symbols used on the map. There is no universally accepted set of standard symbols, but some that are more widely used are given in Fig. D-2. In addition to the graphic symbols in Fig. D-2, letter symbols are sometimes used to designate rock units. Such a symbol contains a letter or letters referring to the geologic column, followed by a letter or letters referring to the specific name of the rock unit. Thus in the symbol *Ot* the "O" stands for Ordovician and the "t" for the Trenton limestone of central New York State. The letters or abbreviations generally used for the geologic column are given in Table D-1.

Sometimes different colors are used to indicate different rock systems. There is no standardized color scheme, but many of the geologic maps of the United States Geological Survey use the following colors, combined with varying patterns, for systems of sedimentary rocks:

Pleistocene	yellow and gray
Paleocene through Pliocene	yellow ocher
Cretaceous	olive-green
Jurassic	blue-green
Triassic	light peacock-blue or bluish gray-green
Mississippian through Permian	blue
Devonian	gray-purple
Silurian	purple
Ordovician	red-purple
Cambrian	brick-red
Precambrian	terra-cotta and gray-brown

No specific colors are designated for igneous rocks, but when colors are used, they are usually purer and more brilliant than those used for sedimentary rocks.

Construction of a Geologic Map

The basic idea of geologic mapping is simple. We are interested first in showing the distribution of the rocks at the earth's surface. Theoretically, all we need to do is plot the occurrence of the different rocks on a base map, and then we have a geologic map. Unfortunately, the process is not quite this simple.

In most areas the bedrock is more or less obscured in one way or another, and only a small amount of outcrop is available for observation, study, and sampling. From the few exposures available, the geologist must extrapolate the general distribution of rock types. In this extrapolation, his field data are obviously of prime importance. But

Table D-1 **Letter Symbols Commonly Used To Designate Units in the Geologic Column**

	Symbol		Symbol
Pleistocene	Q	Permian	Cpm
Pliocene	Tpl	Pennsylvanian	Cp
Miocene	Tm	Mississippian	Cm
Oligocene	To	Devonian	D
Eocene	Te	Silurian	S
Paleocene	Tp	Ordovician	O
Cretaceous	K	Cambrian	€¢
Jurassic	J	Precambrian	P€
Triassic	℞		

492

he will also be guided by changes in soil, vegetation, and landscape, as well as by patterns that can be detected on aerial photographs. Furthermore, he may be aided by laboratory examination of field samples and by the records of both deep and shallow wells. The geologist may also have available to him geophysical data that help determine the nature of obscured bedrock. Eventually, when he has marshaled as many data as possible, he draws the boundaries delineating the various rock types.

In addition to the distribution of rock types, the geologist is also concerned with depicting, as accurately as he can, the ages of the various rocks and their arrangement beneath the surface. These goals, also, will be realized in part through direct observations in the field and in part through other lines of evidence. The preparation of an accurate, meaningful, geologic map demands experience, patience, and judgment.

Geologic Cross Sections

A geologic map tells us something of how rocks are arranged in the underground. Often, to show these relations more clearly, we find it convenient to draw geologic cross sections. Such a section is really a diagram showing a side view of a block of the earth's crust as it would look if we could lift it up to view. We have used cross sections in many illustrations throughout this book.

A geologic cross section is drawn, insofar as possible, at right angles to the general strike of the rocks. The general manner in which a geologic cross section is projected from a geologic map is shown in Fig. D-3. If the projection is made onto a topographic profile in which the vertical scale has been exaggerated, then the angle of the dip of the rocks should be exaggerated accordingly.

Figure D-3   Construction of a geologic cross section from a geologic map.

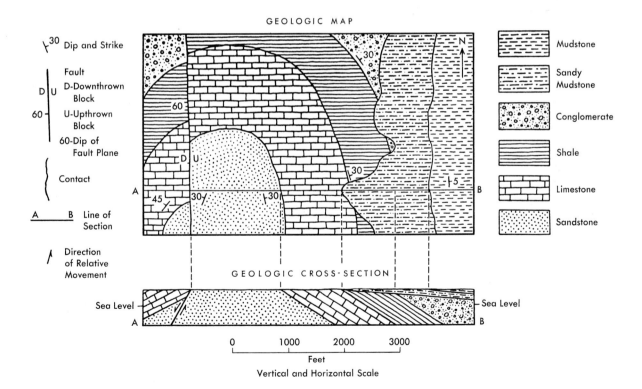

Glossary

A Abbreviation for angstrom, a unit of length, 10^{-8} cm.

Ablation As applied to glacier ice, the process by which ice below the snow line is wasted by evaporation and melting.

Abrasion Erosion of rock material by friction of solid particles moved by water, ice, wind, or gravity.

Absolute date A date expressed in terms of years and related to the present by a reliable system of reckoning.

Absolute time Geologic time measured in terms of years. Compare with *relative time*.

Actinolite A metamorphic ferromagnesian mineral. An asbestos.

Adaptation Any specific characteristic of an organism that is of value to its survival in a given situation. The term may also apply to the process by which such beneficial characteristics are achieved or accumulated.

Aeolian Pertaining to wind. Designates rocks and soils whose constituents have been carried and laid down by atmospheric currents. It is also applied to erosive and other geologic effects accomplished by wind.

Aftershock An earthquake that follows a larger earthquake and originates at or near the focus of the larger earthquake. Generally, major shallow earthquakes are followed by many aftershocks. These decrease in number as time goes on, but may continue for many days or even months.

Agate A variety of chalcedony with alternating layers of chalcedony and opal.

Age A period of earth history of unspecified duration characterized by a dominant or important life form; i.e., the Age of Fishes. Also, a time when a particular event occurred, such as the Ice Age. Age may also refer to the position of anything in the geologic time scale; if possible, it may be expressed in years.

A-horizon The soil zone immediately below the surface, from which soluble material and fine-grained particles have been moved downward by water seeping into the soil. Varying amounts of organic matter give the A-horizon a gray to black color.

Albite The feldspar in which the diagnostic positive ion is Na^+. Sodic feldspar, $Na(AlSi_3O_8)$. One of the plagioclase feldspars.

Algae Any member of a numerous group of simple plants usually classified as a subdivision of the *Thallophyta*. Algae contain chlorophyll and are capable of photosynthesis. They may appear blue-green, green, red, or brown and are classified accordingly. Forms capable of secreting calcium carbonate are important rock-builders.

Alluvial fan The land counterpart of a delta. An assemblage of sediments marking the place where a stream moves from a steep gradient to a flatter gradient and suddenly loses its transporting power. Typical of arid and semiarid climates, but not confined to them.

Almandite A deep red garnet of iron and aluminum formed during regional metamorphism.

Alpha particle A helium atom lacking electrons and therefore having a double positive charge.

Alpine Glacier A glacier confined to a stream valley. Usually fed from a cirque. Also called *valley glacier* or *mountain glacier*.

Amino acid Any of a large group of nitrogenous organic compounds that serve as structural units in the proteins and are essential to all forms of life.

Ammonite Any member of an extinct group of marine molluscs, whose fossil remains are especially important as index fossils in the Permian Period and the Mesozoic Era. Typically, they possess a coiled, many-chambered shell with complex crenulations along the edges of the septa between the chambers.

Amorphous A state of matter in which there is no orderly arrangement of atoms.

Amphibole group Ferromagnesian silicates with a double chain of silicon-oxygen tetrahedra. Common example: hornblende. Contrast with *pyroxene group*.

Amphibolite A faintly foliated metamorphic rock developed during the regional metamorphism of simatic rocks. Composed mainly of hornblende and plagioclase feldspars.

Amphibolite facies An assemblage of minerals formed at moderate to high pressures between 850°F and 1300°F (450°C and 700°C) during regional metamorphism.

Andalusite A silicate of aluminum built around independent tetrahedra. Al_2SiO_5. Characteristic of middle-grade metamorphism. Compare with *kyanite*, which has the same composition and forms under similar conditions, but has a different crystal habit. Contrast with *sillimanite*, which has the same composition but different crystal habit and forms at highest metamorphic temperatures.

Andesite A fine-grained igneous rock with no quartz or orthoclase, composed of about 75 per cent plagioclase feldspars and the balance ferromagnesian silicates. Important as lavas, possibly derived by fractional crystallization from basaltic magma. Widely characteristic of mountain-making processes around the borders of the Pacific Ocean. Confined to continental sectors.

Andesite line A map line designating the petrographic boundary of the Pacific Ocean. Extrusive rocks on the Pacific side of the line are basaltic and on the other side andesitic.

Angiosperm Any member of the advanced group of plants that carries its seeds in a closed ovary and has floral reproductive structures.

Angstrom A unit of length, equal to one hundred-millionth of a centimeter, 10^{-8} cm. Abbreviation, A.

Angular Momentum A vector quantity, the product of mass times radius of orbit times velocity. The energy of motion of the solar system.

Angular unconformity An unconformity or break between two series of rock layers such that rocks of the lower series meet rocks of the upper series at an angle; in other words, the two series are not parallel.

Anhydrite The mineral calcium sulfate, $CaSO_4$, which is gypsum without water.

Anorthite The feldspar in which the diagnostic positive element is Ca^{2+}. Calcic feldspar, $Ca(Al_2Si_2O_8)$. One of the plagioclase feldspars.

Antecedent stream A stream that maintains after uplift the same course it originally followed prior to uplift.

Anthracite Hard coal; compact, dense, very black with a hardness of 2.0 to 2.5 and a specific gravity of 1.4 to 1.8. Anthracite has 80 to 90 per cent fixed carbon and burns with a short flame and great heat.

Anthropology The study of man, especially his physical nature and the ways in which he has modified or been modified by external forces.

Anticlinal theory The theory that water, petroleum, and natural gas accumulate in up-arched strata in the order named (water lowest), provided the structure contains reservoir rocks in proper relation to source beds and capped by an impervious barrier.

Anticline A configuration of folded, stratified rocks in which the rocks dip in two directions away from a crest, as the principal rafters of a common gable roof dip away from the ridgepole. The reverse of a *syncline*. The "ridgepole," or crest is called the axis.

Aquifer A permeable material through which ground water moves.

Aragonite Calcium carbonate $(CaCO_3)$ with crystals in the orthorhombic system. As a constituent of some shells it is less stable than calcite.

Archeo- Combining form meaning "ancient"; from Gr. *archaios*, ancient.

Arête A narrow, saw-toothed ridge formed by cirques developing from opposite sides into the ridge.

Arkose A detrital sedimentary rock formed by the cementation of individual grains of sand size and predominantly composed of quartz and feldspar. Derived from the disintegration of granite.

Arroyo Flat-floored, vertically walled channel of an intermittent stream typical of semiarid climates. Often applied to such features of southwestern United States. Synonymous with *wadi* and *wash*.

Artesian water Water that is under pressure when tapped by a well and is able to rise above the level at which it is first encountered. It may or may not flow out at ground level.

Arthropod Any member of the great animal phylum that is characterized by jointed appendages, a bilaterally symmetrical body, and usually an external chitinous skeleton.

Artifact Anything of a material nature produced by human skill.

Asbestos A general term applied to certain fibrous minerals that display similar physical characteristics although they differ in composition. Some asbestos has fibers long enough to be spun into fabrics with great resistance to heat, such as those used for automobile brake linings. Types with shorter fibers are compressed into insulating boards, shingles, etc. The most common asbestos mineral (95 per cent of U.S. production) is chrysotile, a variety of serpentine, a metamorphic mineral.

Asexual reproduction Reproduction by one individual independent of others.

Ash In geology, the finest rock material from volcanic explosions.

Asphalt A brown to black solid or semisolid bituminous substance. Occurs in nature but is also obtained as a residue from the refining of certain hydrocarbons (then known as "artificial asphalt").

Asymmetric fold A fold in which one limb dips more steeply than the other.

Atoll A roughly circular, elliptical, or horseshoe-shaped island or ring of islands of reef origin, composed of coral and algal rock and sand and rimming a lagoon in which there are no islands of noncoral origin.

Atom A combination of protons, neutrons, and electrons. Ninety-two kinds are found in nature; 102 kinds are now known.

Atomic energy Energy associated with the nucleus of an atom. It is released when the nucleus is split, or is derived from mass that is lost when a nucleus is fused together.

Atomic mass The nucleus of an atom contains 99.95 per cent of its mass. The total number of protons and neutrons in the nucleus is called the *mass number*.

Atomic number The number of positive charges on the nucleus of an atom; the number of protons in the nucleus.

Atomic size The radius of an atom (average distance from the center to the outermost electron of the neutral atom). Commonly expressed in angstroms.

Augite A rock-forming ferromagnesian silicate mineral built around single chains of silicon-oxygen tetrahedra.

Aureole A zone in which contact metamorphism has taken place.

Axial plane A plane through a rock fold that includes the axis and divides the fold as symmetrically as possible.

Axis The ridge, or place of sharpest folding, of an anticline or syncline.

B Symbol for bulk modulus.

Backset beds Inclined layers of sand developed on the gentler dune slope to the windward. These beds may constitute a large part of the total volume of a dune, especially if there is enough vegetation to trap most of the sand before it can cross over to the slip face.

Back swamp Marshy area of a flood plain at some distance from and lower than the banks of a river confined by natural levees.

Barchan A crescent-shaped dune with wings or horns pointing downwind. Has a gentle windward slope and steep lee slope inside the horns. About 100 feet in height and 1,000 feet wide from horn to horn. Moves with the wind at about 25 to 50 feet per year across a flat, hard surface where a limited supply of sand is available.

Barrier island A low, sandy island near the shore and parallel to it, on a gently sloping offshore bottom.

Barrier reef A reef that is separated from a landmass by a lagoon of varying width and depth opening to the sea through passes in the reef.

Basalt A fine-grained igneous rock dominated by dark-colored minerals, consisting of over 50 per cent plagioclase feldspars and the balance ferromagnesian silicates. Basalts and andesites represent about 98 per cent of all extrusive rocks.

Base level (1) For a *stream,* a level below which it cannot erode. There may be temporary base levels along a stream's course, such as those established by lakes, or resistant layers of rock. Ultimate base level for a stream is sea level. (2) For a *region,* a plane extending inland from sea level sloping gently upward from the sea. Erosion of the land progresses toward this plane, but seldom, if ever, quite reaches it.

Basement complex Undifferentiated rocks underlying the oldest identifiable rocks in any region. Usually sialic, crystalline, metamorphosed. Often, but not necessarily, Precambrian.

Basic Widely, but loosely, applied to rocks with a relatively low content of silica and a correspondingly high content of minerals rich in iron, lime, or magnesia, such as amphibole, pyroxene, and olivine. The content of silica in so-called basic rocks is on the order of 45 to 52 per cent. Because basic, as applied to rocks, has no direct relation to *base* in the chemical sense, it is being replaced by the term *subsilicic.*

Basin A depression in the land surface. In geology, it is an area in which the rocks dip toward a central spot. Basins tend to be accentuated by continued downsinking and thus receive thicker deposits of sediment than surrounding areas. An example is the Michigan Basin.

Batholith A very large mass of intrusive rock, generally composed of granite or granodiorite, which in most cases cuts across the invaded rocks and shows no direct evidence of having a floor of older solid rock. A surface exposure exceeding 40 square miles has been suggested as a lower size limit.

Bauxite The chief ore of commercial aluminum. A mixture of hydrous aluminum oxides.

Bay barrier A sandy beach, built up across the mouth of a bay, so that the bay is no longer connected to the main body of water.

Bed "Bed" and "layer" refer to any tabular body of rock lying in a position essentially parallel to the surface or surfaces on or against which it was formed, whether these be a surface of weathering and erosion,

planes of stratification, or inclined fractures.

Bedding (1) A collective term used to signify the existence of beds or layers in sedimentary rocks. (2) Sometimes synonymous with *bedding plane.*

Bedding plane The surface that separates a layer of stratified rock from an overlying or underlying layer.

Bed load Material in movement along a stream bottom, or, if wind is the moving agency, along the surface. Contrast with material carried in suspension or solution.

Bedrock The more or less solid undisturbed rock in place either at the surface or beneath superficial deposits of gravel, sand, or soil.

Beheaded stream The lower section of a stream that has lost its upper portion through *stream piracy.*

Belemnite A general name for any ancient squid-like cephalopod with a pointed, cylindrical, internal skeleton of solid calcium carbonate.

Belt of soil moisture Subdivision of zone of aeration. Belt from which water may be used by plants or withdrawn by soil evaporation. Some of the water passes down into the intermediate belt, where it may be held by molecular attraction against the influence of gravity.

Bentonite A rock composed of clay minerals and derived from the alteration of volcanic tuff or ash. The color range of fresh material is from white to light green, or light blue. On exposure the color may darken to yellow, red, or brown.

Bergschrund The gap or crevasse between glacier ice and the headwall of a cirque.

Berms In the terminology of coastlines, berms are stormbuilt beach features that resemble small terraces; on their seaward edges are low ridges built up by storm waves.

B-horizon The soil zone of accumulation that lies below the A-horizon. Here is deposited some of the material that has moved downward from the A-horizon.

Binding energy The amount of energy that must be supplied to break an atomic nucleus into its component fundamental particles. It is equivalent to the mass that disappears when fundamental particles combine to form a nucleus.

Biochemical rock A sedimentary rock made up of deposits resulting directly or indirectly from the life processes of organisms.

Biotite "Black mica," ranging in color from dark brown to green. A rock-forming ferromagnesian silicate mineral with its tetrahedra arranged in sheets.

Bituminous coal A compact, brittle coal of a gray-black to velvet-black color. It burns with a yellow flame and gives off a strong bituminous odor. Generally, there are no traces of organic structures visible to the eye.

Bivalve An invertebrate animal whose shell is divided into two equal or subequal parts, or valves. Brachiopods, pelecypods, and ostracods are examples.

Blastoid Any of a large group of extinct marine echinoderms that possess a stem and a bud-like head, or theca. They range from the Ordovician to the Permian.

Blowout A basin, scooped out of soft, unconsolidated deposits by the process of deflation. Ranges from a few feet to several miles in diameter.

Body wave Push-pull, or shake, earthquake wave that travels through the body of a medium, as distinguished from waves that travel along a free surface.

Bond See *covalent bond; ionic bond.*

Borderland An actual or hypothetical land mass occupying a position on or near the edge of a continent and supplying sediment to a geosyncline or site of deposition on the continent.

Bornite A mineral, CU_5FeS_4. An important ore of copper.

Bottomset bed Layer of fine sediment deposited in a body of standing water beyond the advancing edge of a growing delta. The delta eventually builds up on top of the bottomset beds.

Boulder size A volume greater than that of a sphere with a diameter of 256 mm, or 10 in.

Boulder train A series of glacier erratics from the same bedrock source, usually with some property that permits easy identification. Arranged across the country in the shape of a fan with the apex at the source and widening in the direction of glacier movement.

Bowen's reaction series A series of minerals for which any early-formed phase tends to react with the melt that remains, to yield a new mineral further along in the series. Thus, early-formed crystals of olivine react with remaining liquids to form augite crystals; these in turn may further react with the liquid then remaining to form hornblende. See also *con-*

tinuous reaction series and *discontinuous reaction series.*

Brachiopod A type of shelled marine invertebrate now comparatively rare but abundant in earlier periods of earth history. Brachiopods are common fossils in rocks of Paleozoic age. They have a bivalve shell and are symmetrical with regard to a plane passing through the beak and the middle of the front margin.

Braided stream A complex tangle of converging and diverging stream channels separated by sand bars or islands. Characteristic of flood plains where the amount of debris is large in relation to the discharge.

Breccia A rock consisting of consolidated angular rock fragments larger than sand grains. It is similar to conglomerate, except that most of the fragments are angular, with sharp edges and unworn corners.

Brown clay An extremely fine-grained deposit characteristic of some deep ocean basins, particularly those of the Pacific.

Bryozoans Aquatic invertebrate animals that individually average less than 1 millimeter in length but that construct large colonial structures that have been preserved as fossils in rocks of all ages from Late Cambrian upward. Only lime-secreting varieties are common as fossils, and bryozoan limestone or marl is widespread. In older textbooks the bryozoans are combined with the brachiopods to constitute the phylum *Molluscoidea;* most recent students treat the bryozoans as a distinct phylum.

Bulk modulus The number that expresses a material's resistance to elastic changes in volume. For example, the number of pounds per square inch necessary to cause a specified change in volume. Represented by the symbol B.

Calcic feldspar Anorthite, whose formula is $Ca(Al_2Si_2O_8)$.

Calcite A common, rock-forming, carbonate mineral whose chemical formula is $CaCO_3$. It has a hardness of 3 and a specific gravity of 2.7. A rock with much calcite is said to be calcareous.

Caldera A roughly circular, steep-sided volcanic basin with a diameter at least three or four times its depth. Commonly at the summit of a volcano. Contrast with *crater.*

Caliche A whitish accumulation of calcium carbonate in the soil profile.

Calving As applied to glacier ice, the process by which a glacier that terminates in a body of water breaks away in large blocks. Such blocks form the icebergs of polar seas.

Capacity The amount of material that a transporting agency such as a stream, a glacier, or the wind can carry under a particular set of conditions.

Capillary fringe Belt above zone of saturation in which underground water is lifted against gravity by surface tension in passages of capillary size.

Capillary size "Hairlike," or very small, such as tubes from .001 to .100 in. in diameter.

Carbohydrate A compound of carbon, hydrogen, and oxygen. Carbohydrates are the chief products of the life process in plants.

Carbonaceous Containing carbon. In geology, containing coal in well-defined beds or small disseminated particles of carbon mingled with inorganic constituents.

Carbonate Any compound formed when carbon dioxide contained in water combines with the oxides of calcium, magnesium, potassium, sodium, and iron. Among the common carbonates are dolomite, siderite, and calcite.

Carbonate mineral Mineral formed by the combination of the complex ion $(CO_3)^{2-}$ with a positive ion. Common example: calcite, $CaCO_3$.

Carbon cycle A cycle of atomic reactions, catalyzed by carbon, in which helium nuclei are formed from hydrogen nuclei. Probable source of the energy radiated by stars.

Carbon-14 Radioactive isotope of carbon, $_6C^{14}$, with a half life of 5,720 years. Used to date events back to about 50,000 years ago.

Carbonization The process of converting a substance into a residue of carbon by removing other ingredients, as in the charring of wood, the natural formation of anthracite, and the fossilization of leaves and other plant organs.

Carbon-ratio A number obtained by dividing the amount of fixed carbon in a coal by the sum of fixed carbon and volatile matter, and multiplying by 100. This is the same as the percentage of fixed carbon, assuming no moisture or ash.

Cassiterite A mineral; tin dioxide, SnO_2. Ore of tin with a specific gravity of 7. Nearly 75 per cent of the world's tin production is from placer deposits, mostly in the form of cassiterite.

Cast A natural or artificial reproduction of an object showing its outward shape. Natural casts are common as fossils.

Catastrophism The belief that the past history of the earth and of living things has been interrupted or greatly influenced by natural catastrophes occurring on a world-wide or very extensive scale.

Cavitation A process of erosion in a stream channel caused by sudden collapse of vapor bubbles against the channel wall.

Cellulose The most abundant carbohydrate, $C_6H_{10}O_5$, with a chain structure like that of the paraffin hydrocarbons. With lignin, an important constituent of plant material, from which coal is formed.

Cement The material that binds the particles of a consolidated sedimentary rock together. Various substances may act as cement, the most common being silica, calcium carbonate, and various iron oxides.

Cementation The process by which a binding agent is precipitated in the spaces between the individual particles of an unconsolidated deposit. The most common cementing agents are calcite, dolomite, and quartz. Others include iron oxide, opal, chalcedony, anhydrite, and pyrite.

Cement rock A clayey limestone used in the manufacture of hydraulic cement. Contains lime, silica, and alumina in varying proportions.

Central vent An opening in the earth's crust, roughly circular, from which magmatic products are extruded. A volcano is an accumulation of material around a central vent.

Cephalopod Any member of a large class of molluscs whose head and mouth are circled with muscular tentacles. Water is drawn in and expelled through a siphon. The eyes are well developed and the whole animal is highly organized for rapid, intelligent action. Many fossil remains have been discovered in rocks of Cambrian age and younger. Modern representatives include the squid, octopus, and pearly nautilus.

Chalcedony A general name applied to fibrous crypto-crystalline silica, and sometimes specifically to the brown, translucent variety with a waxy luster. Deposited from aqueous solutions and frequently found lining or filling cavities in rocks. *Agate* is a variety with alternating layers of chalcedony and opal.

Chalcocite A mineral, copper sulfide, Cu_2S, sometimes called *copper glance*. One of the most important ore minerals of copper.

Chalcopyrite A mineral, a sulfide of copper and iron, $CuFeS_2$. Sometimes called copper pyrite or yellow copper ore.

Chalk A variety of limestone made up in part of biochemically derived calcite, in the form of the skeletons or skeletal fragments of microscopic oceanic plants and animals which are mixed with very fine-grained calcite deposits of either biochemical or inorganic chemical origin.

Chemical energy Energy released or absorbed when atoms form compounds. Generally becomes available when atoms have lost or gained electrons, and often appears in the form of heat.

Chemical rock In the terminology of sedimentary rocks, a chemical rock is composed chiefly of material deposited by chemical precipitation, either organic or inorganic. Compare with *detrital sedimentary rock*. Chemical sedimentary rocks may have either a clastic or nonclastic (usually crystalline) texture.

Chemical weathering The weathering of rock material by chemical processes that transform the original material into new chemical combinations. Thus, chemical weathering of orthoclase produces clay, some silica, and a soluble salt of potassium.

Chert A very dense, usually light-colored siliceous rock usually found associated with limestone, either in the form of nodular or concretionary masses or as distinct beds.

Chitin A horny organic substance, chemical composition $C_{32}H_{54}N_4O_{21}$. It is present in the skeletons and protective coverings of most arthropods and in some sponges, coelenterates, and worms.

Chlorite A family of tetrahedral sheet silicates of iron, magnesium, and aluminum characteristic of low-grade metamorphism. Green color, with cleavage like that of mica, except that small scales of chlorite are not elastic whereas those of mica are.

Chlorophyll The pigment of green plants that is involved in photosynthesis.

C-horizon The soil zone that contains partially disintegrated and decomposed parent material. It lies directly under the B-horizon and grades downward into unweathered material.

Chromite A mineral. An oxide of iron and chromium. $FeCr_2O_4$, the only ore of commercial chromium. It is one of the first minerals to crystallize from a magma and is concentrated within the magma.

Chrysotile A metamorphic mineral, an asbestos, the fibrous variety of serpentine. A silicate of magnesium, with tetrahedra arranged in sheets.

Chute, or chute cutoff As applied to stream flow, the term "chute" refers to a new route taken by a stream when its main flow is diverted to the inside of a bend, along a trough between low ridges formed by deposition on the inside of the bend where water velocities were reduced. Compare with *neck cutoff*.

Cinder Rough, slag-like fragment from a hundredth of an inch to an inch across, formed from magma blown into the air during an eruption.

Cinder cone Built exclusively or in large part of pyroclastic ejecta dominated by cinders. Parasitic to a major volcano, it seldom exceeds 1,500 feet in height. Slopes up 30° to 40°. Example: Parícutin.

Cirque A steep-walled hollow in a mountainside at high elevation, formed by ice-plucking and frost action, and shaped like a half-bowl or half-amphitheater. Serves as principal gathering ground for the ice of a valley glacier.

Clastic rocks Include those deposits that are made up of fragments of pre-existing rocks or of the solid products that are formed during the chemical weathering of such older rocks.

Clastic texture Texture shown by sedimentary rocks formed from deposits of mineral and rock fragments.

Clay minerals Finely crystalline, hydrous silicates that form as a result of the weathering of such silicate minerals as feldspar, pyroxene, and amphibole. The most common clay minerals belong to the kaolinite, montmorillonite, and illite groups.

Clay size A volume less than that of a sphere with a diameter of 1/256 mm (.004 mm, or .00015 in.).

Cleavage (1) *Mineral cleavage.* A property possessed by many minerals of breaking in certain preferred directions along smooth plane surfaces. The planes of cleavage are governed by the atomic pattern, and represent directions in which atomic bonds are relatively weak. (2) *Rock cleavage.* A property possessed by certain rocks of

breaking with relative ease along parallel planes or nearly parallel surfaces. Rock cleavage is designated as *slaty, phyllitic, schistose,* and *gneissic*.

Coal A general name for combustible, solid, black, or brownish-black carbonaceous materials formed through the partial decomposition of vegetable debris. Its formation is distinctly traceable through a series of gradational steps starting with peat and passing through lignite, bituminous coal, and anthracite to a final theoretical limit of nearly pure carbon. It is usually distinctly stratified and is found in association with ordinary sedimentary rocks such as shale and sandstone and, more rarely, limestone.

Cobble size A volume greater than that of a sphere with a diameter of 64 mm (2.5 in.), and less than that of a sphere with a diameter of 256 mm (10 in.).

Coelenterate One of the animal phylum *Coelenterata*, characterized by a hollow body cavity, radial symmetry, and stinging cells; includes jellyfish, corals, and sea anemones.

Col A pass through a mountain ridge. Created by the enlargement of two cirques on opposite sides of the ridge until their headwalls meet and are broken down.

Colloidal size Between two-tenths of a micron and one micron (.0002 mm to .001 mm, or 8×10^{-6} in. to 4×10^{-5} in.).

Colonial animal An individual that lives in close association with others of the same species. Usually it cannot exist as a separate individual.

Column A column or post of dripstone joining the floor and roof of a cave; the result of joining of a stalactite and a stalagmite.

Columnar jointing A pattern of jointing that blocks out columns of rock. Characteristic of tabular basalt flows or sills.

Columnar section A geologic illustration that shows in a graphic manner, and by use of conventional symbols for rock types, the successive rock units that occur throughout a given area or at a specific locality.

Compaction Reduction in pore space between individual grains as a result of pressure of overlying sediments or pressures resulting from earth movement.

Competence The maximum size of particle that a transporting agency, such as a stream, a glacier, or the wind, can move.

Composite volcanic cone Composed of interbedded lava flows and pyroclastic material. Characterized by slopes of close to 30° at the summit, reducing progressively to 5° near the base. Example: Mayon.

Compound A combination of the atoms or ions of different elements. The mechanism by which they are combined is called a *bond*.

Conchoidal fracture A mineral's habit of breaking in which the fracture produces curved surfaces like the interior of a shell (*conch*). Typical of glass and quartz.

Concordant pluton An intrusive igneous body with contacts parallel to the layering or foliation surfaces of the rocks into which it was intruded.

Concretion An accumulation of mineral matter that forms around a center or axis of deposition after a sedimentary deposit has been laid down. Cementation consolidates the deposit as a whole, but the concretion is a body within the host rock that represents a local concentration of cementing material. The enclosing rock is less firmly cemented than the concretion. Commonly spheroidal or disk-shaped, and composed of such cementing agents as calcite, dolomite, iron oxide, or silica.

Cone of depression A dimple in the water table, which forms as water is pumped from a well.

Cone sheet A dike that is part of a concentric set that dips inward, like an inverted cone.

Conformity The mutual relationships between sedimentary beds laid down in orderly sequence with little or no evidence of time lapses and, specifically, without any evidence that the lower beds were folded, tilted, or eroded before the higher beds were laid down.

Conglomerate The consolidated equivalent of gravel. The constituent rock and mineral fragments may be of varied composition and range widely in size. The matrix of finer material between the larger fragments may be sand, silt, or any of the common natural cementing materials such as calcium carbonate, silica, clay, or iron oxide. The rock fragments are rounded and smoothed from transportation by water or from wave action.

Conodont Any small, tooth-like fossil of phosphatic composition. Conodonts range through rocks of Ordovician to Triassic age. Their origin is uncertain. They have been variously assigned to vertebrates and several invertebrate phyla.

Connate water Water that was trapped in a sedimentary deposit at the time the deposit was laid down.

Consequent stream A stream following a course that is a direct consequence of the original slope of the surface on which it developed.

Consolidation In geology, any or all of the processes whereby loose, soft, or liquid earth materials become firm and coherent. Any action that increases the solidity, firmness, and hardness of earth materials is important in consolidation.

Contact The surface, in many cases irregular, which constitutes the junction of two bodies of rock.

Contact metamorphism Metamorphism at or very near the contact between magma and rock during intrusion.

Continental crust Portion of the earth's crust composed of two layers: first layer, sialic rock, 10 to 15 miles thick; second layer, simatic rock, 10 to 15 miles thick.

Continental deposits Deposits laid down on land or in bodies of water not connected with the ocean. The term is applicable whether the land mass is a true continent or only an island. The continental environment embraces fluviatile, lacustrine, glacial, and aeolian conditions.

Continental drift The process, considered by some to be theoretical and by others to be a fact, whereby one or more large land masses split apart and "drifted" laterally to form the present-day continents.

Continental glacier A large ice sheet that completely covers a large section of a continent, covering mountains and plains in an unbroken expanse.

Continental shelf The gently sloping belt of shallowly submerged land that fringes the continents. It may be broad or narrow. The slope is roughly 1 in 540 and the break of slope into deeper water is generally at a depth of about 600 feet. The geology of the continental shelves is similar to the geology of the adjacent emergent land.

Continental slope Portion of the ocean floor extending from about 600 feet (100 fathoms), at the seaward edge of the continental shelves, to the ocean deeps. Continental slopes are steepest in their upper portion, and commonly extend more than 12,000 feet (2,000 fathoms) downward.

Continuous reaction series That branch of Bowen's reaction series (*q.v.*) comprising the plagioclase feldspars, in which reaction of early-formed crystals with later liquids takes place continuously—that is, without abrupt phase changes.

Convection A mechanism by which material moves because its density is different from that of surrounding material. The density differences are frequently brought about by heating.

Convection cell A pair of *convection currents* adjacent to each other.

Convection current A closed circulation of material sometimes developed during convection. Convection currents normally develop in pairs; each pair is called a *convection cell*.

Convergence In terms of living things, convergence is the gradual process by which two or more originally unlike organisms become more and more similar in form, function, or reactions.

Coquina A coarse-grained, porous, friable variety of clastic limestone made up chiefly of fragments of shells.

Coral A general name for any of a large group of marine invertebrate organisms that belong to the phylum *Coelenterata*, which are common in modern seas and have left an abundant fossil record in all periods later than the Cambrian. The term "coral" is commonly applied to the calcareous skeletal remains. As found in the fossil state, coral consists almost exclusively of calcium carbonate.

Coral reef A reef, usually very large, and made up chiefly of fragments of corals, coral sands, and the solid limestone resulting from their consolidation.

Core A cylindrical piece of material cut and brought to the surface by special types of rock-cutting bits during the process of drilling. Also, the innermost part of the earth, surrounded by the mantle.

Core drilling Drilling with a hollow bit and barrel, which cut out and recover a solid core of the rock penetrated.

Coriolis effect The tendency of any moving body, on or starting from the surface of the earth, to continue in the direction in which the earth's rotation propels it. The direction in which the body moves because of this tendency, combined with the direction in which it is aimed, determines the ultimate course of the body relative to the earth's surface.

In the Northern Hemisphere, the coriolis effect causes a moving body to veer or try to veer to the right of its direction of forward motion; in the Southern Hemisphere, to the left. The magnitude of the effect is proportional to the velocity of a body's motion. This effect causes cyclonic stormwind circulation to be counterclockwise in the Northern Hemisphere and clockwise in the Southern, and determines the final course of ocean currents relative to trade winds.

Correlation The process of determining the position or time of occurrence of one geologic phenomenon in relation to others. Usually, and in the narrowest sense, it means determining the equivalence of geologic formations in separated areas through a comparison and study of fossil remains or lithologic peculiarities. In a wider sense, it applies to the cause-and-effect relationships of all geologic events in time and space and to the establishment of these phenomena in a logical and complete chronological system, such as the geologic time scale.

Cosmology The science that deals with the universe, its parts, and the laws governing its operation.

Cosmopolitan As applied to fossil organisms, the term "cosmopolitan" implies a widespread geographic distribution.

Covalent bond A bond in which atoms combine by the sharing of their electrons.

Crater A roughly circular, steep-sided volcanic basin with a diameter less than three times its depth. Commonly at the summit of a volcano. Contrast with *caldera*.

Creep As applied to soils and surficial material, slow downward movement of a plastic type. As applied to elastic solids, slow permanent yielding to stresses which are less than the yield point if applied for a short time only.

Creodont One of the groups of early, primitive, carnivorous mammals included in the suborder *Creodonta*. They flourished early in the Tertiary Period.

Crevasse (1) A deep crevice or fissure in glacier ice. (2) A breach in a natural levee.

Crinoid An exclusively marine invertebrate animal belonging to the phylum *Echinodermata*. Fossil crinoids are found in Late Cambrian and younger rocks. Typically, they are attached by a jointed stem, and

their shape suggests a lily-like plant, hence the name "sea lily," by which they are commonly known. Crinoids were especially abundant in Devonian and Mississippian time, declined at the end of the Paleozoic Era, and achieved a secondary maximum in the middle of the Mesozoic Era. About 650 species are still in existence.

Crosscutting relationships, law of A rock is younger than any rock across which it cuts.

Crossopterygian A type of fish considered to be ancestral to land vertebrates and characterized especially by a stout, muscular fin with a bony axis.

Cross section A geologic diagram or actual field exposure showing the geologic formations and structures transected by a given plane. Cross-section diagrams are commonly used in conjunction with geologic maps and contribute to an understanding of the subsurface geology. The formations, faults, veins, and so forth, are shown by conventional symbols or colors, and the scale is adapted to the size of the features present. Unless otherwise noted, cross sections are drawn in a vertical plane.

Crust In a general sense, the crust of the earth is the outermost shell from 20 to 30 miles thick that encloses the weaker, less well-known, central part of the earth. The term "crust" is frequently used to mean the outermost part of the earth in which relatively low velocities of earthquake waves prevail above the first major discontinuity, the so-called Moho-rovičić discontinuity.

Cryptocrystalline A state of matter in which there is actually an orderly arrangement of atoms characteristic of crystals, but in which the units are so small (that is, the material is so fine-grained) that the crystalline nature cannot be determined with the aid of an ordinary microscope.

Crystal A solid with orderly atomic arrangement. May or may not develop external faces that give it crystal form.

Crystal form The geometrical form taken by a mineral, giving an external expression to the orderly internal arrangement of atoms.

Crystalline structure The orderly arrangement of atoms in a crystal. Also called crystal structure.

Crystallization The process through which crystals separate from a fluid, viscous, or dispersed state.

Curie temperature The tempera-

ture above which ordinarily magnetic material loses its magnetism. On cooling below this temperature it regains its magnetism. Example: iron loses its magnetism above 1400°F (760°C) and regains it as it cools below this temperature. This is its curie temperature.

Current ripple marks Ripple marks, asymmetric in form, formed by air or water moving more or less continuously in one direction.

Cutoff See *chute cutoff; neck cutoff*.

Cycad A plant of the class *Gymnospermae*, having a short, pithy trunk; a thin, woody covering marked by numerous leaf-base scars, and palm-like leaves and cones.

Cycle of erosion A qualitative description of river valleys and regions passing through the stages of youth, maturity, and old age with respect to the amount of erosion that has been effected.

Cyclothem A succession of beds deposited during a single sedimentary cycle of the type that prevailed during the Pennsylvanian Period. The orderly repetition of a sequence of various kinds of strata in a series of cyclothems reflects a similar repetition of conditions of deposition over fairly wide areas of shallow sea and adjacent low-lying land areas.

Cystoid Any member of a class of echinoderms with a box- or cyst-like body constructed of numerous plates that may be arranged regularly or irregularly. The plates may be perforated by many pores, and the creature may have a stem and short food-gathering appendages. The known geologic range is from the Ordovician to the Devonian.

Debris slide A small, rapid movement of largely unconsolidated material that slides or rolls downward to produce an irregular topography.

Decomposition Synonymous with *chemical weathering*.

Deep focus Earthquake focus deeper than 200 miles (300 km). The greatest depth of focus known is 435 miles (700 km).

Deep-sea trenches See *island arc deeps*.

Deflation The erosive process in which the wind carries off unconsolidated material.

Deformation of rocks Any change in the original shape or volume of rock masses. Produced by mountain-building forces. Folding, faulting, and plastic flow are common modes of rock deformation.

Delta A plain underlain by an

assemblage of sediments that accumulate where a stream flows into a body of standing water where its velocity and transporting power are suddenly reduced. Originally so named because many deltas are roughly triangular in plan, like the Greek letter *delta* (Δ), with the apex pointing upstream.

Dendritic pattern An arrangement of stream courses that, on a map or viewed from the air, resembles the branching habit of certain trees, such as the oaks or maples.

Dendrochronology The science of dating and correlating that involves matching growth rings of trees or other vegetation.

Density A number that measures the concentration of matter, expressed as the mass per unit volume. (Mass equals weight divided by acceleration of gravity.)

Density current A current due to differences in the density of sea water from place to place caused by changes in temperature and variations in salinity or the amount of material held in suspension. Also called turbidity current.

Deposit Anything laid down. A natural accumulation of mineral matter in the form of solidified rock, unconsolidated material, useful ores, or organic materials such as coal and oil.

Depositional remanent magnetism Magnetism resulting from the tendency of magnetic particles such as magnetite to orient themselves in the earth's magnetic field as they are deposited. Their orientation is maintained as the soft sediments are lithified and thus records the earth's field when the particles were laid down. Abbreviation, DRM.

Derived Fossils or rock fragments that have been removed by erosion or some other process from their original sites and re-deposited in later formations are said to be derived.

Desert pavement A thin layer of rock fragments, usually of pebble size, left as a cover in desert regions after the wind has removed the finer material. They may be very extensive and one pebble thick.

Desiccation Loss of water from pore spaces of sediments through compaction or through evaporation caused by exposure to air.

Detrital sedimentary rocks Rocks formed from accumulations of minerals and rocks derived either from erosion of previously existing rock or from the weathered products of these rocks.

Detritus Any material worn or broken from rocks by mechanical means. The composition and dimensions are extremely variable. The deposits produced by accumulation of detritus constitute the detrital sediments.

Diabase A basic igneous rock of the basalt-gabbro series in which the essential minerals are plagioclase and augite, with the plagioclase in long, narrow, lath-shaped crystals oriented in all directions and the augite filling the interstices.

Diamond A mineral composed of the element carbon; the hardest substance known. Used as a gem and industrially in cutting tools.

Diastem A minor or obscure break in sedimentary rocks that involves only a very minor time loss. A short interval.

Diastrophism The process or processes that deform the earth's crust.

Diatom A microscopic aquatic plant (one of the algae) that secretes a siliceous skeleton, or test. A sediment made of diatoms is called diatomite.

Diatomaceous ooze A siliceous deep-sea ooze made up of the cell walls of one-celled marine algae known as diatoms.

Differential weathering The process by which different sections of a rock mass weather at different rates. Caused chiefly by variations in composition of the rock itself but also by differences in intensity of weathering from one section to another in the same rock. The result is usually that harder materials stand higher or protrude above softer materials.

Dike A sheet-like body of igneous rock that fills a fissure in older rocks which it entered while in a molten condition. Dikes occur in all types of material—igneous, metamorphic, and sedimentary; if in sedimentary rocks or bedded volcanic rocks, dikes "cut" the formations or transect the beds at an angle.

Dinosaur Any of a large number of extinct reptiles, usually of large size and belonging to either the *Saurischia* or the *Ornithischia*. The dinosaurs were confined to the Mesozoic Era and were characterized by diapsid skull structure, three bones uniting to form the hip joint, and other peculiar structural features.

Diorite A coarse-grained igneous rock with the composition of andesite (no quartz or orthoclase), composed of about 75 per cent plagioclase feldspars

and the balance ferromagnesian silicates.

Dip (1) The acute angle that a rock surface makes with a horizontal plane. The direction of the dip is always perpendicular to the strike. (2) See *magnetic declination*.

Dipole Any object that is oppositely charged at two points. Most commonly refers to a molecule that has concentrations of positive or negative charge at two different points.

Dipole magnetic field The portion of the earth's magnetic field that can best be described by a dipole passing through the earth's center and inclined to the earth's axis of rotation. See also *nondipole field* and *external magnetic field*.

Dip pole See *magnetic pole*.

Discharge With reference to stream flow, the quantity of water that passes a given point in unit time. Usually measured in cubic feet per second, abbreviated cfs.

Disconformity A break in the orderly sequence of stratified rocks above and below which the beds are parallel. The break is usually indicated by erosion channels with sand or conglomerate, which indicate a lapse of time or absence of part of the rock sequence.

Discontinuity (within the earth's interior) Sudden or rapid changes with depth in one or more of the physical properties of the materials constituting the earth, as evidenced by seismic data.

Discontinuous reaction series That branch of Bowen's reaction series (*q.v.*) including the minerals olivine, augite, hornblende, and biotite, for which each change in the series represents an abrupt phase change.

Discordant pluton An intrusive igneous body with boundaries that cut across surfaces of layering or foliation in the rocks into which it has been intruded.

Disintegration Synonymous with *mechanical weathering*.

Dispersal The spread of a species from its point of origin into other territory where its existence is possible.

Distillation The process of creating fossils by eliminating the liquid or gaseous constituents from an organic substance so that only a carbonaceous residue remains.

Distributary channel or stream A river branch that flows away from a main stream and does not rejoin it.

Characteristic of deltas and alluvial fans.

Divide Line separating two drainage basins.

Dolerite (1) Loosely, any dark igneous rock whose constituents cannot be easily determined megascopically. (2) Any coarse basalt. (3) Any rock of the composition of basalt regardless of grain size. (4) A rock of the diorite or gabbro clan with uniform medium to small grains.

Dolomite A mineral composed of the carbonate of calcium and magnesium, $CaMg(CO_3)_2$. Also used as a rock name for formations composed largely of the mineral dolomite.

Dome An upfold in which the strata dip downward in all directions from a central point or area. It is the reverse of a basin.

Drainage basin The area from which a given stream and its tributaries receive their water.

Drift Any material laid down directly by ice, or deposited in lakes, oceans, or streams as a result of glacial activity. Unstratified glacial drift is called *till* and forms *moraines*. Stratified glacial drift forms *outwash plains, eskers, kames,* and *varves*.

Drill hole An artificial hole cut or drilled in the earth to explore for valuable minerals or to secure scientific data.

Dripstone Calcium carbonate deposited from solution by underground water entering a cave in the zone of aeration. Sometimes called *travertine*.

DRM See *depositional remanent magnetism*.

Drumlin A smooth, streamlined hill composed of till. Its long axis is oriented in the direction of ice movement. The blunt nose points upstream and a gentler slope tails off downstream with reference to the ice movement. In height, drumlins range from 25 feet to 200 feet, with the average somewhat less than 100 feet. Most drumlins are between a quarter and a half mile in length. The length is commonly several times the width. Diagnostic characteristics are the shape and the composition of unstratified glacial drift, in contrast to kames, which are of random shapes and stratified glacial drift.

Dune A mound or ridge of sand piled by wind.

Dust-cloud hypotheses Theories that the solar system was formed from the condensation of interstellar dust clouds.

Dust size A volume less than that of a sphere with a diameter of $\frac{1}{16}$ mm (.06 mm or .0025 in.). Used in reference to particles carried in suspension by wind.

Earth (1) The solid matter of the globe as contrasted with water and air. (2) The loose or softer material composing part of the surface of the globe as distinguished from the firm rock. The word is rather indefinite in this sense, meaning about the same as, but not technically synonymous with, the term "soil."

Earthflow A combination of slump and mudflow.

Earthquake Waves in the earth generated when rocks break after being distorted beyond their strength.

Earthquake sounds Sounds in air generated by earthquake waves of audible frequencies.

Echinoderm Any member of the phylum *Echinodermata*. The chief characteristics are radial symmetry and a spiny skin. Common living examples are the starfish, sand dollar, and sea urchin. Extinct forms include blastoids and cystoids.

Echinoid Any of a number of marine invertebrate animals belonging to the class *Echinoidea* of the phylum *Echinodermata*. Recent forms are variously known as sea urchins, sand dollars, and sea porcupines. They are abundant in present-day seas and have left a fossil record extending back to the Ordovician Period. Certain forms are useful guide fossils for some formations of Mesozoic and Cenozoic age.

Ecliptic The apparent path of the sun in the heavens; the plane of the planets' orbit.

Ecology The study of the relations between organisms and environment. *Paleoecology* is the same study applied to past conditions.

Edentate Any member of the mammalian order *Edentata*, a group characterized chiefly by degenerate teeth. Living examples include the armadillo and the sloth.

Elastic deformation A nonpermanent deformation after which the body returns to its original shape or volume when the deforming force is removed.

Elastic energy The energy stored within a solid during elastic deformation, and released during elastic rebound.

Elasticity A property of materials that defines the extent to which they resist small deformation from which they recover completely when the deforming force is removed. Elasticity = stress/strain.

Elastic limit The maximum stress that produces only elastic deformation.

Elastic rebound The recovery of elastic strain when a material breaks or when the deforming force is removed.

Elastic solid A solid that yields to applied force by changing shape or volume, or both, but returns to its original condition when the force is removed. The amount of yield is proportional to the force.

Electrical energy The energy of moving electrons.

Electric charge A property of matter resulting from an imbalance between the number of protons and the number of electrons in a given piece of matter. The electron has a negative charge, the proton a positive charge. Like charges repel each other, unlike attract.

Electric log A record of the electrical responses of the geological materials encountered in a drill hole. Electric logs are useful in locating changes in composition and in making local correlations.

Electron A fundamental particle of matter, the most elementary negative electrical charge. Its mass is .00055 unit.

Electron shell An imaginary spherical surface representing all possible paths of electrons with the same average distance from a nucleus and with approximately the same energy.

Element A unique combination of protons, neutrons, and electrons that cannot be broken down by ordinary chemical methods. The fundamental properties of an element are determined by its number of protons. Each element is assigned a number that corresponds to its number of protons. Combinations containing from 1 through 102 protons are now known.

End moraine A ridge or belt of till marking the farthest advance of a glacier. Sometimes called *terminal moraine*.

Energy The capacity for producing motion. Energy holds matter together. It can become mass, or can be derived from mass. It takes such forms as kinetic, potential, heat, chemical, electrical, and atomic energy, and can be changed from one of these forms to another.

Energy level The distance from an

atomic nucleus at which electrons can have orbits. May be thought of as a shell surrounding the nucleus.

Entrenched meander A meander cut into underlying bedrock when regional uplift allows the originally meandering stream to resume downward cutting.

Epeirogenic Pertaining to or designating the deformation of broad tracts of the earth's crust; contrasts with *orogenic*.

Epicontinental Resting on a continent, as an epicontinental sea.

Epidote A silicate of aluminum, calcium, and iron characteristic of low-grade metamorphism and associated with chlorite and albite in the greenschist facies. Built around independent tetrahedra.

Epidote-amphibolite facies An assemblage of minerals formed between 500°F and 850°F (250°C and 450°C) during regional metamorphism.

Epoch A unit of geologic time; subdivision of a period. Some geologists restrict the term to the equivalent of a rock series, such as the Eocene Epoch or Series of the Tertiary Period or System.

Era One of the major divisions of geologic time, including one or more periods. The eras usually recognized are the Archeozoic, Proterozoic, Paleozoic, Mesozoic, and Cenozoic.

Erg A unit of energy, the capacity for doing work. The energy expended when a force of one dyne acts through a distance of one centimeter.

Erosion The wearing away and removal of materials of the earth's crust by natural means. As usually employed, the term includes weathering, solution, corrosion, and transportation. The agents that accomplish the transportation and cause most of the wear are running water, waves, moving ice, and wind currents. Most writers include under the term all the mechanical and chemical agents of weathering that loosen rock fragments before they are acted on by the transporting agents; a few authorities prefer to include only the destructive effects of the transporting agents.

Erosional flood plain A flood plain that has been created by the lateral erosion and the gradual retreat of the valley walls.

Erosional unconformity A break in the continuity of deposition of a rock series that is made manifest by evidences of erosion. The strata above and below the break may be parallel, with no evidence of folding of the lower beds during the lapse in sedimentation.

Erratic A rock fragment, usually large, that has been transported from a distant source, especially by the action of glacial ice. In the terminology of glaciation, an erratic is a stone or boulder carried by ice to a place where it rests on or near bedrock of different composition.

Esker A widening ridge of stratified glacial drift, steepsided, 10 to 100 feet in height, and from a fraction of a mile to over a hundred miles in length.

Eurypterid An extinct type of arthropod with pincher-like claws and 13 abdominal segments.

Eustatic change of sea level A change in sea level produced entirely by an increase or a decrease in the amount of water in the oceans, hence worldwide.

Evaporation The process by which a liquid becomes a vapor at a temperature below its boiling point.

Evaporite A rock composed of minerals that have been precipitated from solutions concentrated by the evaporation of solvents. Examples: rock salt, gypsum, anhydrite.

Evolution The unfolding or development of an organism so that it becomes more perfectly or completely adapted to the environments that become available to it with the passage of time. The implication of organic evolution is that all life has been derived from one or a few simple beginnings.

Exfoliation The process by which plates of rock are stripped from a larger rock mass by physical forces.

Exfoliation dome A large, rounded domal feature produced in homogeneous coarse-grained igneous rocks and sometimes in conglomerates by the process of exfoliation.

Exoskeleton A hard, outer skeleton or protective covering to which muscles are attached. The integument of the arthropod is a typical exoskeleton.

Exposure An unobscured outcrop of either solid rock or unconsolidated superficial material. In one sense or another, the term embraces all earth materials appearing at the surface that are not hidden by vegetation, water, or the works of man.

External magnetic field A component of the earth's field originating from activity above the earth's surface. Small when compared with the dipole and nondipole components of the field, which originate beneath the surface.

Extrusive rock A rock that has solidified from material poured or thrown out upon the earth's surface by volcanic ash.

Facies A term with many shades of meaning and hence difficult to define. In general, the term "facies" designates the aspect or appearance of a mass of earth material different in one or several respects from surrounding material. The features on which facies are named and recognized are usually selected more or less arbitrarily and may be lithologic (lithofacies) or biologic (biofacies). Two usages seem to be evident. The first applies only within a specific rock or time unit. A facies within the specific interval then designates some particular or general feature by which a part differs from other parts deposited at the same time and usually in physical continuity.

Facies changes Lateral or vertical changes in the lithologic or paleontological characteristics of contemporaneous deposits. Since facies relationships are usually complex, the exact features selected for mapping or discussion should be clearly designated.

Fault A break in materials of the earth's crust on which there has been movement parallel with the surface along which the break occurs. A fault occurs when rocks are strained past the breaking point and yield along a crack or series of cracks so that corresponding points on the two sides are distinctly offset. One side may rise or sink or move laterally with respect to the other side.

Fault-block mountain A mountain bounded by one or more faults.

Fauna The aggregation of animal species characteristic of a certain locality, region, or environment. The animals found fossilized in certain geologic formations or occurring in specified time intervals of the past may be referred to as fossil faunas.

Faunal succession The observed sequence of life forms through past ages. The total aspect of life at any one period is different from that of preceding and succeeding periods. Faunal succession implies but does not prove evolution.

Feldspars Silicate minerals composed of silicon-oxygen and aluminum-oxygen tetrahedra linked together in three-dimensional networks with positive ions fitted into the interstices of the negatively charged framework of tetrahedra. Classed as aluminosilicates. When the positive ion is K^+, the mineral is orthoclase; when it is Na^+, the mineral is albite; when it is Ca^{2+}, the mineral is anorthite.

Felsite A general term for light-colored, fine-grained igneous rocks.

Ferromagnesian silicate A silicate in which the positive ions are dominated by iron, magnesium, or both.

Fibrous fracture A mineral's habit of breaking into splinters or fibers.

Fiord A glacially deepened valley that is now flooded by the sea to form a long, narrow, steep-walled inlet.

Firn Granular ice formed by the recrystallization of snow. Intermediate between snow and glacier ice. Sometimes called *névé*.

Fissility A property of splitting along closely spaced parallel planes more or less parallel to the bedding. Its presence distinguishes shale from mudstone.

Fission tracks Minute tubes formed in certain minerals such as mica by fragments of radioactive elements that have undergone fission in place.

Fissure eruption Extrusion of lava from a fissure in the earth's crust.

Flint A dense, hard, siliceous rock composed of very finely crystalline and amorphous silica.

Flood basalt Basalt poured out from fissures in floods that tend to form great plateaus. Sometimes called *plateau basalt*.

Flood plain A strip of relatively smooth land bordering a stream, built of sediment carried by the stream and dropped in the slack water beyond the influence of the swiftest current. It is called a living flood plain if it is overflowed in times of high water but a fossil flood plain if it is beyond the reach of the highest flood.

Flood plain of aggradation A flood plain formed by the building up of the valley floor by sedimentation.

Flora The assemblage of plants of a given geologic formation, environment, region, or time interval.

Fluid Material that offers little or no resistance to forces tending to change its shape.

Focus The source of a given set of earthquake waves.

Fold A bend, flexure, or wrinkle in rock produced when the rock was in a plastic state.

Foliation A layering in some rocks caused by parallel alignment of minerals. A textural feature of some metamorphic rocks. Produces rock cleavage.

Footwall One of the blocks of rock involved in fault movement. The one that would be under the feet of a person standing in a tunnel along or across the fault. Opposite the hanging wall.

Foraminifera An important order of one-celled animals (protozoa) that have left an extensive fossil record in rocks of Ordovician and younger age. They are almost all marine and have durable shells, or tests, capable of fossilization. Being small, their remains are readily recovered from well cores and cuttings and have become very important in correlating oil-bearing rocks. Thousands of fossil species have been discovered and they are especially useful as guide fossils in rocks of late Paleozoic, Cretaceous, and Tertiary age.

Fore dune A dune immediately back of the shoreline of an ocean or large lake.

Foreset beds Inclined layers of sediment deposited on the advancing edge of a growing delta or along the lee slope of an advancing sand dune.

Foreshock A relatively small earthquake that precedes a larger earthquake by a few days or weeks and originates at or near the focus of the larger earthquake.

Formation The formation is the fundamental unit in the local classification of rocks. The larger units, groups, and series may be regarded as assemblages of formations and the smaller units as subdivisions of formations. The discrimination of sedimentary formations is based on the local sequence of rocks, lines of separation being drawn at points in the stratigraphic column where lithologic characters change or where there are significant breaks in the continuity of sedimentation or other evidences of important geologic events.

Fossil Originally, any rock, mineral, or other object dug out of the earth. Now restricted to any evidence of the existence or nature of an organism that lived in ancient times and that has been preserved in materials of the earth's crust by natural means. The term is not restricted to petrified remains—i.e., those of a stony nature—and includes besides actual remains such indirect evidences as tracks and trails. Fossils are, with few exceptions, prehistoric, but no age limit in terms of years can be set. Fossils are useful in studying the evolution of present life forms and in determining the relative ages of rock strata. The term also is frequently, but loosely, used in connection with ancient inorganic objects and markings, such as fossil ripple marks or rain prints.

Fossil assemblage All the fossil organisms that can be found or collected from a single bed or formation and that are assumed to have lived at the same time.

Fossil fuels Organic remains (once living matter) used to produce heat or power by combustion. Include petroleum, natural gas, and coal.

Fractional distillation The recovery, one or more at a time, of fractions of a complex liquid, each of which has a different density.

Fractionation A process whereby crystals that formed early from a magma have time to settle appreciably before the temperature drops much further. They are effectively removed from the environment in which they formed.

Fracture As a mineral characteristic, the way in which a mineral breaks when it does not have cleavage. May be conchoidal (shell-shaped), fibrous, hackly, or uneven.

Fracture cleavage A system of joints spaced a fraction of an inch apart.

Fringing reef A reef attached directly to a landmass.

Front In connection with concepts of granitization, the limit to which diffusing ions of a given type are carried. The *simatic front*, for example, is the limit to which diffusing ions carried the calcium, iron, and magnesium that they removed from the rocks in their paths. The *granitic front* is the limit to which diffusing ions deposited granitic elements.

Frost action Process of mechanical weathering caused by repeated cycles of freezing and thawing. Expansion of water during the freezing cycle provides the energy for the process.

Frost heaving The heaving of unconsolidated deposits as lenses of ice grow below the surface by acquiring capillary water from below.

Fundamental particles Protons, neutrons, and electrons. These combine to form atoms. Each particle is defined in terms of its *mass* and its *electric charge*.

Fusuline, fusulinid Any of an important group of extinct, marine, one-celled animals (class *Sarcodina*, phylum *Protozoa*) that have left an extensive fossil record from late Paleozoic time. Owing to their small size, they are easily recovered from well cuttings and have proved of great value in correlating oilbearing rocks.

G   Symbol for rigidity modulus.

Gabbro   A coarse-grained igneous rock with the composition of basalt.

Galaxy   A portion of space in which stars, dust, gas, and matter in general are concentrated.

Galena   A mineral; lead sulfide, PbS. The principal ore of lead.

Garnet   A family of silicates of iron, magnesium, aluminum, calcium, manganese, and chromium, which are built around independent tetrahedra and appear commonly as distinctive twelve-sided fully developed crystals. Characteristic of metamorphic rocks. Generally cannot be distinguished from one another without chemical analysis.

Gas   (1) A state of matter that has neither independent shape nor volume, can be compressed readily, and tends to expand indefinitely. (2) In geology, the word "gas" is sometimes used to refer to *natural gas*, the gaseous hydrocarbons that occur in rocks, dominated by methane. Compare with use of the word "oil" to refer to *petroleum*.

Gastropod   Any member of a large and important class of molluscs that typically possess a coiled, single-chambered shell. Marine, fresh-water, and terrestrial forms exist, and the group has left fossil representatives in Cambrian and all younger rocks. The gastropods are extremely numerous at present and have been important throughout the Cenozoic Era. Snails are the best-known representatives.

Gene   An hereditary determiner, located in a chromosome.

Genus (pl. genera)   A group of closely related species of organisms.

Geochemistry   The chemistry of the earth.

Geochronology   The study and classification of time in relation to the history of the earth.

Geode   A roughly spherical, hollow or partially hollow accumulation of mineral matter from a few inches to more than a foot in diameter. An outer layer of chalcedony is lined with crystals that project inward toward the hollow center. The crystals, often perfectly formed, are usually quartz, although calcite and dolomite are also found and, more rarely, other minerals. Geodes are most commonly found in limestone, and more rarely in shale.

Geographic poles   The points on the earth's surface marked by the ends of the earth's axis of rotation.

Geologic age   The time of existence of a fossil organism or the occurrence or duration of a particular event as stated in terms of the conventional geological time scale. Any event not datable in terms of years is usually assigned a relative geologic age.

Geologic column   (1) A chronologic arrangement of rock units in columnar form with the oldest units at the bottom and the youngest at the top. (2) A diagram showing the subdivisions of part or all of geologic time or the rock formations of a particular locality.

Geologic map   A map on which geologic information is plotted. The distribution of the formations is shown by means of symbols, patterns, or colors. The surficial deposits may or may not be mapped separately. Folds, faults, mineral deposits, and so on, are indicated by appropriate symbols.

Geologic time   The segment of time that elapsed before written history began. Although no precise limits can be set, the term implies extremely long duration or remoteness in the past.

Geologic time-scale   A chronologic sequence of units of earth time.

Geology   The science that treats of the origin, composition, structure, and history of the earth, especially as revealed by the rocks, and of processes by which changes in the rocks are brought about. Included is the study of the origin and evolution of living organisms, especially in prehistoric times. There are many subdivisions of the science, of which the following are important: historical geology, physical geology, economic geology, structural geology, mineralogy, mining geology, physiography, geomorphology, petrography, petrology, vulcanology, stratigraphic geology, and paleontology.

Geomagnetic poles   The dipole best approximating the earth's observed field is one inclined $11\frac{1}{2}°$ from the axis of rotation. The points at which the ends of this imaginary magnetic axis intersect the earth's surface are known as the geomagnetic poles. They should not be confused with the magnetic, dip poles or the virtual geomagnetic poles.

Geophysical prospecting   Mapping rock structures by methods of experimental physics. Includes measuring magnetic fields, the force of gravity, electrical properties, seismic wave paths and velocities, radioactivity, and heat flow.

Geophysics   Broadly, the physics of the earth, including the fields of meteorology, hydrology, oceanography, seismology, vulcanology, magnetism, and geodesy. In the more popular and practical sense, the term implies the application of electrical, thermal, magnetic, gravimetric, and seismic methods to the search for petroleum, metals, and underground supplies of water.

Geosyncline   Literally, a great, elongate downfold in the earth's crust. In general, the surface dimensions must be measured in terms of scores of miles, and the thickness of accumulated rocks must be on the order of 30,000 to 40,000 feet. A typical geosyncline comes into being through long-continued, gradual subsidence with simultaneous filling by shallow-water sediments. Geosynclines usually originate between or adjacent to the more solid shield or platform areas of the globe. They may become, with suitable structural evolution, the sites of large-scale deformation, and it is recognized that many major mountain systems are formed of compressed geosynclinal sediments.

Geyser   A special type of thermal spring which intermittently ejects its water with considerable force.

Glacial drift   As used today, the term "glacial drift" embraces all rock material in transport by glacial ice, all deposits made by glacial ice, and all deposits predominantly of glacial origin laid down in the sea or in bodies of glacial meltwater, whether rafted in icebergs or transported in the water itself. It includes till and scattered rock fragments.

Glaciation   A period of intensive ice action; also, the geologic work accomplished by ice masses.

Glacier   A mass of ice, formed by the recrystallization of snow, that flows forward, or has flowed at some time in the past, under the influence of gravity. By convention we exclude icebergs from this definition even though they are large fragments broken from the seaward end of glaciers.

Glacier ice   A unique form of ice developed by the compression and recrystallization of snow, and consisting of interlocking crystals.

Glass   A form of matter that exhibits the properties of a solid but has the atomic arrangements, or lack of order, of a liquid.

Globigerina ooze   A deep-sea calcareous ooze in which limy shells of minute one-celled animals called *Globigerina* abound.

Glossopteris flora   A late Paleozoic assemblage of fossil plants named for the seed fern *Glossopteris,* one of the plants in the flora. Widespread in South America, South Africa, Australia, India, and Antarctica.

Gneiss   A banded metamorphic rock with alternating layers of unlike minerals. Usually, equigranular minerals alternate with tabular minerals.

Gneissic cleavage   Rock cleavage in which the surfaces of easy breaking, if developed at all, are from a few hundredths of an inch to half an inch or more apart.

Goethite   Hydrous iron oxide; the formula is FeO(OH).

Gondwanaland   A hypothetical continent formed by the union of South America, Africa, Australia, India and Antarctica. This land mass is thought to have broken into its present fragments in the Mesozoic Era.

Gradation   Leveling of the land. This is constantly being brought about by the forces of gravity and such agents of erosion as water at the surface and underground, and wind, glacier ice, and waves.

Grade   A term used to designate the extent to which metamorphism has advanced. Found in such combinations as high-grade or low-grade metamorphism. Compare with *rank.*

Graded bedding   The type of bedding shown by a sedimentary deposit when particles become progressively finer from bottom to top.

Gradient   Slope of a stream bed.

Granite   A coarse-grained igneous rock dominated by light-colored minerals, consisting of about 50 per cent orthoclase, 25 per cent quartz, and the balance plagioclase feldspars and ferromagnesian silicates. Granites and granodiorites constitute 95 per cent of all intrusive rocks.

Granitic   Having the general character of granite, especially the structure of interlocking crystals. The mineral composition may or may not be the same as true granite.

Granitization   A special type of metasomatism by which solutions of magmatic origin move through solid rocks, change ions with them, and convert them into rocks which achieve granitic character without having passed through a magmatic stage.

Granodiorite   A coarse-grained igneous rock intermediate in composition between granite and diorite.

Graphic structure   An intimate intergrowth of potassic feldspar and quartz with the long axes of quartz crystals lining up parallel to a feldspar axis. The quartz part is dark and the feldspar is light in color, so the pattern suggests Egyptian hieroglyphs. Commonly found in pegmatites.

Graphite   A mineral composed entirely of carbon. "Black lead." Very soft because of its crystalline structure, in contrast to diamond, which has the same composition but is the hardest substance known.

Graptolite   Any of a large number of extinct marine invertebrates that occur as fossils from late in the Cambrian Period to the Mississippian Period. Their zoological affinities are obscure, but they have been recently assigned to the phylum *Protochordata* and are thus distantly related to vertebrates. They are especially useful as guide fossils in Ordovician rocks.

Gravel   Loose, or unconsolidated, coarse granular material larger than sand grains, resulting from erosion of rock by natural agencies. The lower size limit is usually set at 2 millimeters.

Gravity anomaly   Difference between observed value of gravity and computed value.

Gravity fault   A fault in which the hanging wall appears to have moved downward relative to the footwall. Also called *normal fault.*

Gravity meter   An instrument for measuring the force of gravity. Also called gravimeter.

Gravity prospecting   Mapping the force of gravity at different places to determine differences in specific gravity of rock masses, and, through this, the distribution of masses of different specific gravity. Done with a gravity meter (gravimeter).

Graywacke   A variety of sandstone generally characterized by its hardness, dark color, and angular grains of quartz, feldspar, and small rock fragments set in a matrix of clay-sized particles.

Greenschist   A schist characterized by green color. The product of regional metamorphism of simatic rocks. The green color is imparted by the mineral chlorite.

Greenschist facies   An assemblage of minerals formed between 300°F and 500°F (150°C and 250°C) during regional metamorphism.

Groundmass   The finely crystalline or glassy portion of a porphyry.

Ground moraine   Till deposited from a glacier as a veneer over the landscape and forming a gently rolling surface.

Ground water   Underground water within the zone of saturation.

Ground-water table   The upper surface of the zone of saturation for underground water. It is an irregular surface with a slope or shape determined by the quantity of ground water and the permeability of the earth materials. In general, it is highest beneath hills and lowest beneath valleys. Also referred to as *water table.*

Group   A unit of stratigraphic classification. A local or provincial subdivision of a system based on lithologic features. A group is usually less than a standard series and contains two or more formations.

Guide fossil   Any fossil that has actual, potential, or supposed value in identifying the age of the rocks in which it is found. Also called index fossil.

Guyot   A flat-topped submarine mountain whose summit is supposed to have been exposed to wave action and planed away to the surface of the ocean. Same as *tablemount.*

Gypsum   Hydrous calcium sulphate, $CaSO_4 \cdot 2H_2O$. A soft, common mineral in sedimentary rocks, where it sometimes occurs in thick beds interstratified with limestones and shales. Sometimes occurs as a layer under a bed of rock salt, since it is one of the first minerals to crystallize on the evaporation of sea water. Alabaster is a fine-grained massive variety of gypsum.

H   Symbol for mineral hardness.

Hackly fracture   A mineral's habit of breaking along jagged, irregular surfaces with sharp edges.

Half life   Time needed for one half of the nuclei in a sample of a radioactive element to decay.

Halite   A mineral; rock salt, or common salt, NaCl. Occurs widely disseminated, or in extensive beds and irregular masses, precipitated from sea water and interstratified with rocks of other types as a true sedimentary rock.

Hanging valley A valley that has a greater elevation than the valley to which it is tributary, at the point of their junction. Often (but not always) created by a deepening of the main valley by a glacier. The hanging valley may or may not be glaciated.

Hanging wall One of the blocks involved in fault movement. The one that would be hanging overhead for a person standing in a tunnel along or across the fault. Opposite the footwall.

Hardness A mineral's resistance to scratching on a smooth surface. The Mohs scale of relative hardness consists of ten minerals. Each of these will scratch all those below it in the scale and will be scratched by all those above it: (1) talc, (2) gypsum, (3) calcite, (4) fluorite, (5) apatite, (6) orthoclase, (7) quartz, (8) topaz, (9) corundum, (10) diamond.

Head Difference in elevation between intake and discharge points for a liquid. In geology, most commonly of interest in connection with the movement of underground water.

Heat energy A special manifestation of kinetic energy in atoms. The temperature of a substance depends on the average kinetic energy of its component particles. When heat is added to a substance, the average kinetic energy increases.

Hematite Iron oxide, Fe_2O_3. The principal ore mineral for about nine-tenths of the commercial iron produced in the United States. Characteristic red color when powdered. The name is derived from the Greek word meaning blood.

Hiatus A break or gap in the geologic record, as when rocks of a particular age are missing. The hiatus of an unconformity refers to the time interval not represented by rocks or to rocks missing by comparison with other areas.

Historical geology The study of the history and development of the earth, including the life forms that have inhabited it, and the sum of that knowledge. Historical geology encompasses what astronomy and geophysics can tell of the earth's origin, the paleontologic evidence of the nature of ancient life and its development through geologic time, and the relations developed by stratigraphy, structural geology, and other branches of geology that place the events of earth history in a sequential order.

Horizon A surface of contact or an imaginary plane without actual thickness that marks a certain level in stratified rocks.

Horn A spire of bedrock left where cirques have eaten into a mountain from more than two sides around a central area. Example: Matterhorn of the Swiss Alps.

Hornblende A rock-forming ferromagnesian silicate mineral with double chains of silicon-oxygen tetrahedra. An amphibole.

Hornfels Dense, granular metamorphic rock. Since this term is commonly applied to the metamorphic equivalent of any fine-grained rock, its composition is variable.

Hornfels facies An assemblage of minerals formed at temperatures greater than 1300°F (700°C) during contact metamorphism.

Hot spring A spring that brings hot water to the surface. A *thermal spring*. Water temperature usually 15°F or more above mean air temperature.

Hydraulic gradient Head of underground water divided by the distance of travel between two points. If the head is 10 feet for two points 100 feet apart, the hydraulic gradient is .1 or 10 per cent. When head and distance of flow are the same, the hydraulic gradient is 100 per cent.

Hydrocarbon A compound of hydrogen and carbon that burns in air to form water and oxides of carbon. There are many hydrocarbons. The simplest, methane, is the chief component of natural gas. Petroleum is a complex mixture of hydrocarbons.

Hydrologic cycle The general pattern of movement of water from the sea by evaporation to the atmosphere, by precipitation onto the land, and by movement under the influence of gravity back to the sea again.

Hydrothermal solution A hot, watery solution that usually emanates from a magma in the late stages of cooling. Frequently contains and deposits in economically workable concentrations minor elements that, because of incommensurate ionic radii or electronic charges, have not been able to fit into the atomic structures of the common minerals of igneous rocks.

Icecap A localized *ice sheet*.

Ice sheet A broad, mound-like mass of glacier ice of considerable extent with a tendency to spread radially under its own weight. Localized ice sheets are sometimes called *icecaps*.

Ichthyosaur Literally "fish lizard," any of the extinct, aquatic, fish-like reptiles belonging to the order *Ichthyosauria*.

Igneous Pertaining to or having the nature of fire. As used in geology to distinguish one of the three great classes of rocks, the name is a misnomer, for there is actually no fire involved; it should be interpreted to mean high temperatures.

Igneous rocks Rocks formed by solidification of hot mobile rock material (magma), including those formed and cooled at great depths (plutonic rocks) that are crystalline throughout and those that have poured out on the earth's surface in the liquid state or have been blown as fragments into the air (volcanic rocks).

Illite A clay mineral family of hydrous aluminous silicates. Structure similar to that of montmorillonite, but with aluminum substituted for 10 to 15 per cent of the silicon, which destroys montmorillonite's property of expanding with the addition of water because weak bonds are replaced by strong potassium-ion links. Structurally, illite is intermediate between montmorillonite and muscovite. Montmorillonite converts to illite in sediments, while illite converts to muscovite under conditions of low-grade metamorphism. Illite is the commonest clay mineral in clayey rocks and recent marine sediments, and is present in many soils.

Induced magnetism In the terminology of rock magnetism one of the components of the rock's natural remanent magnetism. It is parallel to the earth's present field and results from it.

Infiltration The soaking into the ground of water on the surface.

Insectivore A member of the order of placental animals, the *Insectivora*. Living examples include the shrews and hedgehog.

Intensity (of an earthquake) A number related to the effects of earthquake waves on man, structures, and the earth's surface at a particular place. Contrast with *magnitude*, which is a number related to the total energy released by an earthquake.

Intermediate belt Subdivision of zone of aeration. The belt that lies between the belt of soil moisture and the capillary fringe.

Intermediate focus Earthquake focus between depths of 40 to 200 miles (60 to 300 km).

Intermittent stream A stream that carries water only part of the time.

Intrusive rock A rock that has solidified from a mass of molten material within the earth's crust but did not reach the surface.

Invertebrate An animal without a backbone; pertaining to such an animal or animals.

Ion An electrically unbalanced form of an atom, or group of atoms, produced by the gain or loss of electrons.

Ionic bond A bond in which ions are held together by the electrical attraction of opposite charges.

Ionic radius The average distance from the center to the outermost electron of an ion. Commonly expressed in angstroms.

Island arc A group of islands having an arc-like pattern. Most island arcs lie near the continental masses, but inasmuch as they rise from the deep ocean floors, they are not a part of the continents proper.

Island arc deeps Arcuate trenches bordering some of the continents. Some reach depths of 30,000 feet or more below the surface of the sea. Also called deep-sea trenches or trenches.

Isolation A term used in biology to designate any process or condition whereby a group of individuals is cut off and separated for a considerable length of time from other areas or groups. The situation need not arise from actual geographical factors. Animals may become isolated as a result of food preferences or because of purely psychological reactions.

Isoseismic line A line connecting all points on the surface of the earth where the intensity of shaking produced by earthquake waves is the same.

Isostasy The ideal condition of balance that would be attained by earth materials of differing densities if gravity were the only force governing their heights relative to each other.

Isotope Alternate form of an element. The fundamental properties of the element, and its place in the table of elements, are determined by the number of protons in its nucleus. Variations in the number of neutrons in the nucleus produce isotopes.

Jasper Granular cryptocrystalline silica usually colored red by hematite inclusions.

Jet or shooting flow A type of flow, related to turbulent flow, occurring when a stream reaches high velocity along a sharply inclined stretch, or over a waterfall, and the water moves in plunging, jet-like surges.

Joint A break in a rock mass where there has been no relative movement of rock on opposite sides of the break.

Juvenile water Water brought to the surface or added to underground supplies from magma.

Kame A steep-sided hill of stratified glacial drift. Distinguished from a drumlin by lack of unique shape and by stratification.

Kame terrace Stratified glacial drift deposited between a wasting glacier and an adjacent valley wall. When the ice melts, this material stands as a terrace along the valley wall.

Kaolinite A clay mineral, a hydrous aluminous silicate. $Al_4Si_4O_{10}(OH)_8$. Structure consists of one sheet of silicon-oxygen tetrahedra each sharing three oxygens to give a ratio of Si_4O_{10}, linked with one sheet of aluminum and hydroxyl. The composition of pure kaolinite does not vary as it does for the other clay minerals, montmorillonite and illite, in which ready addition or substitution of ions takes place.

Karst topography Irregular topography characterized by sinkholes, streamless valleys, and streams that disappear into the underground, all developed by the action of surface and underground water in soluble rock such as limestone.

Kettle A depression in the ground surface formed by the melting of a block of ice buried or partially buried by glacial drift, either outwash or till.

Key bed A well-defined and easily recognizable bed that serves to facilitate correlation in geologic work. The term is also applied to the horizon or bed on which elevations are taken or to which elevations are finally reduced in making a structure contour map. The term is used interchangeably with "key horizon."

Kinetic energy Energy of movement. The amount of kinetic energy possessed by an object or particle depends on its mass and speed.

Kyanite A silicate mineral characteristic of the temperatures of middle-grade metamorphism. Al_2SiO_5 in bladed blue crystals is softer than a knife along the crystal's length, harder across. Its crystalline structure is based on independent tetrahedra. Compare with *andalusite*, which has the same composition and forms under similar conditions, but has a different crystal habit. Contrast with *sillimanite*, which has the same composition but different crystal habit and forms at highest metamorphic temperature.

L Symbol for earthquake surface waves.

Labyrinthodont Pertaining to a peculiar tooth structure characterized by deep infolding of the enamel. This type of tooth is possessed by extinct amphibians and related ancestral fish.

Laccolith A concordant pluton that has domed up the strata into which it was intruded.

Lake A considerable body of inland water or an expanded part of a river.

Laminar flow Mechanism by which a fluid such as water moves slowly along a smooth channel, or through a tube with smooth walls, with fluid particles following straightline paths parallel to the channel or walls. Contrast with *turbulent flow*.

Land bridge A land area, usually narrow and subject to submergence, that connects land masses and serves as a route of dispersal for land plants and animals.

Land form The term "land form" is applied by physiographers to each of the multitudinous features that taken together make up the surface of the earth. It includes all broad features such as plains, plateaus, and mountains, and also all the minor features, such as hills, valleys, slopes, canyons, arroyos, and alluvial fans. Most of these features are the products of erosion, but the term also includes all forms that result from sedimentation and from movements within the crust of the earth.

Landslide A general term for relatively rapid mass movement, such as slump, rock slide, debris slide, mudflow, and earthflow.

Large waves Earthquake surface waves.

Latent heat of fusion The number of calories per unit volume that must be added to a material at the melting point to complete the process of melting. These calories do not raise the temperature.

Lateral moraine A ridge of till along the edge of a valley glacier. Composed largely of material that fell to the glacier from valley walls.

Laterite Tropical soil rich in hydroxides of aluminum and iron formed under conditions of good drainage.

Laurasia A hypothetical land mass composed of Asia, North America, and other minor land masses of the Northern Hemisphere.

Lava A general name for molten

rock poured out on the surface of the earth by volcanoes and for the same material that has cooled and solidified as solid rock.

Law of superposition   The general law which states that, if undisturbed, any sequence of sedimentary rocks will have the oldest beds at the base and the youngest at the top.

Levee (natural)   Bank of sand and silt built by a river during floods, where suspended load is deposited in greatest quantity close to the river. The process of developing natural levees tends to raise river banks above the level of the surrounding flood plains. A break in a natural levee is sometimes called a crevasse.

Lignite   A low-grade coal with about 70 per cent carbon and 20 per cent oxygen. Intermediate between peat and bituminous coal.

Limb   One of the two parts of an anticline or syncline on either side of the axis.

Limestone   A sedimentary rock composed largely of the mineral calcite, $CaCO_3$, which has been formed by either organic or inorganic processes. Most limestones have a clastic texture, but nonclastic, particularly crystalline, textures are common. The carbonate rocks, limestone and dolomite, constitute about 22 per cent of the sedimentary rocks exposed above sea level.

Limonite   Iron oxide with no fixed composition or atomic structure. Always of secondary origin and not a true mineral. Is encountered as ordinary rust, or the coloring material of yellow clays and soils.

Lithification   The process by which unconsolidated rock-forming materials are converted into a consolidated or coherent state.

Lithology   The study of stones or rocks, especially those of sedimentary origin. Also, the description of the total physical characteristics of specified samples or formations.

"Living fossil"   A term applied to any organism with a long geologic history, usually one that has outlived the forms with which it was once associated.

Load   The amount of material that a transporting agency, such as a stream, a glacier, or the wind, is actually carrying at a given time.

Loess   An unconsolidated, unstratified aggregation of small, angular mineral fragments, usually buff in color. Generally believed to be wind-deposited. Characteristically able to stand on very steep to vertical slopes.

Log   A record of the earth materials passed through in digging or drilling a test pit or well. It may contain, in addition, notes regarding geologic structure, water conditions, casing used, and so on. Special types of logs are electric, caliper, radioactivity, sample, and so forth.

Longitudinal dune   A long ridge of sand oriented in the general direction of wind movement. A small one is less than 10 feet in height and 200 feet in length. Very large ones are called seif dunes.

Magma   Hot mobile rock material generated within the earth, from which igneous rock results by cooling and crystallization. It is usually conceived of as a pasty or liquid material, or a mush of crystals together with a noteworthy amount of liquid phase having the composition of silicate melt.

Magnetic declination   The angle of divergence between a geographic meridian and a magnetic meridian. It is measured in degrees east and west of geographic north.

Magnetic inclination   The angle that the magnetic needle makes with the surface of the earth. Also called dip of the magnetic needle.

Magnetic pole   The north magnetic pole is the point on the earth's surface where the north-seeking end of a magnetic needle free to move in space points directly down. At the south magnetic pole the same needle points directly up. These poles are also known as *dip poles*.

Magnetite   A mineral; iron oxide, Fe_3O_4. Black, strongly magnetic. An important ore of iron.

Magnitude (of an earthquake)   A number related to the total energy released by an earthquake. Contrast with *intensity*, which is a number related to the effects of earthquake waves at a particular place.

Mammal   A vertebrate animal characterized by warm blood, a covering of hair, live birth (2 egg-laying exceptions), and the ability to suckle its young.

Mantle   In the geophysical sense, the part of the earth between the surface and the core, excluding the part above the Mohorovičić discontinuity. The term is occasionally used without this exclusion (see *crust*). In a more general sense, mantle refers to the loose material at or near the surface, above bedrock. In zoology, the mantle is the membrane lining the respiratory cavity of molluscs or brachiopods. It also secretes the shell substance.

Marble   Metamorphic rock of granular texture, no rock cleavage, and composed of calcite or dolomite or both.

Marsh gas   Methane, CH_4, the simplest paraffin hydrocarbon. The dominant component of natural gas.

Marsupial   Any of the group of mammals that lack a placenta and have an abdominal pouch in which the immature young remain for some time after birth. Examples are the kangaroo and opossum.

Mass   A number that measures the quantity of matter. It is obtained on the earth's surface by dividing the weight of a body by the acceleration due to gravity.

Massive pluton   Any pluton that is not tabular in shape.

Mass movement   Surface movement of earth materials induced by gravity.

Mass number   Number of protons and neutrons in the nucleus of an atom.

Mass unit   One-sixteenth the mass of the oxygen atom. Approximately the mass of the hydrogen atom.

Matter   Anything that occupies space. Usually defined by describing its states and properties: solid, liquid, or gaseous; possesses mass, inertia, color, density, melting point, hardness, crystal form, mechanical strength, or chemical properties. Composed of atoms.

Meander   (1) A turn or sharp bend in a stream's course. (2) To turn, or bend sharply. Applied to stream courses in geological usage.

Meander belt   The zone along a valley floor that encloses a meandering river.

Mechanical weathering   The process by which rock is broken down into smaller and smaller fragments as the result of energy developed by physical forces. Also known as *disintegration*.

Medial moraine   A ridge of till formed by the junction of two lateral moraines when two valley glaciers join to form a single ice stream.

Member   A subdivision of a geologic formation that is identified by lithologic characteristics such as color, hardness, composition, and similar features and that has considerable geographic extent. Members may receive formal names.

Metal   A substance that is fusible and opaque, is a good conductor of electricity, and has a characteristic luster. Examples: gold, silver, aluminum. Over three-fourths of the elements are metals.

Metamorphic facies   An assemblage

of minerals that reached equilibrium during metamorphism under a specific range of temperature.

Metamorphic rocks (1) "Changed-form rocks." Any rock that has been changed in texture or composition by heat, pressure, or chemically active fluids after its original formation. (2) One of the three great groups of rocks. Metamorphic rocks are formed from original igneous or sedimentary rocks through alterations produced by pressure, heat, or the infiltration of other materials at depths below the surface zones of weathering and cementation. Rocks that have undergone only slight changes are not usually considered metamorphic; for practical purposes, the term is best applied to rocks in which transformation has been almost complete or at least has produced characteristics that are more prominent than those of the original rock.

Metamorphic zone An area subjected to metamorphism and characterized by a certain metamorphic mineral that formed during the process.

Metamorphism A process whereby rocks undergo physical or chemical changes, or both, to achieve equilibrium with conditions other than those under which they were originally formed. Weathering is arbitrarily excluded from the meaning of the term. The agents of metamorphism are heat, pressure, and chemically active fluids.

Metasomatism A process whereby rocks are altered when volatiles exchange ions with them.

Meteoric water Ground water derived primarily from precipitation.

Meteorite A mass of mineral or rock matter coming to the earth from space.

Methane The simplest paraffin hydrocarbon, CH_4. The principal constituent of natural gas. Sometimes called marsh gas.

Micas A group of silicate minerals characterized by perfect sheet or scale cleavage resulting from their atomic pattern, in which silicon-oxygen tetrahedra are linked in sheets. Biotite is the ferromagnesian black mica. Muscovite is the potassic white mica.

Microfossil Any fossil too small to be studied without magnification. Includes single organisms, fragments of complete organisms, or colonies of many organisms.

Micropaleontology The branch of paleontology dealing with fossils so small that they require magnification for identification and study.

Microseism A small shaking. Specif-ically limited in technical usage to earth waves generated by sources other than earthquakes, and most frequently to waves with periods of from a second to about 9 seconds from sources associated with atmospheric storms.

Migmatite A mixed rock produced by an intimate interfingering of magma and an invaded rock.

Mineral A naturally occurring solid element or compound, exclusive of biologically formed carbon components. It has a definite composition, or range of composition, and an orderly internal arrangement of atoms known as crystalline structure, which gives it unique physical and chemical properties, including a tendency to assume certain geometrical forms known as *crystals*.

Mineral deposit A local accumulation or concentration of mineral substances or of a single mineral, either metallic or nonmetallic, which is of economic or potentially economic value.

Mobile belt A belt or tract of the earth's crust, usually long and relatively narrow, which displays evidence of greater geologic activity such as geosynclines, folds, faults, and volcanic activity. Contrasts with stable blocks.

Mohorovičić discontinuity A level of major change in the interior of the earth. It is found just beneath the crust at depths ranging from 5 to 20 miles.

Mold An impression of the exterior or interior of an object from which it is possible to obtain a cast or reproduction of its outward shape.

Molecule The smallest unit of a compound which displays the properties of that compound.

Mollusc Any member of the numerous group of animals constituting the phylum *Mollusca*. In general, they are soft-bodied and are protected by a calcareous shell of their own making. There are marine, fresh-water, and terrestrial forms, and the range of the phylum is from the Early Cambrian to present.

Monadnock A hill left as a residual of erosion, standing above the level of a peneplain.

Monel metal Steel containing 68 per cent nickel.

Montmorillonite A clay mineral family, a hydrous aluminous silicate with a structural sandwich of one ionic sheet of aluminum and hydroxyl between two (Si_4O_{10}) sheets. These sandwiches are piled on each other with water between them, and with nothing but weak bonds to hold them together. As a result, additional water can enter the lattice readily. This causes the mineral to swell appreciably and further weakens the attraction between structural sandwiches. Consequently, a lump of montmorillonite in a bucket of water slumps rapidly into a loose, incoherent mass. Compare with the other clay minerals, *kaolinite* and *illite*.

Moraine A general term applied to certain landforms composed of till.

Mosasaur A large extinct marine lizard commonly found in Upper Cretaceous rocks. Mosasaurs averaged about 15 to 20 feet in length.

Mountain Any part of a landmass that projects conspicuously above its surroundings.

Mountain chain A series or group of connected mountains having a well-defined trend or direction.

Mountain glacier Synonymous with *alpine glacier*.

Mountain range A series of more or less parallel ridges, all of which were formed within a single geosyncline or on its borders.

Mountain structure Structure produced by the deformation of rocks.

Mudcracks Cracks caused by the shrinkage of a drying deposit of silt or clay under surface conditions.

Mudflow Flow of a well-mixed mass of rock, earth, and water that behaves like a fluid and flows down slopes with a consistency similar to that of newly mixed concrete.

Mudstone Fine-grained, detrital sedimentary rock made up of silt and clay-sized particles. Distinguished from shale by lack of fissility.

Multituberculate An extinct mammal of the order *Multituberculata*, which existed in the Late Mesozoic and Early Tertiary. Their teeth are characterized by numerous cusps, and their habits and appearance were evidently somewhat like those of modern rodents.

Muscovite "White mica." A non-ferromagnesian rock-forming silicate mineral with its tetrahedra arranged in sheets. Sometimes called potassic mica.

Mutation An inherited change stemming from modification of the hereditary material in the reproductive cells. The change may be slight or great.

Native state State in which an element occurs uncombined in nature. Usually applied to the metals, as in native copper, native gold, etc.

Natural gas Gaseous hydrocarbons that occur in rocks. Dominated by methane.

Natural remanent magnetism The magnetism of a rock. May or may not coincide with present magnetic field of the earth. Abbreviation, NRM.

Natural selection The complex process whereby organisms are eliminated or preserved according to their fitness or adaptation to their surroundings, especially to changes in the environment.

Nautiloid Any of a large group of marine invertebrate organisms constituting a division of the class *Cephalopoda* of the phylum *Mollusca*. Typically, they have a straight, curved, or coiled, many-chambered shell. The edges of the septa between chambers have a straight or curved pattern and are not acutely angular or crenulated as in the ammonoids. They range from the Cambrian to the present with a maximum development in the Silurian.

Nebula Faintly luminous object or appearance seen in the heavens. Some nebulae within the Milky Way are masses of gas and dust; others, outside of the local galaxy, are clusters of stars.

Neck cutoff The breakthrough of a river across the narrow neck separating two meanders, where downstream migration of one has been slowed and the next meander upstream has overtaken it. Compare with *chute cutoff*.

Neutron A proton and an electron combined and behaving like a fundamental particle of matter. Electrically neutral, with a mass of 1.00896 units. If isolated, it decays to form a proton and an electron.

Névé Granular ice formed by the recrystallization of snow. Intermediate between snow and glacier ice. Sometimes called *firn*.

Nickel steel Steel containing 2.5 to 3.5 per cent nickel.

Nivation Erosion beneath and around the edges of a snowbank.

Nodule An irregular, knobby-surfaced body of mineral that differs in composition from the rock in which it is formed. Silica in the form of chert or flint is the major component of nodules. They are commonly found in limestone and dolomite.

Nonconformity A type of unconformity in which an older, eroded sequence of rocks meets a younger, overlying sequence at an angle. Tilting and erosion of the lower sequence before deposition of the higher beds is implied. Some geologists use nonconformity only for cases where the older rock is of plutonic origin; both usages are evidently correct.

Nondipole magnetic field That portion of the earth's magnetic field remaining after the dipole field and the external field are removed.

Nonferromagnesians Silicate minerals that do not contain iron or magnesium.

Nonmetal An element that is not a metal, such as oxygen, carbon, sulphur, phosphorus, and boron.

Normal fault A fault in which the hanging wall appears to have moved downward relative to the footwall. Opposite of a thrust fault. Also called *gravity fault*.

Nova Literally a "new" star but more accurately one that increases suddenly in size and brilliance. After expending tremendous energy for a short while, it fades to obscurity.

NRM See *natural remanent magnetism*.

Nucleus (atomic) The protons and neutrons constituting the central part of an atom.

Nuée ardente (pl. nuées ardentes) "Hot cloud." A French term applied to a highly heated mass of gas-charged lava ejected more or less horizontally from a vent or pocket at the summit of a volcano, onto an outer slope down which it moves swiftly, however slight the incline, because of its extreme mobility.

Nummulite Any of a large group of foraminiferal protozoans having coin-like shells. They are common in the Early Tertiary rocks of the warmer regions of the earth.

Obsidian Glassy equivalent of granite.

Oceanic crust Portion of the earth's crust composed of one layer of simatic rock 20 to 30 miles thick.

Offlap The arrangement of nonconformable sedimentary units in a depositional basin whereby the shoreward edge of each succeeding younger unit is farther offshore than the unit on which it lies.

Oil In geology, refers to petroleum (*q.v.*).

Oil shale Shale containing such a proportion of hydrocarbons as to be capable of yielding petroleum on slow distillation.

Olivine A rock-forming ferromagnesian silicate mineral that crystallizes early from a magma and weathers readily at the earth's surface. Its crystal structure is based on isolated SiO_4 ions and positive ions of iron or magnesium, or both. General formula: $(Mg,Fe)_2SiO_4$.

Oölites Spheroidal grains of sand size, usually composed of calcium carbonate, $CaCO_3$, and thought to have originated by inorganic precipitation. Some limestones are made up largely of oölites.

Ooze Ooze in a sedimentary sense is any soupy deposit covering the bottom of any water body. Specifically, the term relates to more or less calcareous or siliceous deposits that cover extensive areas of the deep-ocean bottom. The marine oozes contain in greater or less quantities the shells of small organisms whose presence in quantities of 25 per cent or more leads to differentiation into varieties based on their presence. Thus, there are the *Globigerina*, Pteropod, Radiolarian, and Diatom oozes. The percentage of the shells of these organisms may range from zero to nearly 100. Other constituents of the oozes are minerals of a wide range and various other kinds of organic matter.

Opal Amorphous silica, with varying amounts of water. A mineral gel.

Order of crystallization The chronological sequence in which crystallization of the various minerals of an assemblage takes place.

Ore A metalliferous mineral deposit.

Organic Pertaining to or derived from life or from an organism. Chemically, an organic compound is one in which hydrogen or nitrogen is directly united with carbon.

Orogenic Pertaining to or designating an orogeny or mountain-building disturbance; contrasts with *epeirogenic*.

Orogeny The process by which great elongate chains and ranges of mountains are formed. Although the process or processes are not well understood, many orogenic movements appear to start with the downwarping of a large trough in the earth's crust, which is filled with sediments. The trough and its included sediments are then mashed, and the width of the belt is greatly shortened by folding and faulting. Igneous activity generally accompanies or follows deformation, and many of the largest bodies of intrusive igneous rocks lie within orogenic belts. The episode of deformation by which a specific system of mountains comes into being may be called an orogeny. The word thus seems to signify not only a process but also an event.

Orthoclase The feldspar in which K^+ is the diagnostic positive ion; $K(AlSi_3O_8)$.

Orthogenesis Evolution or development along definite lines as the result of a supposed directing influence.

Ostracod   Any of a great number of small aquatic invertebrates of the phylum *Arthropoda* (class *Crustacea*, subclass *Ostracoda*). Typically, their bodies are small, segmented, and encased in a bivalved, horny, or calcareous shell. There are both marine and nonmarine species, and they range from the Ordovician to the present. They are valuable guide fossils for many marine formations and are of special importance in correlating nonmarine continental rocks.

Outcrop   Part of a body of rock that appears bare and exposed at the surface of the ground. In a more general sense, the term also applies to areas where the rock formation occurs next beneath the soil, even though it is not exposed.

Outwash   Material carried from a glacier by meltwater. Laid down in stratified deposits.

Outwash plain   Flat or gently sloping surface underlain by outwash.

Overthrust fault   In a general sense, any reverse fault with low dip; more specifically, a low-angle fault on which the mass above has demonstrably moved or been pushed over a relatively stable mass below the fault. Usually a reverse fault having a dip of less than 20 degrees and a displacement measured in miles.

Overturned fold   A fold in which at least one limb is overturned—that is, has rotated through more than 90°.

Oxbow   An abandoned meander, caused by a neck cutoff.

Oxbow lake   An abandoned meander isolated from the main stream channel by deposition, and filled with water.

Oxide mineral   A mineral formed by the direct union of an element with oxygen. Examples: ice, corundum, hematite, magnetite, cassiterite.

P   Symbol for earthquake primary waves.

Paired terraces   Terraces that face each other across a stream at the same elevation.

Paleo-   A combining form denoting the attribute of great age or remoteness in the past; e.g., *paleobotany*, the study of fossil plants.

Paleoecology   The study of ancient ecology or the relations of fossils to their environment.

Paleogeographic map   A map that shows the reconstructed geographic features of some specified period in the ancient past.

Paleogeography   The study of ancient geography.

Paleolithic   Pertaining to the earliest stage in use of stone by mankind, the Old Stone Age.

Paleomagnetism   The study of the earth's magnetic field as it has existed during geologic time.

Paleontology   A study of the plant and animal life of past periods. It is based on the fossil remains found in the earth.

Pangaea   A hypothetical continent from which all others are postulated to have originated through a process of fragmentation and drifting.

Parabolic dune   A dune with a long, scoop-shaped form that, when perfectly developed, exhibits a parabolic shape in plan, with the horns pointing upwind. Contrast *barchan*, in which the horns point downwind. Characteristically covered with sparse vegetation, and often found in coastal belts.

Paraconformity   An obscure or uncertain unconformity above and below which the beds are parallel and there is little physical evidence of a long lapse in deposition.

Particles, fundamental   See *fundamental particles*.

Pater noster lakes   A chain of lakes resembling a string of beads along a glaciated valley where ice-plucking and gouging have scooped out a series of basins.

Peat   Partially reduced plant or wood material containing approximately 60 per cent carbon and 30 per cent oxygen. An intermediate material in the process of coal formation.

Pebble size   A volume greater than that of a sphere with a diameter of 4 mm or $\frac{5}{32}$ in., and less than a sphere of 64 mm or 2.5 in.

Pedalfer   A soil characterized by the accumulation of iron salts or iron and aluminum salts in the B-horizon. Varieties of pedalfers include red and yellow soils of the southeastern United States, and podsols of the northeastern quarter of the United States.

Pediment   Broad, smooth erosional surface developed at the expense of a highland mass in an arid climate. Underlain by beveled rock, which is covered by a veneer of gravel and rock debris. The final stage of a cycle of erosion in a dry climate.

Pedocal   A soil characterized by an accumulation of calcium carbonate in its profile. Characteristic of low rainfall. Varieties include black and chestnut soils of the northern Plains states, and the red and gray desert soils of the drier western states.

Pedology   The science that treats of soils—their origin, character, and utilization.

Pegmatite   A small pluton of exceptionally coarse texture, with crystals up to 40 feet in length, commonly formed at the margin of a batholith and characterized by graphic structure. Nearly 90 per cent of all pegmatites are simple pegmatites of quartz, orthoclase, and unimportant percentages of micas. The others are extremely rare ferromagnesian pegmatites and complex pegmatites. Complex pegmatites have as their major components the sialic minerals of simple pegmatites, but they also contain a variety of rare minerals.

Pelagic deposit   Material formed in the deep ocean and deposited there. Example: ooze.

Peneplain   An extensive, nearly flat surface developed by subaerial erosion, and close to base level, toward which the streams of the region are reducing it. Originally defined as forming in a humid climate.

Perched water table   The top of a zone of saturation that bottoms on an impermeable horizon above the level of the general water table in the area. Is generally near the surface, and frequently supplies a hillside spring.

Peridotite   A coarse-grained igneous rock dominated by dark-colored minerals, consisting of about 75 per cent ferromagnesian silicates and the balance plagioclase feldspars.

Period   The fundamental unit of the standard geologic time scale, the time during which a standard system of rocks was formed. Examples are the Devonian, Cretaceous, and Tertiary periods.

Permafrost   Permanently frozen ground, or more correctly, ground that remains below freezing temperatures for two or more years.

Permeability   For a rock or an earth material, the ability to transmit fluids. Permeability for underground water is sometimes expressed numerically as the number of gallons per day that will flow through a cross section of 1 square foot, at 60°F, under a hydraulic gradient of 100 per cent. Permeability is equal to velocity of flow divided by hydraulic gradient.

Petrifaction   The process of petrifying, or changing into stone; conversion of organic matter, including shells, bones, and the like, into stone or a substance of stony hardness. Petrifaction is produced by the infiltration of water containing dissolved mineral matter such as calcium carbonate, silica, and so on, which replaces the organic material particle by particle, sometimes with original structure retained.

Petrify To convert organic material such as wood or bone into stone.

Petroleum A complex mixture of hydrocarbons, accumulated in rocks, and dominated by paraffins and cycloparaffins. Crude petroleums are classified as *paraffin-base* if the residue left after volatile components have been removed consists principally of a mixture of paraffin hydrocarbons; as *asphalt-base* if the residue is primarily cycloparaffins.

Phase (in physical chemistry) A homogeneous, physically distinct portion of matter in a system that is not homogeneous, as in the three phases—ice, water, and aqueous vapor.

Phenocryst A crystal significantly larger than the crystals of surrounding minerals.

Phosphate rock A sedimentary rock containing calcium phosphate.

Photogeology The study of geology from photographs, usually those taken from aircraft.

Photosynthesis The process by which carbohydrates are compounded from carbon dioxide and water in the presence of sunlight and chlorophyll. The synthesis of carbohydrates by green plants in the presence of sunlight.

Phyllite A clayey metamorphic rock with rock cleavage intermediate between slate and schist. Commonly formed by the regional metamorphism of shale or tuff. Micas characteristically impart a pronounced sheen to rock cleavage surfaces. Has phyllitic cleavage.

Phyllitic cleavage Rock cleavage in which flakes are produced that are barely visible to the unaided eye. Coarser than slaty cleavage, finer than schistose cleavage.

Phylogeny The history of any race or group. *Phylogenetic* is the adjective.

Phylum A large group of plants or animals; a major division of a kingdom. Usually divided into subphyla or classes.

Physical geology The branch of geology that deals with the nature and properties of material composing the earth, distribution of materials throughout the globe, the processes by which they are formed, altered, transported, and distorted, and the nature and development of landscape.

Phytosaur An extinct reptile somewhat like a crocodile in appearance that is included in the order *Theco-*

donta. Phytosaurs are characteristic of the Late Triassic.

Piedmont glacier A glacier formed by the coalescence of valley glaciers and spreading over plains at the foot of the mountains from which the valley glaciers came.

Pirate stream One of two streams in adjacent valleys that has been able to deepen its valley more rapidly than the other, has extended its valley headward until it has breached the divide between them, and has captured the upper portion of the neighboring stream.

Placental Pertaining to or possessing the embryonic organ known as the placenta, which attaches the embryo to the uterine wall.

Placer A deposit of sand or gravel, usually of river or beach origin, containing particles of gold or other valuable minerals.

Plagioclase feldspars Albite and anorthite.

Planetesimal Literally, "little planet," meaning a small body in space that behaves like a small planet in following an orbit around the sun. Planetesimals may be somewhat hypothetical entities but are required in certain theories of earth origin.

Plastic deformation Permanent change in shape or volume that does not involve failure by rupture, and that, once started, continues without increase in the deforming force.

Plastic solid A solid that undergoes change of shape continuously and indefinitely after the stress applied to it passes a critical point.

Plateau basalt Basalt poured out from fissures in floods that tend to form great plateaus. Sometimes called *flood basalt.*

Playa The flat-floored center of an undrained desert basin.

Playa lake A temporary lake formed in a playa.

Pleochroic halo Minute, concentric spherical zones of darkening or coloring that form around inclusions of radioactive minerals in biotite, chlorite, and a few other minerals. About .003 in. in diameter.

Plesiosaur Any of the extinct marine reptiles characterized by a long, flexible neck and flattened body which make up the order *Plesiosauria.*

Plunge The acute angle that the axis of a folded rock mass makes with a horizontal plane.

Pluton A body of igneous rock that is formed beneath the surface of the earth by consolidation from magma.

Sometimes extended to include bodies formed beneath the surface of the earth by the metasomatic replacement of older rock.

Plutonic igneous rock A rock formed by slow crystallization, which yields coarse texture. Once believed to be typical of crystallization at great depth, but that is not a necessary condition.

Pluvial lake A lake formed during a pluvial period (*q.v.*).

Pluvial period A period of increased rainfall and decreased evaporation, which prevailed in nonglaciated areas during the time of ice advance elsewhere.

Podsol An ashy gray or gray-brown soil of the pedalfer group. This highly bleached soil, low in iron and lime, is formed under moist and cool conditions.

Polar compound A compound, such as water, with a molecule that behaves like a small bar magnet with a positive charge on one end and a negative charge on the other.

Polar wandering A movement of the magnetic poles during past geologic time in relation to the present positions.

Porosity The percentage of open space or interstices in a rock or other earth material. Compare with *permeability.*

Porphyritic A textural term for igneous rocks in which larger crystals, called phenocrysts, are set in a finer ground mass, which may be crystalline or glassy, or both.

Porphyry An igneous rock containing a considerable proportion, say 25 per cent or more by volume, of large crystals or phenocrysts set in a finer groundmass of small crystals or glass, or both.

Portland cement A hydraulic cement consisting of compounds of silica, lime, and alumina.

Positive area A relatively large tract or segment of the earth's crust that has tended to rise over fairly long periods with respect to adjacent areas.

Potassic feldspar Orthoclase, $K(AlSi_3O_8)$.

Potential energy Stored energy waiting to be used. The energy that a piece of matter possesses because of its position or because of the arrangement of its parts.

Pothole A hole ground in the solid rock of a stream channel by sands, gravels, and boulders caught in an eddy of turbulent flow and swirled for a long time over one spot.

Prairie soils Transitional soils between pedalfers and pedocals.

Precambrian Pertaining to or designating all rocks formed prior to the Cambrian Period. The term "Precambrian" is used as a noun as well as an adjective by some geologists.

Precipitation The discharge of water, in the form of rain, snow, hail, sleet, fog, or dew, on a land or water surface. Also, the process of separating mineral constituents from a solution by evaporation (halite, anhydrite) or from magma to form igneous rocks.

Prehistoric time The interval of time preceding the historic period or the invention of writing.

Pressure Force per unit area applied to the outside of a body.

Primary waves Earthquake body waves that travel fastest and advance by a push-pull mechanism. Also known as longitudinal, compressional, or P-waves.

Primate Any member of the placental mammal order *Primates*, characterized by large brains, prehensile hands, and five digits on hands and feet.

Primitive Pertaining to the origin or beginning of anything; also, rudimentary.

Proton A fundamental particle of matter with a positive electrical charge of 1 unit (equal in amount but opposite in effect to the charge of an electron), and with a mass of 1.00758 units.

Protore The original rock, too poor in mineral values to constitute an ore, from which desired elements have been leached and redeposited as an ore. The process of leaching and redeposition of desired elements is sometimes called supergene enrichment, or secondary sulfide enrichment.

Pseudofossil An object of inorganic but natural origin that might resemble or be mistaken for a fossil.

Pterodactyl Any member of the reptilian order *Pterosauria*, or flying reptiles.

Pteropod ooze A calcareous deep-sea ooze dominated by the remains of minute molluscs of the group *Pteropoda*.

Pumice Pyroclastic rock filled with gas-bubble holes. Cellular in texture, with many open compartments sealed from one another, it is usually buoyant enough to float on water.

Push-pull wave A wave that advances by alternate compression and rarefaction of a medium, causing a particle in its path to move forward and backward along the direction of the wave's advance. In connection with waves in the earth, also known as *primary wave*, or compressional wave, longitudinal wave, or P-wave.

Pyrite A sulfide mineral. Iron sulfide, FeS$_2$.

Pyroclastic rock Fragmental rock blown out by volcanic explosion and deposited from the air. Includes bomb, block, cinder, ash, tuff, and pumice.

Pyroxene group Ferromagnesian silicates with a single chain of silicon-oxygen tetrahedra. Common example: augite. Compare with *amphibole group* (example: hornblende), which has a double chain of tetrahedra.

Pyrrhotite A mineral; iron sulfide. So commonly associated with nickel minerals that it has been called "the world's greatest nickel ore."

Quartz A silicate mineral, SiO$_2$, composed exclusively of silicon-oxygen tetrahedra with all oxygens joined together in a three-dimensional network. Crystal form is a six-sided prism tapering at the end, with the prism faces striated transversely. An important rock-forming mineral.

Quartzite Metamorphic rock commonly formed by the metamorphism of sandstone and composed of quartz. Has no rock cleavage. Breaks through sand grains as contrasted to sandstone, which breaks around the grains.

Radial adaptation or adaptive radiation The general process whereby a related group of organisms becomes adapted for life in all suitable environments which become available to it.

Radial drainage An arrangement of stream courses in which the streams radiate outward in all directions from a central zone.

Radioactive disintegration The change an element or isotope undergoes during radioactivity.

Radioactive isotope A variety of any element that has a different atomic weight from other isotopes of the same element and is radioactive. Carbon-14 is a radioactive isotope of carbon.

Radioactivity The spontaneous breakdown of an atomic nucleus, with emission of radiant energy.

Radiogenic Formed by or resulting from radioactive processes, such as radiogenic heat.

Radiolarian ooze A siliceous deep-sea ooze dominated by the delicate and complex hard parts of minute marine protozoa called *Radiolaria*.

Radiometric Pertaining to measurements based on radioactive processes.

Rank A term used to designate the extent to which metamorphism has advanced. Compare with *grade*. Rank is more commonly employed in designating the stage of metamorphism of coal.

Reaction series See *Bowen's reaction series*.

Recessional moraine A ridge or belt of till marking a period of moraine formation, probably in a period of temporary stability or a slight re-advance, during the general wastage of a glacier and recession of its front.

Rectangular pattern An arrangement of stream courses in which tributaries flow into larger streams at angles approaching 90°.

Recumbent fold A fold in which the axial plane is more or less horizontal.

Red beds Red sedimentary rocks of any age.

Reef An aggregation of organisms with hard parts that live or have lived at or near the surface of a body of water, usually marine, and that build up a mound or ridge-like elevation. Reefs are considered sedimentary accumulations.

Refractory A mineral or compound that resists the action of heat and of chemical reagents.

Regional metamorphism Metamorphism occurring over tens or scores of miles.

Rejuvenation A change in conditions of erosion that causes a stream to begin more active erosion and a new cycle.

Relative age The age of a given geologic feature, form, or structure stated in terms of comparison with its immediate surroundings; that is, not stated in terms of years or centuries.

Relative dating The placement of an object or event in its proper chronological order in relation to other things or events without reference to its actual age in terms of years.

Relative time Dating of events by means of their place in a chronologic order of occurrence rather than in terms of years. Compare with *absolute time*.

Replacement The process whereby the substance of a rock, mineral, ore, or organic fragment is slowly removed by solution and material of a different composition is deposited in its place.

Reverse fault A fault in which the hanging wall appears to have moved upward relative to the footwall. Also called *thrust fault*. Contrast with *normal* or *gravity fault*.

Revolution A period of large-scale crustal disturbances and other physical changes having continental or world-wide effects and constituting a critical period in the evolution of organisms.

Reworked A fragment of rock or a fossil removed by natural means from its place of origin and deposited in recognizable form in a younger deposit is said to be reworked.

Rhyolite A fine-grained igneous rock with the composition of granite.

Rift zone A system of fractures in the earth's crust. Often associated with extrusion of lava.

Rigidity Resistance to elastic shear.

Rigidity modulus The number that expresses a material's rigidity. For example, the number of pounds per square inch necessary to cause a specified change of shape. Represented by the symbol G.

Ring dike An arcuate, rarely circular, dike with steep dip.

Ripple mark The undulating surface sculpture of ridges and troughs produced in noncoherent granular materials such as loose sand by the wind, by currents of water, and by agitation of water in wave action.

Roche moutonnée (pl. roches moutonnées) A sheep-shaped knob of rock that has been rounded by the action of glacier ice. Usually only a few feet in height, length, and breadth. A gentle slope faces upstream with reference to the ice movement. A steeper slope attributed to plucking action of the ice represents the downstream side.

Rock In the popular and also in an engineering sense, the term "rock" refers to any hard, solid matter derived from the earth. In a strictly geological sense, a rock is any naturally formed aggregate or mass of mineral matter, whether or not coherent, constituting an essential and appreciable part of the earth's crust. A few rocks are made up of a single mineral, as a very pure limestone. Two or more minerals usually are mixed together to form a rock.

Rock cycle A concept of the sequences through which earth materials may pass when subjected to geological processes.

Rock flour Finely divided rock material pulverized by a glacier and carried by streams fed by melting ice.

Rock flow The movement of solid rock when it is in a plastic state.

Rock-forming silicate minerals Minerals built around a framework of silicon-oxygen tetrahedra. Olivine, augite, hornblende, biotite, muscovite, orthoclase, albite, anorthite, quartz.

Rock glacier A tongue of rock waste found in the valleys of certain mountainous regions. Characteristically lobate and marked by a series of arcuate, rounded ridges that give it the aspect of having flowed as a viscous mass.

Rock melt A liquid solution of rock-forming mineral ions.

Rock salt Halite, or common salt, NaCl.

Rock slide Sudden and rapid slide of bedrock along planes of weakness.

Rossi-Forel scale A scale for rating earthquake intensities. Devised in 1878 by de Rossi of Italy and Forel of Switzerland.

Runoff Water that flows off the land.

Rupture A breaking apart or state of being broken apart.

S Symbol for secondary wave.

Salt (1) Any of a class of compounds derived from acids by replacement of part or all of the acid hydrogen by a metal or metal-like radical; $NaHSO$ and Na_2SO_4 are sodium salts of sulphuric acid (H_2SO_4). (2) Halite, common salt, Sodium chloride, NaCl.

Saltation Mechanism by which a particle moves by jumping from one point to another.

Salt dome A mass of NaCl generally of roughly cylindrical shape and with a diameter of about a mile near the top. These masses have been pushed through surrounding sediments into their present positions, sometimes as far as 20,000 feet. Reservoir rocks above and alongside salt domes sometimes trap oil and gas.

Sand Clastic particles of sand size, commonly but not always composed of the mineral quartz.

Sand size A volume greater than that of a sphere with a diameter of $\frac{1}{16}$ mm (.0625 mm or .0025 in.), and less than that of a sphere with a diameter of 2 mm or $\frac{5}{64}$ in.

Sandstone A consolidated rock composed of sand grains cemented together. The size range and composition of the constituents are the same as for sand, and the particles may be rounded or angular. Although sandstones may vary widely in composition, they are usually made up of quartz; and if the term is used without qualification, a siliceous composition is implied.

Sapropel An aquatic ooze or sludge that is rich in organic matter. Believed to be the source material for petroleum and natural gas.

Schist A crystalline metamorphic rock that has closely spaced foliation and tends to split readily into thin flakes or slabs. Dominantly composed of fibrous or platy minerals.

Schistose cleavage Rock cleavage in which grains and flakes are clearly visible and cleavage surfaces are rougher than in slaty or phyllitic cleavage.

Sea arch The roof of a cave cut by the sea through a headland.

Sea cave A cave formed by the erosive action of sea waves.

Seamount An isolated, steep-sloped peak rising from the deep ocean floor but submerged beneath the ocean surface. Most have sharp peaks, but some have flat tops and are called *guyots* or *tablemounts*. Seamounts are probably volcanic in origin.

Secondary wave An earthquake body wave slower than the primary wave. A *shear*, *shake*, or *S-wave*.

Secular variation of the magnetic field A change in inclination, declination, or intensity of the earth's magnetic field. Detectable only from long historical records.

Sediment In the singular the word is usually applied to material in suspension in water or recently deposited from suspension. In the plural the word is applied to all kinds of deposits from the waters of streams, lakes, or seas, and in a more general sense to deposits of wind and ice. Such deposits that have been consolidated are generally called *sedimentary rocks*.

Sedimentary facies An accumulation of deposits that exhibits specific characteristics and grades laterally into other sedimentary accumulations formed at the same time but exhibiting different characteristics.

Sedimentary rocks Sedimentary rocks are composed of sediment: mechanical, chemical, or organic. They are formed through the agency of water, wind, glacial ice, or organisms and are deposited at the surface of the earth at ordinary temperatures. The materials from which they are made must originally have come from the disintegration and decomposition of older rocks, chiefly igneous. They cover about 75 per cent of the land area of the globe.

Sedimentation Strictly, the act or process of depositing sediment from suspension in water. Broadly, all the processes whereby particles of rock material are accumulated to form sedimentary deposits. Sedimentation, as commonly used, involves not only aqueous but also glacial, aeolian, and organic agents.

Seif dune A very large longitudinal dune. As high as 300 feet and as long as 60 miles.

Seismic prospecting A method of determining the nature and structure of buried rock formations by generating waves in the ground (commonly by small charges of explosive) and measuring the length of time these waves require to travel different paths.

Seismic seawave A large wave in the ocean generated at the time of an earthquake. Popularly, but incorrectly, known as a *tidal wave*. Sometimes called a *tsunami*.

Seismogram The record obtained on a seismograph.

Seismograph An instrument for recording vibrations, most commonly employed for recording earth vibrations.

Seismology The scientific study of earthquakes and other earth vibrations.

Serpentine A silicate of magnesium common among metamorphic minerals. Occurs in two crystal habits, one platy, known as antigorite, the other fibrous, known as chrysotile. Chrysotile is an asbestos. The name "serpentine" comes from mottled shades of green on massive varieties, suggestive of the markings of a serpent.

S.G. Symbol for specific gravity.

Shake wave Wave that advances by causing particles in its path to move from side to side or up and down at right angles to the direction of the wave's advance, a shake motion. Also called *shear wave* or *secondary wave*.

Shale A general term for lithified muds, clays, and silts, that are fissile and break along planes parallel to the original bedding. A typical shale is so fine-grained as to appear homogeneous to the unaided eye, is easily scratched, and has a smooth feel. The lamination, or fissibility, is usually best displayed after weathering.

Shallow focus Earthquake focus within 40 miles (60 km) or less of the earth's surface.

Shear Change of shape without change of volume.

Shear modulus See *rigidity modulus*.

Shear wave Wave that advances by shearing displacements (which change the shape without changing the volume) of a medium. This causes particles in its path to move from side to side or up and down at right angles to the direction of the wave's advance. Also called *shake wave* or *secondary wave*.

Sheeting Joints that are essentially parallel to the ground surface. They are more closely spaced near the surface and become progressively farther apart with depth. Particularly well-developed in granitic rocks, but sometimes in other massive rocks as well.

Shell (1) The crust of the earth or some other continuous layer beneath the crust. (2) A thin layer of hard rock. (3) The hard outer covering of an organism or the petrified remains of the covering.

Shield The Precambrian nuclear mass of a continent, around which and to some extent on which the younger sedimentary rocks have been deposited. The term was originally applied to the shield-shaped Precambrian area of Canada but is now used for the primitive areas of other continents, regardless of shape.

Shield volcano A volcano built up almost entirely of lava, with slopes seldom as great as 10° at the summit and 2° at the base. Examples: the five volcanoes on the island of Hawaii.

Sial A term coined from the symbols for silicon and aluminum. Designates the composite of rocks dominated by granites, granodiorites, and their allies and derivatives, which underlie continental areas of the globe. Specific gravity considered to be about 2.7.

Sialic rock An igneous rock composed predominantly of silicon and aluminum. The term is constructed from "si" for silicon and "al" for aluminum. Average specific gravity about 2.7.

Siderite A mineral; iron carbonate, $FeCO_3$. An ore of iron.

Silica Silicon dioxide, SiO_2. Silica forms the natural crystalline minerals quartz, cristobalite, and tridymite, and the noncrystalline mineral opal, which carries 2-13 per cent water. Quartz is the most abundant mineral in the visible portions of the earth's crust and occurs in a great variety of igneous, metamorphic, and sedimentary rocks and as the filling in veins.

Silicate minerals Minerals with crystal structure containing SiO_4 tetrahedra arranged as (1) isolated units, (2) single or double chains, (3) sheets, or (4) three-dimensional networks.

Silicic Pertaining to or derived from silica or silicon; specifically, designating compounds of silicon, as silicic acid.

Silicon-oxygen tetrahedron A complex ion composed of a silicon ion surrounded by 4 oxygen ions. It has a negative charge of 4 units, is represented by the symbol $(SiO_4)^{4-}$, is the diagnostic unit of silicate minerals, and is the central building unit of nearly 90 per cent of the materials of the earth's crust.

Silification The process of combining with or being impregnated with silica. A common method of fossilization.

Sill A tabular body of igneous rock that has been injected while molten between layers of sedimentary or igneous rocks or along the foliation planes of metamorphic rocks. Sills are relatively more extensive laterally than they are thick.

Sillimanite A silicate mineral, Al_2SiO_5, characteristic of highest metamorphic temperatures and pressures. Occurs in long slender crystals, brown, green, white. Its crystalline structure is based on independent tetrahedra. Contrast with *kyanite* and *andalusite*, which have the same composition but different crystal habits and form at lower temperatures.

Silt size A volume greater than that of a sphere with a diameter of $\frac{1}{256}$ mm (.0039 mm or .00015 in.), and less than that of a sphere with a diameter of $\frac{1}{16}$ mm (.0625 mm or .0025 in.).

Sima A term coined from "si" for silicon and "ma" for magnesium. Designates a worldwide shell of dark, heavy rocks. The sima is believed to be the outermost rock layer under deep, permanent ocean basins, such as the mid-Pacific. Originally, the sima was considered basaltic in composition, with a specific gravity of about 3.0. It has been suggested also, however, that it may be peridotitic in composition, with a specific gravity of about 3.3.

Simatic rock An igneous rock composed predominantly of ferromagnesian minerals. The term is constructed from "si" for silicon and "ma" for magnesium. Average specific gravity 3.0 to 3.3.

Sink A sinkhole.

Sinkhole Depression in the surface of the ground caused by the collapse of the roof over a solution cavern.

Skeleton The hard structure that constitutes the framework supporting the soft parts of any organism. It may be internal as in the vertebrates, or external as in the invertebrates.

Slate   A fine-grained metamorphic rock with well-developed slaty cleavage. Formed by the low-grade regional metamorphism of shale.

Slaty cleavage   Rock cleavage in which ease of breaking occurs along planes separated by microscopic distances.

Slip-face   The steep face on the lee side of a dune.

Slope failure   See *slump*.

Slope wash   Soil and rock material that is being or has been moved down a slope predominantly by the action of gravity assisted by running water that is not concentrated into channels. The term applies to the process as well as the materials.

Slump   The downward and outward movement of rock or unconsolidated material as a unit or as a series of units. Also called *slope failure*.

Snowfield   A stretch of perennial snow existing in an area where winter snowfall exceeds the amount of snow that melts away during the summer.

Snowline   The lower limit of perennial snow.

Soapstone   See *talc*.

Sodic feldspar   Albite, $Na(AlSi_3O_8)$.

Soil   The superficial material that forms at the earth's surface as a result of organic and inorganic processes. Soil varies with climate, plant and animal life, time, slope of the land, and parent material.

Soil horizon   A layer of soil approximately parallel to the land surface with observable characteristics that have been produced through the operation of soil-building processes.

Solid   Matter with a definite shape and volume and some fundamental strength. May be crystalline, glassy, or amorphous (*q.v.*).

Solifluction   Mass movement of soil affected by alternate freezing and thawing. Characteristic of saturated soils in high latitudes.

Space lattice   In the crystalline structure of a mineral, a three-dimensional array of points representing the pattern of locations of identical atoms or groups of atoms which constitute a mineral's *unit cell* (*q.v.*). There are 230 pattern types.

Species   A group of plants or animals that normally interbreed producing fertile offspring and that resemble each other in structure, habits, and functions.

Specific gravity   A number that represents the ratio between the weight of a given volume of a material and the weight of an equal volume of water at 4°C (39.2°F).

Specific heat   The amount of heat necessary to raise the temperature of one gram of any material through one degree Centigrade.

Sphalerite   A mineral; zinc sulfide, ZnS. Nearly always contains iron, $(Zn,Fe)S$. The principal ore of zinc. Also known as Zinc Blende or Black Jack.

Spheroidal weathering   The spalling off of concentric shells from rock masses of various sizes as a result of pressures built up during chemical weathering.

Spirifer   A general name for brachiopods with wide, pointed, or winged shells.

Spit   A sandy bar built by currents into a bay from a promontory.

Spontaneous generation   The appearance of life or living things from dead material without the intervention of outside or supernatural forces.

Spring   A place where the water table crops out at the surface of the ground and where water flows out more or less continuously.

Stack   A small island that stands as an isolated, steep-sided rock mass just off the end of a promontory. Has been isolated from the land by erosion and by weathering concentrated just behind the end of a headland.

Stage   The time-stratigraphic unit next in rank below a series. It is the fundamental working unit in local time-stratigraphic correlation and therefore is employed most commonly to relate any of the various types of minor stratigraphic units in one geologic section or area to the rock column of another nearby section or area with respect to time of origin.

Stalactite   Icicle-shaped accumulation of dripstone hanging from a cave roof.

Stalagmite   Post of dripstone growing upward from the floor of a cave.

Staurolite   A silicate mineral characteristic of middle-grade metamorphism. Its crystalline structure is based on independent tetrahedra with iron and aluminum. It has a unique crystal habit that makes it striking and easy to recognize: six-sided prisms intersecting at 90° to form a cross, or at 60° to form an X.

Stegocephalian   Any large extinct amphibian with a broad, flat, bone-covered skull.

Stock   A discordant pluton that increases in size downward, has no determinable floor, and shows an area of surface exposure less than 40 square miles. Compare with *batholith*.

Stoping   A mechanism by which batholiths have moved into the crust by the breaking off and foundering of blocks of rock surrounding the magma chamber.

Strain   Change of dimensions of matter in response to stress. Commonly, unit strain, such as change in length per unit length (total lengthening divided by original length), change in width per unit width, change in volume per unit volume. Contrast with *stress*.

Strata   The plural of stratum.

Stratification   The characteristic structural feature of sedimentary rocks produced by the deposition of sediments in beds, layers, strata, laminae, lenses, wedges, and other essentially tabular units. Stratification stems from many causes—differences of texture, hardness, cohesion or cementation, color, mineralogical or lithological composition, and internal structure.

Stratigrapher   One who studies, or who has expert knowledge of, stratigraphy.

Stratigraphic trap   A structure that traps petroleum or natural gas because of variation in permeability of the reservoir rock, or the termination of an inclined reservoir formation on the up-dip side.

Stratigraphy   The branch of geology that deals with the definition and interpretation of the stratified rocks, the conditions of their formation, their character, arrangements, sequence, age, distribution, and especially their correlation, by the use of fossils and other means. The term is applied both to the sum of the characteristics listed above and to the study of these characteristics.

Stratum   A single layer of homogeneous or gradational lithology deposited parallel to the original dip of the formation. It is separated from adjacent strata or cross strata by surfaces of erosion, nondeposition, or abrupt changes in character. Stratum is not synonymous with the terms "bed" or "lamination" but includes both. "Bed" and "lamination" carry definite connotations of thickness.

Streak   The color of the fine powder of a mineral. May be different from the color of a hand specimen. Usually determined by rubbing the mineral on a piece of unglazed porcelain (hardness about 7), known as a streak plate, which is, of course, useless for minerals of greater hardness.

Stream capture See *stream piracy*.

Stream piracy The process whereby a stream rapidly eroding headward cuts into the divide separating it from another drainage basin, and provides an outlet for a section of a stream in the adjoining valley. The lower portion of the partially diverted stream is called a *beheaded stream*.

Stream terrace A surface representing remnants of a stream's channel or flood plain when the stream was flowing at a higher level. Subsequent downward cutting by the stream leaves remnants of the old channel or flood plain standing as a terrace above the present level of the stream.

Strength The stress at which rupture occurs or plastic deformation begins.

Stress Force applied to material that tends to change the material's dimensions. Commonly, unit stress, or total force divided by the area over which it is applied. Contrast with *strain*.

Striation A scratch or small channel gouged by glacial action. Bedrock, pebbles, and boulders may show striations produced when rocks trapped by the ice are ground against bedrock or other rocks. Striations along a bedrock surface are oriented in the direction of ice flow across that surface.

Striations (of a mineral) Parallel thread-like lines or narrow bands on the face of a mineral; reflect the internal atomic arrangement.

Strike The direction of the line formed by intersection of a rock surface with a horizontal plane. The strike is always perpendicular to the direction of the dip.

Strike-slip fault A fault in which movement is almost in the direction of the fault's strike.

Structural geology The study of the architecture of the earth insofar as it is determined by earth movements. "Tectonics" and "tectonic geology" are terms that are synonymous with structural geology. The movements that affect solid rock result from forces within the earth and cause folds, joints, faults, and cleavage. The movement of magma, because it is often intimately associated with the displacement of solid rocks, is also a subject that lies within the domain of structural geology.

Sublimation The process by which solid material passes into the gaseous state without first becoming a liquid.

Subsequent stream A tributary stream flowing along beds of less erosional resistance, parallel to beds of greater resistance. Its course is determined subsequent to the uplift that brought the more resistant beds within its sphere of erosion.

Subsidence A sinking of a large area of the earth's crust.

Subsurface Pertaining to, formed, or occurring beneath the surface of the earth.

Subsurface water Water below the surface of the ground. Also referred to as *underground water*, and *subterranean water*.

Subterranean water Water below the surface of the ground. Also referred to as *underground water*, and *subsurface water*.

Sulfate mineral (sulphate mineral) Mineral formed by the combination of the complex ion $(SO_4)^{2-}$ with a positive ion. Common example: gypsum, $CaSO_4 \cdot 2H_2O$.

Sulfide mineral (sulphide mineral) Mineral formed by the direct union of an element with sulfur. Examples: argentite, chalcocite, galena, sphalerite, pyrite, and cinnabar.

Superheat Heat added to a substance after melting is complete.

Superimposed stream A stream whose present course was established on young rocks burying an old surface. With uplift, this course was maintained as the stream cut down through the young rocks to and into the old surface.

Superposition The natural order in which rocks are accumulated in beds one above the other. See *law of superposition*.

Surface wave Wave that travels along the free surface of a medium. Earthquake surface waves are sometimes represented by the symbol L.

Suspended water Underground water held in the zone of aeration by molecular attraction exerted on the water by the rock and earth materials and by the attraction exerted by the water particles on one another.

Symmetrical fold A fold in which the axial plane is essentially vertical. The limbs dip at similar angles.

Syncline A configuration of folded stratified rocks in which the rocks dip downward from opposite directions to come together in a trough. The reverse of an *anticline*.

System A fundamental division or unit of rocks. It is of world-wide application and consists of the rocks formed during a period, as the Cambrian System.

Tablemount See *guyot*.

Tabular A shape with large area relative to thickness.

Taconite Unleached iron formation of the Lake Superior District. Consists of chert with hematite, magnetite, siderite, and hydrous iron silicates. An ore of iron. It averages 25 per cent iron, but natural leaching turns it into an ore with 50 to 60 per cent iron.

Talc A silicate of magnesium common among metamorphic minerals. Its crystalline structure is based on tetrahedra arranged in sheets. Greasy and extremely soft. Sometimes known as *soapstone*.

Talus A slope established by an accumulation of rock fragments at the foot of a cliff or ridge. The rock fragments that form the talus may be rock waste, sliderock, or pieces broken by frost action. Actually, however, the term "talus" is widely used to mean the rock debris itself.

Tarn A lake formed in the bottom of a cirque after glacier ice has disappeared.

Taxonomy The science of classification, especially the classification of living things.

Tectonic Pertaining to rock structures formed by earth movements, especially those movements that are widespread.

Tectonic change of sea level A change in sea level produced by land movement.

Tektite A rounded object of glass-like appearance presumed to be of extraterrestrial origin, although none have been observed to fall. The chemical composition is different from obsidian, more like that of shale.

Temperature An arbitrary number that represents the activity of atoms. Degree of heat.

Temporary base level A base level that is not permanent, such as that formed by a lake.

Terminal moraine A ridge or belt of till marking the farthest advance of a glacier. Sometimes called *end moraine*.

Terminal velocity The constant rate of fall eventually attained by a grain when the acceleration caused by the influence of gravity is balanced by the resistance of the fluid through which the grain falls.

Terrace A nearly level surface,

relatively narrow, bordering a stream or body of water, and terminating in a steep bank. Commonly the term is modified to indicate origin, as in *stream* terrace and *wave-cut* terrace.

Terrigenous deposit Material derived from above sea level and deposited in deep ocean. Example: volcanic ash.

Tetrahedron (pl. tetrahedra) A four-sided solid. Used commonly in describing silicate minerals as a shortened reference to the silicon-oxygen tetrahedron (*q.v.*).

Texture The general physical appearance of a rock, as shown by the size, shape, and arrangement of the particles that make up the rock.

Therapsid Any member of the extinct reptilian order *Therapsida*. The various species had many mammal-like characteristics, and there were both herbivorous and carnivorous forms of varied size.

Thermal gradient In the earth, the rate at which temperature increases with depth below the surface. A general average seems to be around 30°C increase per kilometer of depth or 150°F per mile.

Thermal spring A spring that brings warm or hot water to the surface. Sometimes called *warm spring,* or *hot spring.* Temperature usually 15°F or more above mean air temperature.

Thermo remanent magnetism Magnetism acquired by an igneous rock as it cools below the curie temperatures of magnetic minerals in the rock. Abbreviation, TRM.

Thin section A slice of rock ground so thin as to be translucent.

Thrust fault A fault in which the upper or "hanging" wall appears to have moved upward at a relatively low angle. Also called reverse fault.

Tidal current A water current generated by the tide-producing forces of the sun and the moon.

Tidal inlet Waterway from open water into a lagoon.

Tidal wave Popular but incorrect designation for *tsunami.*

Tide Alternate rising and falling of the surface of the ocean, other bodies of water, or the earth itself, in response to forces resulting from motion of the earth, moon, and sun relative to each other.

Till Unstratified and unsorted glacial drift deposited directly by glacier ice.

Tillite Indurated till. The term is reserved for pre-Pleistocene tills that

have been indurated or consolidated by processes acting after deposition.

Time-rock unit (time-stratigraphic unit) A mass of rock defined on the basis of arbitrary time limits and not physical characteristics. The *Cambrian System* is a time-rock unit including all rocks deposited during the Cambrian Period.

Tombolo A sand bar connecting an island to the mainland, or joining two islands.

Tongue A subdivision of a formation that passes in one direction into a thicker body of similar type of rock and dies out in the other direction.

Topographic deserts Deserts deficient in rainfall either because they are located far from the oceans toward the center of continents, or because they are cut off from rainbearing winds by high mountains.

Topset bed Layer of sediment constituting the surface of a delta. Usually nearly horizontal, and covers the edges of inclined foreset beds.

Toreva block A large-scale prehistoric slump characteristic of now arid and semiarid sections, as in New Mexico.

Tourmaline A silicate mineral of boron and aluminum, with sodium, calcium, fluorine, iron, lithium, or magnesium. Formed at high temperatures and pressures through the agency of fluids carrying boron and fluorine. Particularly associated with pegmatites.

Traction The process of carrying material along the bottom of a stream. Traction includes movement by saltation, rolling, or sliding.

Transition element An element in a series in which an inner shell is being filled with electrons after an outer shell has been started. All transition elements are metallic in the free state.

Transpiration The process by which water vapor escapes from a living plant and enters the atmosphere.

Transverse dune A dune formed in areas of scanty vegetation and in which sand has moved in a ridge at right angles to the wind. It exhibits the gentle windward slope and the steep leeward slope characteristic of other dunes.

Travertine A form of calcium carbonate, $CaCO_3$, formed in stalactites, stalagmites, and other deposits in limestone caves, or as incrustations around the mouths of hot and cold calcareous springs. Sometimes known as *tufa,* or *dripstone.*

Trellis pattern A roughly rectilinear arrangement of stream courses in a pattern reminiscent of a garden trellis, developed in a region where rocks of differing resistance to erosion have been folded, beveled, and uplifted.

Trilobite A general name for an important group of extinct marine animals (phylum *Arthropoda,* class *Crustacea*) whose remains are found in rocks of Paleozoic age. They have a compressed trilobate body with numerous segments in the thoracic region. Some forms are especially valuable guide fossils for the Cambrian Period.

Tritium A radioactive isotope of hydrogen that is produced in the upper atmosphere as a result of cosmic-ray activity. It has a half-life of 12.5 years, and it can be used in tracing and dating water masses in the ocean or underground.

TRM See *thermo remanent magnetism.*

Tropical deserts Deserts lying between 5° to 30° north and south of the equator.

Truncated spur The beveled end of a divide between two tributary valleys where they join a main valley that has been glaciated. The glacier of the main valley has worn off the end of the divide.

Tsunami (pl. tsunami) A large wave in the ocean generated at the time of an earthquake. Popularly, but incorrectly, known as a *tidal wave.* Sometimes called *seismic seawave.*

Tufa Calcium carbonate, $CaCO_3$, formed in stalactites, stalagmites, and other deposits in limestone caves, as incrustations around the mouths of hot and cold calcareous springs, or along streams carrying large amounts of calcium carbonate in solution. Sometimes known as *travertine,* or *dripstone.*

Tuff Rock consolidated from volcanic ash.

Tundra A stretch of arctic swampland developed on top of permanently frozen ground. Extensive tundra regions have developed in parts of North America, Europe, and Asia.

Turbidite A deposit laid down by a turbidity (density) current.

Turbidity current A current in which a limited volume of turbid or muddy water moves relative to surrounding water because of its greater density.

Turbulent flow Mechanism by which a fluid such as water moves near a rough surface. Fluid not in contact with the irregular boundary outruns that which is slowed by friction or deflected by the uneven surface. Fluid particles move in a series of eddies or whirls. Most stream flow is turbulent, and turbulent flow is important in both erosion and transportation. Contrast with *laminar flow.*

Type locality The place from which the name of a geologic formation is taken or from which the type specimen of an organism comes.

Ultimate base level Sea level, the lowest possible base level for a stream.

Unconformity A buried erosion surface separating two rock masses, the older of which was exposed to erosion for a long interval of time before deposition of the younger. If, in the process, the older rocks were deformed and were not horizontal at the time of subsequent deposition, the surface of separation is an *angular unconformity.* If the older rocks remained essentially horizontal during erosion, the surface separating them from the younger rocks is called a *disconformity.* An unconformity that develops between massive igneous rocks that are exposed to erosion and then covered by sedimentary rocks is called a *nonconformity.*

Underground water Water below the surface of the ground. Also referred to as *subsurface water,* and *subterranean water.*

Uneven fracture A mineral's habit of breaking along rough, irregular surfaces.

Uniformitarianism The belief or principle that the past history of the earth and its inhabitants is best interpreted in terms of what is known about the present. Uniformitarianism would explain the past by appealing to known laws and principles acting in a gradual, uniform way through past ages.

Unit cell In the crystalline structure of a mineral, a parallelepiped enclosing an atom or group of atoms arbitrarily selected so that the mineral's structure is represented by periodic repetition of this unit in a *space lattice (q.v.).*

Unpaired terrace A terrace formed when an eroding stream, swinging back and forth across a valley, encounters resistant rock beneath the unconsolidated alluvium and is deflected, leaving behind a single terrace with no corresponding terrace on the other side of the stream.

Upwarp A broad area uplifted by internal forces.

Valley glacier A glacier confined to a stream valley. Usually fed from a cirque. Sometimes called *alpine glacier* or *mountain glacier.*

Valley train Gently sloping plain underlain by glacial outwash and confined by valley walls.

Valve The one or several pieces which make up the shell of an animal.

Van Allen belts Belts composed mostly of energetic ionized nuclei of hydrogen atoms and electrons, trapped in the outer atmosphere by the earth's magnetic field.

Variety A subdivision of a species.

Varves The regular layers or alternations of material in sedimentary deposits that are caused by annual seasonal influences. Each varve represents the deposition during a year and consists ordinarily of a lower part deposited in summer and an upper, fine-grained part deposited in the winter. Varves of silt and clay-like material occur abundantly in glacial-lake sediments, and varves are believed to have been recognized in certain marine shales and in slates. The counting of varves and correlation of sequences have been applied toward establishing both the absolute and relative ages of Pleistocene glacial deposits. Varved "clays" of glacial origin commonly consist largely of very finely divided quartz, feldspar, and micaceous minerals rather than mostly true clay minerals.

Vascular plant Any plant with tissues specifically adapted to conduct liquids or gas.

Velocity of a stream Rate of motion of a stream measured in terms of the distance its water travels in a unit of time, usually in feet per second.

Ventifact A pebble, cobble, or boulder that has had its shape or surface modified by wind-driven sand.

Vertebrate An animal with a backbone.

Virtual geomagnetic pole For any one locality the pole consistent with the magnetic field as measured at that locality. The term refers to magnetic-field direction of a single point, in contrast to "geometric pole," which refers to the best fit of a geocentric dipole for the entire earth's field. Most paleomagnetic readings are expressed as virtual geomagnetic poles.

Viscosity An internal property of rocks that offers resistance to flow. The ratio of deforming force to rate

at which changes in shape are produced.

Volatile components Materials in a magma, such as water, carbon dioxide, and certain acids, whose vapor pressures are high enough to cause them to become concentrated in any gaseous phase that forms.

Volcanic ash The unconsolidated, fine-grained material thrown out in volcanic eruptions. It consists of minute fragments of glass and other rock material, and in color and general appearance may resemble organic ashes. The term is generally restricted to deposits consisting mainly of fragments less than 4 millimeters in size. Very fine volcanic ash composed of particles less than 0.05 millimeter may be called **volcanic dust.** The indurated equivalent of volcanic ash is **tuff.**

Volcanic block An angular mass of newly congealed magma blown out in an eruption. Contrast with *volcanic bomb.*

Volcanic bomb A rounded mass of newly congealed magma blown out in an eruption. Contrast with *volcanic block.*

Volcanic dust Pyroclastic detritus consisting of particles of dust size.

Volcanic earthquakes Earthquakes caused by movements of magma or explosions of gases during volcanic activity.

Volcanic eruption The explosive or quiet emission of lava, pyroclastics, or volcanic gases at the earth's surface, usually from a volcano but rarely from fissures.

Volcanic neck The solidified material filling a vent or pipe of a dead volcano.

Volcanism The phenomena related to or resulting from the action or actions of a volcano.

Volcano A landform developed by the accumulation of magnetic products near a central vent.

Warm spring A spring that brings warm water to the surface. A *thermal spring.* Temperature 15°F or more above mean air temperature.

Water gap The gap cut through a resistant ridge by a superimposed or antecedent stream.

Water table The upper surface of the zone of saturation for underground water. It is an irregular surface with a slope or shape determined by the quantity of ground water and the permeability of the earth materials. In general, it is highest beneath hills and lowest beneath valleys.

Weathering The response of materials that were once in equilibrium within the earth's crust to new conditions at or near contact with water, air, or living matter.

Wind gap The general term for an abandoned water gap.

Xenolith A strange rock broken from the wall surrounding a magma chamber and frozen in the intrusion as it solidified.

Yardang A sharp-edged ridge between two troughs or furrows excavated by wind action.

Yardang trough A trough excavated by wind action, between two yardangs.

Yazoo-type river A tributary that is unable to enter its main stream because of natural levees along the main stream. The Yazoo-type river flows along the back-swamp zone parallel to the main stream.

Yield point The maximum stress that a solid can withstand without undergoing permanent deformation either by plastic flow or by rupture.

Zone A subdivision of stratified rock based primarily on fossil content. It may be named after the fossil or fossils it contains. Strictly speaking, the zone of paleontological stratigraphy is based not on one but on two or more designated fossils. No fixed thickness or lithology is implied by the term "zone."

Zone of aeration A zone immediately below the surface of the ground, in which the openings are partially filled with air, and partially with water trapped by molecular attraction. Subdivided into (a) belt of soil moisture, (b) intermediate belt, and (c) capillary fringe.

Zone of flow The subsurface part of the earth in which the breaking of material is prevented by pressure and all deformation is by some type of flow. The term is also used in reference to the deeper parts of glaciers where fracturing of the ice does not take place.

Zone of fracture The upper portion of the earth's crust in which rocks are deformed mainly by fracture. The term is also applied to the outer part of glaciers where fracturing occurs.

Zone of saturation Underground region within which all openings are filled with water. The top of the zone of saturation is called the *water table*. The water that is contained within the zone of saturation is called *ground water*.

Index

GEOLOGIC MAP

QUATERNARY

Rocks and unconsolidated deposits of Pleistocene and Recent age

TERTIARY

Rocks of Paleocene, Eocene, Oligocene, Miocene, and Pliocene age

MESOZOIC

Rocks of Triassic, Jurassic, and Cretaceous age

LATE PALEOZOIC

Rocks of Devonian, Mississippian, Pennsylvanian, and Permian age

EARLY PALEOZOIC

Rocks of Cambrian, Ordovician, and Silurian age

PRECAMBRIAN

A variety of igneous, metamorphic, and sedimentary rocks (includes some metamorphosed paleozoic locally)

EXTRUSIVE IGNEOUS ROCKS

Chiefly lava flows of Tertiary and Quaternary age

INTRUSIVE IGNEOUS ROCKS

(includes some metamorphic rocks)
Granitoid rocks of various ages

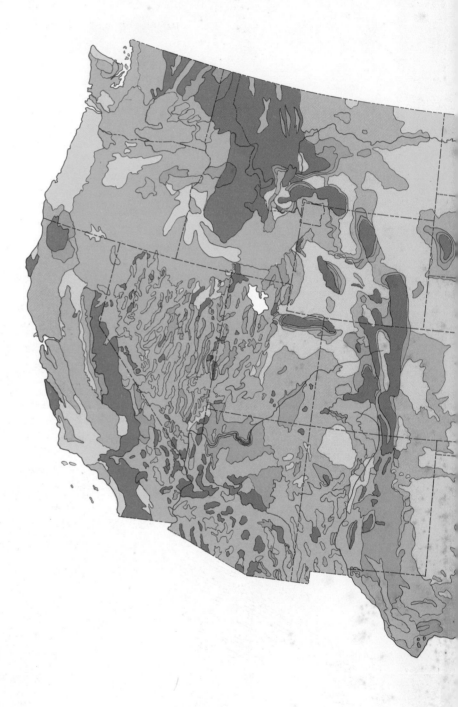